The Dalmatian that Lost its Spots

By Helen Haraldsen

Illustrated by Steve Hutton

The Dalmatian that Lost its Spots

www.helenharaldsen.co.uk

Illustrated by Steve Hutton

Editing, Cover Design and Formatting by Let's Get Booked:
www.letsgetbooked.com

Paperback ISBN: 978-1-913953-01-0

eBook ISBN: 978-1-913953-02-7

Book 1

For Lucy, my friend. Beautiful inside and out.

ONE

Lucy the Dalmatian was nick named Lucy Leopard by her humans because she was spotty, like a leopard. She liked swimming, doing forward rolls and getting in people's way so they fell over her. Lucy was often admired for her beautiful spots and received lots of compliments. She always gave people a nice smile and a tail wag to thank them for their kind words.

Lucy lived with Petra; a pointer. Her humans called her The Crazy Pointer because she loved running around the house with a shoe in her mouth, or rummaging in the woods looking for pheasants to chase. She even caught hedgehogs in the garden and brought them into the house. Petra did everything at 100 miles per hour. Her feet even twitched when she was asleep as she ran everywhere in her dreams.

The two dogs were the best of friends. They did everything together and were never apart. They ate together, slept together, played together and even went on holiday together. Although they had very different personalities, they were inseparable.

One day their humans, Mr and Mrs Daley, took them for a walk. Although it was only spring, the day was warm so they all got in the car and headed off to a lake. The sun was shining, the birds were singing and everyone was happy. Lucy practiced her forward rolls as they walked along the lake-side path, until she got told off for squashing the bluebells. So, instead, she paddled in the water and swam out to fetch sticks her humans threw into the lake.

Meanwhile, Petra vanished, as usual. No-one knew where she was until they heard the startled call of a pheasant and saw it come flapping out of the long grass, closely followed by The Crazy Pointer with a big grin on her face.

By the time they got nearly halfway around the lake, the Daleys were getting sick of tripping over Lucy, who kept stopping in the middle of the path. They were also sick of shouting for Petra, who was forever scrambling up the steep banks beside the path and disappearing, so they decided to stop and have their picnic.

Both of the dogs loved picnics, but especially Lucy, who started drooling the minute the sandwiches were unpacked. She turned her soft brown eyes towards the Daleys and gave them a look that she hoped would convince them to share their lunch. As usual, it worked. Both dogs got bits of sandwich, some tasty crisps and pieces of crunchy apple that made them lick their lips.

All too soon, the food was eaten up and it was time to continue their walk. They came to a field with a herd of sheep, so the dogs got put on their leads because

Petra would chase and frighten the sheep. Lucy wouldn't bother them, but the Daleys liked to treat both dogs the same.

After the field, they followed a track until they were on the other side of the lake and the dogs were allowed off their leads again. Petra immediately hurtled off into the trees, but Lucy stayed with the Daleys. She liked to keep an eye on them and make sure they were okay, plus she couldn't keep up with The Crazy Pointer who ran up and down steep slopes like a mountain goat.

After a little while, Petra hadn't returned and no pheasants had been sighted to signal her whereabouts. Mrs Daley started whistling and calling her name. They waited for her to appear, and Lucy sat down, knowing that this could take a while.

Petra didn't return.

Lucy wasn't worried. Petra always came back eventually. Wherever she was, Petra wouldn't be stuck. She was an experienced escape artist and could always get out of any predicament she found herself in. But the Daleys were getting cross. Their shouts had gotten louder and more urgent and they'd started to retrace their steps back the way they'd been. When they went around a corner, out of sight, Lucy got up and trotted after them, not wanting to be left by herself.

Sometime later, there was still no sign of Petra. Lucy and the Daleys left the track and climbed into the woods in search of her. Lucy *was* starting to get worried now. It was getting cold and the sky was darkening. The Daleys were still shouting and whistling, but Lucy could hear that they sounded anxious rather than annoyed. She sniffed the ground to see if she could pick up Petra's scent, but The Crazy Pointer had run all over the place in loops, making it impossible to follow her trail.

As the sun lowered in the sky, the Daleys reluctantly returned to the path and trudged back to the car. Lucy could see that they were tired and upset. Petra was still missing and they didn't want to go home without her, but there were still miles to walk to get back and it would soon be dark.

Eventually, in pitch blackness, the group of three got back to the car and drove home in silence. Everybody was thinking about where Petra could be and hoping that wherever she was, she was safe.

When they got back to their house and put the lights on, Mrs Daley gave Lucy some food and patted her.

"Don't worry, Leopard," she said, using Lucy's pet name. "We'll go back and find her first thing in the morning." Mrs Daley paused and looked at Lucy closely. Then she bent over and ran her hands over the dog's coat.

“Hmmm,” she said, as her husband came into the kitchen. “Lucy looks different somehow. I can’t tell what it is. What do you think?”

"You're just imagining it because you're tired and worried," he replied, giving Lucy a quick glance and a hurried pat. "Come on, let's go to bed and everything will look better in the morning."

Lucy did feel a little strange. Her fur felt all tingly and twitchy. *It must just be because I'm worried about Petra,* she thought. *I'll be back to normal by the morning.* Giving herself a little scratch, she plonked herself wearily in her bed, gazing forlornly at the empty one beside her where Petra should be.

Where are you Petra? she wondered, before falling into a deep, deep sleep.

TWO

When Mr Daley came into the kitchen the next morning and saw Lucy in her bed, beside Petra's empty one, it wasn't the empty space that got his attention. He rubbed his eyes and looked again. He couldn't believe what he was seeing. It seemed he hadn't lost one dog but two, for the dog looking back at him from Lucy's bed and wearing Lucy's collar was no Dalmatian. It was completely white apart from its black nose.

When his wife came in to see him just standing, staring, she stared too.

"What do we do now?" Mrs Daley eventually said. "Go back and keep looking for Petra or take this dog to *Peregrine Pets*, the animal rescue place?"

"This dog? It's Lucy!"

"It can't be Lucy. It's got no spots! They can't have *disappeared*! Someone must have stolen her!"

"And left a white dog in her place?" asked Mr Daley, checking the door and finding it still locked. "It's definitely Lucy. Look – I'd recognise her lovely heart-shaped nose anywhere."

Mrs Daley bent down to examine the white dog. Lucy whined and thumped her tail. She'd known as soon as she woke up that something was wrong. At first she'd thought it was just the upsetting sight of Petra's empty bed that troubled her, reminding her that her best friend was missing, but it was more than that. She didn't feel herself, somehow. Something was missing. Just as she'd been trying to work out what it was, Mr Daley had appeared in the doorway and stared at her like he didn't know her. Then Mrs Daley had come and hadn't recognised her either. And that's when she knew what was wrong. She'd lost her spots. She was a spot-less Dalmatian! Her heart sank. Would the Daleys still want her without her beautiful spots? She licked Mrs Daley on the nose and held her paw out to her. *I'm still Lucy,* she tried to say, in every way she could.

"You're right." Mrs Daley peered at Lucy. "She's got Leopard's big square head and her heart-shaped nose." She looked down. "Both of her front paws have one black nail like Lucy… and here's the little lump she has on her shoulder," she said, feeling all over the white dog's body. "I can't believe it. It *is* our Lucy, but what's happened to her spots?"

Worried that there must be something terribly wrong with their dog, the Daleys whisked her straight to the vet, where a quick scan with a microchip reader revealed that the white dog was indeed Lucy.

"I've never seen anything like it!" the young vet exclaimed, her eyes wide behind her spectacles. "It could be some new condition that makes Dalmatians lose their spots. I could be the one to discover a cure. This could make me famous!" The vet pushed her specs up her nose as she stared at Lucy, her eyes still round with excitement.

"We're not interested in fame," Mrs Daley said. "We just want to make sure she's alright."

"Oh, oh, yes of course!" The vet said, but in her mind, she was imagining herself on the front cover of PetVet magazine. "That's no problem. I understand your other dog is missing? Why don't you go and look for her and leave Lucy here? I'll run some tests to see what I can find. She'll be perfectly safe here with me."

Reluctantly, the Daleys left Lucy with the vet while they headed off to continue their search for Petra. Lucy cried and struggled against the vet, who smelled of so many things it was alarming. Lucy detected guinea pig, cat, some kind of bird, blood and antiseptic. It made her heart pound. She needed to get away. She needed to help look for Petra. Humans were useless: they couldn't see very far and they had no sense of smell. They'd never find Petra without her help.

But the vet wouldn't let her go. She held on to Lucy's lead and stopped her when she tried to follow her humans. Mr Daley gave Lucy a pat on the head.

"Don't worry, Leopard," he said. "The vet's going to look after you and find a way to get your spots back. We'll all be back together soon."

Lucy whimpered and tried to follow him. She knew the vet wouldn't be able to do anything about her missing spots because the only cure was to find Petra. Lucy was certain they had disappeared because she was so worried and unhappy that her best friend was missing. While Petra was lost, so were her spots. But she had no way of letting the humans know.

Lucy spent several hours being poked and prodded by the vet as she ran lots of tests to try and find out what might have caused Lucy's spots to vanish. But, of course, she found nothing.

Disappointed, she put Lucy in a cage in the back room where poorly animals were recovering.

Frantically, Lucy scrabbled at the cage door, trying to get out. But the door was fastened on the outside. She was trapped.

"Oi. Can you cut that out? I'm trying to sleep. Please stop making that racket."

Lucy looked in the direction of the voice and saw a pug, curled up in a plush bed under a bench containing the vet's supplies. He wasn't trapped in a cage like her.

"Please help me," Lucy pleaded. "I need to get out of here."

"Don't worry," sighed the pug. "Whatever's wrong with you, my owner will fix you. She's the vet. It's her job to make animals better."

"But there's nothing wrong with me!" Lucy howled, and explained her problem to the pug. "So, I really need you to come and help get me out of this cage so I can go and help find my best friend. *Please.*"

"I don't believe you," said the pug, getting out of his bed to take a look at Lucy. "It's not possible for a Dalmatian to lose its spots. You're just a plain white dog who tells porky pies for attention." And with that, the pug turned around and went back to his bed.

"I'm not lying!" Lucy howled again. "I have to get out of here and help find my friend before it's too late. Something's happened to her. She could be injured. She probably won't have anything to eat or drink. You've got to help me!"

"Oh, for goodness sake," said thc pug, getting out of bed again. "If only to shut you up. How's anyone meant to get their nap with you making all that noise?" He waddled back to Lucy's cage on his short little legs.

"Thank you!" Lucy gave the pug one of her nicest smiles. "You just need to reach up and nudge the door's catch up, then slide it across. Then the door will open."

The pug stood up on his back legs and tried to do as Lucy said. But being so small, he could barely reach the door catch, and his flat wrinkly face meant that he had no muzzle to nudge it with.

"Sorry," he wheezed. "I can't do it." He sat down beside Lucy's cage to get his breath back.

Dejected, Lucy lay down. It looked like she would just have to wait for the Daleys to come back for her later. Hopefully, they would have found Petra, then her spots would come back and they could all go home together.

THREE

Later that day, the phone rang. Lucy listened as the vet answered it. She couldn't hear who was speaking at the other end, but from what the vet said, she knew it was her humans.

"No, I'm afraid she's still spot-less," the vet said. "I've done some tests and... I'll get the results back tomorrow. You might as well leave her here tonight and I'll try some other things tomorrow. I...er...I have medicine I can try. It's my own invention. I think it might help to bring her spots back."

Lucy didn't understand every word humans said but she knew enough to know she didn't like the sound of that.

"Did you find your missing dog?" the vet asked, into the telephone.

Lucy waited, hopeful for the reply.

“Oh, dear. That’s a shame. Well, maybe you’ll find her tomorrow.”

Lucy’s heart sank. Petra was still missing and needed her help, but she was going to be trapped here in this cage, unable to look for her. She needed to do something, but what?

Just as she was trying to think of a new plan, the vet came into the room and opened the back door. She told the pug who was snoring in his bed that he could go outside for some fresh air if he liked. The pug continued to snore.

“You lazy boy,” she said, patting him. “Well, I’ll leave the door open and you can go out when you wake up.”

After the vet left, Lucy looked out of the open door. She could see an enclosed grass area with a fence and hedge around it. On the grass, paddling its feet for worms, was a giant white seagull. Lucy had an idea.

"Excuse me, seagull? Could you help me?" Lucy called, raising her voice so the gull outside could hear her. The gull didn't react and continued paddling. "Hello, seagull?" Lucy repeated, even louder. Still, the bird didn't respond.

"What are you doing now?" said the pug, grumpy at being woken by Lucy again.

"I'm trying to speak to this seagull. I want to ask him if he will fly around and have a look for Petra. He can travel far and look from above. Maybe he could get some other birds to help."

"Well firstly, he is a she. And do you speak Tweet?"

"Pardon?" Asked Lucy.

"Well, you're a dog. We speak the language of Woof. Cats speak the language of Miaow. Birds speak Tweet. So, unless you're bi-lingual, you can't talk to her, can you?"

“Oh. I didn’t think of that.” Lucy slumped against her cage.

Seeing how downhearted she was, the pug decided to help.

“You might not be able to speak Tweet,” he said, “but I’m here every day. I’ve picked up a bit of other animals’ languages. I’ll try for you.”

And with that, he raised his head and pulled his shoulders back, before strutting out onto the grass. Lucy saw him approaching the gull, who was still paddling. He made a series of high-pitched squeaks and whistles that she couldn’t understand. The gull shook her head and made a loud ‘*keow*’ sound before pulling a large juicy worm out of the ground and flying away with it.

“She said no, she’s too busy looking for food,” reported the pug.

Lucy lowered her head onto her paws.

"But I'll ask some other birds," he said, his heart softening when he saw how disappointed Lucy was.

The pug tried asking a jackdaw, a blackbird and a robin but none of them would help.

"Sorry," the pug told Lucy. "They're all too busy nesting and finding food for their chicks, I'm afraid. They can't help."

Before Lucy had a chance to reply, the vet came into the room and gave all the animals in the cages some food. Lucy tried to barge past her and escape, but the vet pushed her back in and closed the door.

"I'm sorry Lucy," the vet told her, "but you'll have to stay here until I can find a way to get your spots back. If I can do that, I'll be on the telly. Everyone will know me." A faraway look glazed her eyes as if she was imagining a future of living in luxury and being a celebrity. "Come on Gomez," she said, dreamily, to the pug. "Let's go home."

"Goodnight," said Gomez, to Lucy, as he followed the vet.

The lights were switched off, the door closed and there was silence in the room, except for the sound of animals crunching their food and the low buzz of a wasp who must have got fastened in when the vet closed all the doors and locked up.

I hope it doesn't sting me, thought Lucy.

Too upset to eat her dinner, Lucy paced around her cage, worrying about Petra and wondering where she could be.

"Excuzzze me," she heard a strange, buzzy voice near her, but couldn't see who or what it was coming from.

"Who's that?"

"Look at your food dish," the voice instructed.

Lucy looked down at her food dish and saw a wasp sitting on the rim. She immediately shrank back as far as she could go in the small space of the cage.

"Wh-wh-at do you want?" she asked.

"To help you," the wasp said. "I heard all about your problem earlier and saw you trying to get help from the birdzzz. Useless, selfish lot, birdzzz. But I can help."

“You? How can you help? And why would you want to help?” Lucy asked, suspicious of its intentions.

The wasp sighed. “Ahhh, everybody alwayzzz thinks wasps are bad. All they want to do is squash uzzz. We get no thanks for everything we do. Without uzzz the world would be overrun with spiderzzz and fliezzz: we feed loads of them to our babiezzz. But does anyone thank uzzz? No. We pollinate plants and crops but doezzz anyone care? No. They love the little furry bumble beezzz but they hate uzzz wasps.”

“Well, there is the fact that you sting, and it hurts.” Lucy pointed out, interrupting the wasp.

“Only to defend ourselvezzz!” The wasp waved its antennae in frustration. “As I said, people are always trying to kill uzzz. And I could never sting anybody. I’m a boy. It’s only the femalezzz that can sting.”

“Oh,” said Lucy, who stopped shrinking into the back of her cage and stepped forward. “Well, I didn’t know that. I'm pleased to meet you. You said you'd like to help me?"

"Ah, yes. I heard all about your problem. Your friend is missing and you need help to find her but you are trapped in here, without your spots. A Dalmatian without its spots is like a wasp without its stripezzz. I will help find your friend, my lady!" The wasp bowed in front of Lucy. "As soon as someone openzzz a window tomorrow, I will begin the search."

"Thank you. But won't it be a bit much for you?" Lucy asked. "You're only very small. All I know is that we were near a lake. I don't know which one or how far away it is: you might have to fly miles to find her. It could take you all week!"

"I won't be searching alone. I will call all of my friendzzz and family. All I have to do is release a chemical from my body to say that I need help and they will all come. We'll have your friend found in no time."

"That's so kind of you, er…Mr Wasp," said Lucy. "I'm sorry, I don't know your name. I'd never have expected this from a wasp. And…" she cocked her head, puzzled, "How is it that I can talk to you? Gomez the pug said that animals all have their own language. I couldn't understand the birds but I can understand you fine. Why is that?"

"I'm a wizzze wasp," he said, proudly. "Wasps don't use wordzzz to communicate, so we don't have namezzz, but I love wordzzz. I've spent lots of time getting close to people and animalzzz to listen to them talking. I'm fluent in Human, Woof and the language of insects. I know a bit of Tweet, but I don't know reptile or rodent languagezzz at all. Now, go to sleep and dream of your friend. Tomorrow we will find her."

FOUR

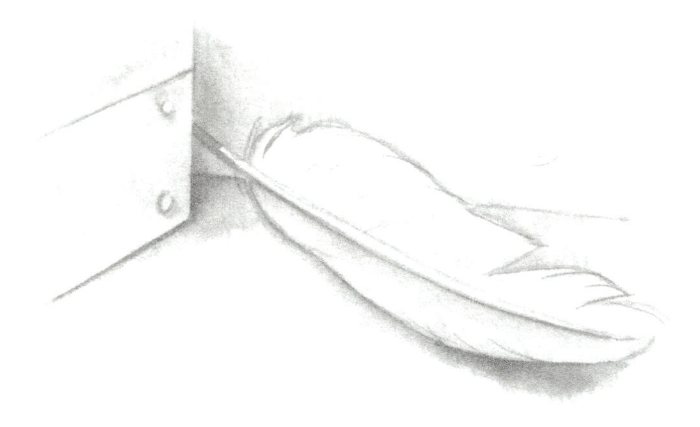

By the time Lucy woke up the next morning, the vet had arrived, the windows were open and the wasp had gone. Lucy paced around her cage again, wondering what he was doing and worrying about the vet and the medication she said she'd give to her.

Her own invention? Lucy didn't like the sound of that. The only cure for her lost spots was finding Petra.

Gomez the pug was back in his bed under the bench, asleep and snoring his head off. Lucy got so used to the sound of his loud snores she didn't hear the buzzing sound straight away.

"Pzzzt."

She eventually noticed a sound coming from her untouched dish of food and looked down. There on the edge was the wasp.

"You're back already?" she cried and wagged her tail. "Did you find her?"

"We did," the wasp replied. "She'zzz in some woodland, quite a way from here. She'zzz fallen down a hole and is stuck, I'm afraid. It's deep and she can't climb out. It could be an old well or mine shaft?"

"Oh no," cried Lucy. "She won't have anything to eat or drink. If she isn't found soon, she'll die! I have to get out of here. You have to take me to her."

"It's a long way away, my lady. It will take you dayzzz to get there on foot. If you're going to travel there, I will guide you but you'd better eat something." He flew away from Lucy's food bowl. "Eat up."

Lucy wasn't worried about the journey – she could walk for miles easily, but she quickly wolfed the food down, not tasting anything in her hurry to get away. But once she had finished, then what? How could she get out of her cage?

"Can you help me get out?" she asked the wasp.

"I'm afraid not, my dear."

"Gomez!" Lucy called to the sleeping pug. "Gomez, WAKE UP!"

"Oh, what now? Leave me alone," Gomez replied sleepily from his bed.

"I need you to get me out of here, NOW." Lucy howled, urgently.

"I tried that yesterday. I can't do it, you know I can't, so leave me alone."

"You can, Gomez. If you look around, I'm sure you could find a pen or a pencil someone has dropped on the floor. You can use it to push the catch up and then drive it open."

"No. Go away." Gomez turned over and went back to sleep.

Desperate to think of a way to get out of the cage, Lucy tried to come up with another strategy, but she could think of nothing else. Gomez was the only chance she had of escape. An idea crept into her mind. It wasn't a very nice idea and normally she would push it away, but this day was not like any other day. This day she would do anything.

"Wasp," she said in a whisper so that Gomez didn't hear her. "I need your assistance to get Gomez to help. I need you to...threaten to sting him unless he gets up and does what I'm asking."

"But I can't sting. I don't have a stinger, I told you," he replied, wiggling his antennae in confusion.

"Yes, but...Gomez doesn't know that." Lucy said, cringing at her words. "If you tell him you'll sting him, he'll believe you. Go on. I wouldn't normally do anything like this, but he's my only hope and I need him. I need *you.* Please wasp."

"You shouldn't ask me this! I spend my life trying to convince everyone that wasps are good and helpful, to stop my friendzzz and family getting squashed. I can't do this! I couldn't bring myself to be so mean."

Lucy closed her eyes, trying to quell the panic that was rising inside her as she thought of poor Petra, trapped and alone in the dark. She must convince the wasp to help her if she was to get to Petra in time.

"Wasp," she said, "think of it like acting. You're just playing a part. You're using words to make something happen, but once it's done, we can explain to Gomez that you wouldn't really have stung him. And we can tell him how he may have helped to save a life. I'm sure that will make up for it." She looked hopefully at the wasp. He was scratching his head. "Don't you want to help me save Petra? You've told me where she is but unless I can get out of here, what good is it? It was a waste of your friends' efforts."

The wasp sighed. "Alright," he said. "I am only acting; really I am being a lifesaver - a hero! And heroezzz must make difficult decisionzzz. Leave this to me."

The wasp started to buzz menacingly and crawled out of one of the wire squares on the front of Lucy's cage. Soon he could be heard playing his part.

"Good dog Gomezzz, your assistance is required in a life-saving mission!" he shouted, flying close to Gomez' head. "Arizzze and join uzzz in our quest."

Gomez curled into a tight ball. “Go away,” he repeated.

“I’m afraid I must insist.” The wasp landed on Gomez’s ear and shouted directly into it. “GET UP OR I WILL STING YOU OVER AND OVER UNTIL YOU DO AS I ASK.”

Gomez jumped out of his bed like a Jack-in-the-Box, suddenly wide awake. “No, no. Please don’t sting me. I’ll do it, I’ll do whatever you want. Just, please don’t sting me!” Gomez’ wrinkles arranged themselves into a picture of worry and his large, bulbous eyes begged for mercy.

“Oh, I’m sorry, I’m sorry, pleazzze forgive me,” the wasp muttered to himself. Lucy spoke up loudly so that her voice drowned out the wasp’s apology. That could come later.

“Oh Gomez, thank you so much, you’re wonderful,” Lucy flattered him. “Just look around and see if you can find anything you could use to lift and push the catch on this cage."

Gomez went on the search. He snuffled around the floor, sniffing everywhere. He scoured every corner of the building but didn't find anything he could use. Normally, he'd have given up then, but the threat of the wasp sting kept him searching. Finally, when he thought there was nowhere else he could look, he saw something poking out from behind a filing cabinet. It was a feather. A large, grey feather. Gomez remembered a pilgrim goose called Daphne who was here a few weeks ago because she had a limp. One of her feathers must have fallen out and been blown behind the cabinet. Gomez seized it and dragged it out. The feather was long with a hard, strong quill. It was a perfect tool for the job.

Gomez trotted proudly over to the cage, carrying the feather in his mouth. It tickled his nose and made him sneeze but he did not drop it. "Look what I've found," he declared, standing in front of Lucy's cage.

"Oh, that's perfect," she said.

"Yes, bravo Gomezzz."

"Now, see if you can use it to nudge the catch up, then push it across," Lucy encouraged.

Gomez had to work hard. The catch was stiff and it took several nudges before it moved up into position, ready to push across. Gomez's hind legs trembled from the effort of standing up on them for so long and his mouth ached from holding the feather tightly. He'd have liked to give up and say he tried his best and couldn't do any more, but the sound of the wasp buzzing nearby made him continue. He pushed the catch to the left. It moved a tiny bit. He tried again. It moved a tiny bit more. Gomez's legs started to wobble like jelly.

The wasp spurred him on. “You’re nearly there my brave pug. Keep going. Push.”

“Yes, go on, push,” Lucy echoed.

It took a painfully long time and Lucy itched with impatience as she watched the catch gradually move across, millimetre by millimetre, but at last, the cage door swung open and Lucy jumped out. She was free.

“I can’t thank you enough,” Lucy brushed her face against Gomez’ to show her affection.

“You’re welcome,” Gomez grinned, now pleased and honoured to have helped. He seemed to have forgotten that he didn’t want to help at first. The wasp chose to remind him.

“I wouldn’t have stung you,” he said. “I couldn’t have. I haven’t got a stinger, but –”

"You tricked me?" Gomez's eyes bulged out of his wrinkly face, making him look both annoyed and upset.

"Well, yes, but I shouldn't have had to. Think about how you feel right now. It feels good to help, yes? Maybe next time someone needzzz your help, you will offer it freely? I'm sorry that I lied, but perhaps you have learned a little lesson from this experience? One day you might need some help yourself. Goodbye, my friend. Now we must leave you. Let's go!"

And with that, Lucy jumped up against the back door and used her paw to press down the handle. The door swung open. Watching them disappear, Gomez shook his head, wondering if he was awake or if he'd just dreamt the whole thing. Getting back into his bed, he did dream. He dreamt about rescuing a wasp who had fallen into his water dish and was drowning. No-one witnessed his selfless act or congratulated him for his kindness, but still, he smiled as he slept and a warm, happy feeling wrapped itself around him.

FIVE

Leaving the vet's building behind them, Lucy and the wasp sneaked out into the open. Normally Lucy couldn't go anywhere without people pointing at her and exclaiming, *'There's a Dalmatian!'* But as a plain white dog, nobody noticed her. She was a ghost. It was what she needed at that moment but still, it hurt her to be so invisible.

Her tail drooped as she followed the wasp through the shadows as they left the town. She had her guide, but without the Daleys by her side, the world seemed a scary place. Cars were fast and noisy and smelled like a cocktail of chemicals. She'd never really noticed before when she'd been on the lead, safely beside her humans, but without them, danger seemed to be everywhere.

Once they left the town with all its cars, people and buildings behind, Lucy relaxed slightly. The wasp got tired from having to fly so far and took a little rest on Lucy's head.

"I'm sorry, wasp, I know your wings need a rest, but you're tickling the top of my head," Lucy said, trying not to do one of her forward rolls to remove the tickle. "Do you think you could move down and sit on my collar instead?"

The wasp did so right away, not wanting to irritate his friend.

The pair of them travelled all day, crossing through fields with difficulty. Petra could have jumped over the fences easily to cross the fields. The Daleys often said that she seemed to have trampolines in her paws, but Lucy wasn't as springy as The Crazy Pointer. She had to look for gaps in fences and hedgerows to squeeze through.

***

Back at the clinic, the vet came through to get Lucy out of her cage to run some more tests on her. She couldn't believe her eyes when she saw the cage door hanging open.

"Aaaaargghh!" she screamed, making Gomez jump out of his skin. He had been enjoying a new dream in which he wore a superhero cape and could fly.

"How has this dog got out? And where is she?"

The vet rushed around, searching madly for Lucy. Gomez shrank away but she was too busy to notice him.

"Oh *NO.*" The open back door answered her question. "She's escaped! I'll have to find her before the owners discover I've lost their dog. I'll be in so much trouble if I don't get her back. Come on Gomez. Let's go!"

The vet put a sign on the door that said, '**Had to close due to emergency**,' locked up and rushed out to her car. With screeching wheels, she sped out of the car park in search of the missing dog.

***

Lucy was tired. A large, sturdy dog, she could usually walk all day without weakening, but that day, she didn't feel herself. The pads on her paws were sore and she was all scratched from the brambles and hawthorns that had pulled at her skin as she pushed through the hedges. Her collar got caught on a nasty, thorny branch and she had to wriggle out of it to avoid being trapped.

"Are we nearly there yet?" she whined to the wasp.

"I'm afraid there'zzz still a way to go," he told her. "We're heading towardzzz those mountainzzz in the distance, see?" He pointed an antenna in a north-westerly direction. "When we can clearly see a pointy rock amongst them, we're close. But we can't see it yet."

"Then we must keep going." Lucy limped forward, prepared to walk all through the night to reach her friend.

"I'm afraid we must stop," the wasp said. "You need to rest."

Lucy started to protest.

"No, no, you'll never make it if you do not rest. Plus, I can't navigate without the sun and I can't fly once it gets cold at night. I need to eat. I'm going to go and find some fruit for my supper. Would you like me to bring you some?"

Lucy shook her head and found a sheltered gap in a hedgerow to rest in. She managed to drink from a water trough in the field, but there was nothing for her to eat. Despite gobbling the contents of a full bowl of food before she left the vet's, Lucy's stomach rumbled. She couldn't understand why she felt so weak.

As the sun dropped behind the distant mountains and the moon sparkled among the stars in the dark, Lucy began to shiver. The wasp was nice and warm, snuggled against Lucy's face. One of her ears covered him like a blanket. His wings tickled her ear but she didn't complain. She needed her guide to get a good rest so that he was ready to continue their journey as soon as it got light in the morning.

As she looked up, wondering if Petra was also looking at the same stars, she was too cold to sleep. She closed her eyes, trying her hardest to ignore the shaking of her body and the rumbling in her tummy, but she could not. All she could picture was her basket next to the radiator in the kitchen at home. Cosy and safe.

She opened her eyes to see a group of sheep and their lambs staring at her. She looked enviously at their warm wool, the frost on top glistening in the moonlight.

"I won't harm you," Lucy told them, knowing that sheep were often frightened of dogs.

The sheep flinched, startled by her voice, but they didn't run away. In fact, they seemed to be coming slightly closer. Even though they spoke different languages, the sheep seemed to understand that Lucy was no threat and that she was freezing. They came closer and closer still. Before she knew it, Lucy found herself surrounded by the flock. The warmth that came from their big fluffy fleeces was like a hug and Lucy snuggled in. She wrinkled her nose against the strong odour that came from their wool but she was exhausted. Soon, she'd drifted off into a welcome slumber.

***

Eventually, the vet had to give up her search for Lucy and go home. She'd been everywhere she could think of. She'd stopped people and asked them if they'd seen a white dog. Nobody had. She'd driven around in the dark, hoping her headlights would search it out. But Gomez was hungry and had started to whine for his supper. The vet knew she would have to give up her search for the night and continue in the morning.

As she put a dish of food on the floor for Gomez and slung a ready meal into the microwave for herself, her phone rang. When she picked it up, she saw she had seventeen missed calls. All from the same number.

"Hello?" she said. As she listened to the voice at the other end, her eyes widened and she started to shake her head.

"Oh, no, no. You can't have her back yet! Err...I mean to say, it's a very delicate time right now, and very important that she isn't disturbed. I...err...yes, I gave her the medicine and her spots looked like they were starting to come back when I left for the day, but she needs to be left in peace to let the process develop fully.

"Yes, yes...I understand but if you move her now, the spots may disappear again and might never come back."

The microwave pinged.

"That's right, yes. I'll see how she is tomorrow and I'll let you know. But she needs to stay with me for at least another day so I can continue to give her more of the...err...the special medicine I've devised to get those spots back. Right, right, yes goodnight. I'm sure everything will work out fine and you'll soon have both of your dogs back with you."

She opened the door of the microwave to pull out the meal, but the plastic container was so hot it burned her hand and she dropped it on the floor. Gomez left his own, rather dull dog food and started to lick it up, not even caring that it burned his tongue as it was so tasty. The vet tried to push him away with her foot, like a little football, but Gomez dribbled around her feet, keeping out of reach.

"Oh, still no luck with finding your other dog?" she said, accidentally standing on one of Gomez's paws, making the little dog yelp. "You're offering a reward if anyone finds her? Yes, that's a good idea. Don't worry about Lucy, she's *fine* and you'll soon have her back. Goodnight then, bye, bye, bye-bye." She hung up the phone and slammed it down on the kitchen counter.

"I have to find that dog. I HAVE to. But I've told them the spots are coming back and they're not. *Why did I say that*? I've no idea how to make them come back. What am I going to do?" She grabbed her hair as she talked to herself and stared down at the mess on the floor, seeming not to see it. Gomez wondered if it was safe to come out of the corner he'd pressed himself into to resume cleaning up the spilt food.

The vet continued clutching her hair while her eyes roamed frantically over the kitchen. Her gaze settled on the large diary pinned to the wall. Hanging from a string next to it was a black marker pen. A permanent marker.

"Ah ha," she cried, grabbing the marker. "I know what to do about some missing black spots!" With that, still clutching the marker pen, she headed upstairs for a bath, leaving the spilt food forgotten on the floor.

SIX

Lucy was awakened by light creeping in under her eyelashes. She yawned and stretched, looking around her. She was still surrounded by the sheep and lambs, who were dozing in the peace of the early morning, listening to the sounds of birds singing happily in the trees.

This is it, Lucy thought. *Today is the day I'll find Petra and get us both home. If I have the strength.* Despite her lovely, snuggly sleep, her body still felt weak.

What is that noise?

"Zzzzzz."

The noise was coming from Lucy's left ear. She shook her head to rid herself of it before she remembered what it was: the sound of a sleeping wasp, snoring.

"Wazzz up?" the wasp said, drowsily.

"I'm sorry to wake you," Lucy said, "but the sun is up. If you can find your way now, we need to get going. We have to find Petra today."

The wasp decided he needed to wash his antennae before setting off on the day's journey.

"I don't mean to hurry you, but do you think we could get going? Time is running out. Lucy was impatient to get started.

"Patience, my dear lady," the wasp said, without speeding up. "I'm just waiting."

"Waiting for what?" Lucy stamped a front paw.

"Not what – who," he replied.

Lucy frowned until she was distracted by a loud humming that filled the air, getting louder and louder.

"What's happening?" she asked anxiously.

“I called for some assistance. But... I wasn’t expecting so many to come.”

The air darkened as a swarm of wasps came twisting and spiralling out of the trees, surrounding them.

“Right, come on then. What are we waiting for? Let’s go.”

Lucy jumped up, ready to follow the wasps, who were already streaming off into the distance, but, before she left, she turned back to the sheep who’d kept her warm all night. “I know you can’t understand me,” she said to them. “But thank you for your help and for trusting me. You’ll never know how much I appreciate what you did.”

The sheep regarded her sleepily, but Lucy was sure one of them – a big, black-faced ewe with twin lambs by her side – nodded at her. Lucy paused and then bowed at the sheep. Her heart leapt in surprise when all of the sheep bowed back.

"Baaaa," said the black-faced ewe in a deep, commanding voice. Lucy had no idea what she was saying but imagined it might be 'go' or 'good luck.'

"Goodbye," Lucy said before she turned and trotted after the wasps.

Many miles were travelled over fields and through woods. Lucy had to wade through streams and swim through deep rivers in her struggle to follow the wasps as they showed her the way. There were no obstacles for them up there in the sky. She was weary and whimpered with relief when the big pointy rock came into view and she knew there wasn't far to go.

But Lucy was fading. She started to slow down and get left behind. The team of wasps noticed and worried that she wouldn't have the energy to get to the final destination. Sighting some tourists having a picnic, they spied an opportunity to get Lucy some food.

"You need to eat something, my lady," the wasp said as Lucy staggered wearily on the uneven, stony ground. "Just a little further. I don't like to do this but needzzz must."

When Lucy was within reach of the tourists, the wasp told her to hide behind a rock and wait. Lucy did as she was told and watched as the swarm swooped in on the picnic, buzzing at full volume, making the picnickers scream, drop their sandwiches and start batting at the air, trying to swat the wasps.

This was Lucy's cue to dive in, while their attention was occupied elsewhere, and grab what she could from the abandoned picnic.

After a ham sandwich, sausage roll and pork pie, Lucy expected to feel a little better and was ready to continue on her way. But as she licked her lips and stood up, her legs still trembled despite the rest and the food. And something else was wrong. It was too quiet. There was no buzzing in the air.

The wasps were gone.

Lucy could still see the pointy rock, up in the mountains, in the distance, but that was just a landmark for guidance. She had no idea which direction to head in to find Petra. She lowered her head and sniffed the ground but there was no scent of her friend to follow. She didn't know what to do. She didn't understand why the wasps would help her to get this far, and to find food, only to then abandon her.

Lucy climbed up onto a big boulder to sniff the air and see if she could find any clues to direct her in which way she should go. She had come so far; she wasn't going to give up now.

And that's when she saw it. Her heart leapt and she let out a little doggy laugh. In the distance, beyond the edge of a lake, were the wasps. They were much too far away to be able to see individually, but they had all come together to make a shape in the sky. The whole swarm had formed themselves into a great dark arrow with the tip of the arrow pointing into a clump of trees.

They had not left her. The wasps had flown on ahead to show her the way. *They're pointing at the exact spot where Petra is,* Lucy realised with a howl of joy. *Oh, beautiful, clever wasps.* Forgetting all of her worries and pains, Lucy hurried in the direction of the arrow. "I'm coming!" she barked. "I'm coming."

By the time Lucy reached the place the wasps were pointing to, the sun was sinking behind the mountains. When they saw that Lucy had found her target, the wasp arrow faded away and they headed back to their nests, leaving her alone. Their job was done.

“Petra!” Lucy called. She was in the area the wasps were pointing at but there was no sign of The Crazy Pointer. “Petra!” Lucy called again, louder.

“Lucy? Is that you? I’m down here,” a voice said so weakly, Lucy could barely hear it.

“I’m here. I’ll find you.” Lucy remembered that the wasp told her Petra had fallen down a hole. She put her nose to the ground and started to sniff every blade of grass. At last, she picked up a weak scent. It was days old now and there was barely anything left of it, but Lucy inhaled deeply and followed it quickly. It lead her to the brink of a hole in the ground. She could feel wooden planks beneath her paws, but they were soggy and rotten. She backed up, feeling like the planks were going to give way under her weight, and heard Petra call out from below her.

“I’m down here. Be careful you don’t fall in too. The ground just disappeared under my paws.”

"Are you alright?" Lucy called down, peering over the edge of the hole the best she could. It was so dark and deep; she couldn't even see Petra.

"Yes," a feeble voice drifted up, out of the hole, "but I can't get out. The walls are too steep and slippery for me to climb."

Lucy didn't know what to do. She couldn't help Petra by herself. But there wasn't time to go and get help either. Even if she could find some humans, how could she explain what she needed from them? They'd probably just bundle her into their car and take her home with them. She couldn't let that happen.

"Don't worry, I'm here now. I'll get you out." Lucy promised, having no idea how she was going to do so.

She looked around in the woods, hoping for a miracle. All she could find were bluebells, pine cones and wild garlic. All very pretty, but of no help whatsoever.

Please, Lucy prayed. *If there's anyone or anything out there that can come to my aid, I really need you now. Please...*

But nothing happened. Lucy ventured further away from the hole in the ground in search of...well, she didn't even know what she was looking for. But she couldn't just sit and do nothing.

And then. There it was. A long, thick, sturdy branch that had snapped off a tree in one of the winter storms. It was bound to be long enough to reach into the hole. Petra was an excellent climber. She could scramble up and over five-barred gates in the blink of an eye. Surely, she would be able to use this branch to climb out to freedom. Lucy just had to get the branch over to the hole and manoeuvre it down into the depths, and hey presto, Petra could get out!

She grabbed one end of the branch in her mouth and pulled with all her might. But it didn't move. She tried again. And again. It was too heavy for her to drag on her own.

Defeated, Lucy sat down in the grass, her head low and her shoulders shaking. There was no sound from Petra. She wasn't calling up to ask what was going on. Lucy had tried so hard to get there to rescue her friend and now there she was, but she was helpless...useless. And Petra remained trapped.

SEVEN

All hope was gone. The wasps had left and the last of Lucy's strength had disappeared. There was nothing else to do but lie down beside the hole. It seemed so cruel for Lucy to have found her friend but not be able to help her. A tear rolled out of her eye and plopped onto the moss in front of her.

Just then, the leaves on the ground started to rustle and Lucy lifted her head to see what it was. It was getting dark, so it was hard to tell, but it looked like lots of black things were moving about under the leaves. *What are they?* she wondered, uneasily. *They're too big and round to be ants or beetles.*

Whatever they were, they were arranging themselves under the heavy branch and nudging it. Lucy's sensitive ears picked out a tiny squeaking noise coming from the helpers, as if they were discussing what to do about the branch. And then they were lifting it, making it move, carrying it towards the hole! The huge branch seemed to slither over the ground like an enormous snake. Then, when one end of the branch was over the hole, the helpers climbed on top of each other to make a tower, lifting the other end of the branch so that it slowly slithered down into the hole. Lucy heard a thud as it hit the bottom.

"Petra!" Lucy barked urgently into the black hole. "Can you see the big branch? Can you climb up it? Up towards my voice?"

"I'll try," came the voice from below.

Lucy stood on the edge, where the wooden planks felt the most secure, and listened. She could hear some faint scratching noises but all she could see was darkness. "I'm here," she called into the hole. "Keep coming towards my voice."

It seemed to take years before she could make out a shape in the gloom, but at last, Petra wobbled into view. She was using all her concentration to keep her balance so she didn't fall back into the hole. When she was within reach, Lucy leant out as far as she could and grabbed Petra by the collar.

Normally such a strong dog, Lucy expected to lift Petra easily as she was so slim and light. And after her days in the hole with nothing to eat, she was even thinner. She should've felt like fresh air to lift. But Lucy had no power. Her grip on Petra's collar slipped and she nearly dropped her back into the hole. Petra had to scrabble and scramble her way up and out. Lucy did her best to help drag her away from the edge.

"You're safe, I've got you!" Lucy was so relieved to see Petra alive and well that she covered Petra's face with affectionate licks, forgetting all about the mysterious helpers who had melted away without a trace. Both dogs were so exhausted that they fell asleep together, cuddled up to keep each other warm.

When the sun came up in the morning, Lucy was the first to wake. Seeing Petra lying beside her filled her with joy. Her tail started wagging and she gave her friend some more face licks. Petra was so tired she didn't wake up, so Lucy lay her head on her paws while she waited.

Half closing her eyes, she looked down at her toes and saw...spots. She lifted her head and looked at her legs. More spots! She turned her head to the left, then the right, trying to see as much of her body as possible. She was covered in spots. A strange memory jumped into Lucy's mind of her spots coming to Petra's rescue the night before, of them taking her shape and working together to move the branch. Such strong spots! No, she shook her head. It couldn't be a memory; that would be impossible. It must have been a dream.

And yet, here they were. Her spots had returned and she felt brilliant. She stood up, her body and legs full of vigour again.

"They're back!" she howled happily. "Wherever they've been, they're back. I'm properly me again." Her celebrations woke Petra up at last.

"Let's go home," Lucy said.

"I can't wait to get back and sleep for a hundred years on the sofa," Petra said, imagining the warmth of her living room and the sofa she wasn't meant to sit on, but did anyway.

"Yes, and the Daleys will be so pleased to have you back, they'll give you loads of treats as well," Lucy said, her mouth filling with saliva as she imagined pieces of mouth-watering chicken and beef.

"Mmmmm, can't wait." Petra got to her feet, but bumped into Lucy as she staggered against her. "Is it far?"

Lucy's heart sank. She didn't know how far away home was. Or even which direction to go. The Daleys brought them to this place in the car and she hadn't paid any attention to the route. *Where's my friendly wasp?* Lucy wondered. *I could really do with him now.*

But there was no sign of the wasp. They were on their own.

"Come on, this way," Lucy said. Her only hope was to lead Petra back the way she came when she followed the wasps and hope that she could work out where to go.

It was slow going as Petra was so weak. She was a long way from being The Crazy Pointer at the moment. But Lucy was patient and walked slowly beside her friend, propping her up as she leaned against Lucy's strong body.

They left the wood and came to a rough, stony path. Lucy remembered that the path lead to a car park and a road. She headed in that direction, hoping that the Daleys might be looking for them there.

They only just made it. By the time they reached the car park, Petra could go no further and slumped down on the ground. Lucy looked around, trying to recognise the Daley's car. She knew that it was blue and there were four blue cars parked there. She barked urgently, hoping that the Daleys would be in one of the cars.

But nothing happened.

Lucy barked some more but the cars were all empty. She didn't know what to do next. She didn't want to leave Petra by herself, but she couldn't find help if she stayed by her side. As she tried to make up her mind what to do, a small grey car pulled into the car park. Lucy didn't pay any attention to it until she heard a familiar voice. She froze. Her first instinct was to run away, but she stopped herself; this could be their only chance to get back home.

The voice belonged to the young vet. She was out looking for Lucy, desperate to find her, draw on some black spots in permanent marker and return her to her owners before she got in trouble for losing their dog. The vet opened one of the car doors and a round, fawn-coloured dog with a flat face plopped out. Gomez!

"Gomez!" Lucy whispered, trying to get the small dog's attention. "GOMEZ," she called again.

He snapped up his little head and peered in Lucy's direction. "Who's there?"

"It's me." Lucy inched out from under the bush she and Petra were resting beneath.

"Who are you?" Gomez asked, cocking his head to one side. "I don't know you."

"What? Of course you do, I'm Lucy. You helped me escape from the clinic with the goose feather."

"No. I helped a white dog. You're a Dalmatian. A completely different dog! How do you know about the goose feather?"

"Because I *am* the white dog! You tried to get the birds to help me but they wouldn't, so then a wasp came and threatened to sting you to get you to let me out. Look Gomez, it's a long story. I'll tell you about it later. There isn't time now. I need your help again. I need you to help me get Petra home. We don't know where to go from here and my friend can't walk anymore."

"Your friend?" Gomez remembered Lucy's story now. "Oh, you actually found her!" His bottom began to wiggle and his tail whisked his back as he recalled his part in the rescue mission. "I'll alert my human.

She's looking for you. She'll be glad to take you home," Gomez panted, worn out by the excitement.

Lucy hesitated. She wasn't sure whether she could trust the vet. There was something about the young woman that made her feel uneasy. "She won't know it's me though. She's looking for a white dog and I've lost my collar with my name tag on."

Gomez squinted into the darkness beside Lucy and could just about make out the outline of another dog, lying on the ground. "We'll have to convince her then. We'd better hurry. Your friend needs help right now; what other options do you have?"

Lucy knew that Gomez was right. There wasn't any other option. She'd have to risk it and hope for the best.

"Alright then."

Gomez went into action, yapping and spinning around in a frenzy.

"What's wrong with you?" the vet snapped impatiently. "I haven't got time to play with you, Go-, I've *got* to find this missing dog today."

Gomez' tongue lolled from his mouth but he continued to yap. Then Lucy stepped forward and barked too, praying she'd be recognised.

The vet became a statue. Her eyes widened and her mouth opened. Lucy's tail gave a little wag. It had worked – the woman knew her.

Then, she laughed. It was a harsh laugh and it made Lucy's hackles rise.

"Oh, well, isn't that funny?" the vet said through clenched teeth. "The very day I'm looking for a Dalmatian, one appears! But of course, the one I want has no spots." She stopped suddenly, and bent down, peering at Lucy. "But I could take you back with me and *pretend* that you're Lucy, couldn't I? Your owners might not notice you're a different dog. They're expecting a Dalmatian. If I give them a Dalmatian, why would they think it's a different dog? Yes, that could work," she said, rubbing her hands. She noticed that Lucy wasn't wearing a collar. "All I need is a new collar, with the name and owner's phone number on and everything will be alright. Come on then dog, come to me."

Dog? Lucy's tail drooped in dismay. The vet didn't recognise her at all.

She patted her hands against her legs to summon Lucy towards her. But Lucy didn't move. She wouldn't leave Petra.

"Come on, nice dally," the vet said, more gently, pulling some treats out of her pocket and holding them out towards Lucy.

Lucy was almost tempted by the delicious smell of the meaty treat the vet was offering her, but still, she wouldn't move away from Petra.

"Come on now, come here." The vet made a grab for her, but Lucy ducked out of her reach and showed the vet her teeth. Lucy often showed her teeth as she smiled all the time, but this time, she wasn't smiling. She was warning the vet that she was not going anywhere without her friend.

Seeing an opportunity to help, Gomez rushed towards Petra and yapped in her ear. He nudged her with his flat forehead and growled, "Petra. Get up. You need to stand up, just for a minute so you can be seen. Get up, come on, get up."

Petra made a huge effort and hauled herself up onto shaky legs.

"What's that? Another dog?" The vet edged closer and peered at Petra.

"It's a pointer," she said quietly to herself. "A pointer and a Dalmatian... it's the *missing* pointer! And this must be the Dalmatian that lost its spots. It's

Lucy! They belong to the same people! Yippee! I've got you both. I'm saved! Come on girls, you come with me and I'll get you back home." She dropped down onto her knees and emptied her pockets, feeding Petra all the treats she had. Lucy's stomach rumbled but she didn't attempt to take anything for herself. She could wait.

Soon both dogs were in the back of the vet's car with Gomez, heading for home. Lucy sighed happily, all her worries gone. She'd done it. She'd found Petra, and her spots. Everything would be alright now.

EIGHT

But the vet didn't take the dogs to their home. She took them back to her clinic and put them in cages, making sure to fasten the catches tightly.

"What are you doing? Take us *home*!" Lucy barked but all the vet heard was "woof, woof, *woof!*" She gave them both a big bowl of food and a dish of water before fishing her phone out of her pocket. She looked at it, deliberating whether or not to make the call. Her plan *had* been to ring the local news to let them know that not only had she found a missing dog, and was about to reunite it with its owners, she'd also found a cure for the Dalmatian that lost its spots. It would make her famous. It could make her rich! But she faltered. Because she knew it was a lie. If anyone were to find out that her miracle medicine didn't exist, no-one would ever trust her again. Her career would be over and her family would be so disappointed in her.

She searched through her phone for a number and dialled, waiting for someone to answer.

"Hello?" she said. "Hi, it's Wren Robbins, the vet. I've got some news for you. Lucy's spots have returned." She paused as she listened to the excited response on the other end. "And there's more. I've found your other dog. I've found Petra. She's here too."

No more than ten minutes later, the Daleys pulled up at the vet's clinic, the tyres of their car squealing as they slammed on the brakes and leapt out, not even bothering to shut the doors.

“Where are they?” said Mrs Daley. Her eyes were all red and her hair was sticking up all over the place like a mop.

“They’re just through here,” the vet opened a door and ushered them through. She explained how she came upon Petra while out walking her own dog that morning and told them where she was. She didn’t mention that she’d actually been looking for Lucy.

“Yes, that’s where we parked on the day we lost her!” Mrs Daley interrupted. “But we’ve been back there loads of times and we’ve never seen her!”

“Well, to be fair, I wouldn’t have seen her either. With her markings, she’s well camouflaged. It was my pug who found her.”

Gomez puffed up his chest and smiled, proud to have been mentioned for his part in getting Petra home.

"And not only have you found Petra; you've brought Lucy's spots back!" Mr Daley said, seeing Lucy in her cage, wagging her tail furiously. "Your miracle medicine works! How much do we owe you for Lucy's treatment? And we'll give you the reward we offered for Petra's return as well."

"Oh, well..." the vet looked at the floor. The lies she'd told made her cheeks burn so she kept her head down. "I'm err...I'm afraid there was no miracle medicine."

"What do you mean?" asked Mr Daley.

The poor young vet had to explain all about how Lucy went missing and how she had to make something up to keep the owners away so they didn't find out.

"I'm sorry I lied, but nobody would trust me with their animals if they found out I'd lost someone's dog," the vet said. "I'm in enough trouble as it is. I didn't know what else to do."

"What trouble?" asked Mrs Daley.

"With this place," the vet gestured around her, "keeping it open. I'm only a tiny practice here. I've just taken it over from my dad. He was a vet too but he's retired now and wants me to keep the family business going. But now that other, much bigger practice has opened in the next town, with its swishy automatic doors and all the best new equipment, people are taking their animals there instead. I'm probably going to have to close down and Dad will be so disappointed. I shouldn't have lied, I know, but I was desperate. Finding those lost spots was the only thing I could think of to keep going. If I could have got on the news with something like that, I'd have made my name and saved the business."

"So…if you didn't cure Lucy, how did she get her spots back?" asked Mr Daley.

"I…I don't know. When I found Petra, Lucy was with her and all her spots were back then. It looks like Lucy escaped from here to go and rescue her friend. I've really no idea how she got out. The pens here are secure. I can only assume that Lucy's spots disappeared due to stress and worry about her missing friend. Once she'd found her, they all came back again. That's the only explanation I can think of."

"Oh, Lucy! You rescued Petra? You brave, clever girl!" Mrs Daley opened the cage door and gave her a huge hug that put white hairs all over her clothes. But she didn't care. She was too happy to notice. She opened Petra's cage and hugged her too.

"Right, we're taking you two home, come on," she said, clipping a lead onto Petra's collar. "And we won't be paying anything for Lucy's *treatment."*

"No, no, of course not." The vet held her hands up to show she wasn't expecting anything.

"I don't think you deserve the reward either, actually, since you only found Petra by accident because you were looking for Lucy, who you'd lost!"

And with that, they left the vet and took the dogs home.

Later that night, when the Daleys were sitting on the sofa, each with a dog on their lap, Mrs Daley spoke up, having spent a few hours thinking over the situation.

"You know," she said, "I've been thinking about the young vet. She didn't have to tell us the truth about the medicine and Lucy's spots, or about Lucy going missing. She could have lied about it all, charged us a fortune and got herself on the telly. If she'd done that, she could have saved her business. She behaved badly, but she did the right thing in the end and told the truth. I don't want her to have to close down... I think I'll phone the local TV news in the morning and see if they'll do a story about Petra's rescue. It would be good publicity for the vet."

"Yes dear," Mr Daley agreed. "You do that."

NINE

On the day of the TV interview, everyone made sure they looked their best. Lucy and Petra were both given a bath and Lucy looked absolutely beautiful with her black spots gleaming against her pristine white coat.

The reporter asked the Daleys lots of questions about the dogs and their recent adventure. They smiled and answered, looking as happy as could be. At the end of the interview, the reporter said to the Daleys, "So you must be very relieved to have both of your dogs back with you?"

"Yes we are," Mr Daley said, "and we'd like to thank this young vet, Miss Robbins. Lucy was the one to find Petra, but Miss Robbins brought them back to us."

The vet smiled and tears brimmed behind her glasses. She was so relieved to have been forgiven. But she hadn't heard the best part yet.

"For what she's done," Mr Daley continued, "we'd like to give her this reward." He passed the young vet a cheque. She looked down at it in shock, seeing the numbers written on it. Her eyes sparkled and a big, fat tear rolled down her face and plopped onto the cheque.

"Oh, you didn't need to do that!" she exclaimed. "That's so kind of you."

"Well, you deserve it," Mrs Daley looked the vet straight in the eyes to show her that she really meant it.

"It's far more than I deserve," she replied, removing her glasses to wipe her eyes. The reporter frowned in confusion, but the Daleys knew exactly what she meant. "If it's alright with you, I'll be donating some of this money to our local animal charity to help them rescue and rehome more abandoned and unwanted pets."

"That's absolutely fine with us," Mrs Daley said, pulling the vet into a big hug. "What a lovely idea."

And the vet did as she said. She made a donation to *Peregrine Pets* and even came away with a rescue dog: a chestnut Staffordshire bull terrier called Gizmo who nobody wanted due to her twisted front leg. Gomez instantly loved her and he and Gizmo became the best of friends straight away, just like Lucy and Petra.

And instead of the vet having to close her doors, the opposite happened. She became famous, just like she wanted. Having seen her on the TV, customers started flocking to her surgery and *Peregrine Pets* invited her to become their official vet. She was so busy, she had to take on more staff to help her.

The vet often thought about how she'd almost tried to get what she wanted through dishonesty, and it made her shudder. How different it could all have been if she'd chosen to lie. She'd still have got the money, much more in fact, if she'd charged for the imaginary miracle medicine, but how guilty she would have felt. It would have weighed on her mind every day and made it impossible to be happy. Now, her family were proud of her and she had nothing on her conscience. She was so pleased she made the right choice; it made her smile all day long. She even became known as 'the smiling vet'.

TEN

The vet wasn't the only one to find fame. After being on the TV news, Lucy was also featured in local newspapers where her story was picked up by the national news. Soon she was in all the newspapers in the country, with the headline 'The Dalmatian that Lost its Spots' and then she was invited onto daytime TV programmes with Petra and the Daleys to talk about their story.

The best thing that happened as a result of it all was that Lucy became the poster dog for *Peregrine Pets* and because she was so well known, the charity found itself flooded with people offering new homes to its rescued animals.

Peregrine
Pets
Animal Shelter
Dalmatian
that lost
its spots...

One day, Lucy and Petra were lying in their back garden, side by side, enjoying the sunshine. There was a buzzing sound and a wasp zig-zagged past them. Petra went to snap at it but Lucy stopped her immediately.

“What?” Petra asked. “Wasps are a nuisance, and they sting.”

“Not all wasps sting,” Lucy replied. “Wasps are actually very helpful creatures, and one of them is a good friend of mine. I hope to see him again sometime.”

“You’ve got a friend who’s a wasp?” Petra asked in disbelief.

“I have. He’s the reason you’re here today, actually. If it hadn’t been for him and all his friends and family, I’d never have found you. I didn’t get a chance to thank them for what they did, but I hope to, one day. They didn’t help because they expected anything in return, or even because they were asked to…they did it because…well, because they're good and kind."

"Oh? I'd like to hear about that," said Petra.

"Alright then, but get ready. It's a long story."

THE END

Thank You

I'd like to first thank Steve Hutton for producing the illustrations for the book and the cover. He used photographs of the real Lucy and Petra and captured them brilliantly. This story is about my own dogs but sadly, Lucy passed away in April 2020. She was a big presence in my life, having a huge personality and being physically larger than average for a Dalmatian, so it's lovely that the illustrations capture her so well.

Choosing the final cover design for this book was a difficult task and I really appreciate the work Amanda at 'Let's Get Booked' put in to creating it. Thanks also to all the people who read the manuscript, voted and gave feedback on the title, cover and blurb, including the pupils at Braithwaite Primary School. Their enthusiasm for the final version of the story was so nice after all the months of work.

Finally, for their support and encouragement, I thank award winning children's authors Tom Palmer and Sam Angus for reading and reviewing the book before publication. Sam gave me pages of advice which definitely helped to improve the story, alongside my editor.

To anyone who helped with this book in any way, I appreciate your time and am grateful for the support and suggestions offered. I hope that you enjoyed reading the story as much as I enjoyed creating it in memory of my lovely Lucy Leopard.

Find out what Lucy and Petra get up to in their next adventure in the sequel:

Petra and the Dogs in Danger

About the Author

Helen lives in Cumbria with her husband and a family of horses, dogs, hens, ducks and geese! As well as writing books, she also teaches English and runs a secondary school library.

Visit **www.helenharaldsen.co.uk** to find out more about Helen and to sign up to her mailing list. You'll receive news, updates, opportunities and free, exclusive bonus material linked to HH Books.

Did you enjoy this book? The author would love to see your reviews on Amazon.

Please feel free to post your comments and let others know about The Dalmatian that Lost its Spots.

Also By This Author

Amber's Pony Tales

A Tale of Two Shoes

Did You Know?

The origins of the Dalmatian breed can be traced back to Croatia and its historical region of Dalmatia. Because they are such a beautiful dog, with great endurance, they were often used in the 18th and 19th century as companions for the carriages of the wealthy. They were trained to trot alongside the carriages to protect the occupants from highwaymen. From puppies, they were kennelled in the stables, where they formed strong bonds with the horses.

Dalmatians also played a vital role with the fire service, back in the days when steam powered pumpers were pulled by horses. Dalmatians would run alongside the horses, keeping pace even when sprinting long distances, helping to clear the way in crowded streets. They also guarded the very valuable horses in their stables.

With the decline of horse-drawn transport, the Dalmatian is now mainly used as a loyal pet, companion and show dog.

The German Shorthaired Pointer was bred in Germany as an all-terrain hunting dog that could effectively hunt all types of game on all types of land, from dense forests to open fields. The dog's job was to locate the game and point – remain still – to allow the hunters time to close in on the quarry. It was also needed to retrieve fallen game both on land and in water. They are intelligent, energetic and affectionate and also excellent escape artists (unless they fall down a very deep well)!

Printed in Great Britain
by Amazon

Biodiversity: An Introduction

SECOND EDITION

Kevin J. Gaston
Professor of Biodiversity and Conservation
Department of Animal & Plant Sciences
University of Sheffield

and

John I. Spicer
Reader in Marine Biology and
Physiological Ecology
School of Biological Sciences
University of Plymouth

350 Main Street, Malden, MA 02148-50120, USA
108 Cowley Road, Oxford OX4 1JF, UK
550 Swanston Street, Carlton, Victoria 3053, Australia

First edition published 1998
Second edition published 2004

Library of Congress Cataloging-in-Publication Data

Gaston, Kevin J.
Biodiversity: an introduction/
Kevin J. Gaston and John I. Spicer. – 2nd ed.
p. cm.
Includes bibliographical references and index.
ISBN 1-4051-1857-1 (pbk.: alk. paper)
1. Biological diversity. I. Spicer, John I. II. Title.
QH541.15.B56G37 2004
333.95'11—dc21 2003011788

A catalogue record for this title is available from the British Library.

Set in 10/13pt Berkeley Old Style
by Graphicraft Limited, Hong Kong
Printed and bound in the United Kingdom
by TJ International, Padstow, Cornwall

For further information on
Blackwell Publishing, visit our website:
http://www.blackwellpublishing.com

Contents

Preface

This is the second edition of *Biodiversity: An Introduction*. Our goal in writing the first edition was to provide a text that both gave an introduction to biodiversity – what it is, how it arose, how it is distributed, why it is important and what should be done to maintain it – and present an entry point into the wider literature on biodiversity. That remains the goal here. However, much has occurred in the intervening years. First, understanding of many key issues has developed rapidly, with important new models having been developed, experiments having been conducted, and measurements made. Some controversies have been settled, and others have arisen. In short, the study of biodiversity remains vibrant and stimulating. Second, and as a consequence of these advances, the literature on biodiversity has continued to blossom with, for example, few issues of some of the major science journals (e.g. *Nature*, *Science*) now passing without containing one or more papers of relevance. Third, there has been a marked change in the structure of botanical, zoological and ecological courses taught in universities, away from inclusion of the more traditional taxonomically centred surveys of different groups of organisms, and towards an approach centred instead on the concept of biodiversity. Fourth, and most importantly, there has been little, if any, reduction in the degree of threat faced by the variety of life on Earth; if anything, there is now a sharpened awareness of how acute that threat is and how pervasive are its implications.

These developments have led us to revise *Biodiversity: An Introduction* substantially. Much of the book has been rewritten, updated and extended. The six chapters address the nature of biodiversity (Chapter 1), the history of biodiversity (Chapter 2), the spatial distribution of biodiversity (Chapter 3), the value of biodiversity (Chapter 4), human impacts on biodiversity (Chapter 5), and the future maintenance of biodiversity (Chapter 6). In each case, we have sought to draw out the major issues and provide actual examples. All the figures in the book can be downloaded from the Blackwell Publishing website (www.blackwellpublishing.com/gaston). Reference is made throughout the text to relevant papers and books, where possible with an emphasis on those that are more readily accessible. In addition, each chapter concludes with suggestions for further reading. These are sources, usually books, that we hope readers will find useful for exploring particular themes in greater detail, but which have often not been cited elsewhere in the chapter.

Many people have generously provided guidance in this endeavour, commenting on drafts of the first edition of *Biodiversity: An Introduction*, suggesting ways in which the published version could be improved and developed, commenting on drafts of chapters for the second edition, and responding to multifarious queries and requests. In particular, we are grateful to Dave Bilton, Steven Chown, Andy Foggo, Sian Gaston, Alison Holt, Rhonda Snook, Richard Thompson, Mick Uttley and Clare Vincent. We would also like to thank the students who have taken module *APS215 Biodiversity* at the University of Sheffield, Tim Caro and the students on his conservation biology course, Lee Hannah, Claudia Moreno and Ana Rodrigues. Rosie Hayden, Cee Pike, Katrina Rainey and Sarah Shannon of Blackwell Publishing cajoled, encouraged and helped steer this volume to its conclusion, with good humour and insight. We are grateful for their assistance.

As before, we dedicate this book to Megan, Ben, Ethan and Ellie, with the desire that their generation is kinder to biodiversity than our own has been.

K.J.G. & J.I.S.
January 2003

Acknowledgements

The authors and publisher gratefully acknowledge the permission granted to reproduce the copyright material in this book:

Fig. 1.2: Fig. 1 from Avise, J.C. & Johns, G.C. (1999) Proposal for a standardized temporal scheme of biological classification for extant species. *Proceedings of the National Academy of Sciences, USA* **96**, 7358–7363. Copyright © 1999 National Academy of Sciences, USA. Reprinted by permission.

Fig. 1.3: Fig. 1 from Purvis, A. & Hector, A. (2000) Getting the measure of biodiversity. *Nature* **405**, 212–219. Reprinted by permission of the publisher and the authors.

Fig. 1.6a: Fig. 4b from Roy, K., Jablonski, D. & Valentine, J.W. (1996) Higher taxa in biodiversity studies: patterns from eastern Pacific marine molluscs. *Philosophical Transactions of the Royal Society, London B* **351**, 1605–1613. Reprinted by permission of the Royal Society.

Fig. 1.6b: Reprinted from *Biological Conservation* **93**, Balmford, A., Lyon, A.J.E. & Lang, R.M. 'Testing the higher-taxon approach to conservation planning in a megadiverse group: the macro fungi', pp. 209–217, Copyright © 2000, with permission from Elsevier.

Fig. 1.6c: Fig. 3.7a from Williams, P.H. & Humphries, C.J. (1996) Comparing character diversity among biotas. In: *Biodiversity: A Biology of Numbers and Difference* (ed. K.J. Gaston), pp. 54–76. Blackwell Science, Oxford. Reprinted by permission of Blackwell Publishing Ltd.

Fig. 1.6d: Fig. 5d from Petchey, O.L. & Gaston, K.J. (2002) Functional diversity (FD), species richness and community composition. *Ecology Letters* **5**, 402–411. Reprinted by permission of Blackwell Publishing Ltd.

Fig. 2.2: Reprinted with permission from Fig. 1, Benton, M.J. (1995) Diversification and extinction in the history of life. *Science* **268**, 52–58. Copyright © 1995 American Association for the Advancement of Science.

Fig. 2.3a: Reprinted with permission from Fig. 3a, Benton, M.J. (1995) Diversification and extinction in the history of life. *Science* **268**, 52–58. Copyright © 1995 American Association for the Advancement of Science.

Fig. 2.3b: Reprinted with permission from Fig. 4a, Benton, M.J. (1995) Diversification and extinction in the history of life. *Science* **268**, 52–58. Copyright © 1995 American Association for the Advancement of Science.

Fig. 2.4: Fig. 28.3b from Van Valkenburgh, B. & Janis, C.M. (1993) Historical diversity patterns in North American large herbivores and carnivores. In: *Species Diversity in Ecological Communities: Historical and Geographical Perspectives* (eds. R.E. Ricklefs & D. Schluter), pp. 330–340. University of Chicago Press, Chicago, IL. Reprinted by permission of University of Chicago Press.

Fig. 2.5: Fig. 1 from Niklas, K.J. (1986) Large-scale changes in animal and plant terrestrial communities. In: *Patterns and Processes in the History of Life* (eds. D.M. Raup & D. Jablonski), pp. 383–405. Springer-Verlag, Heidelberg. Reprinted by permission of Springer-Verlag.

Fig. 2.6: Fig. 1 from Benton, M.J. (1985) Mass extinction among non-marine tetrapods. *Nature* **316**, 811–814. Reprinted by permission of the publisher.

Fig. 2.7a: Fig. 5.2 from Boulter, M. (2002) *Extinction, Evolution and the End of Man*. Fourth Estate, London. Reprinted by permission of the author.

Fig. 2.7b: Fig. 5.3 from Boulter, M. (2002) *Extinction, Evolution and the End of Man*. Fourth Estate, London. Reprinted by permission of the author.

Fig. 2.8: Fig. 2 from Slowinski, J.B. & Guyer, C. (1989) Testing the stochasticity of patterns of organismal diversity: an improved null model. *American Naturalist* **134**, 907–921. Reprinted by permission of University of Chicago Press.

Fig. 2.9: Fig. 1 from Raup, D.M. (1994) The role of extinction in evolution. *Proceedings of the National Academy of Sciences, USA* **91**, 6758–6763. Reprinted by permission of the National Academy of Sciences.

Fig. 2.10: Fig. 2 from Raup, D.M. (1994) The role of extinction in evolution. *Proceedings of the National Academy of Sciences, USA* **91**, 6758–6763. Reprinted by permission of the National Academy of Sciences.

Fig. 2.12a: Fig. 1a from Dworschak, P.C. (2000) Global diversity in the Thalassinidea (Decapoda). *Journal of Crustacean Biology* **20** (Special Number 2), 238–245. Reprinted by permission of The Crustacean Society.

Fig. 2.12b: *Mammal Species of the World*, edited by Don E. Wilson and DeeAnn Reeder. (Washington, DC, Smithsonian Institution Press). Copyright © 1993 by the Smithsonian Institution. Used by permission of the publisher.

Fig. 2.13: Map from Hockey, P. (1997a) New Birds in Africa. *Africa – Birds and Birding* **2**, 39–44. Reprinted by permission of Africa – Birds and Birding.

Fig. 3.1a: Fig. 3 from Lonsdale, W.M. (1999) Global patterns of plant invasions and the concept of invisibility. *Ecology* **80**, 1522–1536. Reprinted by permission of The Ecological Society of America.

Fig. 3.1b: Fig. 1 from Azovsky, A.I. (2002) Size-dependent species–area relationships in benthos: is the world more diverse for microbes? *Ecography* **25**, 273–282. Reprinted by permission of Blackwell Publishing Ltd.

Fig. 3.3a: Fig. 2 from Ellison, A.M. (2002) Macroecology of mangroves: large-scale patterns and processes in tropical coastal forests. *Trees* **16**, 181–194. Reprinted by permission of Springer-Verlag.

Fig. 3.3c: Fig. 4b from Bini, L.M., Diniz Filho, J.A.F., Bonfim, F. & Bastos, R.P. (2000) Local and regional species richness relationships in viperid snake assemblages from South America: unsaturated patterns at three different spatial scales. *Copeia* **2000**, 799–805. Reprinted by permission of the American Society of Ichthyologists and Herpetologists.

Fig. 3.3d: Reprinted with permission from Fig. 3, Ricklefs, R.E. (1987) Community diversity: relative roles of local and regional processes. *Science* **235**, 167–171. Copyright © 1987 American Association for the Advancement of Science.

Fig. 3.4: Fig. 1 from Olson, D.M., Dinerstein, E., Wikramanayake, E.D., Burgess, N.D., Powell, G.V.N., Underwood, E.C., D'Amico, J.A., Itoua, I., Strand, H.E., Morrison, J.C., Loucks, C.J., Allnutt, T.F., Ricketts, T.H., Kura, Y.,

Lamoreux, J.F., Wettengel, W.W., Hedao, P. & Kassem, K.R. (2001) Terrestrial ecoregions of the world: a new map of life on Earth. *BioScience* **51**, 933–938. Copyright © American Institute of Biological Sciences. Reprinted by permission of the publisher.

Fig. 3.5: Fig. 2 from Olson, D.M., Dinerstein, E., Wikramanayake, E.D., Burgess, N.D., Powell, G.V.N., Underwood, E.C., D'Amico, J.A., Itoua, I., Strand, H.E., Morrison, J.C., Loucks, C.J., Allnutt, T.F., Ricketts, T.H., Kura, Y., Lamoreux, J.F., Wettengel, W.W., Hedao, P. & Kassem, K.R. (2001) Terrestrial ecoregions of the world: a new map of life on Earth. *BioScience* **51**, 933–938. Copyright © American Institute of Biological Sciences. Reprinted by permission of the publisher.

Fig. 3.6: Reprinted from *Ecological Geography of the Sea*, Longhurst, A. (Academic Press, San Diego). Copyright © 1998 with permission from Elsevier.

Fig. 3.8: Fig. 1 from Myers, N., Mittermeier, R.A., Mittermeier, C.G., da Fonseca, G.A.B. & Kent, J. (2000) Biodiversity hotspots for conservation priorities. *Nature* **403**, 853–858. Reprinted by permission of the publisher.

Fig. 3.9a: Fig. 1b from Cowling, R.M. & Samways, M.J. (1995) Predicting global patterns of endemic plant species richness. *Biodiversity Letters* **2**, 127–131. Reprinted by permission of Blackwell Publishing Ltd.

Fig. 3.9b: Fig. 1b from Ceballos, G. & Brown, J.H. (1995) Global patterns of mammalian diversity, endemism and endangerment. *Conservation Biology* **9**, 559–568. Reprinted by permission of Blackwell Publishing Ltd.

Fig. 3.10: Fig. 1a from Cowling, R.M. & Samways, M.J. (1995) Predicting global patterns of endemic plant species richness. *Biodiversity Letters* **2**, 127–131. Reprinted by permission of Blackwell Publishing Ltd.

Fig. 3.11: Fig. 7 from Stattersfield, A.J., Crosby, M.J., Long, A.J. & Wege, D.C. (1998) *Endemic Bird Areas of the World. Priorities for Biodiversity Conservation*. BirdLife International, Cambridge. Reprinted by permission of Birdlife International.

Fig. 3.12a: Fig. 1 from Oberdorff, T. & Guégan, J.-F. (1999) Patterns of endemism in riverine fish of the Northern Hemisphere. *Ecology Letters* **2**, 75–81. Reprinted by permission of Blackwell Publishing Ltd.

Fig. 3.12b: Fig. 4 from Ceballos, G. & Brown, J.H. (1995) Global patterns of mammalian diversity, endemism and endangerment. *Conservation Biology* **9**, 559–568. Reprinted by permission of Blackwell Publishing Ltd.

Fig. 3.13a: Fig. 1a from Enquist, B.J. & Niklas, K.J. (2001) Invariant scaling relations across tree-dominated communities. *Nature* **410**, 655–660. Reprinted by permission of the publisher and authors.

Fig. 3.13b: Fig. 1c from Oberdorff, T., Guégan, J.-F. & Hugueny, B. (1995) Global scale patterns of fish species richness in rivers. *Ecography* **18**, 345–352. Reprinted by permission of Blackwell Publishing Ltd.

Fig. 3.13d: Fig. 2a from Kaufman, D.M. & Willig, M.R. (1998) Latitudinal patterns of mammalian species richness in the New World: the effects of sampling method and faunal group. *Journal of Biogeography* **25**, 795–805. Reprinted by permission of Blackwell Publishing Ltd.

Fig. 3.14a: Reprinted from *Deep Sea Research I* **47**, Culver, S.J. & Buzas, M.A., Global latitudinal species diversity gradient in deep-sea benthic foraminifera, pp. 259–275. Copyright © 2000 with permission from Elsevier.

Fig. 3.14b: Fig. 12 from Dolan, J.R. & Gallegos, C.L. (2001) Estuarine diversity of tintinnids (planktonic ciliates). *Journal of Plankton Research* **23**, 1009–1027. By permission of Oxford University Press.

Fig. 3.14c: Fig. 2 from Dworschak, P.C. (2000) Global diversity in the Thalassinidea (Decapoda). *Journal of Crustacean Biology* **20** (Special Number 2), 238–245. Reprinted by permission of The Crustacean Society.

Fig. 3.14d: Fig. 1 from Flessa, K.W. & Jablonski, D. (1995) Biogeography of recent marine bivalve molluscs and its implications for paleobiogeography and the geography of extinction: a progress report. *Historical Biology* **10**, 25–47.

Reprinted by permission of Taylor & Francis Ltd, http://www.tandf.co.uk/journals

Fig. 3.15: Fig. 2 from Gaston, K.J., Williams, P.H., Eggleton, P. & Humphries, C.J. (1995) Large scale patterns of biodiversity: spatial variation in family richness. *Proceedings of the Royal Society, London B* **260**, 149–154. Reprinted by permission of the Royal Society.

Fig. 3.16: Reprinted with permission from Fig. 2 (Angiosperms), Crane, P.R. & Lidgard, S. (1989), Angiosperm diversification and paleolatitudinal gradients in Cretaceous floristic diversity, *Science* **246**, 675–678. Copyright © 1989 American Association for the Advancement of Science.

Fig. 3.17: Fig. 2 from Eggleton, P. (1994) Termites live in a pear-shaped world: a response to Platnick. *Journal of Natural History* **28**, 1209–1212. Reprinted by permission of Taylor & Francis Ltd, http://www.tandf.co.uk/journals

Fig. 3.18a: Fig. 1 from Dixon, A.F.G., Kindlmann, P., Leps, J. & Holman, J. (1987) Why are there so few species of aphids, especially in the tropics? *American Naturalist* **129**, 580–592. Reprinted by permission of University of Chicago Press.

Fig. 3.18b: Fig. 2 from Price, P.W., Fernandes, G.W., Lara, A.C.F., Brawn, J., Barrios, H., Wright, M.G., Ribeiro, S.P. & Rothcliff, N. (1998) Global patterns in local number of insect galling species. *Journal of Biogeography* **25**, 581–591. Reprinted by permission of Blackwell Publishing Ltd.

Fig. 3.18c: Fig. 2 from Kouki, J., Niemelä, P. & Viitasaari, M. (1994) Reversed latitudinal gradient in species richness of sawflies (Hymenoptera, Symphyta). *Annales Zoologici Fennici* **31**, 83–88. Reprinted by permission of the Finnish Zoological and Botanical Publishing Board.

Fig. 3.18d: Fig. 1 from Järvinen, O., Kouki, J. & Häyrinen, U. (1987) Reversed latitudinal gradients in total density and species richness of birds breeding on Finnish mires. *Ornis Fennica* **64**, 67–73. Reprinted by permission of the Finnish Ornithological Society.

Fig. 3.19a: Fig. 2 from Kerr, J.T & Packer, L. (1999) The environmental basis of North American species richness patterns among *Epicauta* (Coleoptera: Meloidae). *Biodiversity and Conservation* **8**, 617–628. With kind permission of Kluwer Academic Publishers.

Fig. 3.19b: Fig. 1 from Roy, K., Jablonski, D., Valentine, J.W. & Rosenberg, G. (1998) Marine latitudinal diversity gradients: tests of causal hypotheses. *Proceedings of the National Academy of Sciences, USA* **95**, 3699–3702. Copyright © 1998 National Academy of Sciences, USA.

Fig. 3.19c: Fig. 3a from Lennon, J.J., Greenwood, J.J.D. & Turner, J.R.G. (2000) Bird diversity and environmental gradients in Britain: a test of the species–energy hypthesis. *Journal of Animal Ecology* **69**, 581–598. Reprinted by permission of Blackwell Publishing Ltd.

Fig. 3.20a: Fig. 2 from Grytnes, J.A. & Vestaas, O.R. (2002) Species richness and altitude: a comparison between null models and interpolated plant species richness along the Himalayan altitudinal gradient, Nepal. *American Naturalist* **159**, 294–304. Reprinted by permission of University of Chicago Press.

Fig. 3.20b: Fig. 1a from Sanders, N.J. (2002) Elevational gradients in ant species richness: area, geometry and Rapoport's rule. *Ecography* **25**, 25–32. Reprinted by permission of Blackwell Publishing Ltd.

Fig. 3.20d: Fig. 1b from Patterson, B.D., Stotz, D.E., Solari, S., Fitzpatrick, J.W. & Pacheco, V. (1998) Contrasting patterns of elevational zonation for birds and mammals in the Andes of southeastern Peru. *Journal of Biogeography* **25**, 593–607. Reprinted by permission of Blackwell Publishing Ltd.

Fig. 3.21: Fig. 2 from Rahbek, C. (1995) The elevational gradient of species richness: a uniform pattern? *Ecography* **18**, 200–205. Reprinted by permission of Blackwell Publishing Ltd.

Fig. 3.22a: Fig. 2 from Svavarsson, J., Strömberg, J.-O. & Brattegard, T. (1993) The deep-sea asellote (Isopoda, Crustacea) fauna of the Northern Seas: species composition, distributional patterns and origin. *Journal of Biogeography* **20**, 537–555. Reprinted by permission of Blackwell Publishing Ltd.

Fig. 3.22b: Fig. 5.2 from Rex, M.A., Etter, R.J. & Stuart, C.T. (1997) Large-scale patterns of species diversity in the deep-sea benthos. In: *Marine Biodiversity: Patterns and Processes* (eds. R.F.G. Ormond, J.D. Gage & M.V. Angel), pp. 94–121. Cambridge University Press, Cambridge. Reprinted by permission of Cambridge University Press.

Fig. 3.22c: Fig. 5a from Morenta, J., Stefanescu, C., Massuti, E., Morales-Nin, B. & Lloris, D. (1998) Fish community structure and depth-related trends on the continental slope of the Balearic Islands (Algerian basin, western Mediterranean). *Marine Ecology Progress Series* **171**, 247–259. Reprinted by permission of the International Ecology Institute, Oldendorf/Luhe, Germany.

Fig. 3.22d: Fig. 4.13 from Angel, M.V. (1994) Spatial distribution of marine organisms: patterns and processes. In: *Large-scale Ecology and Conservation Biology* (eds. P.J. Edwards, R.M. May & N.R. Webb), pp. 59–109. Blackwell Science, Oxford. Reprinted by permission of Blackwell Publishing Ltd.

Fig. 3.23: Fig. 5a from Macpherson, E. & Duarte, C.M. (1994) Patterns in species richness, size and latitudinal range of East Atlantic fishes. *Ecography* **17**, 242–248. Reprinted by permission of Blackwell Publishing Ltd.

Fig. 3.24a: Fig. 4 from Martin, J. & Gurrea, P. (1990) The peninsula effect in Iberian butterflies (Lepidoptera: Papilionoidea and Hesperioidea). *Journal of Biogeography* **17**, 85–96. Reprinted by permission of Blackwell Publishing Ltd.

Fig. 3.24b: Fig. 2.22 from Gaston, K.J. & Blackburn, T.M. (2000) *Pattern and Process in Macroecology*. Blackwell Science, Oxford. Reprinted by permission of Blackwell Publishing Ltd.

Fig. 3.24c: Fig. 3 from Rapoport, E.H. (1994) Remarks on marine and continental biogeography: an aerographical viewpoint. *Philosophical Transactions of the Royal Society, London B* **343**, 71–78. Reprinted by permission of the Royal Society.

Fig. 3.25: Fig. 5.8 from Balmford, A. (2002) Selecting sites for conservation. In: *Conserving Bird Biodiversity: General Principles and their Applications* (eds. K. Norris & D.J. Pain), pp. 74–104. Cambridge University Press, Cambridge. Reprinted by permission of Cambridge University Press.

Fig. 4.1: Fig. 1 from Naeem, S. (1998) Species redundancy and ecosystem reliability. *Conservation Biology* **12**, 39–45. Reprinted by permission of Blackwell Publishing Ltd.

Fig. 4.2: Fig. 2 from Naeem, S. (2002) Functioning of biodiversity. In: *Encyclopedia of Global Environmental Change*, Vol. 2 (ed. T. Munn), pp. 20–36. Copyright © 2002 John Wiley & Sons Limited. Reproduced with permission.

Fig. 5.1: Fig. 5.3 from Pimm, S.L., Moulton, M.P. & Justice, L.J. (1995) Bird extinctions in the central Pacific. In: *Extinction Rates* (eds. J.H. Lawton & R.M. May), pp. 75–87. Oxford University Press, Oxford. Reprinted by permission of Oxford University Press.

Fig. 5.2: Reprinted from *Trends in Ecology and Evolution* **8**, Smith, F.D.M., May, R.M., Pello, R., Johnson, T.H. & Walter, K.R, How much do we know about the current extinction rate? pp. 375–378, Copyright © 1993, with permission from Elsevier.

Fig. 5.3: Fig. 1 from Pauly, D., Christensen, V., Guénette, S., Pitcher, T.J., Sumaila, U.R., Walters, C.J., Watson, R. & Zeller, D. (2002) Towards sustainability in world fisheries. *Nature* **418**, 689–695. Reprinted by permission of the publisher and authors.

Fig. 5.4: Fig. 26 from Grainger, R.J.R. & Garcia, S.M. (1996) Chronicles of marine fishery landings (1950–1994): trend analysis and fisheries potential. *FAO Fisheries Technical Paper* **359**, 1–51. Reprinted by permission of the Food and Agriculture Organization of the United Nations.

Fig. 5.6: Reprinted with permission from Fig. 1, Green, G.M. & Sussman, R.W. (1990) Deforestation history of the eastern rain forests of

Madagascar from satellite images, *Science* **248**, 212–215. Copyright © 1990 American Association for the Advancement of Science.

Fig. 5.7: From Anon. (1994) *Biodiversity: The UK Action Plan*. HMSO, London. Reprinted by permission of HMSO.

Fig. 5.8: Fig. 1 from Ruesink, J.L., Parker, I.M., Groom, M.J. & Kareiva, P.M. (1995) Reducing the risks of nonindigenous species introductions. *BioScience* **45**, 465–477. Copyright © American Institute of Biological Sciences.

Fig. 5.9: Fig. 1 from Vitousek, P.M., Mooney, H.A., Lubchenco, J. & Melillo, J.M. (1997) Human domination of Earth's ecosystems. *Science* **277**, 494–499.

Fig. 5.10: From *Terrestrial Ecoregions of the Indo-Pacific: A Conservation Assessment*, by Eric Wikramanayake, Eric Dinerstein, Colby Loukes, et al. Copyright © 2002 Island Press. Republished by permission of Island Press.

Fig. 5.11a: Fig. 2 from Thompson, K. & Jones, A. (1999) Human population density and prediction of local plant extinction in Britain. *Conservation Biology* **13**, 185–189. Reprinted by permission of Blackwell Publishing Ltd.

Fig. 5.11b: Fig. 3 from Hoare, R.E. & du Toit, J.T. (1999) Coexistence between people and elephants in African savannas. *Conservation Biology* **13**, 633–639. Reprinted by permission of Blackwell Publishing Ltd.

Fig. 5.12: Fig. 2 from Woodroffe, R. (2000) Predators and people: using human densities to interpret declines of large carnivores. *Animal Conservation* **3**, 165–173. Reprinted by permission of Cambridge University Press.

Fig. 5.13: Fig. 5.3 from Cohen, J.E. (1995) *How Many People Can the Earth Support?* W.W. Norton, New York.

Fig. 6.1: Fig. 2 from Green, M.J.B. & Paine, J. (1997) State of the world's protected areas at the end of the twentieth century. Paper presented at IUCN World Commission on Protected Areas symposium 'Protected areas in the twenty-first century: from islands to networks'. Albany, Australia. Copyright © 1997 WCMC. Reprinted by permission of UNEP-WCMC, Cambridge.

Fig. 6.2: Fig. 3 from Green, M.J.B. & Paine, J. (1997) State of the world's protected areas at the end of the twentieth century. Paper presented at IUCN World Commission on Protected Areas symposium 'Protected areas in the twenty-first century: from islands to networks'. Albany, Australia. Copyright © 1997 WCMC. Reprinted by permission of UNEP-WCMC, Cambridge.

Fig. 6.3: From *Requiem for Nature*, by John Terborgh. Copyright © 1999 by John Terborgh. Republished by permission of Island Press/Shearwater Books.

Fig. 6.4: Fig. 15.2 from Huston, M.A. (1994) *Biological Diversity: The Coexistence of Species on Changing landscapes*. Cambridge University Press, Cambridge. Reprinted by permission of Cambridge University Press.

Fig. 6.5: Reprinted with permission from Fig. 2, Soulé, M.E. (1991), Conservation: tactics for a constant crisis, *Science* **253**, 744–749. Copyright © 1991 American Association for the Advancement of Science.

Table 2.3: Table 2 from McKinney, M.L. (1997) Extinction, vulnerability and selectivity: combining ecological and paleontological views. With permission, from the *Annual Review of Ecology and Systematics*, volume 28 © 1997, by Annual Reviews www.annualreviews.org.

Table 2.4: Table 3.1–2 from Hawksworth, D.L. & Kalin-Arroyo, M.T. (1995) Magnitude and distribution of biodiversity. In: *Global Biodiversity Assessment* (ed. V.H. Heywood), pp. 107–199. Cambridge University Press, Cambridge. Reprinted by permission of Cambridge University Press.

Table 3.1: Table 7–1 from Reaka-Kudia, M.L. (1997) The global biodiversity of coral reefs: a comparison with rain forests. In: *Biodiversity II: Understanding & Protecting our Biological Resources* (eds. M.L. Reaka-Kudia, D.E. Wilson & E.O. Wilson), pp. 83–108. Joseph Henry, Washington, DC. Reprinted with permission from *Biodiversity II* © 1996 by the National Academy of Sciences, courtesy of the National Academies Press, Washington, DC.

Table 4.1: Table 1.1 from Lovelock, J. (1989) *The Ages of Gaia: A Biography of our Living Earth*. Oxford University Press, Oxford. Reprinted by permission of Oxford University Press.

Table 5.2: Table 2 from Hannah, L., Carr, J.L. & Lankerani, A. (1995) Human disturbance and natural habitat: a biome level analysis of a global data set. *Biodiversity and Conservation* 4, 128–155. With kind permission of Kluwer Academic Publishers.

Table 5.4: Excerpted from *A Plague of Rats and Rubbervines: The Growing Threat of Species Invasions*, by Yvonne Baskin. Copyright © 2002 The Scientific Committee on Problems of the Environment (SCOPE). Reprinted by permission of Island Press/Shearwater Books.

Every effort has been made to trace copyright holders and to obtain their permission for the use of copyright material. The publisher apologizes for any errors or omissions in the above list and would be grateful if notified of any corrections that should be incorporated in future reprints or editions of this book.

1 What is biodiversity?

1.1 Marion Island

The biotas of a few sites around the world have received disproportionate attention from biologists. One such is Marion Island, the larger of the two islands that make up the Prince Edward archipelago. Small (c. 290 km^2) and remote (c. 2300 km southeast of Cape Town, South Africa), and with no permanent human population, the principal attractions that have led numerous scientists to conduct studies here in the midst of the vast Southern Ocean have been the, often charismatic, birds and mammals that are present. Marion Island is home to breeding populations of about 50,000 elephant seals and fur seals, and perhaps a million seabirds, including penguins, albatrosses, petrels and shearwaters. But these are just some of the more obvious inhabitants, and closer inspection reveals many more kinds of organisms. There are about 150 known species of invertebrates, including 44 species of insects and about 69 species of mites. And then there are, of course, the plants. There are 24 naturally occurring and 13 introduced species of vascular plants on Marion Island, and over 80 species of mosses, 45 species of liverworts, and 100 species of lichens have been identified.

Even given the intensity of study that Marion Island has received much remains unknown. No one has studied the nematode worms, although there seem likely to be more than 50 species present. The protists, bacteria

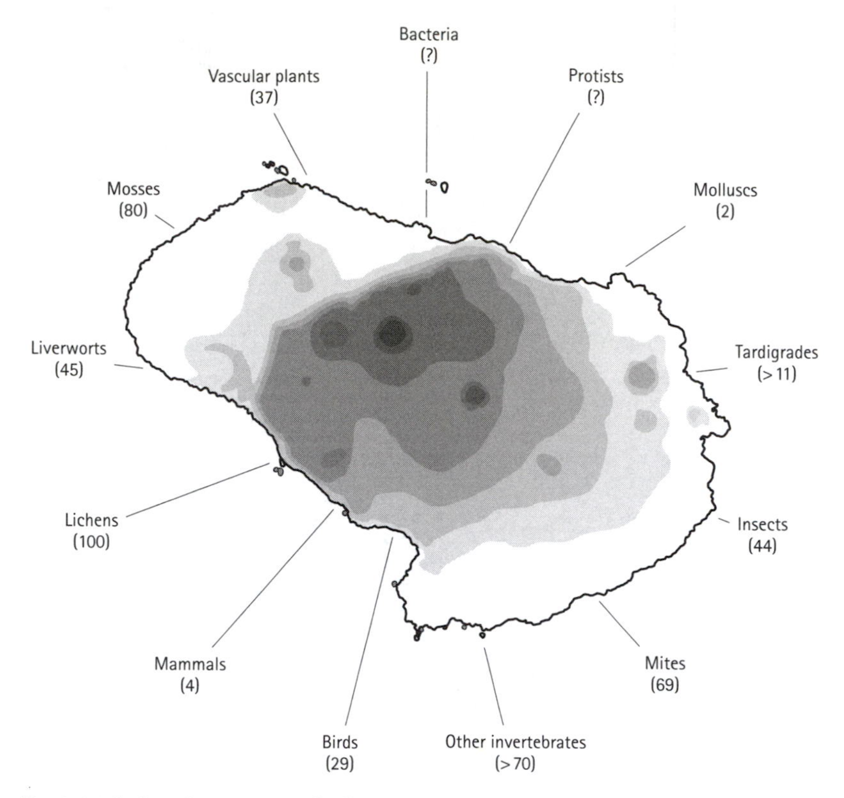

Fig. 1.1 The breeding species of sub-Antarctic Marion Island, one of the two remote Prince Edward Islands. Grey scales indicate variation in elevation. (Data from a variety of sources, including Gremmen 1981; Hänel & Chown 1999; Gaston et al. 2001; Øvstedal & Gremmen 2001; S.L. Chown pers. comm.)

and viruses also remain largely unexamined. Many of the species occurring on the island doubtless have associated parasites, but these also are mostly unknown. Indeed, there is a total of more than 500 species inhabiting Marion Island (Fig. 1.1).

Each of these species embraces a diverse range of evolutionary history, genetics, morphology, physiology and ecology. Each typically also comprises many tens of thousands of individuals, sometimes considerably less, but sometimes orders of magnitude more. For the majority, rather few of these individuals actually occur on Marion Island itself (although there are some species that occur nowhere else), but are scattered over the land- or seascape across many hundreds of square kilometres. Most of these individuals will have a unique genetic make-up, and, if only in the fine details, a unique morphology, physiology and ecology.

Such variety is echoed time and again across the Earth. Indeed, although it is important because some species found there occur nowhere else, and because of the large breeding populations of birds and mammals, Marion

Island would scarcely register on any league table of biological variation. It is by most standards a very depauperate place – as well as being small and remote, it is also cool (mean annual air temperature c. 5°C), wet (annual rainfall > 2.5 m), windy (gale-force winds blow for at least 1 h on nearly a third of all days) and was extensively covered in ice during recent periods of glaciation, a combination that would not predispose it to 'Eden-like' tendencies. Many areas have many more species, individuals of which exhibit greater diversities of form and function. For example:

- 173 species of lichens have been recorded on a single tree in Papua New Guinea (Aptroot 1997);
- 814 species of trees have been recorded from a 50 ha study plot in Peninsular Malaysia (Manokaran et al. 1992);
- 850 species of invertebrates are estimated to occur at a sandy beach site in the North Sea (Armonies & Reise 2000);
- c. 1300 species of butterflies have been recorded on five field trips, averaging less than 3 weeks each, to an area of < 4000 ha in Brazil (Robbins & Opler 1997);
- 245 resident species of birds have been recorded holding territories on a 97 ha plot in Peru (Terborgh et al. 1990);
- > 200 species of mammals may occur at some sites in the Amazonian rain forest (Voss & Emmons 1996);
- 55–135 animal species have been recorded in individual 30 × 30 cm cores of ocean floor sediment from 2100 m depth (Grassle & Maciolek 1992).

1.2 What is biodiversity?

Most straightforwardly, biological diversity or biodiversity is 'the variety of life', and refers collectively to variation at all levels of biological organization. Thus, one can, for example, speak equally of the biodiversity of some small or large part of Marion Island, of the island as a whole, of the islands of the Southern Ocean, of a continent or an ocean basin, or of the entire Earth. Many more formal definitions of biological diversity or biodiversity (we shall use the two terms interchangeably) have been proposed, which develop this simple one (DeLong 1996 reviewed 85 such definitions!). Of these, perhaps the most important and far-reaching is that contained within the Convention on Biological Diversity (the definition is provided in Article 2). This landmark treaty was signed by more than 150 nations on 5th June 1992 at the United Nations Conference on Environment and Development, held in Rio de Janeiro, and came into force approximately 18 months later (we shall subsequently refer to it simply as 'the Convention', although elsewhere you will commonly find it referred to by its acronym, CBD).

The Convention states that:

'Biological diversity' means the variability among living organisms from all sources including, inter alia, *terrestrial, marine and other aquatic ecosystems and the ecological complexes of which they are part; this includes diversity within species, between species and of ecosystems.*

['*inter alia*' means 'among other things'.] Biodiversity is the variety of life, in all of its many manifestations. It encompasses all forms, levels and combinations of natural variation and thus serves as a broad unifying concept.

For the purposes of the exploration of biodiversity embodied in this book we will amplify the full definition from the Convention in one way. At present it does not obviously take into account the tremendous variety of biological life that occurred in the past, some of which is preserved in the fossil record. However, we will want to trace the origins of present-day biodiversity and this will necessitate delving into the past (Chapter 2). To avoid any possible confusion therefore, we will explicitly interpret the definition to embrace the variability of all organisms that have ever lived, and not simply those that are presently extant.

The actual definition of biodiversity, as given above, is neutral with regard to any importance it may be perceived to have. The Convention is, in contrast, far from a neutral document, as amply revealed by its objectives (Article 1), which are:

. . . the conservation of biological diversity, the sustainable use of its components and the fair and equitable sharing of the benefits arising out of the utilization of genetic resources, including by appropriate access to genetic resources and by appropriate transfer of relevant technologies, taking into account all rights over those resources and to technologies, and by appropriate funding.

Likewise, much of the usage of the term 'biodiversity' is value laden. It carries with it connotations that biodiversity is *per se* a good thing, that its loss is bad, and that something should be done to maintain it. Consequently, it is important to recognize that there is rather more to use of the term than a formal definition in the Convention, or for that matter elsewhere, and its application often reveals just as much about the values of the person using it (see Section 1.4.2 and Chapter 4). This should always be borne in mind when interpreting what is being said about biodiversity, particularly now that the term has become a familiar feature of news programmes and papers, and importance is attached to it by environmental groups, political decision-makers, economists and ordinary citizens alike. Many users assume everyone shares the same intuitive definition, but this is not necessarily the case.

Table 1.1 Elements of biodiversity. (Adapted from Heywood & Baste 1995.)

Ecological diversity	Genetic diversity	Organismal diversity
Biomes		Domains or Kingdoms
Bioregions		Phyla
Landscapes		Families
Ecosystems		Genera
Habitats		Species
Niches		Subspecies
Populations	Populations	Populations
	Individuals	Individuals
	Chromosomes	
	Genes	
	Nucleotides	

1.3 Elements of biodiversity

The variety of life is expressed in a multiplicity of ways. Some sense of this variety can begin to be made by distinguishing between different key elements. These are the basic building blocks of biodiversity. They can be divided into three groups: (i) genetic diversity; (ii) organismal diversity; and (iii) ecological diversity (Table 1.1). Genetic diversity encompasses the components of the genetic coding that structures organisms (nucleotides, genes, chromosomes) and variation in the genetic make-up between individuals within a population and between populations. Organismal diversity encompasses the taxonomic hierarchy and its components, from individuals upwards to species, genera and beyond. Ecological diversity encompasses the scales of ecological differences from populations, through niches and habitats, on up to biomes. Although presented separately, the groups are intimately linked, and in some cases share elements in common (e.g. populations appear in all three).

Some of these elements are more readily, and more consistently, defined than are others. When we consider genetic diversity, nucleotides, genes and chromosomes are discrete, readily recognizable, and comparative units. Things are not quite so straightforward and neat when we move up to individuals and populations, with complications being introduced by, for example, the existence of clonal organisms and difficulties in identifying the spatial limits to populations. When we come to organismal diversity most of the elements are perhaps best viewed foremost simply as convenient human constructs for grouping evolutionarily related sets of individuals (although they do not always manage to do so). For instance, debate persists over exactly how many taxonomic kingdoms of organisms there should be, with a three domain natural classification being increasingly widely accepted (Bacteria and Archaea (prokaryotes), and Eukarya (eukaryotes)). When we refer to orders, families, genera or species of different groups we are not necessarily comparing like with like, although within a group examples of a given taxonomic level (e.g. different genera) may be broadly comparable. Thus, some species placed in different genera of cichlid fishes last shared common ancestors within the last few thousand years, some species placed in different families of primates diverged within the last few million years, and some species in the genus *Drosophila* diverged more than 40 million years ago (Fig. 1.2). Even the reality and recognition of species, for long considered one of the few biologically meaningful elements, has been a recurrent theme of debate for many decades, and a broad range of opinions and viewpoints have been voiced (Table 1.2; Section 1.4.4). Finally, and perhaps most problematic, is exactly how we define the various elements of ecological diversity. In most cases these elements constitute useful ways of breaking up continua of phenomena. However, they are difficult to distinguish without recourse to what ultimately constitute some essentially arbitrary rules. For example, whilst it is helpful to be able to label different habitat types, it is not always obvious precisely where one should end and another begin, because no such beginnings and endings really exist.

While many of the elements of biodiversity may be difficult to define rigorously, and in some cases may have no strict biological reality, they remain useful and important tools for thinking about and studying biodiversity. Thus, the elements of biodiversity, however defined, are not independent. Within each of the three groups of genetic, organismal and ecological diversity, the elements of biodiversity can be viewed as forming nested hierarchies (see Table 1.1); which serves also to render the complexity of biodiversity more tractable. For example, within genetic diversity, populations are constituted of individuals, each individual has a complement of chromosomes, these chromosomes comprise numbers of genes, and genes are constructed from nucleotides. Likewise, within organismal diversity kingdoms, phyla, families, genera, species, subspecies, populations and individuals form a nested sequence, in which all elements at lower levels belong to one example of each of the elements at higher levels. Along with the evolutionary process, this hierarchical organization of biodiversity reflects one of the central organizing principles of modern biology.

Whether any one element of biodiversity, from each or all of the three groups, can be regarded in some way as the most fundamental, essential or even natural is a contentious issue. For some, genes are the basic unit of life. However, in practice, it is often the species that is treated as the most fundamental element of biodiversity. Whether or not such an approach is useful, never mind correct, we will return to shortly (Section 1.4.4).

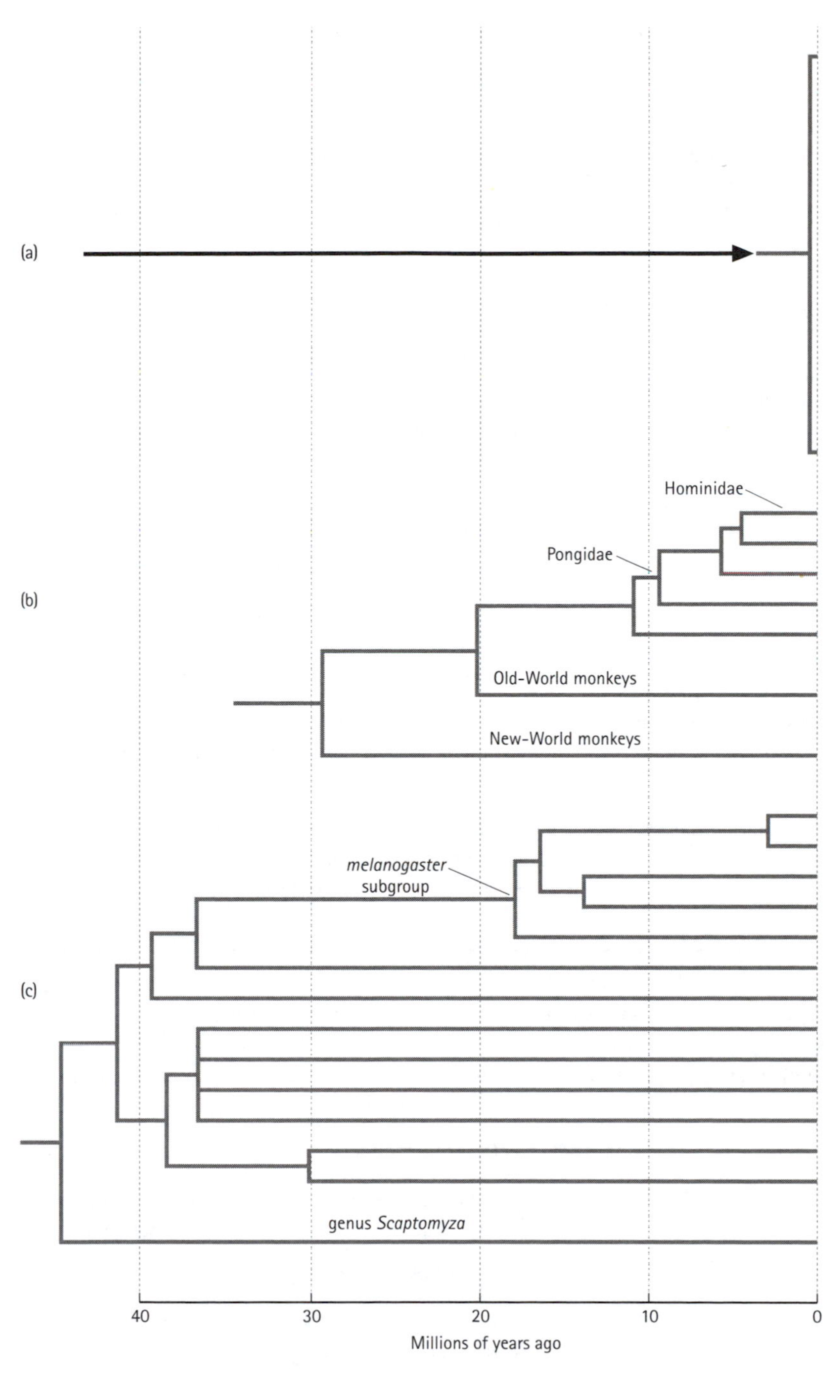

Fig. 1.2 Examples of disparities of taxonomic assignments in classifications of representatives of: (a) cichlid fish in Lake Victoria (14 species in nine genera); (b) anthropoid primates (seven species of several families); and (c) the genus *Drosophila* (13 species). (From Avise & Johns 1999.)

Table 1.2 (a) Species concepts; and (b) their strengths and weaknesses. (Adapted from Bisby 1995.)
(a)

Species concept	Definition
Biological species	A group of interbreeding natural populations that do not successfully mate or reproduce with other such groups (and, some would add, which occupy a specific niche)
Cohesion species	The smallest group of cohesive individuals that share intrinsic cohesive mechanisms (e.g. interbreeding ability, niche)
Ecological species	A lineage which occupies an adaptive zone different in some way from that of any other lineage in its range and which evolves separately from all lineages outside its range
Evolutionary species	A single lineage of ancestor–descendant populations which is distinct from other such lineages and which has its own evolutionary tendencies and historical fate
Morphological species	The smallest natural populations permanently separated from each other by a distinct discontinuity in heritable characteristics (e.g. morphology, behaviour, biochemistry)
Phylogenetic species	The smallest group of organisms that is diagnostically distinct from other such clusters and within which there is parental pattern of ancestry and descent
Recognition species	A group of organisms that recognize each other for the purpose of mating and fertilization

(b)

Species concept	Practical application	Strengths/weaknesses
Biological	Difficult	Popular, irrelevant to asexual organisms, complicated by natural hybridization, polyploidy, etc.
Cohesion	Difficult	Cohesion is difficult to recognize
Ecological	Difficult	Adaptive zones difficult to define, assumes two species cannot occupy same niche for even a short period
Evolutionary	Difficult	Criteria vague and difficult to observe
Morphological	Common	Morphological criteria may not reflect actual links that hold organisms together into a natural unit
Phylogenetic	Increasing	Will give rise to recognition of many more species than more traditional concepts
Recognition	Difficult	Determining if a feature is used to recognize potential mates is difficult or impossible in many populations

1.4 Measuring biodiversity

1.4.1 Number and difference

For many purposes the concept of biodiversity is useful in its own right, as it can provide a valuable shorthand expression for what is a very complex phenomenon. However, for more general applicability, one needs to be able to measure biodiversity – to quantify it in some way. Only then can one address such fundamental questions as how biodiversity has changed through time, where it occurs, and how it can be maintained.

From the definition alone, it is clear that no single measure of biodiversity will be adequate. Indeed, given its great complexity, it would be foolish to believe that the variety of life in an area, however small or large that area might be, could be captured in a single number. Measures of diversity in general, and not solely of biodiversity, are commonly found in basic ecological texts. Essentially, many of these measures have two components: (i) the number of entities; and (ii) the degree of difference (dissimilarity) between those entities. For example, species richness (the number of species) places emphasis on the number of elements. But, weighting each of these species by, say, the numbers of individuals, would be one way of incorporating a metric of the differences between them into a measure (Fig. 1.3). In the case of biodiversity the entities are one of its elements.

In measuring biodiversity, the breadth of ways in which differences can be expressed is potentially infinite. Think, for example, of the ways in which one could discriminate between just two species. These might include facets of their biochemistry, biogeography, evolutionary history, genetics, morphology or physiology, or perhaps the ecological role they play in a particular community (shredder, decomposer, predator, etc.) (cf. Table 1.2). As a result of the variety of elements of biodiversity, and of differences between them, there is no single all-embracing measure of biodiversity – nor will there ever be one! This means that it is impossible to state categorically what is the biodiversity of an area or of a group of organisms. Instead, only measures of certain components can be obtained, and even then such measures are only appropriate for restricted purposes.

Whilst one may feel uncomfortable with this notion, it is important to realize that it also applies, though perhaps not so obviously, in making many other concepts operational. For example, the topic of complex systems is attracting wide interest across a spectrum of fields of research (including physics), but there is no single measure of complexity (or simplicity for that matter). Instead there are many measures, none necessarily any more correct than the others, and which quantify rather different

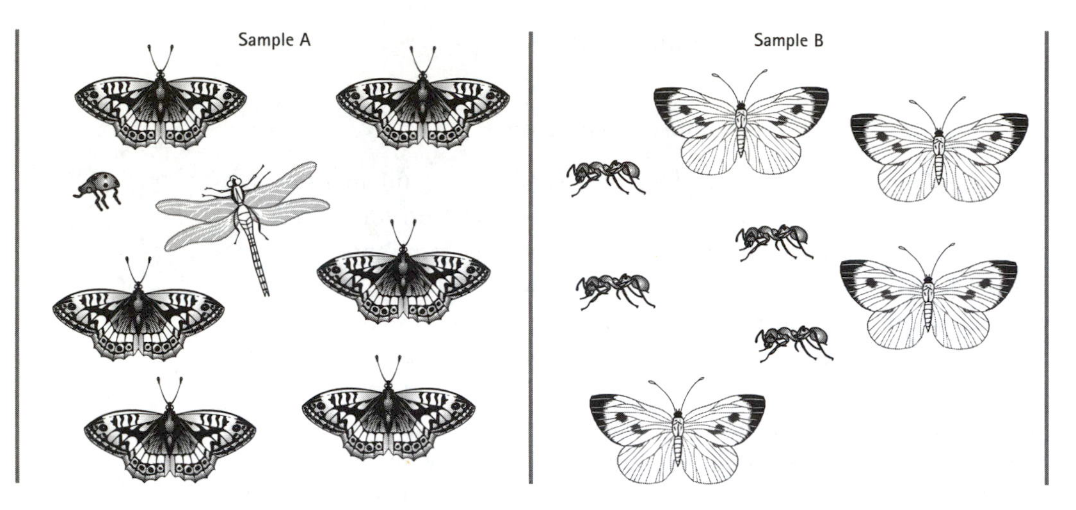

Fig. 1.3 Two samples of insects from different locations, illustrating two of the many different measures of biodiversity: species richness and species evenness. Sample A could be described as being the more diverse as it contains three species to sample B's two. However, in sample B there is less chance than in sample A that two randomly chosen individuals will be of the same species. (From Purvis & Hector 2000.)

components of complexity. To take an example closer to home, the concept of body size is utilized widely in biology. For example, one can recognize that relationships exist between body size and latitude (the biggest butterflies are found in the tropics) or between body size and abundance (elephants are rarer than many species of mice). And yet there is no such thing as the body size of an organism. Rather, size can be (and is) expressed in a variety of ways, none of which has any obvious logical precedence. Consider two individuals similar in body mass, but differing in linear dimensions. Which is the larger?

1.4.2 Value

Measures of biodiversity are commonly used as bases for making decisions about conservation action, or for planning more generally. It should now be clear that the choice of measure employed might not be neutral with regard to the outcome of such decisions. Different measures of biodiversity may suggest different answers. Moreover, it is important to remember that concentration on a particular element of biodiversity essentially places differential value on that facet of the variety of life. Both what you are measuring and how you are measuring it reveal something about what you most value. For example, if we use measures of ecological diversity as a basis for decision-making this implies that this is the dimension of biodiversity that is of most importance to us.

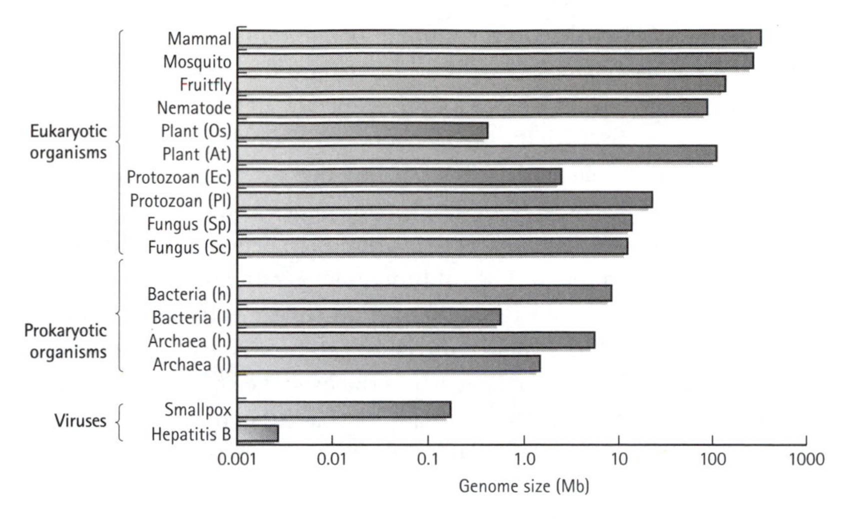

Fig. 1.4 Genome size for a range of organisms and viruses for which there are complete sequences (data derived from Genome Monitoring Table at http://www2.ebi.ac.uk/genomes/mot and Genomes online database at http://wit.integratedgenomics.com/GOLD). Abbreviations: l, lowest value for the grouping; h, highest value for the grouping; Os, *Oryza sativa*; At, *Arabidopsis thaliana*; Ec, *Encephalitozoon cuniculi*; Pl, *Plasmodium falciparum*; Sp, *Schizosaccharomyces pombe*; Sc, *Saccharomyces cerevisiae*.

1.4.3 Genetic diversity as a critical component

Few would disagree that genetic diversity is a critical component of biodiversity. This can be measured both directly (identifying and cataloguing variation in nucleotides, genes and chromosomes; see Table 1.1) or indirectly (quantifying variation in phenotypic features shown – or often just assumed – to have a genetic basis). Genes are constructed from strings of nucleotides (DNA). The total number, position and identity (there are four different types) of the nucleotides are all critical in the coding of biological information. Thus, determining nucleotide sequences is arguably one of the strongest measures of genetic diversity, although a large number of other techniques involving DNA analysis are also prevalent (restriction fragment length polymorphism (RFLP), DNA fingerprinting, random amplified polymorphic DNAs (RAPDs), microsatellite variation), their usage being dependent on the precise question being addressed.

Huge variation is encountered in the size and composition of the small, but steadily increasing, number of genomes sequenced to date (Fig. 1.4). Generally, multicellular organisms tend to have more DNA than single-celled organisms but there are exceptions. Similarly, although there appears to be an overall trend of increasing genome size with increasing morphological complexity, this is not invariant. For example, the lungfish (which still has not been fully sequenced) seems to have approximately

40 times more DNA than the mammal example in Fig. 1.4. This said, many of these discrepancies can be accounted for if comparison is limited to functional portions of DNA, those that encode for functional RNA and proteins. The species with the greatest amount of DNA has about 100,000 times as much as that with the least, but the species with the largest number of genes has only 20 times as many genes as that found in many bacteria. In other words, much of the variation in genomes is attributable not to differences in the number of functional genes, but in the amounts of non-coding DNA. One of the most striking findings from comparative genomics is that there are many 'universal' gene segments (e.g. those that code for ATP-binding sites), suggesting the existence of an ancient minimal set of DNA sequences that all cells must have. There is some evidence that nucleotide sequence divergence increases with increasing taxonomic diversity.

Nucleotide variation may give rise to changes in the character of the actual protein coded for. Until recently allelic variation determined in this way was one of the most commonly used (and cheapest) measures of genetic diversity. It was assessed using allozyme electrophoresis that identifies protein alleles, as different forms of a protein migrate at different rates on a gel. Allozyme electrophoresis has revealed an enormous amount of variation at all hierarchical levels.

Genes are located on chromosomes. All eukaryotic cells contain chromosomes, and their number, size and shape in an individual is referred to as the karyotype. Variation in karyotype has been investigated in detail mainly within species of plants, insects, amphibians and mammals. Most eukaryotes possess between 10 and 50 chromosomes, but there is huge variation both within and between groupings, with the overall range being from one to more than 200 (Fig. 1.5). There is no obvious relationship between chromosome number and any other measure of genetic diversity.

It is difficult to see at present how the various measures of genetic diversity discussed above map onto, or relate to, other measures of biodiversity, and how they could be employed as the primary measures of biodiversity. In the former case, much of the difficulty lies in the limited understanding of how genetic diversity matches up with the results of its expression, phenotypic diversity, although great strides are being made in this area. In the latter case, the difficulty rests in the limited amount of data that are available on genetic diversity through time and space, although the quantity is growing rapidly and the means of obtaining it are becoming more rapid.

1.4.4 Species richness as a common currency

Whilst biodiversity can be measured in a host of ways, in practice it tends most commonly to be measured in terms of species richness, the number of species. There are several reasons why this is so.

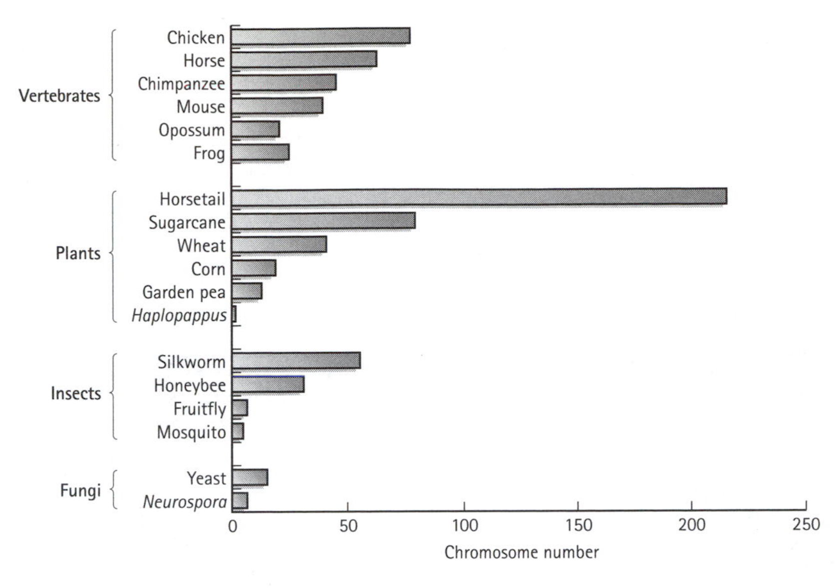

Fig. 1.5 Chromosome number for a range of organisms. (Data from various sources.)

1 *Practical application*. Species richness has proven to be measurable in practice, at least to the point where different workers will provide much the same estimation of the number of species of a given status (e.g. present, breeding, wintering) in a given taxon in a given area at a given time.

2 *Existing information*. A substantial amount of information already exists on patterns in species richness, and this has been made available in the scientific literature. Moreover, further information on this can readily be extracted from existing museum collections (which globally comprise many millions of biological specimens) and their associated literature (many millions of volumes), particularly as greater efforts are made to catalogue these collections in computerized databases that are accessible from remote locations.

3 *Surrogacy*. Species richness acts as a surrogate measure for many other kinds of variation in biodiversity. In general, as long as the numbers involved are at least moderate, greater numbers of species tend to embody more genetic diversity (in the form of a greater diversity of genes through to populations), more organismal diversity (in the form of greater numbers of individuals through to higher taxa), and greater ecological diversity (from representatives of more niches and habitats through to more biomes) (Fig. 1.6).

4 *Wide application*. The species unit is commonly seen as the unit of practical management, of legislation, of political discourse, and of tradition (folk taxonomies have frequently been found to conform closely to modern ones). For a wide range of people, variation in biodiversity is pictured as variation in species richness.

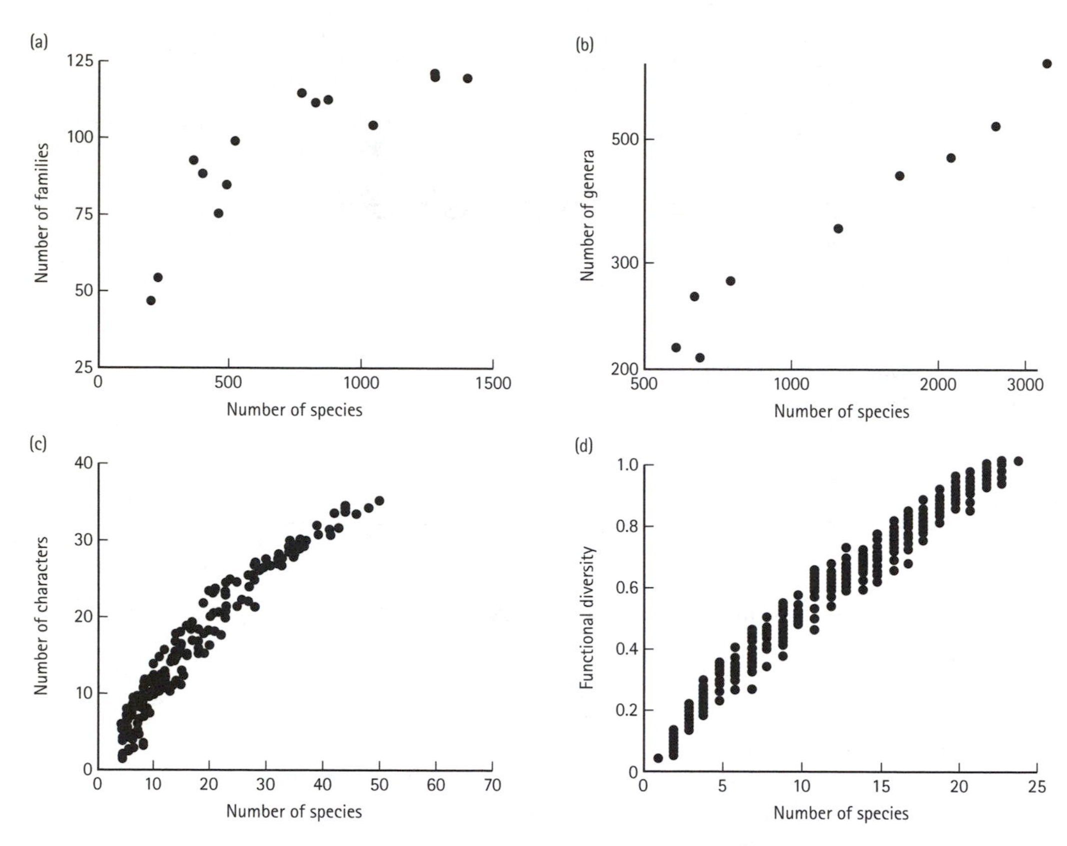

Fig. 1.6 Relationships between species richness and: (a) family richness for eastern Pacific benthic molluscs in different latitudinal bands; (b) generic richness for macromycete fungi for areas of the UK; (c) character richness for bumblebees among 611,000 km^2 grid cells; and (d) functional diversity (a measure of the extent of functional differences amongst a set of species) for Patagonian forbs. (a, From Roy et al. 1996; b, from Balmford et al. 2000; c, from Williams & Humphries 1996; d, from Petchey & Gaston 2002.)

The above said, the measurement of biodiversity in terms of species richness does have some significant limitations:

• *Definition of species.* The foremost difficulty is the lack of agreement as to precisely what constitutes a species. In major part this results because species can to a large extent be regarded as hypotheses, opinions or concepts, as much as real robust entities. There are at least seven major species concepts, each with their own strengths and weaknesses, from either theoretical or practical perspectives (see Table 1.2). The application of these different concepts can lead to the recognition of different numbers of species. For example, populations of seemingly coherent morphospecies (species separated on the basis of distinct discontinuities in one or more heritable characteristics, such as morphological features) may actually exhibit levels of genetic divergence typical of different species identified on this alternative basis, and thus constitute so-called cryptic species. Likewise, using a biological species concept, 40–42 species of birds-of-paradise (Paradisaeidae) have been distinguished in Australasia, but using a phylogenetic species concept pushes this figure up to 90 (Cracraft 1992). In practice, such problems are, however, commonly not as severe as this might seem to imply. As the vast majority of groups of organisms have been, and are still being, described based on collections of preserved specimens using differences in morphological characteristics, references to species richness more often than not concern 'morphological' species richness or are very close to estimates based on such a species concept (with some particular level of morphological difference being regarded as sufficient to confer species status). Fortunately, this method of defining a species continues to be relatively effective for most needs (although it may be woefully inadequate for groups such as prokaryotes). There is general consensus amongst appropriate specialists as to the overall numbers of species in a reasonably well-studied group occurring in an area or globally, and radical shifts in the number of species recognized do not tend to occur.

- *Different kinds of diversity*. An additional limitation of species richness as a measure of biodiversity has frequently been illustrated with reference to the issue of whether an assemblage of a small number of closely related species, say two species of mouse, is more or less biodiverse than an equivalent sized assemblage of more distantly related species, say a species of mouse and a species of shrimp. While the latter assemblage would, intuitively, seem to be the more diverse (in terms of morphological variation, differences in evolutionary history, etc.), in terms of species richness the assemblages are equally diverse. The extent to which this is a weakness of using species richness as a measure of biodiversity depends, however, perhaps less on the outcomes of such simple scenarios than on scenarios more typical of studies of biodiversity, which commonly involve assemblages numbering at least tens, if not hundreds or thousands, of species. Here, it seems that species richness is often strongly positively correlated with many other measures of biodiversity; i.e. it is a good surrogate (Gaston 1996a).

Species richness has, in some sense, become the common currency of much of the study of biodiversity. If one wishes to explore and discuss the origin, patterns and maintenance of biodiversity, such a currency certainly makes the task manageable. Although we will also have recourse to some other measures, throughout the rest of this book we will essentially treat species richness as equivalent to biodiversity, notwithstanding the facts that it remains only one among many measures, and retains some significant and important limitations. In so doing, we do not wish to imply that the problems associated with using this one measure are either trivial or unimportant. However, progress can be made using it, provided one remains alert to its limitations.

1.5 Summary

1 Biodiversity is the variety of life, in all its manifestations.
2 Key elements of this variety can be recognized, comprising three nested hierarchies of genetic, organismal and ecological diversity.
3 Because the variety of life can be expressed in a multiplicity of ways, there is no single overall measure of biodiversity, rather there are multiple measures of different facets.
4 The measure of biodiversity chosen may influence the findings of a particular study, and may reveal something about the values placed on a particular facet of the variety of life by an investigator.
5 Whilst it has some significant limitations, species richness has become the common currency of much of the study of biodiversity, and has proven valuable for many heuristic and practical purposes.

Further reading

For this chapter

Carroll, S., Grenier, J. & Weatherbee, S. (2001) *From DNA to Diversity: Molecular Genetics and the Evolution of Animal Design*. Blackwell Science, Oxford. (*An excellent advanced undergraduate text that genuinely tries to link genetic diversity to morphology and evolutionary diversity*.)

Claridge, M.F., Dawah, H.A. & Wilson, M.R. (eds.) (1997) *Species: The Units of Biodiversity*. Chapman & Hall, London. (*An in-depth exploration of the meaning of species*.)

Gaston, K.J. (1996) What is biodiversity? In: *Biodiversity: A Biology of Numbers and Difference* (ed. K.J. Gaston), pp. 1–9. Blackwell Science, Oxford. (*Takes a different view from the one proffered here, distinguishing between biodiversity as a concept, a measurable entity, and a social/political construct*.)

Hawksworth, D.L. (ed.) (1995) *Biodiversity: Measurement and Estimation*. Chapman & Hall, London. (*An important, if somewhat eclectic, set of papers*.)

Hey, J. (2001) *Genes, Categories and Species*. Oxford University Press, Oxford. (*An unusual, at times erratic, but interesting book*.)

Magurran, A.E. (1988) *Ecological Diversity and its Measurement*. Croom Helm, London. (*Lucid review, and a good point of entry into this field*.)

Noss, R.F. (1990) Indicators for monitoring biodiversity: a hierarchical approach. *Conservation Biology* 4, 355–364. (*Distinguishes an alternative hierarchical organization to biodiversity, based on composition, structure and function*.)

General texts on biodiversity

Dobson, A.P. (1996) *Conservation and Biodiversity*. Scientific American, New York. (*Beautifully produced and reasonably comprehensive, with a good bibliography – very accessible*.)

Gaston, K.J. (ed.) (1996) *Biodiversity: A Biology of Numbers and Difference*. Blackwell Science, Oxford. (*A wide-ranging, but far from comprehensive, examination of the measurement of temporal and spatial patterns in, and the conservation and management of, biodiversity.*)

Groombridge, B. & Jenkins, M.D. (2002) *World Atlas of Biodiversity: Earth's Living Resources in the 21st Century*. University of California Press, London. (*A wide-ranging overview, with lots of maps, tables and graphs.*)

Heywood, V.H. (ed.) (1995) *Global Biodiversity Assessment*. Cambridge University Press, Cambridge. (*A major review of the different facets of biodiversity, from characterization to economic importance. A formidable tome!*)

Huston, M.A. (1994) *Biological Diversity: The Coexistence of Species on Changing Landscapes*. Cambridge University Press, Cambridge. (*A very ecological perspective on biodiversity.*)

Jeffries, M.J. (1997) *Biodiversity and Conservation*. Routledge, London. (*A gentle introduction to these topics.*)

Karp, A., Ingram, D.S. & Isaac, P.G. (eds.) (1997) *Molecular Tools for Screening Biodiversity*. Kluwer Academic, Dordrecht. (*Comprehensive description and evaluation of a range of molecular techniques for use in addressing different questions concerning diversity.*)

Levin, S.A. (ed.) (2001) *Encyclopedia of Biodiversity*, Vols. 1–5. Academic Press, San Diego, CA. (*A fantastic resource, covering the length and breadth of the field.*)

Perlman, D.L. & Adelson, G. (1997) *Biodiversity: Exploring Values and Priorities in Conservation*. Blackwell Science, Oxford. (*Basic text on the concepts and their implications.*)

Reaka-Kudla, M.L., Wilson, D.E. & Wilson, E.O. (eds.) (1997) *Biodiversity II: Understanding and Protecting our Biological Resources*. Joseph Henry Press, Washington, DC. (*The sequel to Wilson & Peter (1988).*)

Solbrig, O.T. (ed.) (1991) *From Genes to Ecosystems: A Research Agenda for Biodiversity*. The International Union of Biological Sciences (IUBS), Paris. (*Identifies some of the major issues to be addressed in the study of biodiversity.*)

Wilson, E.O. (1992) *The Diversity of Life*. Penguin Books, London. (*A popular, wide-ranging, and very readable account by perhaps the most influential proponent of biodiversity.*)

Wilson, E.O. & Perlman, D.L. (2000) *Conserving Earth's Biodiversity* (CD-ROM). Island Press, Washington, DC. [Demonstration version at http://www.islandpress.org/wilsoncd/index.ssi] (*There are surprisingly few CD-ROM and other such resources available on the topic of biodiversity; this is perhaps the best general one.*)

Wilson, E.O. & Peter, F.M. (eds.) (1988) *BioDiversity*. National Academy Press, Washington, DC. (*Where it all began? The 'milestone' volume that drew attention to the importance of biodiversity.*)

World Conservation Monitoring Centre (1992) *Global Biodiversity: Status of the Earth's Living Resources*. Chapman & Hall, London. (*A useful collation of essays and data.*)

World Conservation Monitoring Centre (comp.), Groombridge, B. (ed.) (1994) *Biodiversity Data Sourcebook*. World Conservation Press, Cambridge. (*An update and expansion of some of the information in the World Conservation Monitoring Centre (1992) volume.*)

World Conservation Monitoring Centre, Groombridge, B. & Jenkins, M.D. (2000) *Global Biodiversity: Earth's Living Resources in the 21st Century*. World Conservation Press, Cambridge. (*The first edition of Groombridge & Jenkins.*)

Surfing the World Wide Web (WWW)

'Biodiversity' on a search engine throws up a whole load of material; some useful, and much not. To save you time there are some lists of biodiversity WWW sites (http://www.groms.de/data/zoology/riede/taxalinks.html; http://biodiversity.uno.edu; http://www.biodiversity.org.uk/ibs/other/env/biodiv.htm). However, there are three web sites that call for special mention:

1 The Convention on Biological Diversity and all of the material associated with it is accessible at http://www.biodiv.org/.

2 The World Resources Institute (WRI) web site (http://wri.igc.org/wri/biodiv) is a valuable source of biodiversity facts and figures.

3 The UNEP-World Conservation Monitoring Centre (UNEP-WCMC) is an internationally recognized body for collation of information on conservation and sustainable use of biodiversity. Visitors to their web site (http://www.unep-wcmc.org) will find good general information and also fairly detailed information in the form of statistics and maps, generated from their databases. These include details of protected areas, national biodiversity strategies and data on threatened species.

2 Biodiversity through time

2.1 Introduction

As well as being of inherent interest, it is not unreasonable to suppose that an understanding of how biodiversity has arisen, and how it has changed in the past, may be important in interpreting its present and future structure. In this chapter, we consider the temporal dynamics of biodiversity – that is, how biodiversity changes with time. We begin by considering the sources of information on which this understanding is founded. We then give a brief overview of the history of life and of the principal historical patterns in the magnitude of biodiversity. We next turn to the major processes that give rise to these patterns, particularly diversification and extinction. Finally, we consider one product of these dynamics, namely the numbers of extant species.

Throughout this chapter, we will be concerned with the broad sweep of history. Those relatively recent, in geological terms, changes in biodiversity that have resulted as a direct or indirect product of human activities will be addressed at some length in Chapter 5.

2.2 Sources of information

Knowledge of the history of biodiversity derives from two primary sources. The first is analyses of data from the fossil record, and the second is analyses of molecular data.

2.2.1 Fossil record

Much of the modern-day geological landscape owes its origins to past biodiversity, which has left behind a rich fossil record. This has provided extraordinary insights into the history of life on Earth. However, working with the fossil record to understand this history is an important constraint for three reasons. First, as recognized by Darwin when marshalling evidence for his theory of evolution, this record is far from perfect or even. The record is much better for some periods than for others, and estimates of the numbers of species leaving a fossil record range from less than one to, at most, a few per cent of those that have ever lived (e.g. Sepkoski 1992). Second, of this fossil record, only a tiny fraction has actually been recovered. Third, the record, and that portion of it that has been recovered, is biased towards the more abundant, the more widespread, and the longer lived species, and more towards some groups of organisms than others. For instance, soft-bodied organisms, such as some cnidarians (jellyfish, sea anemones) are rarely fossilized and are exceptional in the fossil record, whereas the number of individual fossils of brachiopods, which are hard-bodied organisms, has been estimated to be in the billions. Some of the major soft-bodied animal groupings have left no fossil remains: animals like the Platyhelminthes (flatworms, flukes and tapeworms). The fossil record for animals with hard body parts, such as the brachiopods and molluscs, echinoderms and vertebrates, while often much better, is still far from complete and not always representative: 95% of all fossil species are marine animals while 85% of today's recorded plants and animals are terrestrial. In short, many of the pages of the history of biodiversity written in the fossil record are missing, and those that have been obtained only capture a biased portion of that history.

The paucity of the fossil record, even with regard to individual taxa, is well illustrated by a group that possesses hard body parts and is relatively well researched, having caught the attention and imagination of people of all ages and from all walks of life: the dinosaurs. Although something of the history of this group is familiar even to many primary/elementary school children, it remains based on a remarkably small window on the past. As of 1990, 900–1200 genera of dinosaurs were estimated to ever have lived (Dodson 1990). Of these, only 285 (336 species) were known from fossils, and nearly half of these were from only a single specimen; complete skulls and skeletons were known from only 20% of known genera. Similarly, it has been estimated that no more than 7% of all the primate species that have existed are known from fossils (Tavaré et al. 2002).

While it is clear that the documented fossil record is far from complete, in many different ways, it still provides an invaluable pictorial history of life on Earth, where many of the major events in that history have left their mark in, or on, the rocks. Notwithstanding its limitations, it is still possible to construct an understanding of changes in biodiversity through geological time using the fossil record (for recent analyses of the robustness of the fossil record, see Benton et al. 2000; Alroy et al. 2001; Smith 2001). However, because of the constraints referred to above, it will often be necessary to make recourse, throughout this chapter, to the temporal dynamics of numbers of higher taxa rather than of species because these are less vulnerable to the constraints. This should not pose too much of a problem, for not only do numbers of higher taxa act as a surrogate for numbers of species (cf. Section 1.4.4), but it is also true that they act as a measure of biodiversity in their own right (see Table 1.1).

2.2.2 Molecular evidence

Whilst the fossil record continues to provide the bulk of insights into the history of biodiversity, molecular evidence is playing an increasingly significant role. Comparison of molecular data for different organisms enables the generation of branching trees representing hypotheses of their patterns of phylogenetic relatedness, with those organisms with sequences that are more different being assumed to have diverged earlier in the evolutionary process. If assumptions are made about the rate at which molecular sequences diverge (a 'molecular clock'), then the timings of different evolutionary events can be estimated.

Fossil and molecular evidence do not always agree, particularly over the dates of first appearance of groups. For example, molecular evidence suggests that at least six animal phyla originated deep in the Precambrian, more than 400 million years (Myr) earlier than their first appearance known from the fossil record (Wang et al. 1999). Likewise, molecular data suggest that primates diverged from other placental mammals c. 90 Myr ago whereas the oldest known fossil primates are from c. 55 Myr ago (Tavaré et al. 2002). The fossil record is always liable to underestimate dates of first appearance, because the likelihood of such early individuals being fossilized and the fossils recovered is low. Equally, of course, the accuracy of first appearances estimated from molecular evidence rests on the interpretation of the molecular divergence data and particularly on the assumptions about the nature and dynamics of the molecular clock. However, together, fossil and molecular evidence provide a powerful combination for unlocking many of the secrets of the past.

2.3 A brief history of biodiversity

2.3.1 Principal features, from the Beginning to the present day

Drawing on insights provided by the fossil record and molecular evidence, some of the major events of life on Earth, together with their

Table 2.1 Geological eras, periods, and the major events associated with them. (Adapted from Schopf 1992.)

Era	Period	Myr ago	Major events
Precambrian	(PC)	4500	Origin of life, first multicellular organisms
Palaeozoic	Cambrian (C)	550	All of the major phyla present in fossil record, including first vertebrates (jawless fish)
	Ordovician (O)	500	First jawed fish
	Silurian (S)	440	Colonization of land by plants and arthropods
	Devonian (D)	410	Diversification of teleosts (bony fish). First amphibians and insects
	Carboniferous (Crb)	360	Extensive forests of vascular plants, origin of reptiles, amphibians dominant
	Permian (P)	290	Mass extinction of marine invertebrates, origins of mammal-like reptiles and 'modern insects'
Mesozoic	Triassic (Tr)	250	Origin and diversification of ruling reptiles, origin of mammals, gymnosperms dominant
	Jurassic (Jur)	210	Dominance of ruling reptiles and gymnosperms, origin of birds
	Cretaceous (Cret)	140	Origin of angiosperms (flowering plants), ruling reptiles and many invertebrate groups go extinct towards end of period
Cenozoic	Tertiary (Tert)	65	Diversification of mammals, birds, pollinating insects and angiosperms. Late Tertiary/early Quaternary – the zenith of biodiversity
	Quaternary (Q)	1.8	Origin of humankind

chronology, are presented in Table 2.1. It is likely that all known organisms originated from a single common ancestor. Self-evidently, biodiversity has increased between this inception, estimated to be about 3.5–4.0 billion years ago (the Earth itself is thought to be more than 4.5–5.0 billion years old, and thus life has been present throughout most of its existence), and the present time – otherwise we would not see the wealth of organisms that we do today. At first this increase appears to have been very slow.

One of the key innovations, which opened the door to a major increase in biodiversity, was the advent of multicellularity (i.e. the appearance of individual organisms being composed of numerous cells, differentiated for the performance of different functions). Multicellular organisms did not begin to diversify until perhaps 1.4 billion years ago, when nearly 60% of the history of life had already passed. Multicellular animals (metazoans) specifically did not begin markedly to diversify until approximately

600 Myr ago, by which time about 80% of the history of life had passed. None of these first fossil metazoans possessed any hard parts and most were no more than a few millimetres long. There are a few tantalizing glimpses of relatively large soft-bodied metazoans in late Precambrian (also known as Vendian) rocks, for example in the Ediacaran fauna in Australia, which has been referred to as comprising either ancestral metazoans, or a parallel unsuccessful metazoan experiment.

It is only with the beginning of the Palaeozoic Era (early life), and in rocks of the Cambrian period (550 Myr ago), that we see the sudden appearance of the first sizeable metazoans with hard parts (as exemplified by the *Wonderful Life* (Gould 1989) of the Burgess Shale fauna from Canada). Not only are the fossils plentiful, but there is a bewildering array of different body plans present, some 'experimental' (or, with hindsight, novel), and relatively short-lived (300 + Myr), but others surviving and remaining to the present. It has been estimated that if the Cambrian explosion of biodiversity had continued at a constant rate to the present day the oceans would be occupied by 10^{60} families of metazoan organisms, instead of the 10^3 there actually are (Sepkoski 1997). In fact, by the end of the Cambrian all of today's major animal groupings (or phyla) are present in the fossil record.

The diversity of body plans displayed by the different phyla belies some important underlying conservatism in their genetic make-up, particularly in the homeotic genes, those genes that regulate the expression of other genes. Some of the best understood are the *Hox* genes. Homologous *Hox* genes are present in nearly all organisms. They have a precise role in the definition of anterior/posterior regional identity. Mutation in a *Hox* gene, or the development of even one novel *Hox* gene, can have profound morphological consequences. Not surprisingly such events have been suggested as providing a mechanism for initial rapid evolution of body plans, leading to the increase in the diversity of phyla around and before the Cambrian period. Figure 2.1 illustrates the relative timing of the major events in *Hox* gene evolution mapped onto a phylogenetic tree of metazoans for which there are data. Cnidarians possess only anterior and posterior *Hox* genes. The remaining animal phyla examined show an expansion of central *Hox* genes (with further specialization accompanying the origin of moulting animals – the ecdysozoans), with echinoderms and chordates being characterized by a further expansion of the posterior *Hox* genes. Vertebrates show duplication of *Hox* genes: sharks and jawless fish possess more than two *Hox* complexes; teleost fish have 5–7 complexes; and the tetrapods have four complexes.

A list of all of the present-day phyla as recognized by one authority is presented in Table 2.2. This is based on a five kingdom system of higher classification, although a three domain system has also been proposed (Woese et al. 1990). Other surveys recognize greater or smaller numbers

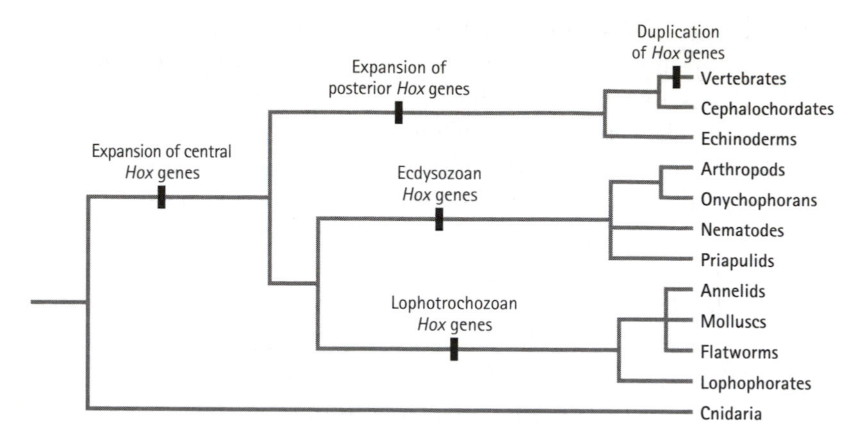

Fig. 2.1 Major events in the evolution of metazoan *Hox* genes. (Data from Rosa et al. 1999.)

Table 2.2 A survey of present-day phyla, based on the classification of Margulis and Schwartz (1998).

		Marine	Freshwater	Terrestrial
Superkingdom: **Prokarya**				
Kingdom: **Bacteria**				
Subkingdom: **Archaea**				
Euryarchaeota	Methanogens and halophils	√	√	√
Crenarchaeota	Thermoacidophils	√	√	
Subkingdom: **Eubacteria**				
Proteobacteria	Purple bacteria	√	√	√
Spirochaetae		√	√	√
Cyanobacteria	Blue-green bacteria and chloroxybacteria, grass green	√	√	√
Saprospirae	Fermenting gliders	√	√	√
Chloroflexa	Green non-sulphur phototrophs		√	√
Chlorobia	Anoxygenic green sulphur bacteria	√	√	√
Aphragmabacteria	Mycoplasmas			√
Endospora	Endospore-forming and related low-G + C Gram-positive bacteria	√	√	√
Pirellulae	Proteinaceous-walled bacteria and relatives		√	
Actinobacteria	Actinomycetes, actinomycota and related high-G + C Gram-positive bacteria		√	√

(cont'd)

Table 2.2 *(cont'd)*

		Marine	Freshwater	Terrestrial
Deinococci	Radiation-resistant or heat-resistant Gram-positive bacteria		√	
Thermotogae	Thermophilic fermenters	√	√	√
Superkingdom: **Eukarya**				
Kingdom: **Protoctista**				
Archaeprotista		√	√	√
Microspora	Microsporida			√
Rhizopoda	Amastigote amoebas and cellular slime moulds	√	√	√
Granuloreticulosa		√	√	
Xenophyophora		√		
Myxomycota	Myxogastria, plasmodial slime moulds			√
Dinomastigota	Dinoflagellata, Dinophyta	√	√	
Ciliophora	Ciliates	√	√	
Apicomplexa	Sporozoa, Telosporidea			√
Haptomonada	Prymnesiophyta, Haptophyta, coccolithophorids	√	√	
Cryptomonada	Cryptophyta	√	√	
Discomitochondria	Flagellates, zoomastigotes, zooflagellates	√	√	√
Chrysomonada	Chrysophyta	√	√	
Xanthophyta		√	√	√
Eustigmatophyta		√	√	
Diatoms	Bacillariophyta	√	√	√
Phaeophyta	Brown algae	√	√	
Labyrinthulata	Slime nets and thraustochytrids	√		
Plasmodiophora				√
Oomycota	Oomycetes, oomycotes		√	√
Hyphochytriomycota			√	√
Haplospora		√		
Paramyxa		√		
Myxospora	Myxozoa, myxosporidians	√	√	
Rhodophyta	Red algae	√	√	√
Gamophyta	Conjugaphyta, conjugating green algae		√	
Actinopoda		√	√	√
Chlorophyta	Green algae	√	√	
Chytridiomycota			√	√
Zoomastigota	Zoomastigotes, zooflagellates	√	√	√

(cont'd on p. 26)

Table 2.2 *(cont'd)*

		Marine	Freshwater	Terrestrial
Kingdom: **Animalia**				
Placozoa	Trichoplaxes	√		
Porifera	Sponges, poriferans	√	√	
Cnidaria	Cnidarians, hydras, jellyfish, sea anemones, corals	√	√	
Ctenophora	Comb jellies	√		
Platyhelminthes	Flatworms	√	√	√
Gnathostomulida	Jaw worms	√		
Rhombozoa	Rhombozoans	√		
Orthonectida	Orthonectids	√		
Nemertea	Ribbon worms, nemertines, Rhynchocoela	√	√	√
Nematoda	Nematodes, thread worms, round worms	√	√	√
Nematomorpha	Gordian worms, horsehair worms, nematomorphs	√	√	√
Acanthocephala	Thorny-headed worms	√	√	√
Rotifera	Rotifers, wheel animals	√	√	√
Kinorhyncha	Kinorhynchs	√		
Priapulida	Priapulids	√		
Gastrotricha	Gastrotrichs	√	√	
Loricifera	Loriciferans	√		
Entoprocta	Entoprocts	√		
Chelicerata	Chelicerates, spiders, scorpions, ticks, mites	√	√	√
Mandibulata (Uniramia)	Mandibulates, mandibulate arthropods	√	√	√
Crustacea	Crustaceans	√	√	√
Annelida	Annelid worms, true worms	√	√	√
Sipuncula	Sipunculans, sipunculids, peanut worms	√		
Echiura	Spoon-worms, echiurans, echiurids	√		
Pogonophora	Beard worms, pogonophorans, tube worms	√		
Mollusca	Molluscs	√	√	√
Tardigrada	Water bears, tardigrades	√	√	√
Onychophora	Velvet worms, onychophorans, peripatuses			√
Bryozoa	Ectoprocta, ectoprocts, moss animals	√	√	
Brachiopoda	Lampshells, brachiopods	√		

(cont'd)

Table 2.2 *(cont'd)*

		Marine	Freshwater	Terrestrial
Phoronida	Phoronids	√		
Chaetognatha	Arrow worms	√		
Hemichordata	Acorn worms, pterobranchs, enteroptneusts, tongue worms	√		
Echinodermata	Echinoderms	√		
Urochordata*	Tunicates, sea squirts, ascidians, larvaceans, salps	√		
Cephalochordata*	Lancelets, Acrania	√		
Craniata*		√	√	√
Kingdom: **Fungi**				
Zygomycota	Zygomycotes, zygomycetes		√	√
Basidiomycota	Basidiomycotes, basidiomycetes		√	√
Ascomycota	Ascomycotes, ascomycetes	√	√	√
Kingdom: **Plantae**				
Bryophyta	Mosses		√	√
Hepatophyta	Liverworts		√	√
Anthocerophyta	Hornworts			√
Lycophyta	Club mosses, lycophytes, lycopods		√	√
Psilophyta	Psilophytes, whisk fern			√
Sphenophyta	Sphenophytes, Equisetophyta, horsetails			√
Filicinophyta	Pterophyta, Pterodatina, Pteridophyta, ferns		√	√
Cycadophyta	Cycads			√
Ginkgophyta				√
Coniferophyta	Conifers			√
Gnetophyta	Gnetophytes			√
Anthophyta	Angiospermophyta, Magnoliophyta, flowering plants	√	√	√

*These phyla comprise the chordates.

of phyla, and different sets thereof (the listing does not include viruses, which are minute and mostly parasitic sub-organisms derived, in many cases it has been suggested, from the nuclear material of organisms). Moreover, new phyla continue to be found. In 1998 alone, some authorities reported more than 20 new divisions of bacteria at the phylum, and possibly higher, level (Fuhrman & Campbell 1998). At the time of writing, the most recent to be discovered has been named the Nanoarchaeota, with as yet a single species, a nano-sized hyperthermophilic microorganism obtained from a submarine hot vent (Huber et al. 2002).

Gould (1989) suggests that anatomical diversity reached a maximum around the time of the Cambrian explosion in biodiversity. The colonization of land by animals and plants (440 Myr ago), and their subsequent diversification, lagged far behind the emergence of multicellular organisms in the oceans. So animal life has gone from a position of relatively few species encompassing many different body plans in the Cambrian ('early experimentation . . .'), up to the present day where we see considerably more species but fewer body plans ('. . . and later standardisation') (Gould 1989).

Broadly speaking, there were relatively few species during the Palaeozoic and early Mesozoic eras (although this has been a matter of some controversy; Signor 1990). However, starting just over 100 Myr ago there was a progressive and substantial increase in biodiversity that culminated at the end of the Tertiary and beginning of the Quaternary (Pleistocene) in there being more extant species and higher taxa of animals and plants (both marine and terrestrial) than at any time before or, indeed, since (Signor 1990). The ancestors of the human lineage emerged from the apes about 5 Myr ago in Africa, the genus *Homo* about 2 Myr ago, and anatomically modern humans 100,000–200,000 years ago. We are living in the Quaternary (Holocene) in a time of decreasing diversity, which is correlated with change in climate and the advent of organized and large-scale human activity (Chapter 5).

There is no consensus as to whether in broad outline the path from one species to many can be explained in terms of a simple mathematical model, and if so what that model might be. Part of the difficulty lies in the fact that once diversification began to occur on a major scale (Cambrian to the present day) it was not, as we have seen above, continuous. Rather, there were periods of dramatic increase, interspersed by some times of major setbacks or periods of relative stasis (or at least no marked directional trend in diversity). Consequently, the history of biodiversity is often presented as one of radiations and stabilizations, punctuated by mass extinctions (Signor 1990; Sepkoski 1992).

Growth in numbers of families of marine organisms exhibits three main phases of diversification (in the early Cambrian, in the Ordovician, and through the Mesozoic and Cenozoic), two main phases of approximate stabilization of diversity (in the mid to late Cambrian, and through most of the Palaeozoic), and five major mass extinctions (Late Ordovician, Late Devonian, Late Permian, Late Triassic, end-Cretaceous) (Fig. 2.2). This has been explained using two sequential S-shaped (logistic) curves, each consisting of an initially slow period of increase, followed by a rapid one, with a final slow approach to an asymptote (Courtillot & Gaudemer 1996). It has also been explained using an underlying exponential curve,

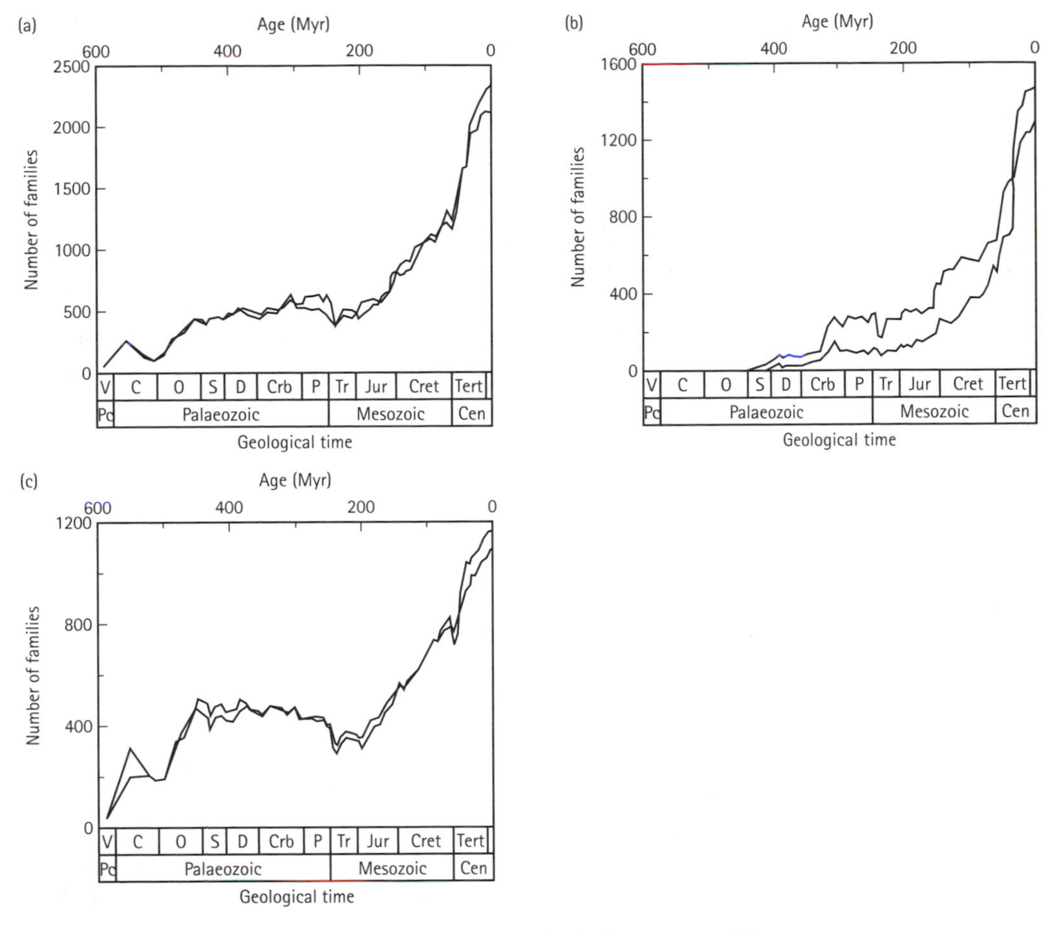

Fig. 2.2 Temporal dynamics of the number of families of: (a) all organisms; (b) continental organisms; and (c) marine organisms. In each case a maximum and minimum curve is shown, based on a combination of stratigraphic and habitat-preference information. C, Cambrian; Cen, Cenozoic; Crb, Carboniferous; Cret, Cretaceous; D, Devonian; Jur, Jurassic; O, Ordovician; P, Permian; Pc, Precambrian; S, Silurian; Tert, Tertiary; Tr, Triassic; V, Vendian. (From Benton 1995.)

about which there is considerable variation in numbers of families (Hewzulla et al. 1999). Growth in numbers of families of continental organisms, and of all organisms (marine + continental) show more continuous patterns of increase (Fig. 2.2; Benton 1995, 1997). These have been explained using exponential curves, with a regular doubling of family numbers within fixed units of time. In none of these cases is there evidence of an obvious long-term limit to the diversity of life that can inhabit the Earth. Presumably, if diversification were to continue, at some point an ultimate ceiling would be attained, but it is not difficult to see that many more different species than are presently extant might be packed onto the Earth before that ceiling was attained. This is important because

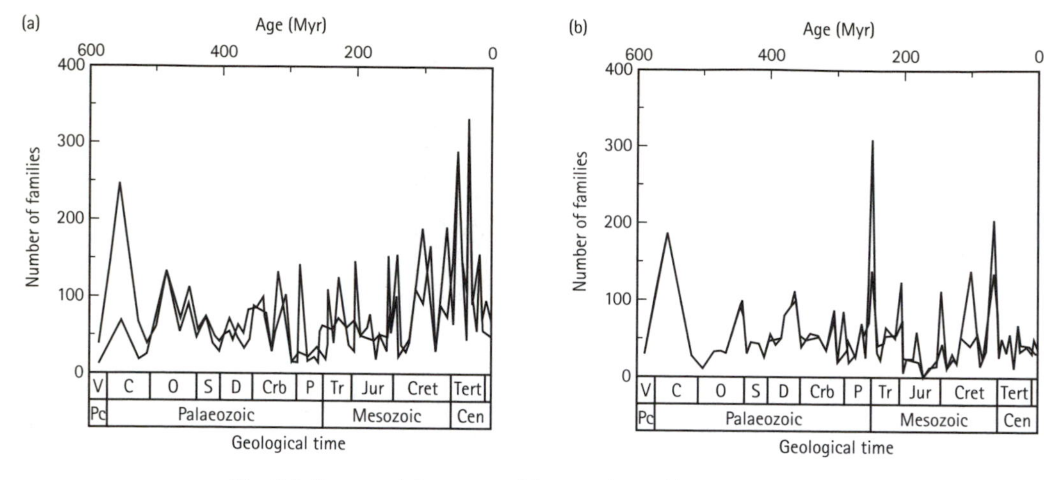

Fig. 2.3 Temporal dynamics of the numbers of family (a) originations and (b) extinctions for all organisms. Maximum and minimum curves are shown and abbreviations are as in Fig. 2.2. (From Benton 1995.)

many models of patterns of species richness both in time and space assume, conversely, that this richness has attained equilibrium.

The number of families in any one period is the number in the preceding period, plus the number of new ones that have appeared, minus the number from the preceding period that have become extinct. The patterns of these originations and extinctions are complex (Fig. 2.3), and numerous studies have sought to identify underlying regularities. The patterns seem to be driven both by internal dynamics of the diversification process and by the influence of external factors.

The broad patterns of temporal change are, to a first approximation, reflected both in global and regional biodiversity and in local biodiversity (Fig. 2.4). This is both interesting and informative, as it means that as biodiversity has increased on a global scale it has tended also to do the same locally. The alternative scenario would have been that biodiversity remained approximately constant locally, with the global increase having resulted solely from a growing differentiation between the occupants of different localities.

Given that there is a pattern of overall increase in biodiversity through time, the obvious question is why? The answer, quite simply, is that we do not know. A number of different factors have been suggested as effecting this increase: external factors such as the break-up of the continents and their subsequent drift (increasing the differentiation between assemblages on different continents and in different ocean basins), and changing climatic conditions and intrinsic factors such as the occupation, through evolutionary time, of more and more of the potential niche space open to organisms (associated with evolutionary 'break-throughs'), and perhaps

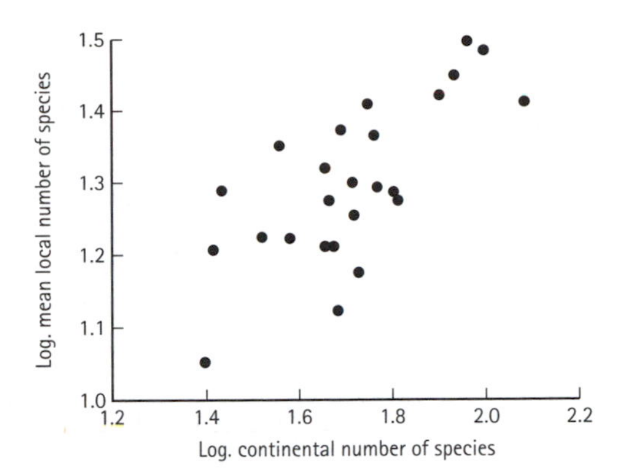

Fig. 2.4 Relationship between local and continental species richness through time for large mammalian carnivore and herbivore species in North America over the last 44 Myr (divided into 25 time intervals, each data point is for one time interval). (From Van Valkenburgh & Janis 1993.)

finer subdivision of this space. The move onto land, for example, opened up many more opportunities for speciation than had previously existed.

2.3.2 Diversification

The overall pattern of diversification is not a product of synchronous changes in the biodiversity of all the component groups of organisms. Rather, some groups underwent differential diversification in particular time periods, often associated with the invasion of new habitats or following major extinction events. Moreover, different groups diversified in different ways (Benton 1997). Some radiated quickly and later also underwent rapid decline in diversity, perhaps to extinction. Some radiated very slowly, and persisted at low diversity. Others continued to radiate at moderate to high rates for very long periods.

This can clearly be seen with reference to land plants and to vertebrate tetrapods. Amongst the land plants, the dominance of primitive vascular plants gave way to pteridophytes (ferns) and lycopsids (club mosses), which in turn gave way to a predominance of gymnosperms (spore bearers), which finally were overtaken by the angiosperms (flower bearers) (Fig. 2.5); there is some evidence that the angiosperms continue their diversification through the present. Amongst vertebrate tetrapods, the early amphibians and reptiles gave way to a number of successful reptile groups (including dinosaurs), which in turn gave way to the modern amphibians and reptiles, the birds and the mammals (Fig. 2.6). It is tempting to interpret these successions as cases of competitive replacement or improvement, with one group being driven out by the growing numbers of species of the ascendant group. However, there is no reason that this interpretation need be correct, and the reasons for these patterns are almost always considerably more complex, and associated with changing environmental conditions and the shifting opportunities associated with these.

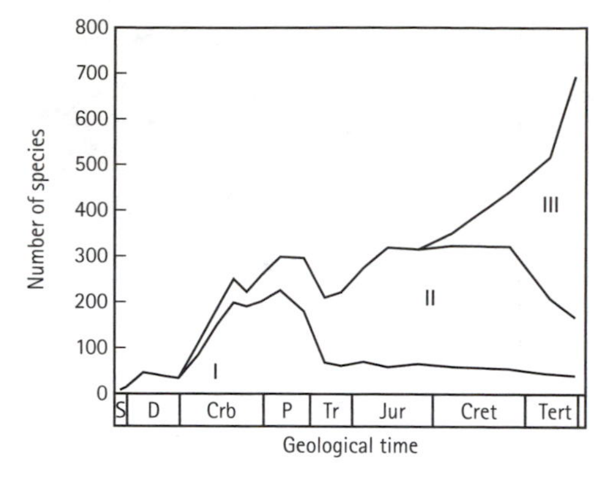

Fig. 2.5 Temporal dynamics of the numbers of fossil species of vascular land plants. I, pteridophytes; II, gymnosperms; III, angiosperms. Abbreviations are as in Fig. 2.2. (From Niklas 1986.)

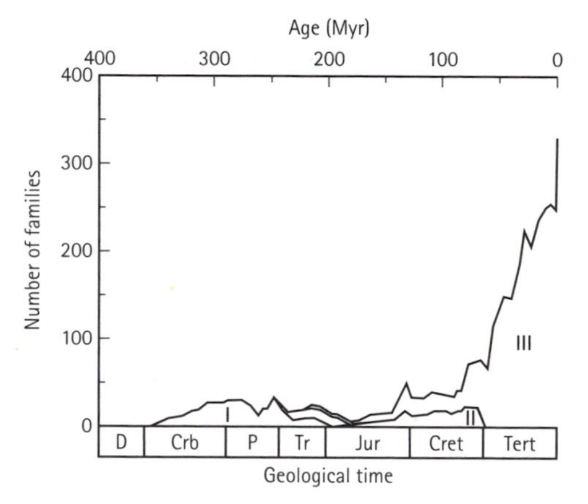

Fig. 2.6 Temporal dynamics of the numbers of families of terrestrial tetrapods. I, early amphibians, early reptiles (anapsids), mammal-like reptiles; II, early diapsids (reptiles), dinosaurs, flying lizards; III, 'modern groups' – amphibians (salamanders and frogs), reptiles (turtles, lizards, snakes and crocodiles), birds and mammals. Abbreviations are as in Fig. 2.2. (From Benton 1985.)

It has been suggested that the rise and fall in the diversity of different groups can, mass extinctions and other such disruptions aside, be reasonably well modelled by a modification of a logistic model, in which a group diversifies initially rather slowly and then more quickly, at some point attaining a peak in richness, and then declines slowly to extinction over some longer period (Fig. 2.7). How general is such a model remains unclear.

Notwithstanding the relatively large number of major body plans, or phyla (see Table 2.2), at any one time much of biodiversity is contributed by just a few groups of organisms, whilst most groups are simply not very diverse. This pattern is repeated at all taxonomic levels. Thus, for example, most species are in the kingdom Animalia, most of the species in the Animalia are in the Arthropoda, most of the species in the Arthropoda are in the class Insecta, and most of the species in the Insecta are in the orders Diptera (the flies), Hymenoptera (the ants, bees and wasps) and Coleoptera (the beetles). Likewise, the largest number of species in the class Mammalia are in the order Rodentia (the rodents), most of the species in the Rodentia are in the family Muridae, and a high proportion of species in the Muridae are in the largest genus in that group.

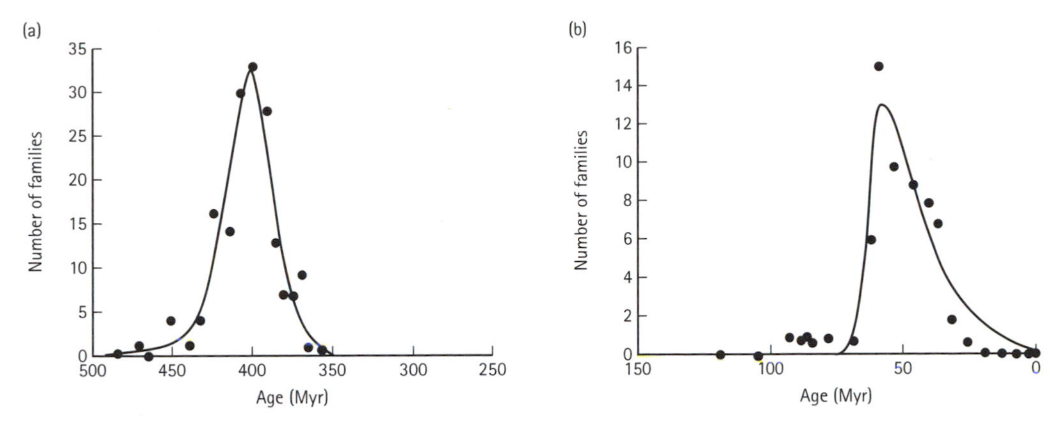

Fig. 2.7 Numbers of families occurring every 1 Myr for: (a) agnathans (jawless vertebrates related to modern lampreys and hagfish); and (b) Cimolesta (small dog-like animals). (From Boulter 2002.)

Three main explanations have been proposed for this clumped pattern of diversity. First, it is possible that this could merely be an artefact of the process of classifying organisms into groups, and may have no biological basis. There is little evidence that this is actually true, because the differences between many groups of organisms are clearly real and reflective of their evolutionary relationships; although curiously, humans do tend to organize sets of differing inanimate objects into a few large groups and many small ones!

Second, the patterns could simply be a matter of chance. Indeed, a pattern in which many groups have a few species and one or a few groups contain a high proportion of species is a likely product of a model of random speciation and extinction. Consider the circumstances in which lineage splitting leads from one ancestral species to four descendant species, and in which at all branching points one ancestral species gives rise to two descendants (dichotomous splitting; Fig. 2.8). Initially an ancestral species splits to give two distinct species. Depending on which of these two speciates, two possible three-species outcomes exist, and depending on which of these three species subsequently speciates, six possible four-species outcomes may result. Of these patterns of phylogeny of four species, only one third (2/6) are symmetrical; an uneven distribution of species is the more likely outcome. Such a pattern is repeated for progressively larger and larger numbers of species (although the possible number of evolutionary trees grows very rapidly; for example by the same set of rules, there are 87,178,291,200 possible trees giving rise to 15 species!). Indeed, models of random speciation and extinction take us a long way towards understanding patterns of diversification, but are not always sufficient. Some groups still have disproportionately more species than would be expected by chance.

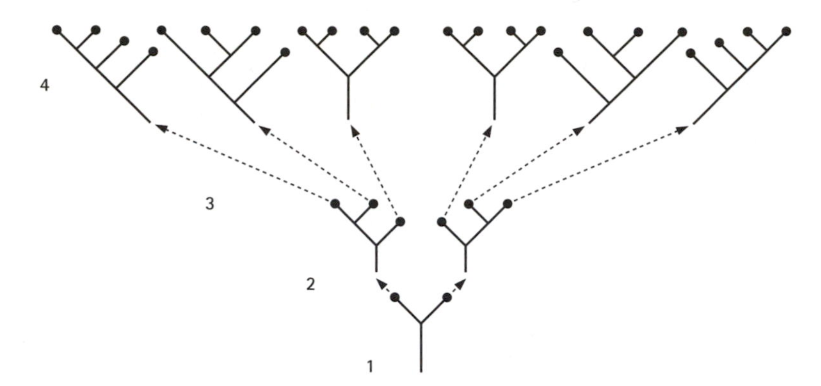

Fig. 2.8 A diagrammatic representation of the possible routes by which lineage splitting leads from one ancestral species to four. (From Slowinski & Guyer 1989.)

This leads us to the third possible reason for the observed pattern, which is that some groups have features that predispose them to diversify disproportionately. Thus, it has been proposed that dispersal by animals has promoted the diversification of some vascular plant groups, the ability to fly has promoted the diversification of some insect groups, and small body size has promoted the diversification of some bird groups. Such suggestions have proven much more difficult to test than was long supposed, and there are many 'just-so' stories (a phrase used by Gould & Lewontin (1979), borrowed from Rudyard Kipling's 1902 book of the same name, to describe a clever explanation of why a given species has a particular trait which is either untested or untestable) for why one group is more diverse than another, with no sound empirical support. Nonetheless, it would seem likely that the evolution of some traits opened up opportunities for some groups to diversify disproportionately more than others. Thus, there is quantitative evidence that the adoption of phytophagy ('plant eating') has been associated with disproportionate diversification in insect groups (Mitter et al. 1988), whilst the adoption of a carnivorous parasitic lifestyle has not (Wiegmann et al. 1993). Much of the history of diversification has been one of specialization in interspecific interactions, be these based on consumption, pollination or dispersal (Thompson 2002).

2.3.3 Extinction

The overall pattern of temporal change in biodiversity results from the difference between rates of speciation (adding species) and rates of extinction (taking species away). If species are being generated faster than they are becoming extinct, then the level of biodiversity will rise. When the rate of extinction equals that of speciation an overall pattern of stability (stasis) will result. Hence if, or when, stasis is observed in the level of

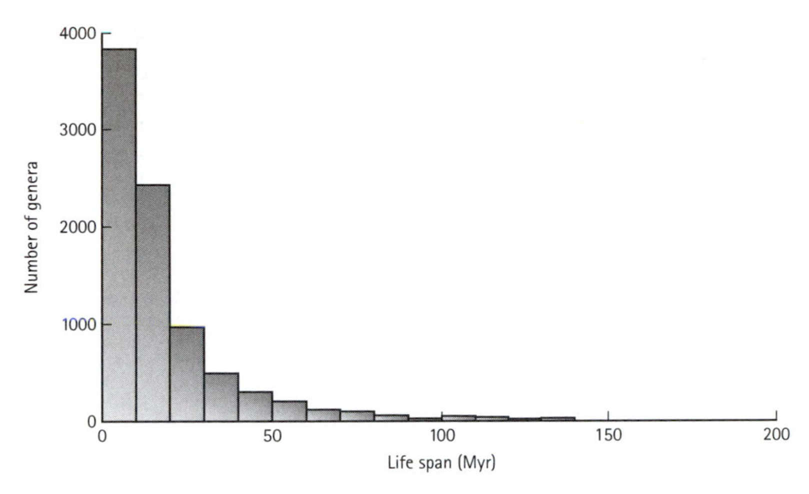

Fig. 2.9 Life spans of c. 17,500 extinct genera of marine animals (vertebrate, invertebrate and microfossil). (From Raup 1994.)

biodiversity this does not necessarily mean that nothing is happening; turnover in the identities of taxa through time could, and frequently will, still be high. When the level of extinction exceeds that of speciation then biodiversity will decline, and if this persisted for a sufficient period then life would ultimately be expunged from the Earth.

Over the history of life on Earth, in excess of 90% of all species (and perhaps closer to 98%) are estimated to have become extinct. Based on evidence from a variety of groups (both marine and terrestrial), the best present estimate is that the average species has had a life span (i.e. from the time a particular species appears in the fossil record until the time it disappears) of around 5–10 Myr (May et al. 1995). Again using a higher taxonomic unit to reduce the sampling problems, Raup (1994) found that the recorded life spans of 17,500 genera of fossil marine animals were strongly right-skewed (Fig. 2.9). Most genera persisted for a relatively short time, whilst a few persisted for a very long period. The real pattern is probably even more skewed, as the very short-lived are unlikely even to be recorded in the fossil record. The pattern is also likely to apply to species. Compared with the duration of life on Earth, however, no genus survived for very long. The longest-lived persisted for about 160 Myr, or about 5% of the history of life.

Some groups tend to have characteristically higher rates of extinction than do others. Thus, there is substantial variation in the estimated periods for which, on average, species in different taxonomic groups persist (Table 2.3). Indeed, natural extinctions tend to be taxonomically clumped, often disproportionately within species-poor groups, which may mean that more genetic diversity is lost than would be expected by chance. Extinctions resulting from human activities tend also to be

Table 2.3 Estimated mean duration (Myr) of fossil species. (From McKinney 1997.)

	Duration (Myr)
Marine	
Reef corals	25
Bivalves	23
Benthic foraminiferans	21
Bryozoa	12
Gastropods	10
Planktonic foraminiferans	10
Echinoids	7
Crinoids	6.7
Non-marine	
Monocotyledonous plants	4
Horses	4
Dicotyledonous plants	3
Freshwater fish	3
Birds	2.5
Mammals	1.7
Insects	1.5
Primates	1

clumped (parrots, pheasants and primates are all disproportionately threatened at present). Such differences may reflect extrinsic factors. Thus, for example, in the fossil record marine groups seem to have lower rates of extinction than do terrestrial groups (Table 2.3), which may perhaps reflect the greater buffering of marine systems to environmental change. However, the differences may also reflect intrinsic factors that make some species more vulnerable to extinction than others, with the relationship between the intrinsic characteristics of species and the likelihood of extinction depending fundamentally on the extrinsic factors that are posing the threat to continued persistence.

The intensity of extinction has varied markedly over time, with comparatively low levels during the majority of periods and high levels during the minority, and an overall right-skewed frequency distribution (Fig. 2.10). The right-hand tail of this continuum comprises what have come to be known as the mass extinctions (the other periods comprise background extinctions), albeit that they clearly do not represent a distinct subset of periods. Although in these short intervals 75–95% of species alive at that time are estimated to have become extinct (Jablonski 1995), in sum the mass extinctions only account for about 4% of all extinctions in the last 600 Myr (Raup 1994). Their importance therefore lies not in their contribution to total extinctions, but in the disruptive effect they have had on the patterns of development of biodiversity. They

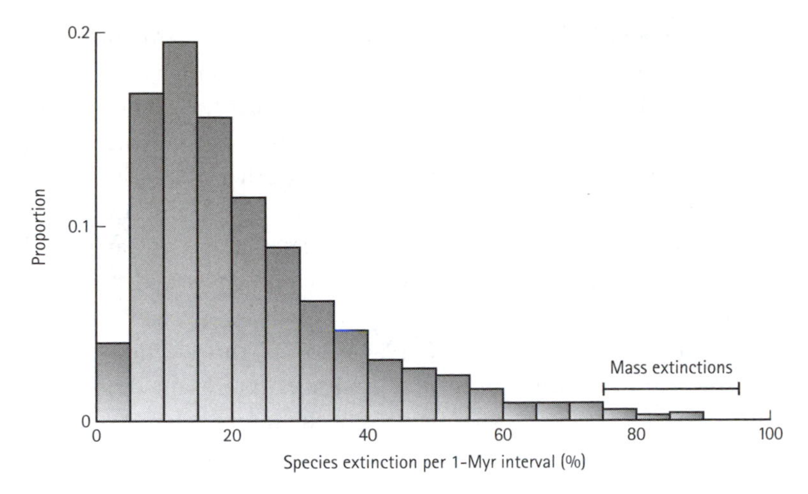

Fig. 2.10 Proportion of 1-Myr intervals during the past 600 Myr with different intensities (percentage of species) of extinction. Mass extinctions occur in the extreme of the right-hand tail. (From Raup 1994.)

reveal that marine and terrestrial biotas are not infinitely resilient but can in some senses be pushed beyond their limits by certain environmental stresses leading to dramatic collapses in diversity (Jablonski 1991). When levels of biodiversity recover, they often have a markedly different composition to those that preceded a mass extinction, with those groups which were previously highly successful in terms of species richness being lost entirely or persisting at reduced numbers.

Although they are the tail of a continuum, the mass extinctions were not simply the result of the chance coincidence of extinctions of very large numbers of species. Indeed, the 'big five' mass extinctions are believed to have had rather different causes (Erwin 2001).

1 *Late Ordovician (440 Myr ago)*. Global climates during the Ordovician were warm, causing a decline in vertical circulation in the oceans, and thence depletion of oxygen in deep waters. The movement of a large amount of continental area near to the South Pole resulted in climatic cooling and the onset of glacial conditions. Sea levels decreased, causing the extinction of marine, particularly deep-water, groups. The end of the glaciation led to a second phase of extinction, with rising sea levels being associated with the spread of low oxygen conditions, leading to the loss of shallow-water groups.

2 *Late Devonian (360 Myr ago)*. Many processes have been suggested to have given rise to this extinction event, including extraterrestrial impact, sea-level fluctuations and spread of anoxic waters, climatic changes and global cooling. There is insufficient evidence to attribute the event solely to any of these, and it may have arisen from a combination of factors.

3 *Late Permian (250 Myr ago)*. Again, the cause of this extinction event, the largest of all (extinguishing 95% of all marine species and 70% of species on land), is debatable. There is evidence that the event coincided with low oxygen levels in the oceans, sea-level rise, and climatic change, some or all of which may have been triggered by other processes.
4 *Late Triassic (210 Myr ago)*. Attempts to explain this event have focussed on extraterrestrial impact, marine anoxia and volcanism (the last giving rise to rapid climatic shifts, volcanic gases and acid rain). Again, however, the patterns of causality are unclear.
5 *End-Cretaceous (65 Myr ago)*. Explanations of this extinction event, best known for the extinction of the dinosaurs, pterosaurs and marine reptiles, have focussed on consequences of the impact of an extraterrestrial object, in particular the global cooling that may have followed from subsequent changes to the atmosphere (particularly dust, smoke, water vapour and sulphur dioxide).

The fossil record reveals that overall levels of biodiversity may recover from mass extinction events very rapidly (for example, the families of marine organisms in Fig. 2.2) on an evolutionary time scale, but the recovery and the re-establishment of some communities still typically requires 2–10 Myr (Jablonski 1995; Erwin 1998). Whilst some lineages may pass on to attain high diversity, others surviving a mass extinction event may fail ever to recover markedly, suggesting an impact that may extend well beyond the actual extinction event itself (a pattern that has been termed 'dead clade walking'; Jablonski 2002). If substantial extinctions occur in the near future, as seems likely if not inevitable (Chapter 5), then the species will not be replaced in short order.

2.4 How many extant species are there?

If the diversity of life has increased through evolutionary time, how many species are presently extant? Although it has received substantial attention, the importance of this question perhaps has less to do with the usefulness of the actual answer than with the challenge it poses to an understanding of how biodiversity is distributed amongst different groups of organisms and across the Earth. It is one of the basic descriptors of life on the planet, to which we should be able to provide a reasonably accurate answer.

On the face of it, the best way of finding out how many extant species there are would simply be to count them! However, the diversity of life is so great that this presents a truly formidable task, and one that has never risen high enough up the agenda of humankind to be given serious consideration. The question of how insurmountable the obstacle would be if substantial resources, technology and ingenuity were brought to bear remains unanswered. Some believe that it is attainable in a matter of decades, but most are unconvinced.

Given the enormity of such a task, all of the many attempts at estimating how many extant species there are have employed indirect measures, and, in the process, have made major assumptions of one kind or another (for reviews, see May 1988, 1990, 1994a; Hammond 1995; Pimm et al. 1995a; Stork 1997). Five main methods have been used to estimate the numbers of extant species in large taxonomic groups or all groups, based on extrapolations from:

1 *Canvassing experts*. This involves estimating overall numbers of species based on the opinions of those experts who have studied particular groups of species over long periods and have gained an understanding of the numbers that are unknown to science. This makes the entirely untestable assumption that these experts know these groups sufficiently well to make reliable estimates.

2 *Patterns of species description*. Overall numbers of species in some groups have been estimated by extrapolating into the future the growth in the cumulative numbers of taxonomically described species through time. This assumes that past patterns of description indicate future patterns.

3 *Proportion of undescribed species*. This approach involves estimating overall numbers of species from the ratio of previously unknown to previously known species in large samples of specimens, and then extrapolating from the overall numbers of known species. This assumes that the samples are representative.

4 *Well-studied areas*. Overall numbers of species globally or in very large regions have been estimated by extrapolating from those few (predominantly temperate) areas for which numbers of species are reasonably well known. This assumes that the areas for which overall species numbers are well known are representative of those for which they are not.

5 *Well-studied groups*. This involves estimating overall numbers of species based on the global numbers in well-known groups and estimates of the ratio of the numbers of species in these groups to others in those few regions where the latter are reasonably well known. This assumes that these ratios of numbers of species in well-known and other groups remain reasonably constant across space.

The assumptions of all of these approaches are seldom precisely met. All also require extrapolation beyond the bounds of available data, something that statisticians, quite correctly, always caution against.

A widely quoted working estimate of extant species numbers, integrating what is presently known based on large numbers of studies, is one of around 13.5 million, with upper and lower estimated numbers of about 3.5 and 111.5 million species, respectively (Table 2.4) (Hawksworth & Kalin-Arroyo 1995; see also World Conservation Monitoring Centre 1992; Hammond 1995). The upper boundary appears wildly improbable,

Table 2.4 Approximate numbers of described species (in thousands) currently recognized, and estimates of possible species richness for groups with more than 20,000 described species and/or estimated to include in excess of 100,000 species. The reliability of all estimates is likely to vary greatly, and a crude indication of the likely accuracy is given. (From Hawksworth & Kalin-Arroyo 1995.)

	Described species	Number of estimated species		Working figure	Accuracy of working figure
		High	Low		
Viruses	4	1000	50	400	Very poor
Bacteria	4	3000	50	1000	Very poor
Fungi	72	2700	200	1500	Moderate
'Protozoa'	40	200	60	200	Very poor
'Algae'	40	1000	150	400	Very poor
Plants	270	500	300	320	Good
Nematodes	25	1000	100	400	Poor
Arthropods					
Crustaceans	40	200	75	150	Moderate
Arachnids	75	1000	300	750	Moderate
Insects	950	100,000	2000	8000	Moderate
Molluscs	70	200	100	200	Moderate
Chordates	45	55	50	50	Good
Others	115	800	200	250	Moderate
Totals	1750	111,655	3635	13,620	Very poor

if for no other reason than that it is not obvious where all the 'missing' species are to be found! Evidence in support of the working estimate or a figure somewhat lower is becoming increasingly convincing, albeit categorical demonstrations of its validity do not exist. Thirteen and a half million species is difficult to visualize. It is about one species for every 450 people in the world, but it is debateable how much that helps to comprehend this extraordinary level of diversity.

The major uncertainties in the overall numbers of species remain in estimates for particular taxonomic groups (e.g. viruses, bacteria, fungi, nematodes, mites, insects), functional groups (e.g. parasites), and habitats or biomes (e.g. soils, tropical forest canopies, deep-ocean benthos; see Section 3.3.5). Indeed, the relative contribution of some groups compared with others continues to be, sometimes vigorously, debated (e.g. see Hammond 1995).

• *Bacteria*. Understanding of the numbers of species of bacteria (and microbes more generally) is complicated by frequent difficulties in applying standard species concepts to these creatures (resort is usually made to operational taxonomic units, OTUs), by the difficulty of culturing the vast majority of these organisms and thereby applying classical identification techniques, and by the unimaginable numbers of individuals that exist (the global number of prokaryotes is estimated to be 4–6 × 10^{30} cells, with a production rate of 1.7 × 10^{30} cells yr^{-1}; Whitman et al. 1998). The numbers of species estimated to occur in even very small areas can vary by several orders of magnitude, depending on the approach taken to estimation (Curtis et al. 2002; Ward 2002). Globally, it is clear that the diversity of bacteria, both in terrestrial and marine systems, may be far larger than many had previously imagined (Fuhrman & Campbell 1998; Torsvik et al. 2002), and may number millions of taxa.

• *Protozoa*. Whilst even very small samples of sediment may contain many species of Protozoa, it is becoming clear that at least in some groups most of these have large geographic ranges and that this local richness may not therefore be indicative of high global richness (Finlay 2002). Thus, of 85 ciliate species found in a volcanic crater-lake in Australia none were unique to the continent (Finlay & Fenchel 1999). Free-living ciliate species have been estimated to perhaps number just 3000, with the number of extant free-living Protozoa totalling perhaps 12,000–19,000 (Fenchel et al. 1997; Finlay et al. 1998; Finlay & Fenchel 1999).

• *Fungi*. A working figure of 1.5 million species of fungi, based primarily on extrapolation from temperate studies, has been widely cited (Hawksworth 1991). On the one hand, some tropical studies suggest that this may constitute a substantial underestimate (Fröhlich & Hyde 1999; Arnold et al. 2000). On the other hand, it has been argued that the frequency of discovery of previously unknown species in areas whose fungi are not well studied suggests that the figure may be a substantial overestimate. Regardless, the scale of fungal diversity may be suggested by the discovery that just three individual plant leaves (two dicotyledonous and one palm leaf) from the Neotropics together supported 108 foliicolous lichen species, 25% of all the taxa known from the region (Lücking & Matzer 2001); lichens comprise a mutualistic relationship between a fungus and an alga or cyanobacterium.

• *Nematodes*. Cobb (1914) observed that 'If all matter in the universe except the nematodes were swept away, our world would still be dimly recognisable, and if, as disembodied spirits, we could then investigate it, we should find its mountains, hills, vales, rivers, lakes and oceans represented by a film of nematodes'. The figure 10^{19} has been suggested as a conservative estimate of the global number of individuals of free-living nematodes (Lambshead, in press). How this vast abundance translates into numbers of species remains unclear. Figures of 1 million to 100 million extant species have been suggested (for a review, see Lambshead, in press), although recent analyses have cast severe doubt on the more extreme upper estimates.

- *Mites*. The mites have long been regarded as a hyperdiverse group of organisms, and studies in the tropics are revealing a richness comparable to that of many insect taxa (Walter & Proctor 1998; Walter et al. 1998; Walter & Behan-Pelletier 1999). Of an estimated total of at least some hundreds of thousands, less than 50,000 species of mites have been described (World Conservation Monitoring Centre 1992; Walter & Behan-Pelletier 1999).
- *Insects*. The total number of all species depends in major part on the number of extant species of insects (because they constitute such a high proportion of all species), for which estimates have ranged particularly widely (see Table 2.4). A number of recent analyses have strongly suggested that the higher estimates are not tenable (e.g. Bartlett et al. 1999; Ødegaard et al. 2000; Dolphin & Quicke 2001; Novotny et al. 2002a), but they continue to be championed in some quarters. Much of the uncertainty rests on the numbers of species that are to be found in the tropical rain forest canopy, the proportion that are restricted to this environment, and the degree of host specificity of herbivorous insects in such forests, which was assumed to be much higher than is actually the case, implying a fine subdivision of plant resources and thereby inflating estimated numbers of insect species (Novotny et al. 2002a,b). Debate continues to surround the issue of which order of insects is most speciose. Evidence that the Coleoptera (beetles) are a more tropical group than some of the others would seem to bolster their claim, but empirical support is quite sparse.

A feature common to most of these groups is that many of their species are parasites. This has led to a lively debate as to whether parasitism is the most common lifestyle on Earth, and whether the majority of species are parasitic rather than free-living (e.g. May 1992a; Poulin 1996; Windsor 1998). Given that parasites are, and will doubtless remain, more poorly known than free-living species, these are important issues in understanding the overall biodiversity of life on Earth. Given that most free-living species harbour many species of parasites, that some of these species are commonly host specialists, and that parasites frequently themselves provide hosts for other parasites, the significance of the parasitic way of life to the global total number of species is indisputable. If you remain unconvinced, then consider that humans alone play host to probably several hundred parasitic species (including microbes).

Significant debate over numbers of extant species also persists for some of what are regarded as better known taxonomic groups. Thus, for example, it appears that the widely quoted figure of c. 250,000 species of angiosperms (seed plants) is a substantial underestimate, with suggestions that there may in fact be 300,000 or even more than 400,000 (Prance et al. 2000; Govaerts 2001; Bramwell 2002). Whilst reliable figures exist for small areas and regions, global estimates are still largely based on extrapolation and assumptions about the overlap in the occurrence of species in different biogeographic regions.

The construction of an inventory of the Earth's species is hampered severely by the fact that only a fraction of the total number of species have been formally taxonomically described. Even determining how large a fraction is complicated by the absence of a definitive listing of all described species and their status (e.g. whether they are presently regarded as valid species or not). There have been several attempts to establish an international programme to generate such a catalogue, but to date these have foundered for lack of the substantial funding that is required. A widely quoted working estimate is that approximately 1.75 million living species have been described, that is about 13% of an estimated total number of extant species of 13.5 million, with the percentage of species in some particular groups that have been described thought to be much smaller (see Table 2.4).

Lists of described species are prone to two kinds of errors. First, the same species name may have been attributed to more than one species, so-called homonymy. Second, more than one species name may have been attributed to the same species, so-called synonymy. For example, of the 59 new species of mammals described from the Neotropics between 1992 and 1998, two (*Coendou koopmani* and *Thryoptera robusta*) were already deemed by 1997 to be synonyms of previously known species (Patterson 2000). Most synonyms take much longer to be recognized, often many decades. The balance of these two kinds of errors seems to lean strongly towards synonymy, with many thousands of species names thought to be synonyms. For example, 20% of extant insect species names may be synonyms, with the proportion being higher for groups that have been intensively studied, have larger geographic ranges and exhibit conspicuous individual variation (Gaston & Mound 1993), and high proportions are also becoming apparent for some better studied or easily collected groups of fungi and molluscs (Altaba 1996; Aptroot 1997; Bouchet 1997). A similar problem plagues lists of fossil species, with analyses of North American fossil mammal species predicting that 24–31% of currently accepted names will prove invalid (Alroy 2002). This suggests two things. First, a substantially smaller total number of species have been described than the number of presently valid species names implies. Second, substantially less than 13% of the estimated total numbers of extant species may have been described. This is less clear, however, because estimates of global numbers of extant or fossil species that are based on extrapolation from lists of known species will also be inflated by these difficulties.

In fact, the situation is yet more dynamic than even this may seem to imply. For example, perhaps reducing the overestimation, recognized synonyms may be reinstated as full species names if subsequent work shows that they did indeed originally refer to genuinely distinct species

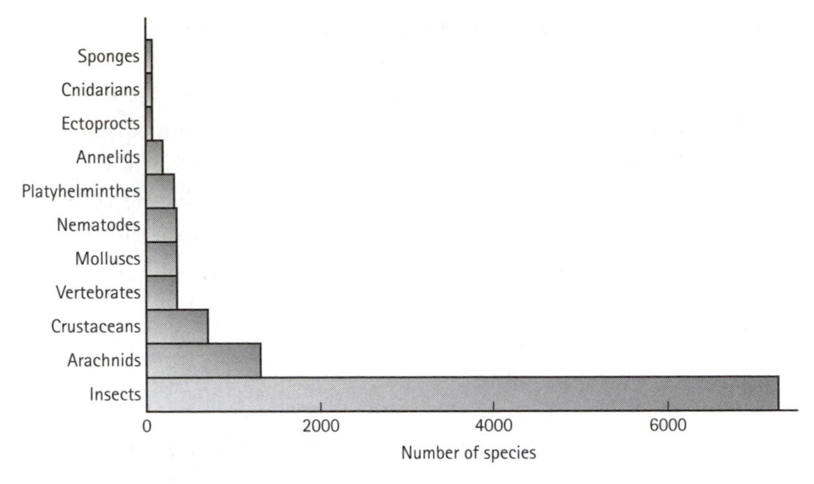

Fig. 2.11 Average number of species described per annum between 1978 and 1987 for major animal groups. (Data from World Conservation Monitoring Centre 1992.)

and not to previously described ones. Thus, since 1982, for the Neotropics, 57 new mammal species have been described, 57 species have been synonymized, and about 150 species have been resurrected from previous synonymy, resulting in a net increase of about 150 species (Patterson 2000).

Additional species are being formally described at a rate of about 13,000 per annum, or about 36 species on the average day (both figures based on formal published descriptions of new species); the breakdown for major groups of animals is given in Fig. 2.11. This rate has remained remarkably constant over past decades (Hawksworth & Kalin-Arroyo 1995). However, the particular group of organisms a taxonomist chooses to study is on the one hand a matter of serendipity and personal choice, and on the other is driven by practical concerns such as the significance of the group in human affairs (e.g. agriculture, medicine) and the availability of funding for research (in some major groups fossil species are being described at higher rates than extant species; Bouchet 1997). Consequently, the catalogue of biodiversity has grown in a somewhat haphazard fashion. Even within those better studied groups, the species that have been described are far from a random subset of all species. On average they are larger-bodied, more abundant (locally or regionally), more widely distributed, occupy a larger number of habitats or life zones, and derive disproportionately from temperate zones (for some groups, rates of description from the tropics appear to have collapsed; e.g. Bouchet 1997). Where species have been formally described, this should not be taken to mean that much is known about them. For example, one estimate suggests that about 40% of described species of beetles are each known from only a single locality (May et al. 1995), usually reflecting the fact that they were captured on just one occasion, often many decades ago (meaning that their present status is unclear; Section 5.2.2).

Inevitably, with so many new species continuing to be found and described, extant representatives of major lineages that were previously unknown continue also to be discovered. The discovery of new phyla has previously been mentioned (Section 2.3.1); other recent examples include a new order of insects (named the Mantophasmatodea; Klass et al. 2002) and a new family of beetles (named the Aspidytidae; Ribera et al. 2002).

Typically, through time the cumulative number of species described in a taxon follows, albeit often only very approximately, an S-shaped function. It increases slowly at first, then goes through a period of rapid growth, before approaching an asymptote when all of the species are known. Such a pattern can be disrupted by changes in the species concept that is generally being employed (see Section 1.4.4), and by variation in the numbers and output of the taxonomists studying a group, but the overall shape is reasonably robust. For well-known groups of organisms the full shape of the function has been revealed, for poorly known ones only the early parts have thus far been attained (Fig. 2.12).

The gap between the number of described animal species and the estimated total number of extant species is due predominantly to ignorance of small-bodied invertebrate taxa; the majority of species are small-bodied. However, it should not be forgotten that numbers of new vertebrate species continue to be discovered. New fish species are described at the rate of about 130–160 each year (Berra 1997). In Africa alone, between 1946 and 1995 some 48 new species of birds were discovered (Fig. 2.13). Globally, from 1980 to mid-2002, 151 extant or recently extinct species of birds were newly described, an average of 6–7 per annum, with several others awaiting description (van Rootselaar 1999, 2002). The majority of these species have been identified using classical taxonomic techniques. However, molecular studies are revealing the existence of many more bird species than had been apparent from morphological studies alone (Martin 1996; Price 1996). Many previously recognized subspecies, races and disjunct populations are as distinct in terms of their degree of molecular divergence as previously recognized species, albeit this may not be as obvious in other regards. This has led to the speculation that there may be 20,000 extant species of birds, twice the present generally accepted number.

Sixteen new, living species of large mammals alone were described during the period 1937 to the early 1990s, about three per decade (Pine 1994). These were two porpoises (*Lagenodelphis hosei*, *Phocoena sinus*), four beaked whales (*Tasmacetus shepherdi*, *Mesoplodon ginkgodens*, *M. carlhubbsi*, *M. peruvianus*), a wild pig (*Sus heureni*), a peccary (*Catagonus wagneri*), four deer (*Mazama chunyi*, *Moschus fuscus*, *Muntiacus atherodes*,

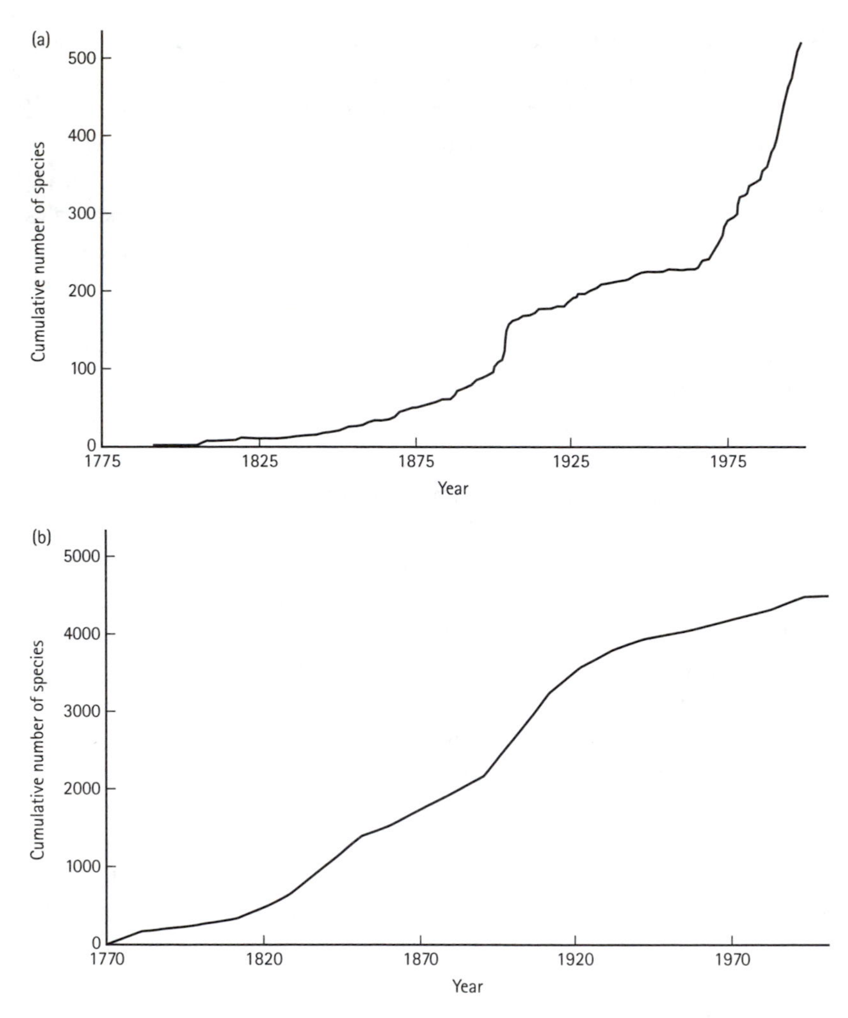

Fig. 2.12 Growth in the cumulative numbers of species described for: (a) thalassinid shrimps; and (b) mammals. (a, From Dworschak 2000; b, from Wilson & Reeder 1993.)

Muntiacus gongshanensis), the kouprey (*Bos sauveli*), a gazelle (*Gazella bilkis*), a wild sheep (*Pseudois schaeferi*) and a 'bovid' (*Pseudoryx nghetinhensis*). Based on historical patterns of species accumulation, Medellín and Soberón (1999) estimate that by the year 2032 an additional 247 mammal species will have been described above the 1992 total of 4628 species. The majority of the new species will be small (< 100 g) and will be in the orders Insectivora, Chiroptera and Rodentia. Given the present rate of loss of biodiversity, it is not unlikely that many presently extant species of mammal will become extinct even before they are described (Chapter 5).

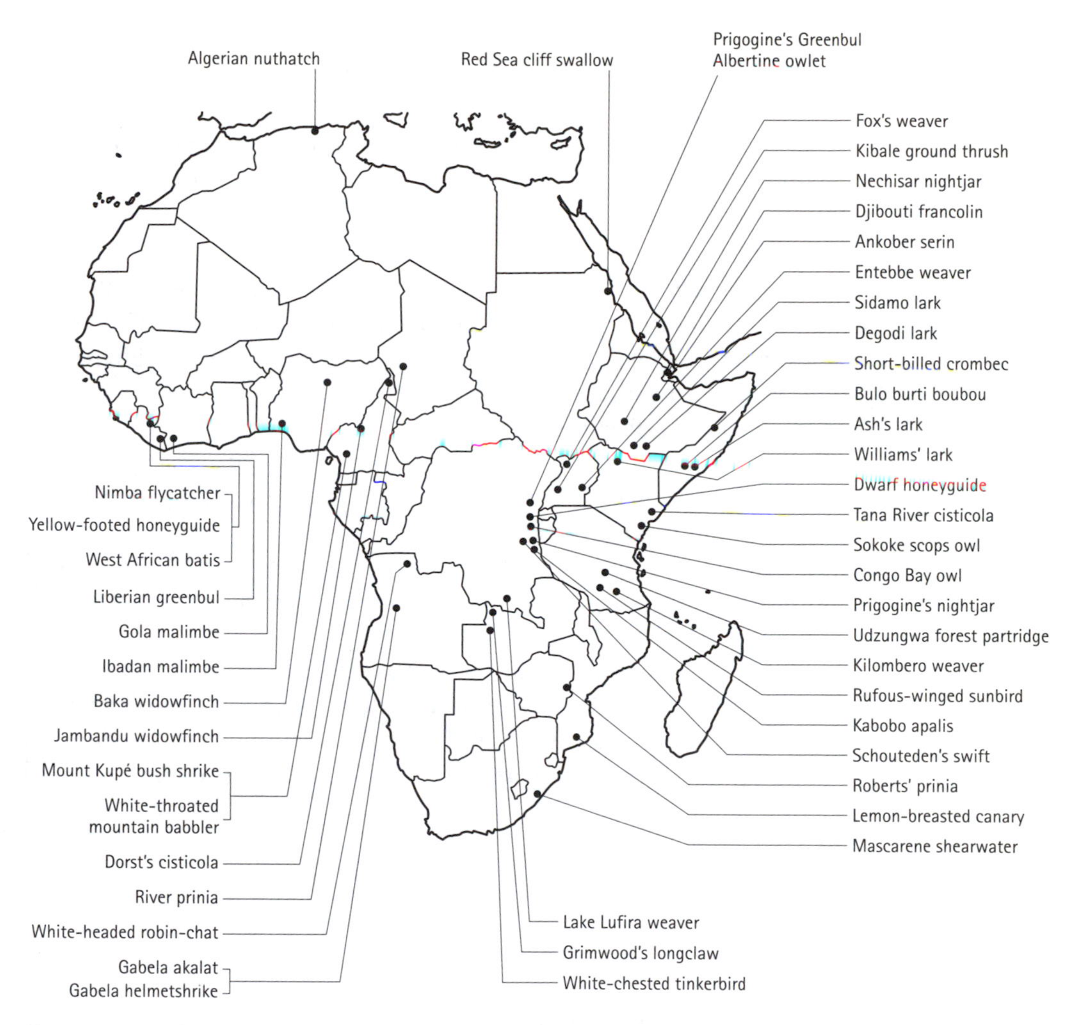

Fig. 2.13 Sites of the discoveries of 47 of the 48 new species of birds recorded from Africa between 1946 and 1995 (in addition, Forbes-Watson's swift was also described from the island of Socotra). (From Hockey 1997a,b.)

There is no likelihood that in the foreseeable future the disparity between the total number of extant species and the number of species that have been described will be markedly closed. This is simply because the taxonomic workforce does not exist to perform the task. In fact, the present workforce is actually in decline (Gaston & May 1992). In the face of this lamentable state of affairs, fulfilment of the task of describing all species will remain a far-distant prospect. What is required is a planned targeting of key groupings, taxa and geographical areas for taxonomic description designed to give a better understanding of the important questions in the study of biodiversity and other fields, rather than the *ad hoc* accumulation of taxa seen at present.

2.5 Summary

1 There has been an overall pattern of increase in biodiversity, from the appearance of the first organism up to the present day, despite the fact that more than 90% of all species that have existed have become extinct.
2 Although it has been described in terms of some simple mathematical models, this increase has not been continuous but is composed of radiations and stabilizations, punctuated by mass extinctions of different taxonomic groups at different times.
3 The mass extinctions are the tail of a continuum of levels of extinction in different periods. Although accounting only for a small proportion of extinctions, they have major disruptive effects on the patterns of development of biodiversity.
4 At any one time, the bulk of biodiversity is contributed by only a relatively few taxonomic groups of organisms; most groups are not particularly diverse.
5 The total number of extant species has been estimated using a variety of extrapolations. The best estimate is that there are approximately 13.5 million species, with only 1.75 million of these currently described. However, there are large potential errors in both these figures.

Further reading

Archibald, J.D. (1996) *Dinosaur Extinction and the End of an Era: What the Fossils Say*. Columbia University Press, New York. (*A readable book, especially for the non-specialist, on the extinction of dinosaurs and other vertebrates.*)

Benton, M.J. (1997) Models for the diversification of life. *Trends in Ecology and Evolution* **12**, 490–495. (*A valuable summary.*)

Brooks, D.R. & McLennan, D.A. (2002) *The Nature of Diversity: An Evolutionary Voyage of Discovery*. University of Chicago Press, Chicago, IL. (*Develops the thesis that historical contingency is vital to understanding the origin of biodiversity.*)

Crawley, M.J. (1997) Biodiversity. In: *Plant Ecology*, 2nd edn. (ed. M.J. Crawley), pp. 595–632. Blackwell Science, Oxford. (*A very useful overview of the biodiversity of plants, with sections on temporal dynamics and aliens.*)

Drury, S. (2001) *Stepping Stones: The Makings of Our Home World*. Oxford University Press, Oxford. (*A short history of the geological and biological origins of our planet.*)

Gee, H. (1996) *Before the Backbone: Views on the Origin of the Vertebrates*. Chapman & Hall, London. (*Extremely well written, state-of-the-art, discussion of vertebrate origins.*)

Hammond, P.M. (1994) Practical approaches to the estimation of the extent of biodiversity in speciose groups. *Philosophical Transactions of the Royal Society, London B* **345**, 119–136. (*A particular viewpoint on estimating the species richness of the very largest groups.*)

Howard, D.J. & Berlocher, S.H. (eds.) (1999) *Endless Forms. Species and Speciation.* Oxford University Press, New York. (*Group of essays presenting current critical thinking on what constitutes a species.*)

Magurran, E.A. & May, R.M. (eds.) (1999) *Evolution of Biological Diversity.* Oxford University Press, Oxford. (*A collection exploring a variety of aspects of the generation of biodiversity.*)

Margulis, L. & Schwartz, K.V. (1998) *Five Kingdoms: An Illustrated Guide to the Phyla of Life on Earth*, 3rd edn. W.H. Freeman & Co., New York. (*The standard work on the higher taxa.*)

Minelli, A. (1993) *Biological Systematics: The State of the Art.* Chapman & Hall, London. (*An accessible overview of biological systematics, including the state of taxonomy of major groups.*)

Raup, D.M. (1994) The role of extinction in evolution. *Proceedings of the National Academy of Sciences, USA* **91**, 6758–6763. (*Simply a great paper.*)

Rosenzweig, M.L. (1995) *Species Diversity in Space and Time.* Cambridge University Press, Cambridge. (*A major review of some of the principal patterns, and the mechanisms which underpin them.*)

Schopf, J.W. (ed.) (1992) *Major Events in the History of Life.* Jones & Bartlett, Boston, MA. (*Contains some very good chapters, written by experts but mainly pitched at undergraduate level, introducing the oldest fossils (chapter 2), the evolution of the earliest animals (chapter 3) and diversification of the vertebrates (chapter 5).*)

Tokeshi, M. (1999) *Species Coexistence: Ecological and Evolutionary Perspectives.* Blackwell Science, Oxford. (*A wide-ranging treatment of the patterns and processes of species diversity and coexistence, unusually blending palaeobiological and contemporary perspectives.*)

3 Mapping biodiversity

3.1 Introduction

Biodiversity is not distributed evenly across the Earth, or through the media (e.g. air, soil, water) that blanket it. Rather, species numbers form a richly textured surface of highs and lows, and species composition (the particular set of species) changes in spatially complex ways. Attempts to understand the distribution of biodiversity have focussed particularly on the identification of general spatial patterns in species richness that transcend this complexity, and on the mechanisms that have given rise to these patterns. Inevitably, such efforts have largely concerned the small number of better known taxa, especially plants, birds and mammals in the terrestrial realm, and molluscs and fish in the marine one. Very little empirical information is available about spatial patterns in the biodiversity of most of the highly speciose groups, such as the bacteria, fungi and insects. For no geographic area, even if only of moderate size, do we as yet have a completed count of all of the species (across all taxa) that occur there.

In this chapter, we do four things. First, we address some issues regarding the effects of spatial scale on observed levels of biodiversity. Second, we identify spatial patterns in the occurrence of areas of extremely high and low biodiversity. Third, we identify spatial gradients in biodiversity, and the mechanisms that have been purported to give rise to them. Finally, we discuss spatial congruence in the biodiversity of different groups, and the prospects for determining the big picture that will allow further generalizations to be made about the distribution of life on Earth.

Throughout this chapter, a distinction is drawn between species richness at local and at regional or large spatial scales. Elsewhere, a distinction is commonly made between alpha, beta and gamma diversities, with alpha diversity being the number of species found within local assemblages or communities, beta diversity being the turnover of species identities between communities, and gamma diversity being the number of species occurring across a region (for a review, see Whittaker et al. 2001).

3.2 Issues of scale

Observed levels of species richness are dependent on spatial scale. There are two principal manifestations of this dependence, species–area relationships and local–regional richness relationships.

3.2.1 Species–area relationships

On average, as the size of an area increases, so does the number of species which it contains (Fig. 3.1; MacArthur & Wilson 1967; Williamson 1988; Rosenzweig 1995). Although other models better fit some data sets, the relationship between species richness and area can commonly be approximated as:

$$S = cA^z$$

or

$$\log S = \log c + z \log A$$

where S is the number of species, A is the area, and z and c are constants (known as the Arrenhius relationship). Relationships of this type characteristically explain more than 50% of the variation in species richness between different areas. The slope of the relationship, z, is commonly found to be about 0.25 to 0.30 (although values span the range 0 to 0.5). This roughly suggests that the loss of 90% of the habitat in an area (i.e. a 10-fold reduction in its extent) will result in the loss of 50% of the species that live exclusively in that habitat. Likewise, the loss of 99% of the habitat will lead to the extinction of 75% of the species. z may vary markedly with whether areas are nested or not (smaller areas lying within the confines of progressively larger ones), whether they are islands or parts of continents, with their latitude, and with the range of sizes of areas (e.g. Palmer & White 1994; Rosenzweig 1995; Crawley & Harral 2001; Lomolino & Weiser 2001; Lyons & Willig 2002).

(a)

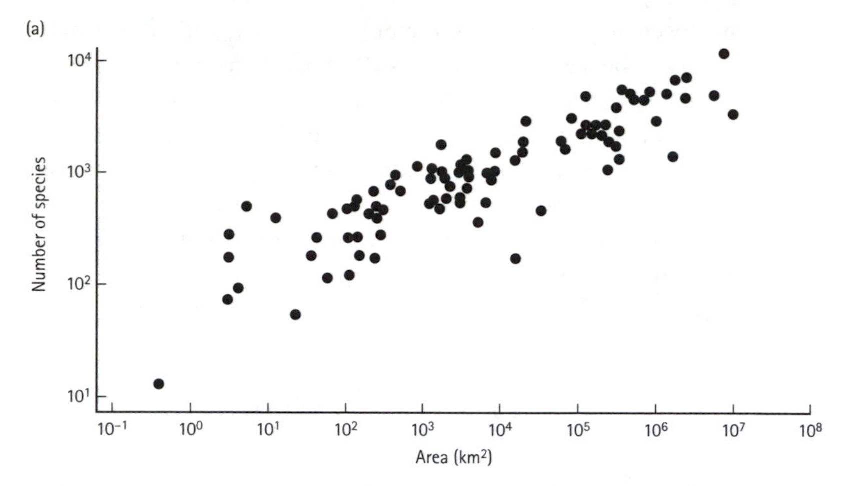

10⁴
10³
10²
10¹
Number of species
10⁻¹ 10⁰ 10¹ 10² 10³ 10⁴ 10⁵ 10⁶ 10⁷ 10⁸
Area (km²)

(b)

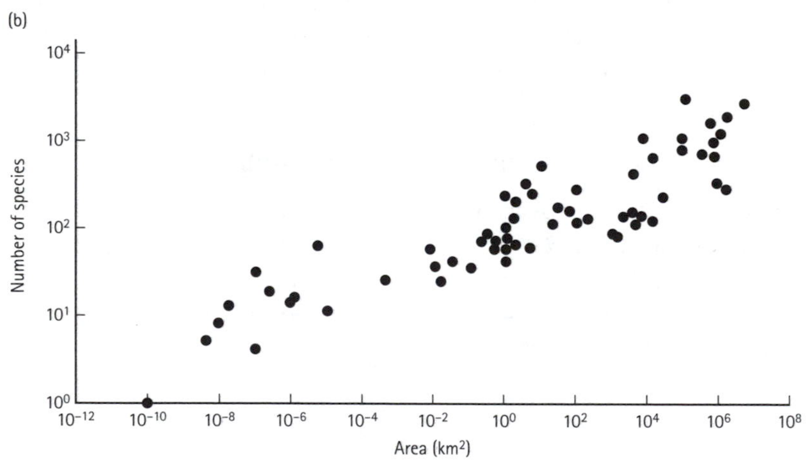

10⁴
10³
10²
10¹
10⁰
Number of species
10⁻¹² 10⁻¹⁰ 10⁻⁸ 10⁻⁶ 10⁻⁴ 10⁻² 10⁰ 10² 10⁴ 10⁶ 10⁸
Area (km²)

(c)

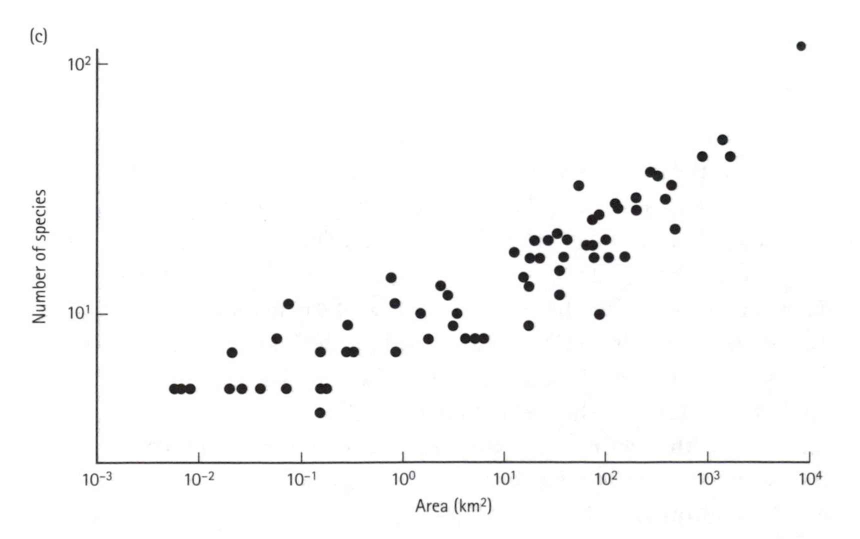

10²
10¹
Number of species
10⁻³ 10⁻² 10⁻¹ 10⁰ 10¹ 10² 10³ 10⁴
Area (km²)

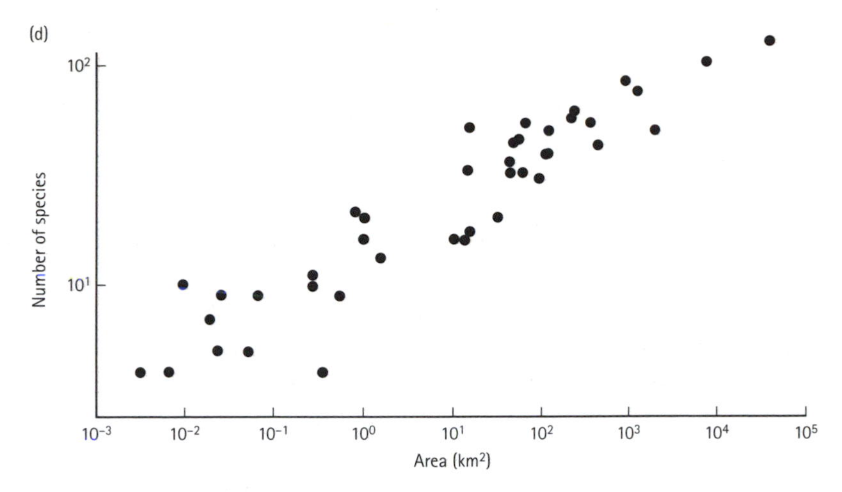

Fig. 3.1 Species–area relationships for: (a) native plant species at sites around the world; (b) benthic macrofaunal species in areas of the Arctic; (c) land snails on Aegean islands; and (d) birds on the Bismarck Islands. (a, From Lonsdale 1999; b, from Azovsky 2002; c, data from Welter-Schultes & Williams 1999; d, data from Mayr & Diamond 2001.)

Four primary reasons have been proposed to explain the species–area relationship.

1 *Sampling*. There may in fact be no underlying relationship between species number and area, with that observed being a statistical artefact of variations in sample size associated with areas of different sizes. More species are recorded from larger areas because more individuals are sampled from those areas.

2 *Habitat diversity*. Larger areas might contain more species because they contain more habitats, and thus more opportunities for different kinds of organisms to establish and persist. Larger areas may contain more habitats because they are topographically and environmentally more diverse.

3 *Colonization/extinction dynamics*. The number of species in an area may result from a dynamic balance between the number of species colonizing from the source pool (e.g. the mainland set of species for many islands), and those going extinct after colonization. Colonization rate is hypothesized to decline as the number of species increases, because there are fewer species remaining to colonize, and because the early colonizers will be those best suited to colonization (e.g. good dispersers). Extinction rate is hypothesized to increase with number of species, as each species has its own finite probability of extinction, and because negative interactions between species (competition, predation, etc.) are more likely when there are more species (although positive interactions may also increase, nullifying this latter effect). Therefore, as the number of species in an area increases, colonization rate declines and extinction rate increases.

4 *Speciation/extinction dynamics*. For very large areas, the influence of immigration on the numbers of species present is relatively small, and the balance between speciation (adding entirely new species) and extinction (removing species) is the most significant process. The larger the area, the larger, on average, are the potential geographic range sizes of the species that occur there. If species with larger geographic ranges have a greater probability of speciating (perhaps because barriers are more likely to subdivide their ranges) and also have a smaller likelihood of extinction (because they contain more individuals, and chance events are less likely to influence them all simultaneously), then more species will accumulate.

These different mechanisms vary in importance with different kinds and sizes of sets of areas. Thus, colonization/extinction dynamics are likely to be very important in genuine island systems, and speciation/extinction dynamics important at the scale of biogeographic provinces.

Differences in the sizes of areas have, with some important exceptions (e.g. see Section 3.3), a pervasive influence on most spatial patterns in biodiversity. This must be borne in mind in much of the subsequent discussion in this chapter. Indeed, species–area relationships will feature as possible explanations of several such patterns. However, the species–area relationship may sometimes be obscured or even reversed by some of the other spatial patterns in biodiversity, especially that with latitude (Section 3.4.1). For example, the small tropical country of Costa Rica (51,100 km^2) contains at least 218 species of reptiles, 796 species of birds and 203 species of mammals, whereas the large temperate country of Canada (9,970,610 km^2) contains 32 species of reptiles, 434 species of birds and 94 species of mammals (Medellín & Soberón 1999).

3.2.2 Local–regional richness relationships

Although it is true that smaller areas tend to contain fewer species than larger areas (Section 3.2.1), the species richness of a small area is not independent of that of the larger area in which it is embedded. Two theoretical types of relationship between the local richness an assemblage might attain and the species richness of the region in which that assemblage resides have been contrasted (Fig. 3.2; Cornell & Lawton 1992). First, local richness may be directly proportional to, but less than, regional richness, following a proportional sampling model (Type I). Alternatively, as regional richness increases, local richness might attain a ceiling above which it does not rise despite continued increases in regional richness (Type II). Acknowledging a number of technical concerns (Huston 1999; Lawton 1999; Srivastava 1999), most real systems, including marine, freshwater and terrestrial assemblages, seem to exhibit an underlying Type I relationship (Fig. 3.3; Cornell & Lawton 1992; Caley & Schluter 1997; Rex et al. 1997; Lawton 1999). Not uncommonly,

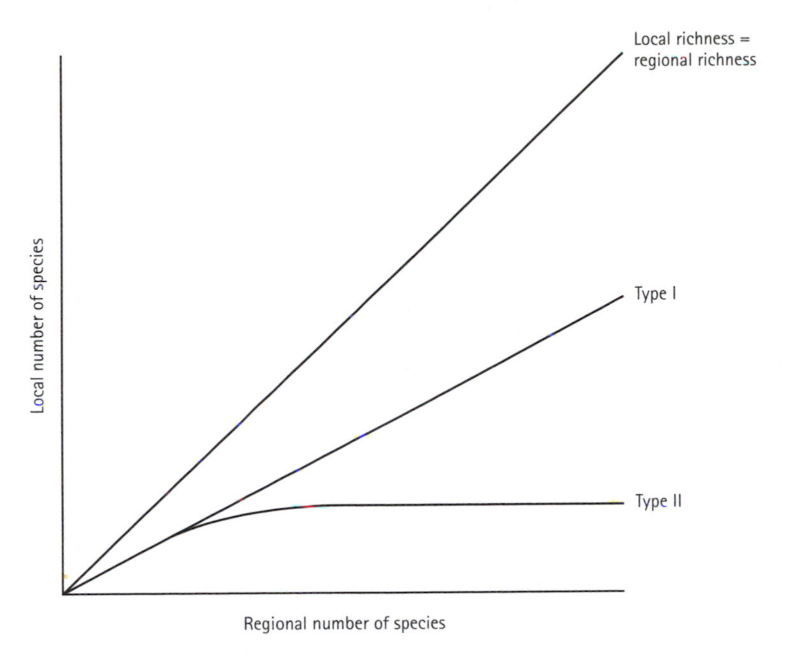

Fig. 3.2 Relationships between local and regional species richness, illustrating the form of Type I and Type II relationships and the limiting condition where local richness equals regional richness.

regional richness explains a large proportion (> 75%) of variance in local richness, and local richness constitutes a marked proportion (> 50%) of regional richness. The predominance of Type I relationships is supported by the observation that some spatial gradients in species richness (e.g. that with latitude) are documented both for localities and regions across those gradients.

The preponderance of examples of Type I relationships, particularly where habitat type has been kept constant, backed up with other evidence (e.g. the limited support for: (i) convergence of communities in comparable environments in regions with different numbers of species; (ii) density compensation among species in assemblages; and (iii) invasion resistance of assemblages), suggests that commonly there are not hard limits to levels of local richness (Cornell 1999). That is, local assemblages do not appear to be saturated with species, in the way one might have expected if ecological interactions (e.g. competition, predation, parasitism) limited local richness. This would fit with the observation that an historical limit has not been reached to the number of species that can be packed onto the Earth (Section 2.3.1).

If the majority of systems exhibit Type I local–regional richness relationships, then a prime driver of local richness appears to be the regional number of species. The importance of regional-scale phenomena for local-scale assemblage structure is a general one (Ricklefs & Schluter

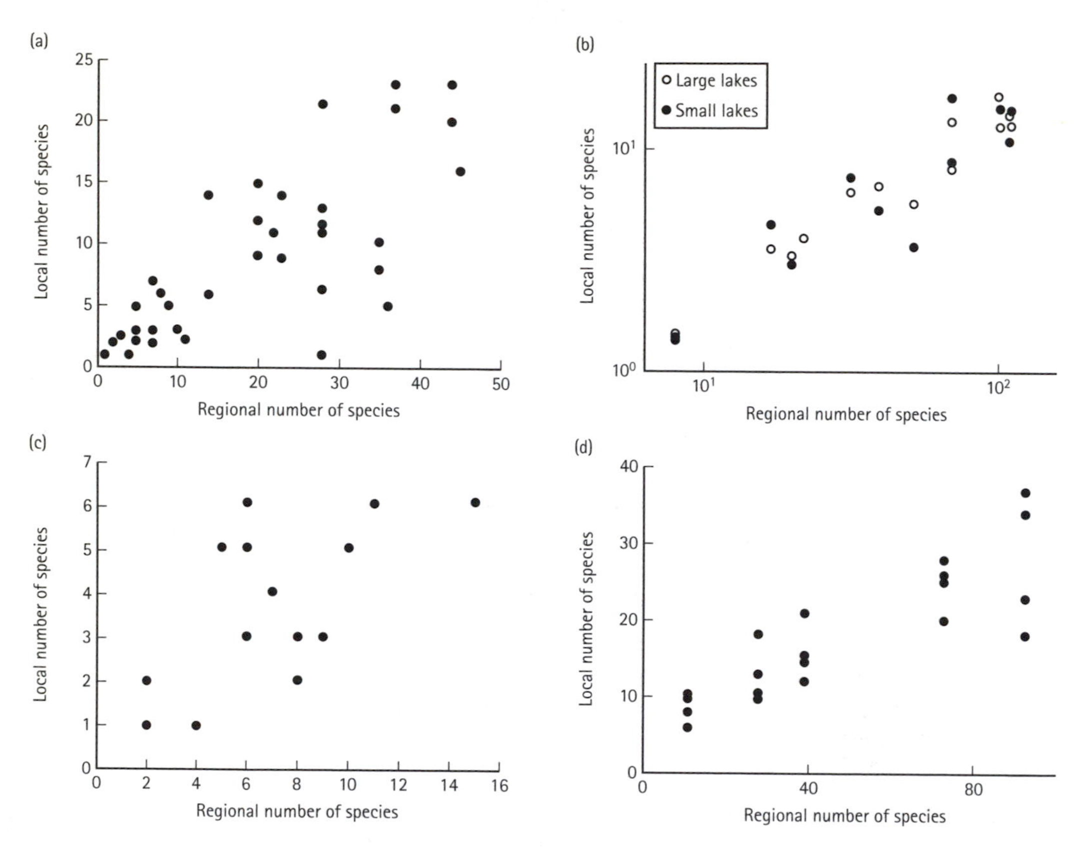

Fig. 3.3 Relationships between local and regional species richness for: (a) mangroves; (b) lacustrine fish in North America; (c) viperid snakes in South America; and (d) birds in the Caribbean. (a, From Ellison 2002; b, data from Griffiths 1997; c, from Bini et al. 2000; d, from Ricklefs 1987.)

1993). A local community is assembled from a regional pool of species (the pool of species in the region that is actually capable of colonizing a given site). The size and structure of this pool are influenced by regional processes, including the effects of the geophysical properties and history of the region (its age, geology, size, climate), and broad-scale ecological or evolutionary processes, such as species migrations, invasions, speciation and regional extinction (Huston 1999). They set the species composition and the abundance, body size and trophic structure of the pool from which local communities are drawn. However, whilst regional pools doubtless play an important role in structuring local assemblages, they are perhaps best seen as contributing to, rather than determining, local assemblage structure: local processes remain important. Resolving the relative contributions of local and regional processes may provide a key to understanding global patterns of biodiversity.

Species–area relationships and local–regional species relationships may be closely related, with some arguing that the latter are a direct consequence of the different forms that the former take (Rosenzweig & Ziv 1999). Whatever its causes, the relationship between local and regional biodiversity underpins the crucial observation that temporal changes in global and regional biodiversity tend to be reflected in local biodiversity, and vice versa (Section 2.3.1). Thus, changes in the numbers of species in local fossil assemblages can often be taken as indicative of the changes occurring at broader scales.

3.3 Extremes of high and low diversity

Some parts of the Earth are far richer or poorer in taxa than are others. Attention is paid particularly to the distribution of the peaks of diversity, partly because of a widespread fascination with why some areas contain large numbers of species, and partly because of the conservation implications.

3.3.1 Biological realms

The oceans cover about 67% and the land about 33% of the 511 million km^2 of the Earth's surface (Table 3.1). One would therefore expect that the oceans would have greater biodiversity. However, whether or not this is so depends on the taxonomic level being considered. Many more phyla are known from marine systems than from terrestrial ones (May 1994b). Of the 96 phyla recognized by Margulis and Schwartz (1998), about 69 have marine representatives and 55 have terrestrial ones (see Table 2.2). The greater diversity of marine systems is also true of some lower taxa, such as classes (Nicol 1971); Reaka-Kudla (1997) states that 90% of all known classes are marine. However, fewer than 15% of species currently named are marine, despite the vastly greater area covered by the

Table 3.1 The areas of different components of the Earth's surface (note some are subsets of others). (From Reaka-Kudla 1997.)

	Area (× 10^6 km^2)	Percentage of the Earth
Global surface area	511	100
Global land area	170.3	33.3
Global rain forests	11.9	2.3
Global oceans	340.1	66.7
Tropical seas	123	24
Global coastal zones	40.9	8
Tropical coastal zones	9.8	1.9
Coral reefs	0.6	0.1

oceans (May 1994b). The extent to which these proportions would change if all of the marine and terrestrial species had been described remains controversial (Section 2.4). Nevertheless, it seems unlikely that anything like parity in richness between the two would be achieved, and that marine systems are genuinely substantially poorer in species numbers.

Five sets of factors have been suggested that might help to explain the contrast in the diversities between land and sea (May 1994b).

1 *Life began in the sea.* This meant that the early diversification of form that led to the different higher taxa that are seen today took place in the sea, with only some of these groups subsequently being able to emerge onto land. Of itself, this does not explain, however, why there should be more species in the terrestrial realm.

2 *Continental environments are more heterogeneous than marine ones.* This observation has long been held to be true, although the complexities of marine environments are increasingly being recognized. The heterogeneity of continental environments would have tended to promote greater levels of speciation on land, especially when coupled with continental drift. The latter resulted in the evolution of sets of distinct floral and faunal assemblages on different land masses, often with species with different evolutionary origins filling similar roles.

3 *The ocean-bed environment is less architecturally elaborate than the terrestrial environment.* Again, if correct, this would tend to promote greater levels of speciation in the terrestrial realm relative to the marine one, although this might arguably be offset by the greater continuous area of the oceans.

4 *Patterns of herbivory differ between sea and land.* Herbivores in marine environments tend to be generalists, whilst those in terrestrial environments tend to be specialists, often feeding on just a single host-plant species and often on only a particular part thereof. Greater specialism gives opportunities for more speciation, but whether this is strictly a cause or a consequence of high species numbers is more debatable.

5 *There are differences in the body size distributions of marine and terrestrial species assemblages.* Primary production, herbivory and predation all tend to involve smaller species in the sea than they do on land (e.g. much of marine productivity results from the huge abundances of microscopic picoplankton). Smaller-bodied species may be able to maintain the contiguity of larger geographic ranges more readily, through having larger numbers of individuals and greater dispersal abilities, perhaps therefore reducing the likelihood of allopatric speciation (speciation by subdivision of the distributions of ancestral species) in marine systems.

The fact that life began in the sea seems to us to be likely to have played an important role in explaining why there are more higher taxa in marine systems than terrestrial ones. The heterogeneity and fragmentation of the land masses seem a likely explanation as to why there are more species in terrestrial systems than in marine ones.

Whilst freshwater systems are not usually regarded as comprising a strict biological realm in their own right, it is instructive to contrast their biodiversity with that of marine and terrestrial systems. There are approximately 55 phyla in freshwater systems, somewhat less than in terrestrial ones (see Table 2.2); however, the number of species is much smaller (70,000 species of freshwater invertebrates have been described, with perhaps another 100,000 awaiting discovery; Strayer 2001). This could simply be an area effect, with lakes and rivers estimated to cover just 1.5 million km^2 (another 16 million km^2 is under ice and permanent snow, and 2.6 million km^2 is wetlands, soil water and permafrost), although the high degree of habitat fragmentation, the wide variation in physical and chemical habitat characteristics, and the limited dispersal abilities of many freshwater organisms have doubtless led to many species having extremely restricted distributions.

3.3.2 Biogeographic regions

Moving down the spatial scales, there have been a number of attempts to divide the land surface of the Earth into broad biogeographic regions, which distinguish areas of marked dissimilarity in the composition of their biota. Comparison of the relative biodiversity of these regions gives a broad-scale picture of its spatial variation. First, of the six to eight biogeographic regions commonly recognized (Fig. 3.4a), the three 'tropical' regions (Neotropics, Indotropics, Afrotropics) perhaps contain two-thirds or more of all extant terrestrial species. Second, the Neotropics is generally recognized to be the region that contains the greatest overall levels of terrestrial biodiversity. Third, the three 'tropical' regions tend to decline in overall biodiversity from the Neotropics to the Indotropics to the Afrotropics. Levels of biodiversity in the first two are probably the more similar to one another, with the Afrotropics being relatively less diverse. In part, this is because the tropical forests of Africa are not as extensive, well developed or rich as those in the other two regions. Fourth, patterns in the biodiversity of different biogeographic regions may not be consistent amongst many groups of organisms. The distribution amongst regions of butterfly species richness, for example, appears to be more similar to that of birds than of mammals (Robbins & Opler 1997).

The different biogeographic regions have also been subdivided into smaller regions, employing a number of schemes, and variously terming the resultant areas as major habitats, vegetation types or biomes. The scheme of Olson et al. (2001) distinguishes 14 such types in the terrestrial realm, on the basis of the similarity of areas in terms of environmental conditions, habitat structure and patterns of biological complexity (Fig. 3.4).

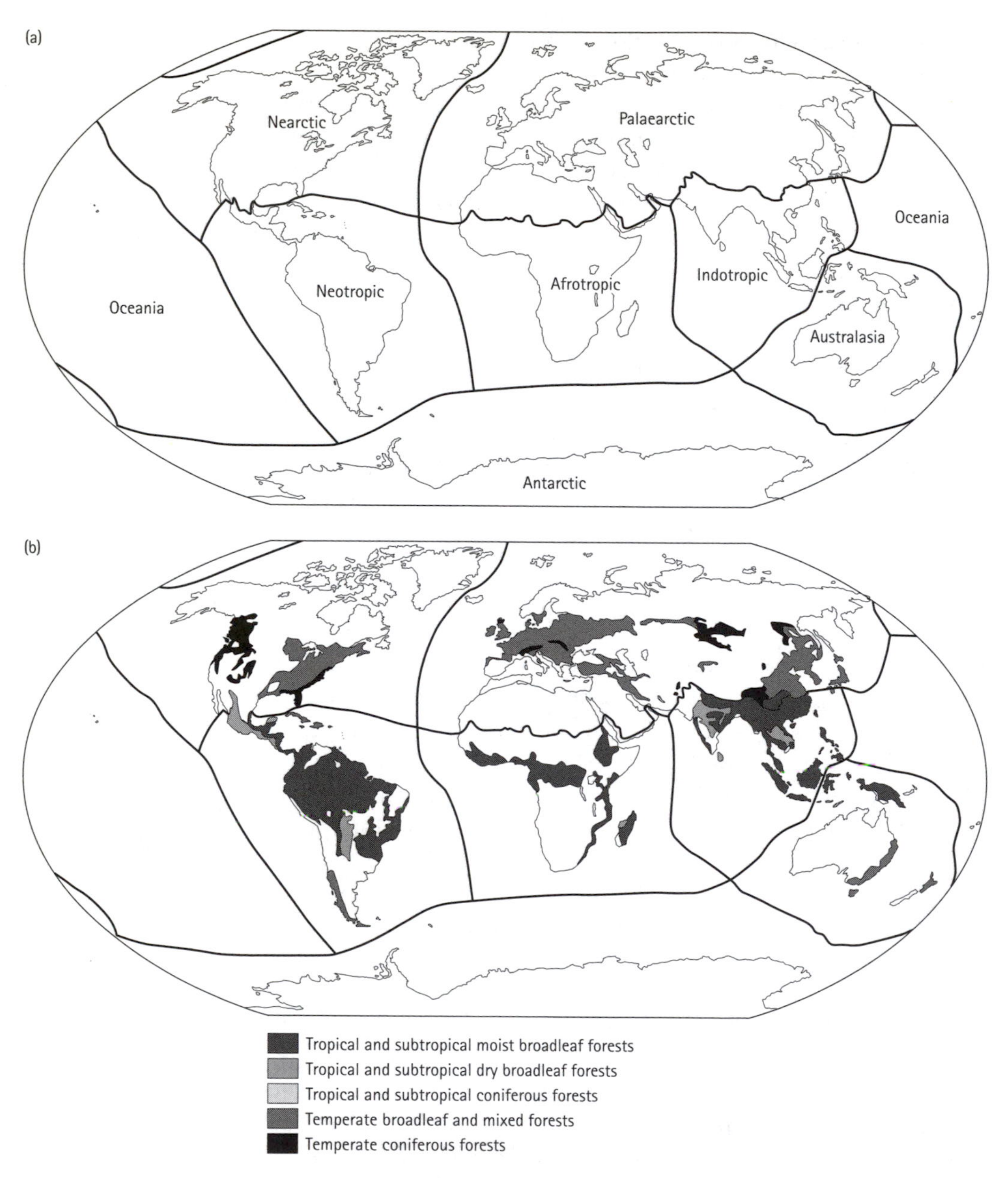

Fig. 3.4 Classification of the terrestrial realm into (a) eight biogeographic regions and (b)–(d) 14 biomes. (From Olson et al. 2001.) (*cont'd*)

These habitat types are: (i) tropical and subtropical moist broadleaf forests; (ii) tropical and subtropical dry broadleaf forests; (iii) tropical and subtropical coniferous forests; (iv) temperate broadleaf and mixed forests; (v) temperate coniferous forests; (vi) boreal forests/taiga; (vii) tropical and subtropical grasslands, savannahs and shrublands; (viii) temperate grasslands, savannahs and shrublands; (ix) flooded grasslands and savannahs; (x) montane grasslands and shrublands; (xi) tundra; (xii)

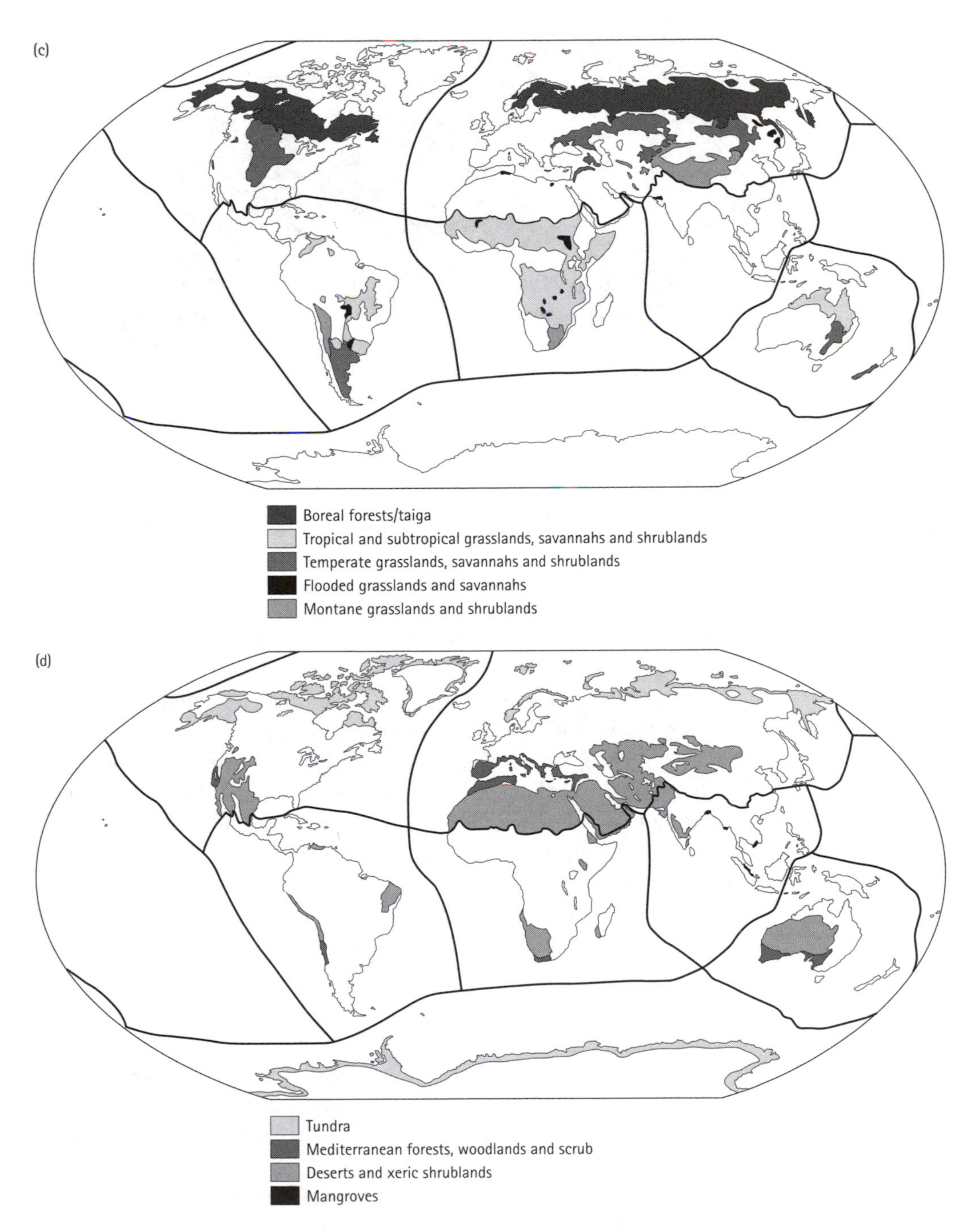

Fig. 3.4 *(cont'd)*

Mediterranean forests, woodlands and scrub; (xiii) deserts and xeric shrublands; and (xiv) mangroves. Nested within these, Olson et al. (2001) recognize 867 ecoregions, representing distinct biotas, and reflecting the distributions of a broad range of flora and fauna (Fig. 3.5).

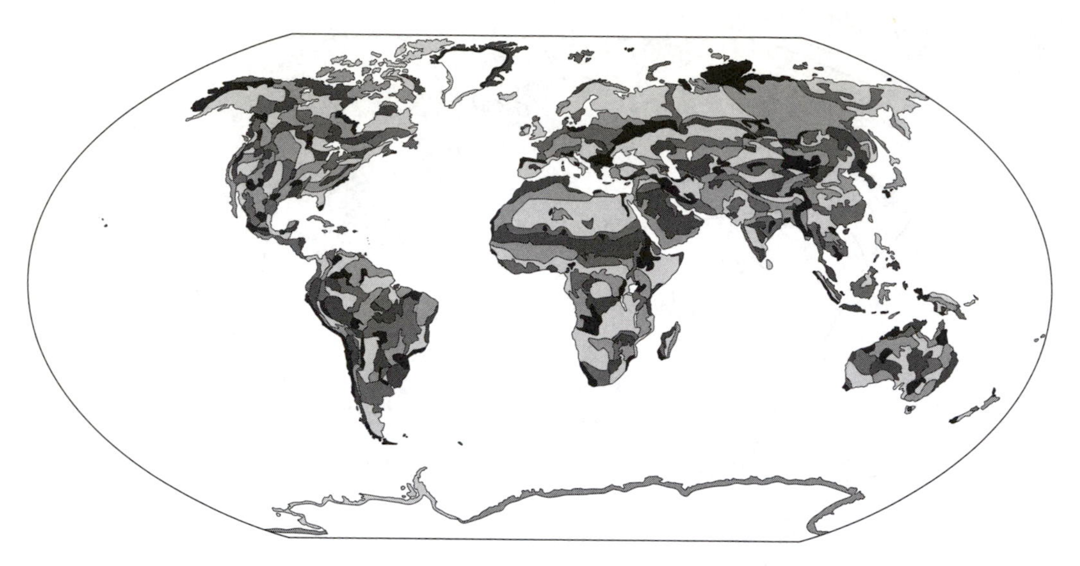

Fig. 3.5 Classification of the terrestrial realm into 867 ecoregions. (From Olson et al. 2001.)

Dividing the marine realm into biogeographic regions has proven much more problematic than has been the case for the terrestrial realm, and arguably the floristic and faunistic discontinuities remain only rather sketchily understood. Much of the problem lies in the enormous extent of the oceans, their three-dimensional complexity, the fact that biological life is found at all depths, from the marine intertidal down to about 11 km, and the associated paucity of sampling, particularly of the sea bed (see below). Of all the species that live in the sea, only about 2% live in mid-water, the remainder living on, or in, the sea bed.

As a result of these difficulties, the marine realm has tended to be divided into regions on the basis of physical characteristics (e.g. temperature regimes, surface currents; Couper 1983; Hayden et al. 1984), but more recently divisions have been recognized in large part on the basis of the algal ecology of the pelagic open ocean (Longhurst 1998). This latter scheme distinguishes four primary biomes: (i) polar; (ii) westerlies; (iii) trades; and (iv) coastal boundary. These biomes are then further subdivided, on the basis principally of biogeochemical features, into 51 provinces (Fig. 3.6).

Relating known patterns of species richness to such schemes for dividing the oceans is not easy. However, marine biodiversity is thought to be highest in the Indo-western Pacific (World Resources Institute 1996; Roberts et al. 2002). Briggs (1996) used data for echinoderms, molluscs, some crustaceans, reef corals, and fish, to show that shelf faunas belonging to the four great tropical regions increased in diversity in the sequence: eastern Atlantic, eastern Pacific, western Atlantic, and Indo-western

Pacific. With a shelf area of 6,570,000 km^2, the diversity of the Indo-western Pacific exceeds the total of the other three, with more than 6000 species of molluscs, 800 species of echinoderms, 500 species of hermatypic (reef-forming) corals and 4000 species of fish (Briggs 1999). This region has been argued to be a centre for the evolutionary radiation of many groups, partly as a consequence of its large area, and because richness declines with distance away from this centre (see also Findley & Findley 2001).

3.3.3 Hotspots

The identification of areas of high biodiversity at yet more moderate scales than those of biogeographic regions has been a topic of some concern, particularly to conservation biologists. Most data at these scales tend to refer to geopolitical units (e.g. states, countries), whose boundaries often do not coincide with biologically meaningful entities, but do reflect an important scale at which many decisions regarding the exploitation and preservation of biodiversity take place (Chapter 6).

The distribution of biodiversity amongst countries is highly skewed, with a few containing a disproportionately large number of species, and most containing a disproportionately small number (Fig. 3.7). For example, Brazil alone contains 50,000–56,000 species of plants, > 3000 species of freshwater fish, 517 species of amphibians, 468 species of reptiles, 1622 species of birds and 524 species of mammals (Mittermeier et al. 1997). Indeed, a set of mega-diversity countries have come to be recognized, comprising the 17 countries which are believed to harbour 66–75% of the world's biodiversity, expressed in terms of species richness (Mittermeier et al. 1997). The list comprises Brazil, Indonesia, Colombia, Mexico, Australia, Madagascar, China, Philippines, India, Peru, Papua New Guinea, Ecuador, USA, Venezuela, Malaysia, South Africa and Democratic Republic of Congo. Much of the variation in biodiversity between countries inevitably results from the dramatic differences in their areas, but it also reflects such characteristics as their latitude, topographical and habitat diversity, and their human history.

Such assessments are based almost exclusively on data for plants and vertebrates. Estimates of the total numbers of species to be found in countries are extremely scarce. Nonetheless, figures have been ventured of 750,000 species for the USA and > 88,000 for the UK (Anon. 1994; Pimentel et al. 1997). Most countries have rather poor inventories of the flora and fauna that lie within their bounds, let alone details of their occurrence. For example, even for those whose faunas have been reasonably well studied, inventories of insect species may remain substantially incomplete (e.g. Japan 29–41% estimated to have been inventoried, Canada 55%, Finland 84%; Gaston 1996a). Moreover, the pattern of

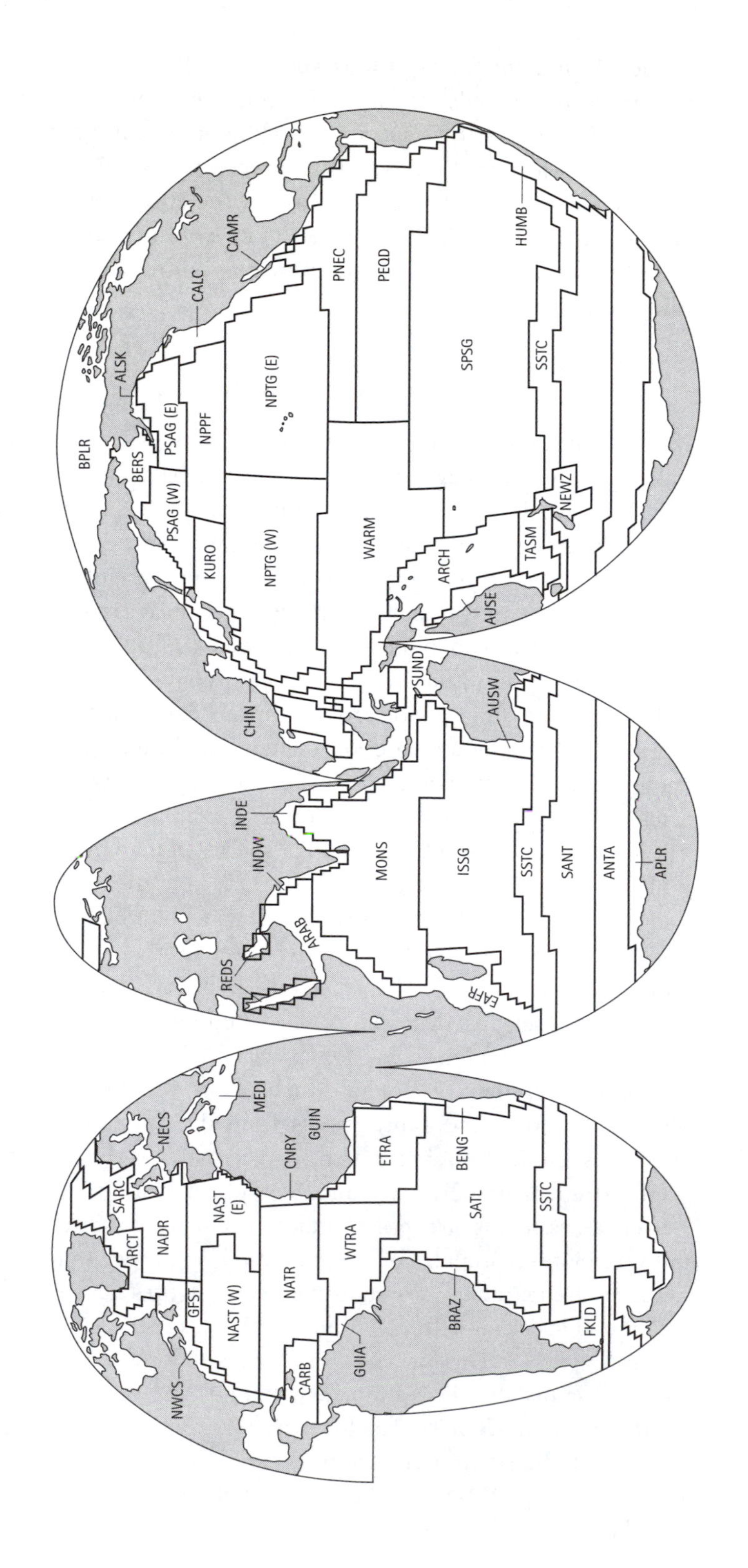
BPLR
BERS
ALSK
CALC
CAMR
PSAG (E)
PSAG (W)
NPPF
NPTG (E)
NPTG (W)
KURO
PNEC
PEQD
WARM
SPSG
HUMB
SSTC
NEWZ
TASM
ARCH
AUSE
SUND
AUSW
CHIN
INDE
INDW
MONS
ISSG
SSTC
SANT
ANTA
APLR
ARAB
REDS
EAFR
MEDI
NECS
SARC
ARCT
NADR
NAST (E)
GFST
NAST (W)
NATR
CNRY
GUIN
ETRA
BENG
SATL
SSTC
WTRA
BRAZ
GUIA
CARB
NWCS
FKLD

Fig. 3.6 Biomes and provinces of the oceans, the former recognized on the basis of algal ecology, and the latter on the basis principally of biogeochemical features. **Antarctic Polar Biome**: ANTA, Antarctic Province; APLR, Austral Polar Province. **Antarctic Westerly Winds Biome**: SANT, Subantarctic Water Ring Province; SSTC, South Subtropical Convergence Province. **Atlantic Coastal Biome**: BENG, Benguela Current Coastal Province; BRAZ, Brazil Current Coastal Province; CNRY, Eastern (Canary) Coastal Province; FKLD, Southwest Atlantic Shelves Province; GUIA, Guianas Coastal Province; GUIN, Guinea Current Coastal Province; NECS, Northeast Atlantic Shelves Province; NWCS, Northwest Atlantic Shelves Province; BPLR, Boreal Polar Province; SARC, Atlantic Subarctic Province. **Atlantic Trade Wind Biome**: CARB, Caribbean Province; ETRA, Eastern Tropical Atlantic Province; NATR, North Atlantic Tropical Gyral Province; SATL, South Atlantic Gyral Province; WTRA, Western Tropical Atlantic Province. **Atlantic Westerly Winds Biome**: GFST, Gulf Stream Province; MEDI, Mediterranean Sea, Black Sea Province; NADR, North Atlantic Drift Province; NAST, North Atlantic Subtropical Gyral Province. **Indian Ocean Coastal Biome**: ARAB, Northwestern Arabian Upwelling Province; AUSW, Australia–Indonesia Coastal Province; EAFR, Eastern Africa Coastal Province; INDE, Eastern India Coastal Province; INDW, Western India Coastal Province; REDS, Red Sea, Persian Gulf Province. **Indian Ocean Trade Wind Biome**: ISSG, Indian South Subtropical Gyre Province; MONS, Indian Monsoon Gyres Province. **Pacific Coastal Biome**: ALSK, Alaska Downwelling Coastal Province; AUSE, East Australian Coastal Province; CALC, California Current Province; CAMR, Central American Coastal Province; CHIN, China Sea Coastal Province; HUMB, Humboldt Current Coastal Province; NEWZ, New Zealand Coastal Province; SUND, Sunda–Arafura Shelves Province. **Pacific Polar Biome**: BERS, North Pacific Epicontinental Sea Province. **Pacific Trade Wind Biome**: ARCH, Archipelagic Deep Basins Province; NPTG, North Pacific Tropical Gyre Province; PEQD, Pacific Equatorial Divergence Province; PNEC, North Pacific Equatorial Countercurrent Province; SPSG, South Pacific Subtropical Gyre Province; WARM, Western Pacific Warm Pool Province. **Pacific Westerly Winds Biome**: KURO, Kuroshio Current Province; NPPF, North Pacific Transition Zone Province; PSAG, Pacific Subarctic Gyres (East and West) Province; TASM, Tasman Sea Province. (From Longhurst 1998.)

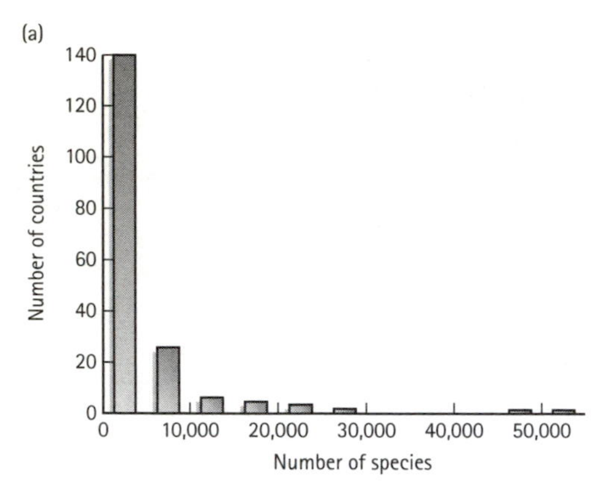

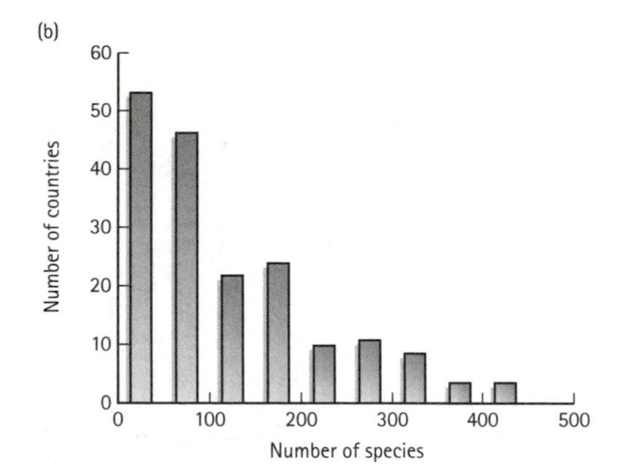

Fig. 3.7 Numbers of species of: (a) flowering plants; and (b) mammals in different countries for which data are available. (Data from World Conservation Monitoring Centre 1994.)

growth in knowledge often does not reflect the distribution of biodiversity. Thus, whilst most species occur in the tropics, as many species of insects are presently being described per unit area from temperate regions as from tropical ones (Gaston 1994).

Besides countries, other schemes have been employed to recognize areas of disproportionately high biodiversity. The most important of these is the identification of 25 biodiversity hotspots (Fig. 3.8), based on areas that contain exceptional concentrations of endemic species and are undergoing exceptional loss of habitat (and are thus facing particularly high threat; Myers et al. 2000; Myers 2001). These areas comprise only 1.4% of the land surface of the Earth, but constitute the remaining habitats for about 135,000 plant species (45% of all extant plant species) and about 9650 vertebrate species (35% of all extant vertebrate species). They also harbour greater amounts of evolutionary history than expected on the basis of species numbers alone (Sechrest et al. 2002). Despite their importance to the maintenance of biodiversity on Earth, knowledge about these areas remains, however, extremely variable, with even the basic summary descriptors of their composition in some cases being little more than best approximations.

3.3.4 Endemism

A taxon is endemic to an area if it occurs there and nowhere else. The area of endemism can either be relatively large (e.g. the three extant species of monotremes, the echidnas *Tachyglossus aculeatus* and *Zaglossus bruijni*, and the platypus *Ornithorhynchus anatinus*, are confined to Australia and New Guinea) or it can be very small (e.g. the 'water bear' *Thermozodium esakii* [Phylum: Tardigrada] is found only in a single Japanese hot spring).

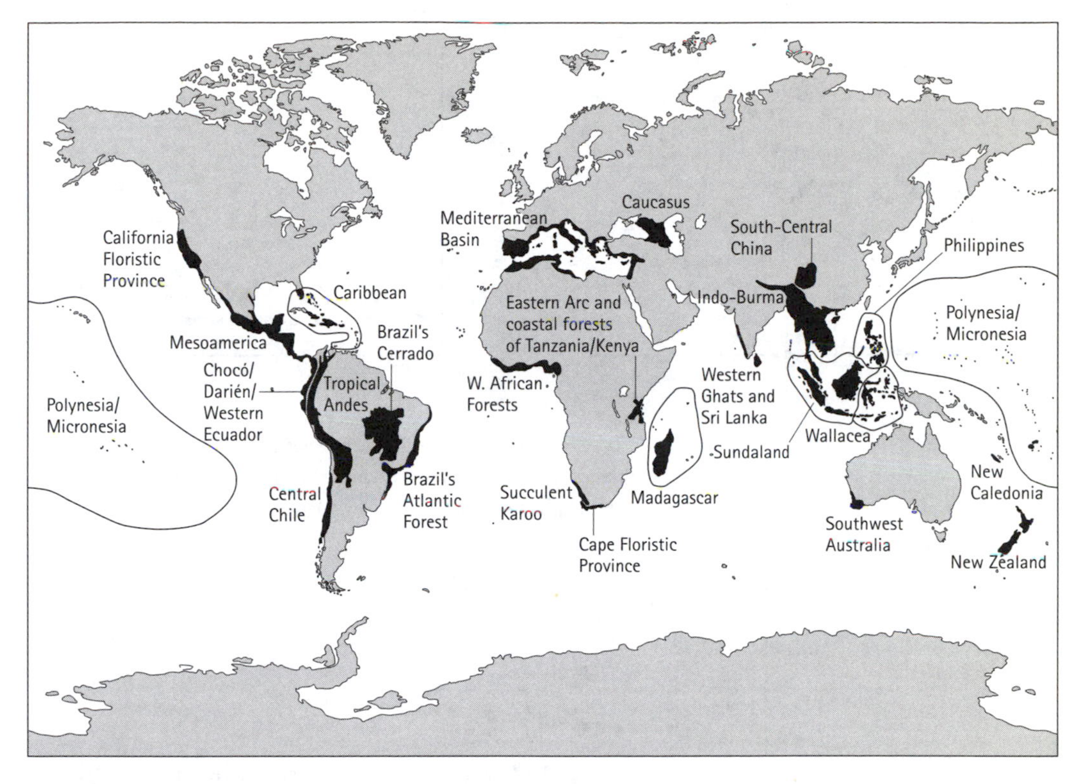

Fig. 3.8 The 25 global hotspots where exceptional concentrations of endemic species are undergoing exceptional habitat loss. (From Myers et al. 2000.)

Some small areas, particularly oceanic islands, can have very high levels of endemism (e.g. Hawaii). Two groups of endemics are commonly recognized. Neoendemics are taxa that have evolved relatively recently, and palaeoendemics are those that may be regarded as evolutionary relicts.

Levels of endemism tend to show patterns of variation with the following:

• *Area*. On average, the number and proportion of taxa that are endemic to a locality or region tends to be an increasing function of area, though such species–area relationships are usually considerably weaker than those based on the sum of all species whether endemic or otherwise (Major 1988; Anderson 1994; McKinney 2002). For example, the number of plant species that are endemic to each of 52 biogeographic provinces (distributed across all major biomes on all continents) tends to increase with their area, and the number of mammal species that are endemic to different countries tends to increase with their area (Fig. 3.9).

• *Latitude*. More importantly, and more markedly, the number of endemics tends to increase towards lower latitudes (Fig. 3.10; Major 1988; Cowling & Samways 1995). This has been graphically demonstrated in a study of birds (Fig. 3.11), which has identified 218 Endemic Bird Areas,

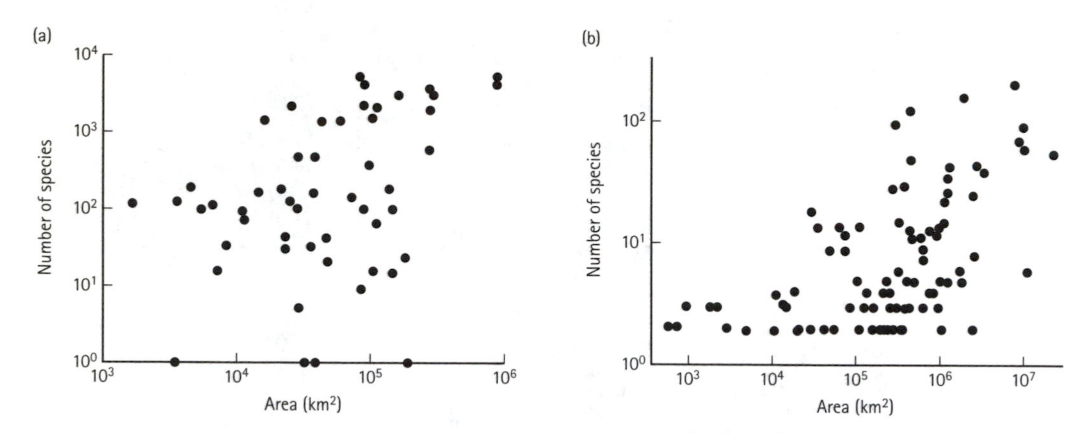

Fig. 3.9 Relationships between number of endemic species and area for: (a) plants in regions on continental land masses; and (b) land mammals in 155 countries. (a, From Cowling & Samways 1995; b, from Ceballos & Brown 1995.)

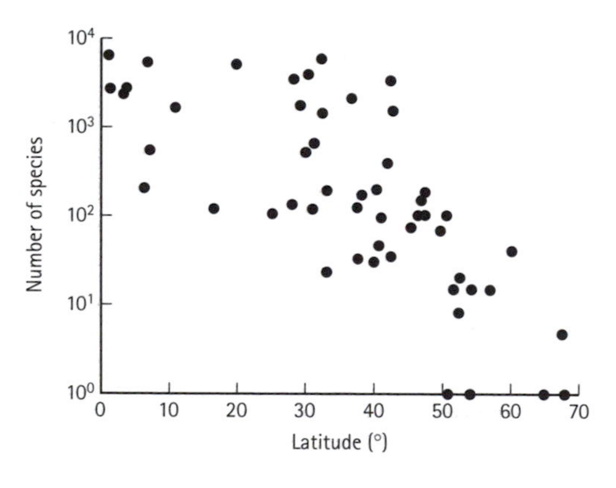

Fig. 3.10 Relationship between number of endemic species and latitude for plants in regions on continental land masses. (From Cowling & Samways 1995.)

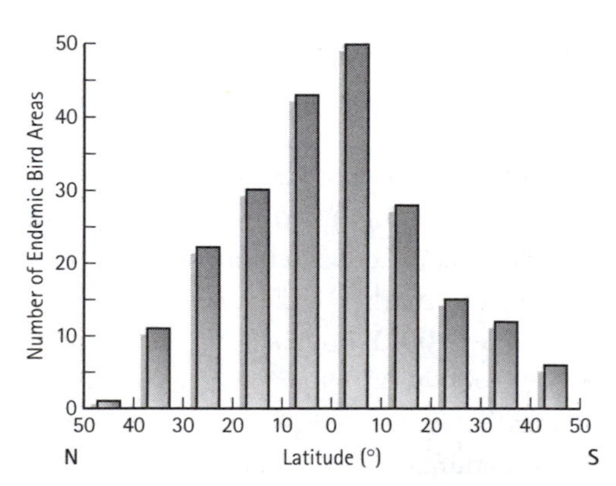

Fig. 3.11 Latitudinal distribution of Endemic Bird Areas (areas supporting two or more species with geographic ranges of < 50,000 km^2). (From Stattersfield et al. 1998.)

defined as areas supporting two or more species with restricted ranges (< 50,000 km^2). In total, these areas occupy a mere 4.5% of the Earth's land surface and contain 73% of all globally threatened bird species; 2649 land bird species (27% of all birds) have breeding ranges of 50,000 km^2 or

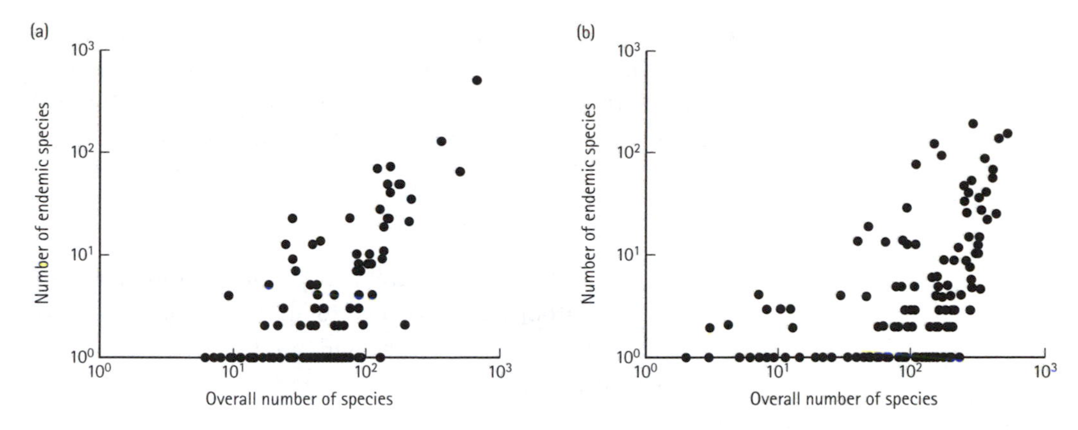

Fig. 3.12 Relationships between numbers of endemic species and overall numbers of species in different areas for: (a) fish in river basins of the northern hemisphere; and (b) land mammals in 155 countries. (a, From Oberdorff et al. 1999; b, from Ceballos & Brown 1995.)

less (Long et al. 1996). Latitudinal gradients in endemism contribute to broader latitudinal trends in the geographic range sizes of species, with the mean range sizes of those present in an area tending to decline particularly from high to intermediate latitudes, and especially in the northern hemisphere (Stevens 1989; Gaston et al. 1998).

• *Species richness*. Levels of endemism and of species richness are not infrequently positively correlated (Fig. 3.12; Balmford & Long 1995). However, there are many exceptions here, with oceanic islands for example tending to have high levels of endemism but relatively low overall numbers of species, and continental peaks of endemism often not being coincident with peaks of species richness (e.g. Seymour et al. 2001; de Klerk et al. 2002).

Reasons given for the occurrence of areas of high levels of endemism are typically: (i) unusual environmental conditions – these may select for independent evolution of local adaptations that enable species to persist under these conditions but prevent them from occurring more widely; (ii) isolation – the separation either by distance or other barriers of individuals from conspecifics enables independent evolution that may give rise to endemic taxa; and (iii) historical – changing environmental conditions (both biotic and abiotic) can constrain previously more widespread species to limited areas (Kruckeberg & Rabinowitz 1985; Major 1988). On continents, high levels of endemism may particularly be associated with areas that have exhibited long-term ecoclimatic stability, enabling populations to survive periods of major global climatic change (e.g. Fjeldså et al. 1999). Such areas may also be evolutionary hotspots, in which multiple evolutionary events have occurred over a significant period (McLennan & Brooks 2002). Historical processes seem to be particularly important, such that the richness of endemics is generally thought to be more difficult to explain in terms of prevailing environmental conditions than is the richness of taxa more generally, although some recent analyses have challenged this notion (Johnson et al. 1998).

3.3.5 Particular environments

The biodiversity associated with different kinds of environments has attracted much interest from biologists. Some of these environments have for practical reasons proven hard to access, and thus important features of this biodiversity continue to be discovered. The following are given by way of a few examples:

- *Tropical forest canopies*. Termed 'the last biotic frontier' (Erwin 1983), despite their large extent (more than 11 million km^2), tropical forest canopies long remained poorly explored. However, their mysteries are now rapidly being exposed through the application of a variety of techniques that have enabled much improved access to this environment (e.g. rope-climbing techniques, aerial walkways, cranes, balloons). These have revealed much higher levels of richness of some groups than had been anticipated, and lower richness of others, but have overall served to confirm the significance of tropical forests for global species numbers.
- *Soils*. Soils have been termed 'the poor man's tropical forest', in homage to the huge numbers of individual organisms that may occur per square metre (Groffman 1997). The small body size of many of the associated species, and the poor efficiency of many extraction methods, have served, however, severely to limit understanding of soil biodiversity, leading to dramatic underestimations both of the local densities of individuals and of species richness (André et al. 2002). Spatial turnover in species composition remains poorly explored, so the basis for estimations of regional or global species richness and patterns is largely lacking.
- *Coral reefs*. The global area covered by coral reefs is only about 600,000 km^2 (c. 0.18% of the total area of oceans). Nonetheless, it has been estimated that up to one quarter of all marine species and one fifth of known marine fish species live in coral reef ecosystems, leading it to be seen as the marine equivalent of tropical forests. Thus, for example, a detailed study involving 400 person-days of collecting at 42 sample stations in a 295 km^2 coral reef complex at a site off New Caledonia yielded 2738 species of molluscs, and a predicted total number of species of more than 3000 (Bouchet et al. 2002). As with all environments that are typically species rich, there are examples of areas of coral reef that naturally are not so, and the 10 richest centres of endemism cover 15.8% of the world's coral reefs but include approximately one half of the species of corals, snails, lobsters and reef fish with restricted ranges (Roberts et al. 2002).

• *Deep ocean*. The biodiversity of the deep ocean remains one of the great imponderables, and a topic of some debate. Areas at depths below 1 km cover more than half of the planet. Some recent studies on the fauna of deep-sea floors in the Atlantic and Pacific have uncovered a high level of species richness (Grassle 1991; Grassle & Maciolek 1992; Poore & Wilson 1993), and it has been suggested that there may be 10 million species in the deep sea (Grassle & Maciolek 1992). Whilst this seems likely to be a marked overestimate (May 1992b), it is undoubtedly the case that large numbers remain to be discovered. For example, knowledge of the sediment-dwelling infauna of the deep sea derives from study of less than 2000 quantitative cores, an estimated area of 500 m^2 (Paterson 1993), and for the meiofauna (the very small animals living between and around the grains of the sediment) alone the area is estimated to be less than 5 m^2 (Lambshead et al. 2000). With the improved access that sophisticated technologies have provided (remotely operated vehicles, bottom landers, submarines, sonar, video), several new kinds of communities of organisms have been identified, such as hydrothermal vents, cold seeps and cold-water coral reefs. Along with seamounts, whilst not especially diverse, these communities are often hotspots of endemism (Tunnicliffe 1991; de Forges et al. 2000; van Dover 2000, 2001).

For reviews of biodiversity in other particular environments: see Marmonier et al. (1993) for ground water; see Körner (2001) for alpine ecosystems; see Convey (2001) for Antarctic ecosystems; see Callaghan et al. (2001) for Arctic ecosystems; and see Hogarth (2001) for mangrove ecosystems.

3.4 Gradients in biodiversity

As has already been observed, spatial variation in biodiversity across the Earth is complex. To aid in understanding this complexity, attention has particularly focussed on how species richness changes along gradients of latitude, elevation and depth, and additionally across peninsulas and bays. Patterns that are manifest along these gradients are abstractions from the broader spatial variation, and need to be interpreted as such. This is particularly so when considering the mechanisms that may give rise to changes in richness with latitude and other such variables. If these mechanisms correctly explain these changes, then they should also explain the wider patterns of variation in species numbers.

3.4.1 Latitude

Perhaps the boldest signature of spatial variation in biodiversity is that associated with latitude. As has long been acknowledged (e.g. Humboldt

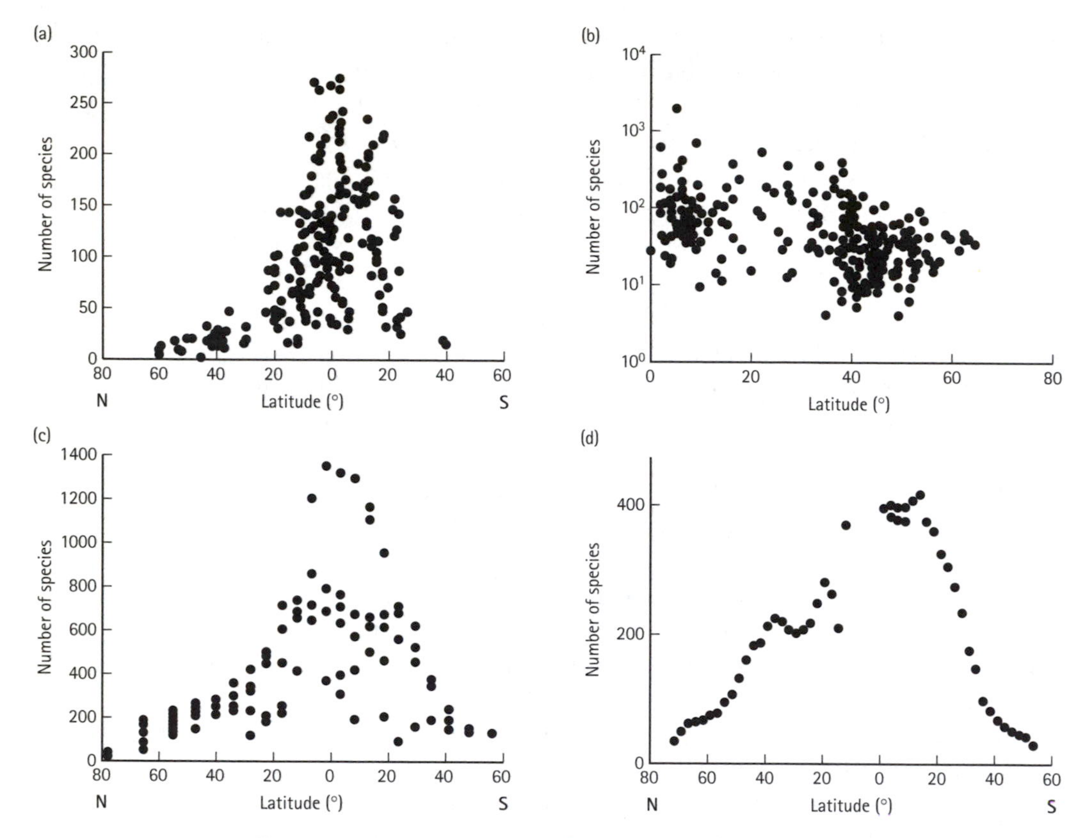

Fig. 3.13 Variation in terrestrial/freshwater species richness with latitude for: (a) trees per 0.1 ha at sites across the Earth; (b) freshwater fish in rivers across the Earth; (c) birds across the New World (grid cells of ~ 611,000 km^2); and (d) mammals across the New World (latitudinal bands of 2.5°). (a, From Enquist & Niklas 2001; b, from Oberdorff et al. 1995; c, adapted from Gaston & Blackburn 2000; d, from Kaufman & Willig 1998.)

& Bonpland 1807; Wallace 1853; Bates 1862), the species richness of most groups of organisms increases from high (temperate) to low (tropical) latitudes (Figs. 3.13 & 3.14). A similar pattern is also frequently observed for the richness of higher taxa, such as genera and families (Fig. 3.15). It is typically manifest whether diversity is determined at local sites, across large regions, or is determined cumulatively across entire latitudinal bands.

Four features of the latitudinal gradient of increasing biodiversity towards lower latitudes are of note.

1 It has been a persistent feature of much of the history of life on Earth. This has been elegantly demonstrated for flowering plants (angiosperms) by Crane and Lidgard (1989), who have shown that the pattern was maintained throughout much of the Cretaceous (Fig. 3.16). Studies of Foraminifera and molluscs suggest that for these groups at least, the

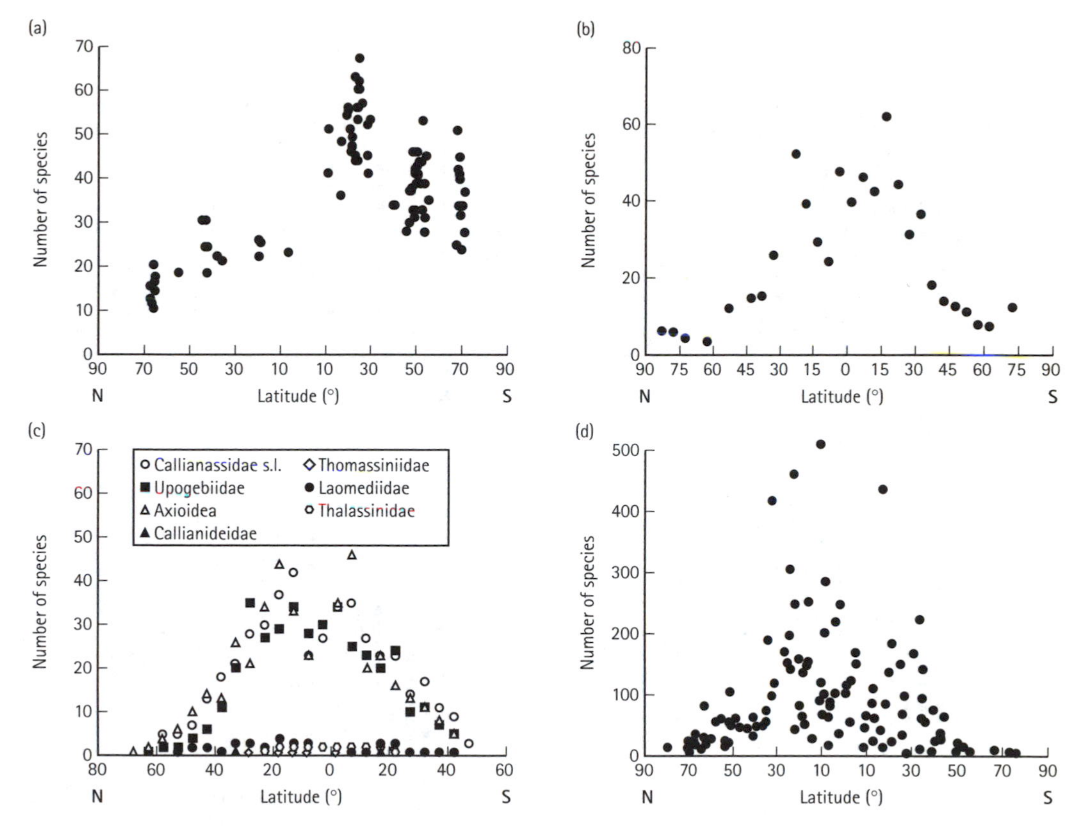

Fig. 3.14 Variation in marine species richness with latitude for: (a) deep-sea benthic Foraminifera; (b) tintinnids (planktonic ciliates); (c) thalassinid shrimp superfamilies; and (d) marine bivalves (at different localities). (a, From Culver & Buzas 2000; b, from Dolan & Gallegos 2001; c, from Dworschak 2000; d, from Flessa & Jablonski 1995.)

gradient may, nonetheless, have become steeper through time (Crame 2001, 2002; Buzas et al. 2002).

2 The peak of diversity is seldom actually at the equator. Rather, it seems often to have an inflection point somewhat further north, often at 20–30°N (e.g. Roy et al. 1998; Crame 2000).

3 The gradient is commonly, though far from universally, asymmetrical about the equator. That is, the pattern of diversity across the Earth is more like a pear (increasing rapidly from northern regions to the equator and declining slowly from the equator to southern regions) than an egg (Platnick 1991, 1992). This is well illustrated by the numbers of genera of termites (Fig. 3.17). In some cases, such effects have been found to result from latitudinal variation in land area (e.g. Kaufman & Willig 1998).

4 The steepness of the gradient may vary markedly. Thus, butterflies are more tropical than birds. Although there are approximately two species of butterflies for every species of bird worldwide, birds greatly outnumber

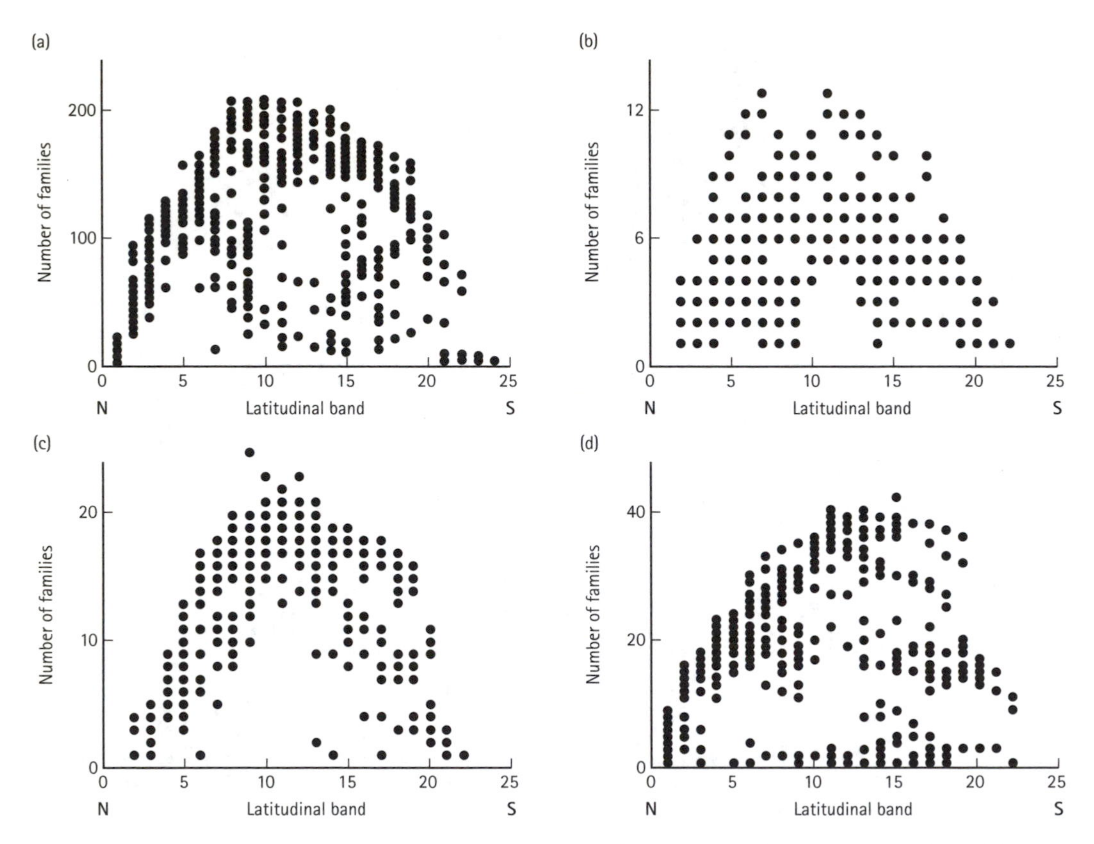

Fig. 3.15 Latitudinal gradients in family richness for: (a) seed plants; (b) amphibians; (c) reptiles; and (d) mammals. Each data point represents the number of species in a cell of a grid of 611,000 km^2 squares, and latitudinal bands run from the north of the northern hemisphere (1) to the south of the southern hemisphere (24). (From Gaston et al. 1995.)

butterflies in the Arctic, have about equal numbers of species in temperate North America, and are outnumbered by butterflies in the Neotropics (Robbins & Opler 1997).

Terrestrial and freshwater systems

The latitudinal gradient in biodiversity is best established for terrestrial and freshwater systems (see Fig. 3.13). Here, exceptions are relatively scarce. They include a variety of usually comparatively minor but sometimes quite major taxa, such as polypore fungi, sawflies, ichneumonid and braconid wasps, aphids and galling insects (Fig. 3.18; Kouki et al. 1994; Reid 1994; Price et al. 1998; Wright & Samways 1998; Kouki 1999). There are also exceptions for some taxonomic groups in some regions of the world or in particular habitat types (e.g. North American grasshoppers, Australian butterflies, breeding birds of eastern USA,

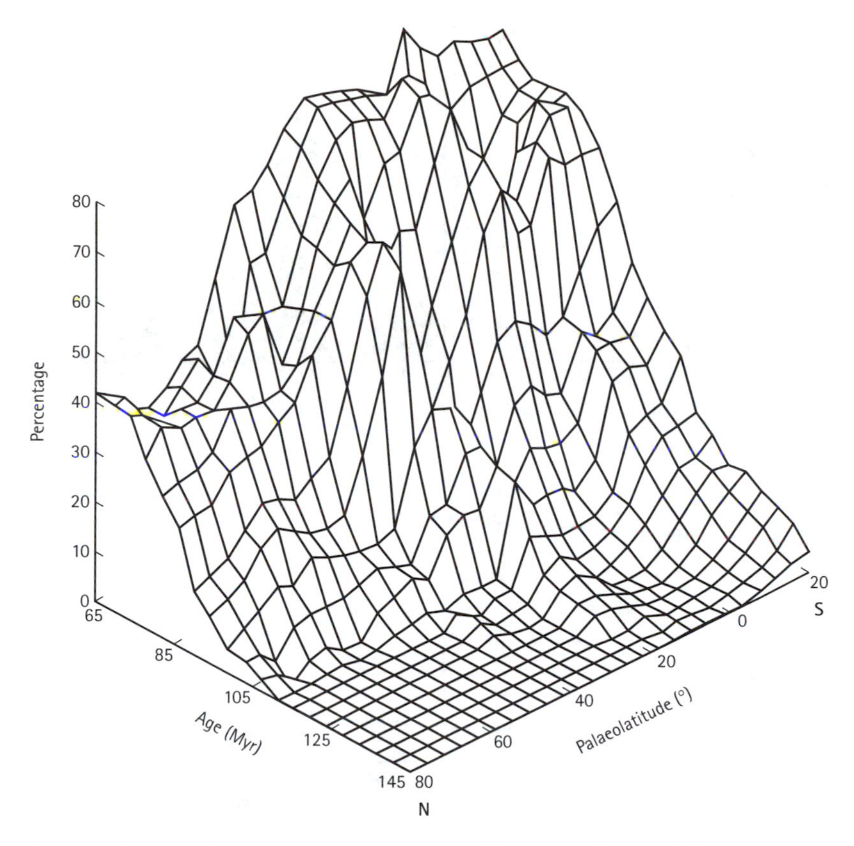

Fig. 3.16 Estimated percentage representation of flowering plants at different geological times and at different palaeolatitudes within Cretaceous palynofloras. (From Crane & Ligard 1989.)

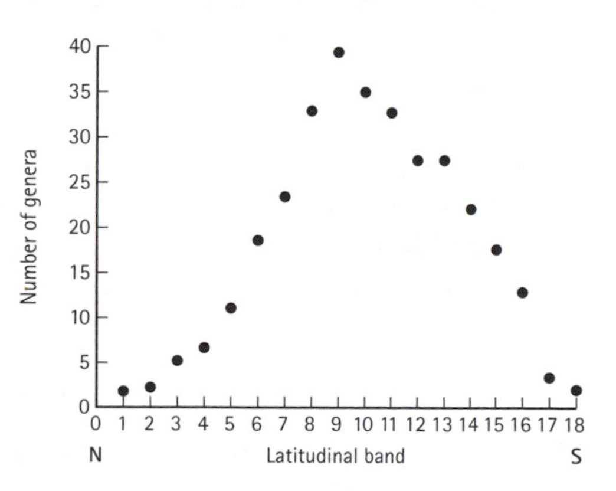

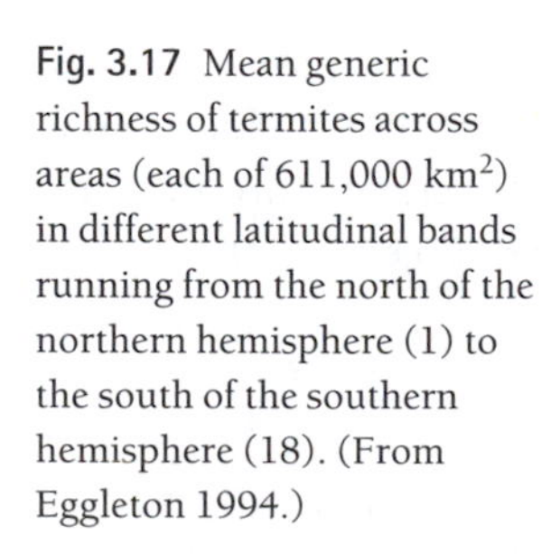

Fig. 3.17 Mean generic richness of termites across areas (each of 611,000 km^2) in different latitudinal bands running from the north of the northern hemisphere (1) to the south of the southern hemisphere (18). (From Eggleton 1994.)

Australian forest mammals; Rabenold 1993; Davidowitz & Rosenzweig 1998; Johnson 1998; Dingle et al. 2000). Although these cases may turn out to apply somewhat more widely, they pose little threat to the generality of the underlying increase in richness towards the tropics.

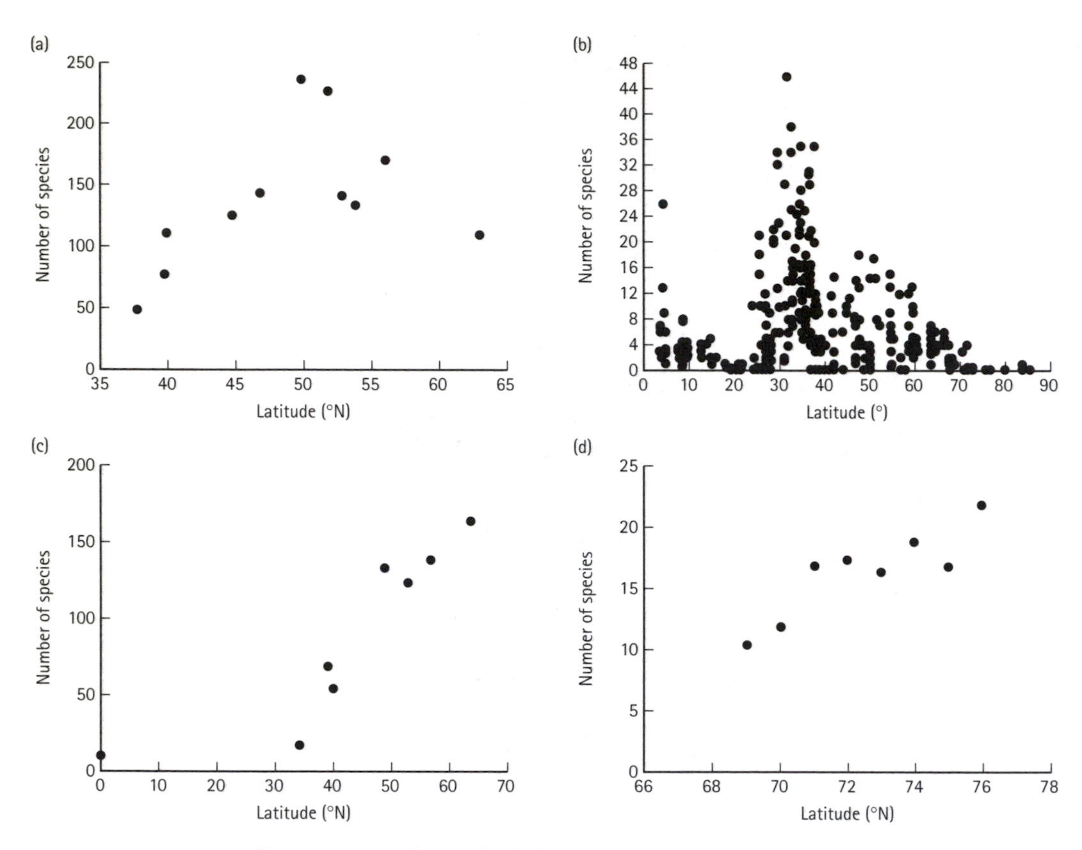

Fig. 3.18 Examples in which decreases in terrestrial species richness with latitude have not been documented: (a) aphid species in areas of 1000 km^2; (b) galling insect species in vegetation samples; (c) sawfly species in areas of 1000 km^2; and (d) breeding bird species on Finnish flark fens. (a, From Dixon et al. 1987; b, from Price et al. 1998; c, from Kouki et al. 1994; d, from Järvinen et al. 1987.)

Curiously, latitudinal gradients in terrestrial systems have also been documented for the diversity of human languages and human ethnic groups, which also tend to increase in number with temperature and rainfall (Mace & Pagel 1995; Cashdan 2001; Collard & Foley 2002).

Marine systems

The question of whether there are latitudinal gradients in biodiversity in marine systems that parallel those in terrestrial ones has given rise to much debate. The detection of latitudinal patterns in these environments has been hampered by the confounding effects of depth (Section 3.4.2) and by the problems of attaining adequate levels of sampling (Section 3.3.5).

Most contention surrounds patterns in shallow waters. Here it seems that whilst there are clear clines of increasing diversity towards lower latitudes for some groups of organisms, most notably molluscs and fish (Rohde 1978, 1992; Vincent & Clarke 1995; Clarke & Crame 1997; Roy et al. 1998), there are not for others (e.g. Kendall & Aschan 1993; Lambshead 1993; Dauvin et al. 1994; Boucher & Lambshead 1995; Vincent & Clarke 1995; Lambshead et al. 2000; Ellingsen & Gray 2002). The reasons for these differences are unclear. However, they may in part result from differences in the way in which comparisons are made. Most of the studies failing to find declines in richness towards high latitudes are for taxa from soft sediments, and are based on point samples. Conversely, most of those studies documenting such patterns are based on pooling data from records of species occurrences across regions. For bryozoans, common benthic organisms, where both analytical approaches have been employed, studies based on local samples failed to find any latitudinal gradient, whilst studies based on regional pools did find them (Clarke & Lidgard 2000), apparently at odds with the existence of any marked local–regional richness relationship (see Section 3.2.2).

Whatever the overall latitudinal pattern of species richness on the continental shelves, it is evident that benthic richness in Antarctic waters may be surprisingly high (Brey et al. 1994; Clarke & Crame 1997). This may, at least in part, result from groups that originally evolved in this region.

In contrast, patterns in the deep sea seem reasonably clear. Latitudinal diversity gradients have been reported in the North Atlantic, and strong inter-regional variation in the South Atlantic, for deep-sea bivalves, gastropods and isopods (Rex et al. 1993, 2000). Poore and Wilson (1993) find a similar pattern for deep-sea isopods, and Culver and Buzas (2000) document decreases in the species richness of deep-sea benthic Foraminifera in both the North and South Atlantic (see Fig. 3.14). These trends were unexpected, as it had long been assumed that the depth of the overlying water would buffer deep-sea assemblages from the environmental variation thought to be associated with such gradients. However, large-scale environmental gradients at the surface may in practice influence deep-sea diversity through, for example, the influence on the pattern and rate of descent of organic matter; with the exception of vent and seep habitats, basal food supply in the deep sea is entirely of extrinsic origin.

Pelagic assemblages also appear to exhibit a latitudinal gradient in richness, though again not necessarily a simple one. For example, declining species richness towards higher latitudes has been documented for ostracods, euphausiids, decapods and fish in the water column to a depth of 2000 m, at a set of stations in the northeast Atlantic (Angel 1993, 1994a). Such gradients may be stepped rather than smooth, as a result of discontinuities such as the polar front and the subtropical convergences (Angel 1994b). The number of species of planktonic Foraminifera peaks at mid-latitudes in all oceans, with tropical latitudes tending to be more species rich than high latitudes (Rutherford et al. 1999). McGowan and Walker (1993) argue that the number of species of pelagic plankton is low at high latitudes, but rather than a regular, systematic increase towards the equator exhibits a sharp gradient at about 40°N. Diversity is high at mid-latitudes, but in the central and eastern Pacific drops to intermediate levels in the equatorial zone. Diversity increases in the South Pacific, and drops to a minimum near Antarctica.

In summary, conflicting evidence and apparently complex patterns in latitudinal clines in the sea mean that these patterns continue to constitute a challenge to the generality of the statement that diversity increases from temperate to tropical regions. However, there is ample evidence that such patterns do exist.

Mechanisms

A large number of possible mechanisms for latitudinal gradients in biodiversity have been proposed (Pianka 1966; Stevens 1989; Rohde 1992; Colwell & Hurtt 1994; Rosenzweig 1995; Turner et al. 1996). These include the effects of competition, mutualism, predation, patchiness, environmental stability, environmental predictability, productivity, area, number of habitats, ecological time, evolutionary time and solar energy (Rohde 1992). At present no consensus view on the cause of the pattern seems to be emerging. However, attention has focussed on three principal mechanisms.

1 *Area effects*. Latitudinal gradients result from the tropical regions having a larger area than temperate ones, and consequently higher rates of speciation and lower rates of extinction (Rosenzweig 1992). The debate as to the evidence for and against this mechanism provides a valuable insight into some of the difficulties that surround identifying the determinants of large-scale patterns in biodiversity (see Rosenzweig 1992, 1995; Blackburn & Gaston 1997; Rohde 1997, 1998; Rosenzweig & Sandlin 1997; Ruggerio 1999; Chown & Gaston 2000; Hawkins & Porter 2001). In this case, there are two critical issues of contention: the first is the most appropriate way in which to divide the world into zones which are biologically meaningful in this sense and whose areas can then be determined; and the second is how differences in these areas influence speciation rates.

2 *Energy availability*. Latitudinal gradients result from higher levels of available energy in low-latitude regions, providing a wider resource base and allowing more species to occur there (Wright 1983; Currie 1991; Wright et al. 1993; Turner et al. 1996). In support of this mechanism, in general those environmental factors that are related to the supply of usable energy (food or limiting nutrient availability, productivity) explain

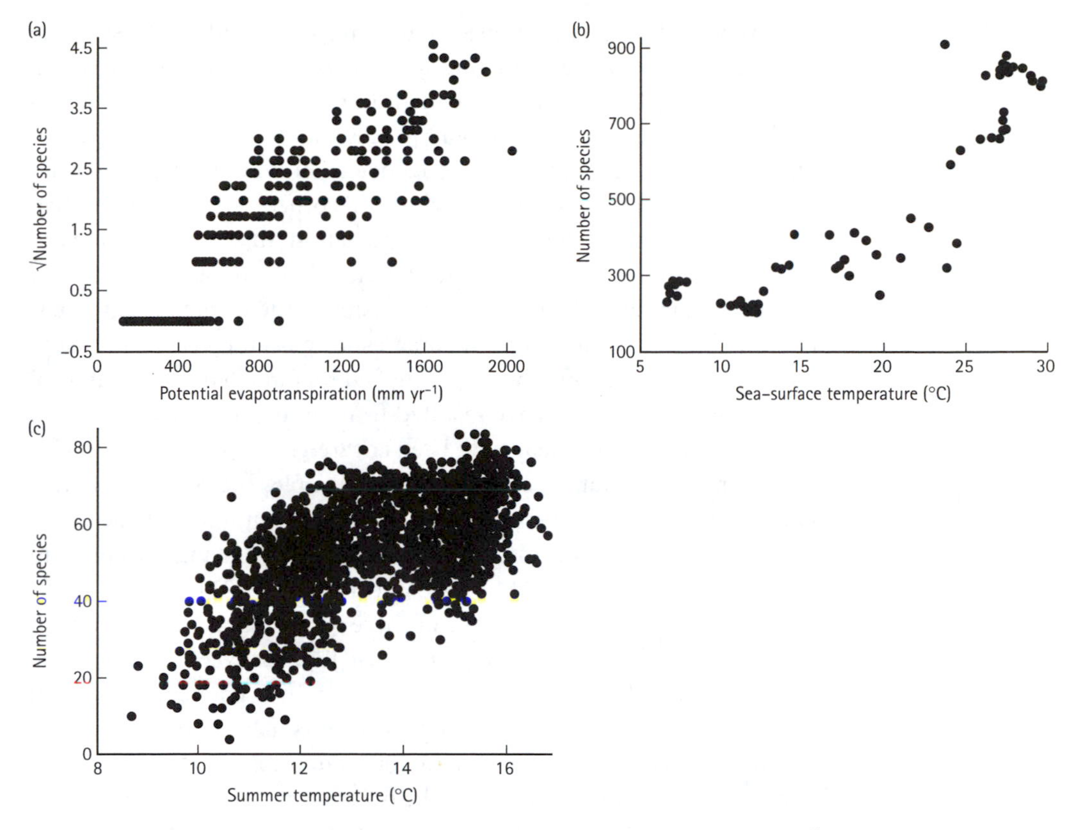

Fig. 3.19 Species–energy relationships for: (a) potential evapotranspiration (mm yr^{-1}) and richness of *Epicauta* beetles (Meloidae) in North America (grid cells of 2.5° × 2.5° south of 50°N, 2.5° × 5° north of 50°N); (b) mean annual sea-surface temperature (°C) and richness of eastern Pacific marine gastropods (bands of 1° latitude); and (c) mean monthly summer temperature (°C) and richness of breeding birds in Britain (grid cells of 10 km × 10 km). (a, From Kerr & Packer 1999; b, from Roy et al. 1998; c, from Lennon et al. 2000.)

more variation in species richness than do those that are not (Wright et al. 1993). However, latitudinal patterns in energy availability may not be simple, and whilst some studies have found relationships between energy and species richness to be broadly positive at large regional scales (particularly across temperate zones) (Fig. 3.19), others have found them to be hump-shaped, with richness declining towards high energy levels (Guégan et al. 1998; Kerr et al. 1998; Chown & Gaston 1999; Kerr & Currie 1999; Balmford et al. 2001). Much may rest on identifying those measures that best reflect available energy and account for temporal patterns in its availability.

3 *Time*. Latitudinal gradients result from the greater length of effective evolutionary time that has been available in the tropics for species

to evolve to fill habitats and niches in those regions (Wallace 1878; Rohde 1992). That is, large-scale environmental perturbations (e.g. glaciation, climatic drying) have been less frequent in the tropics, and so have provided more time for the evolutionary process (and perhaps lower rates of extinction), with the emphasis on effective evolutionary time (the product of absolute time and the rate at which this process occurs) rather than simply on absolute time, and the supposition that tropical climates increase the rate of the evolutionary process. Unfortunately, it is as yet unclear whether evolutionary rates are faster in the tropics, and there is substantial evidence that tropical climates have been considerably more unstable than was commonly supposed, and that much of the richness of tropical assemblages may have resulted from quite recent diversification (given that some regions may have been covered in tropical vegetation for more than 100 million years). Thus, for example, the Neotropical tree genus *Inga* appears to be species rich not because it gradually accumulated species over a long geological period but because it underwent rapid diversification in the past 10 Myr (Richardson et al. 2001).

There is no logical reason why any of these mechanisms need operate in isolation. Indeed, there are potentially close links between each of them, suggesting that the prevalence of the latitudinal gradient in species richness may result because different mechanisms all pull in the same direction. Moreover, the effects of any of these mechanisms are likely to be modified, and in some cases may be overridden, by a number of other factors, such as habitat heterogeneity (e.g. Kerr & Packer 1997; Kerr et al. 2001).

This said, ultimately, spatial variation in biodiversity is a product of patterns in rates of origination, immigration, extinction and emigration. At large spatial scales it will tend solely to be a product of origination and extinction. The tropics have thus variously been argued to represent a cradle of diversity exhibiting high origination rates, a museum of diversity with low extinction rates, or some combination of the two. Jablonski (1993), in an analysis of post-Palaeozoic marine orders, has found that there have been significantly more first appearances in tropical waters, whether defined latitudinally or biogeographically, than expected from sampling alone. This provides direct evidence that tropical regions have been a major source of evolutionary novelty.

3.4.2 Altitude and depth

In considering species–area relationships (Section 3.2.1) and latitudinal gradients in biodiversity (Section 3.4.1), very little allowance was made for the fact that, quite literally, the Earth is not flat; its surface, above and below water, is moulded into mountains and valleys both by local and global geological processes. Whilst for some purposes it may be useful to refer to the Earth's surface using measures of area, the three-dimensional structure of land- and seascapes means that sometimes one should really be dealing in volumes.

Altitude

In the terrestrial realm, the third spatial dimension is commonly construed as the altitude or elevation of land. Altitude could arguably be ignored when considering large areas, because its magnitude is small compared with those of longitude or latitude (mean elevation is 840 m, Mt Everest is 8848 m high). However, it must be remembered that a moderate increase in altitude has, for example, an associated temperature change corresponding to a latitudinal separation perhaps of several hundred kilometres; a change of 2–3°C is experienced over some 10° of latitude or approximately 700 m of altitude in the hills of northern Britain (Whittaker & Tribe 1996).

In terrestrial systems, it is generally accepted that species richness declines towards high elevations (Fig. 3.20; Rahbek 1995; Sanders 2002). However, the details of this pattern are quite variable. Some groups apparently show a relatively simple decline. Others show a pronounced hump-shaped relationship in which richness at first increases from low to mid-elevations and then declines towards high elevations; although even here, diversity at low elevations almost invariably exceeds that at the highest ones.

Elevational gradients in species richness are typically explained in terms of one or more of four principal factors (Lomolino 2001; Sanders 2002).

1 *Area*. Land area varies with elevation, thus it is possible that observed patterns in richness may be driven by the same processes as give rise to species–area relationships (Section 3.2.1). Certainly, accounting for variation in area can change observed relationships between richness and elevation, confirming that area does exert an influence. Thus, Rahbek (1995, 1997) has shown, for example, that when data are not standardized for differences in area then South American tropical land birds exhibit a steady decline in richness with elevation, but when these same data are standardized for area a hump-shaped pattern emerges (Fig. 3.21).

2 *Energy availability*. Just as variation in energy availability may contribute to latitudinal gradients in species richness, it may also explain altitudinal gradients in species numbers. Energy availability may peak at low to intermediate elevations, particularly because day-time temperatures enable higher rates of photosynthesis and cool evenings enable

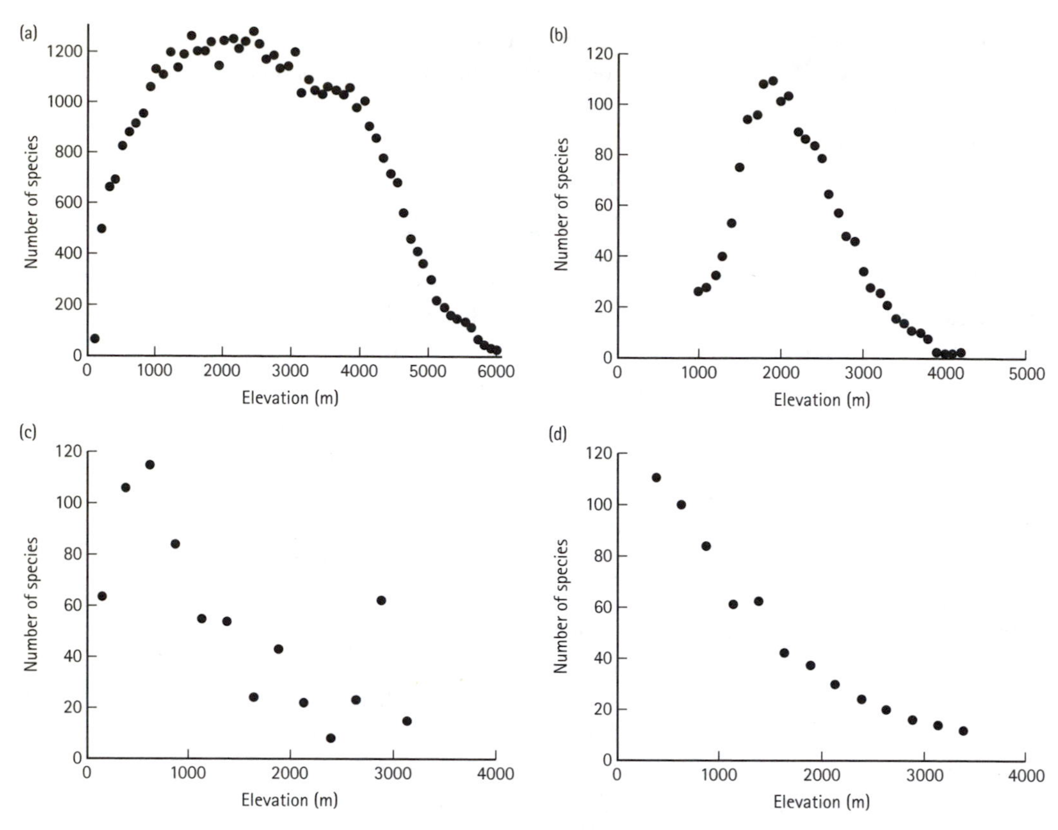

Fig. 3.20 Variation in number of species with elevation for: (a) flowering plants in Nepal; (b) ants in Colorado; (c) treehoppers in Colombia; and (d) bats in Manu National Park & Biosphere Reserve, Peru. (a, From Grytnes & Vetaas 2002; b, from Sanders 2002; c, data from Olmstead & Wood 1990; d, from Patterson et al. 1998.)

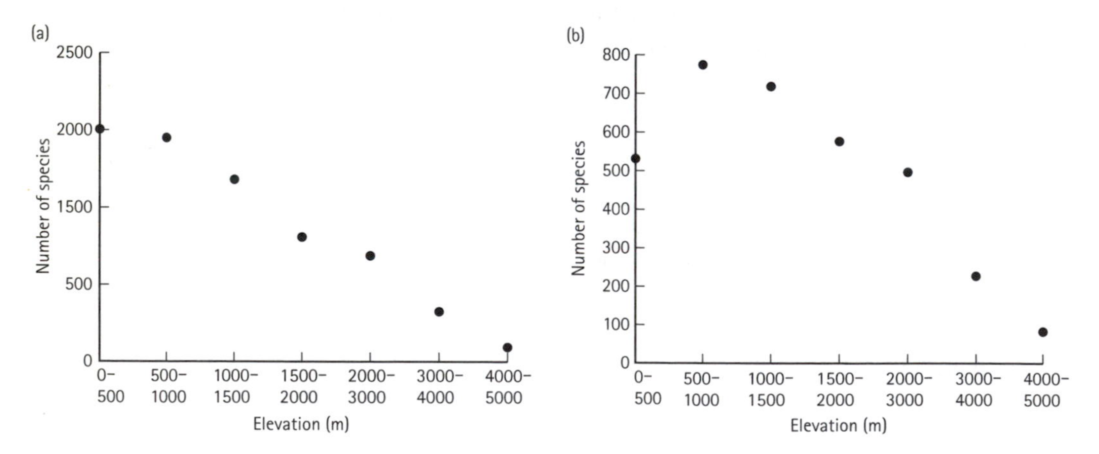

Fig. 3.21 Altitudinal gradient in the species richness of South American tropical land birds, based on data: (a) not standardized for elevational variation in area; and (b) standardized for such variation. (From Rahbek 1995.)

lower plant respiration, providing a wider resource base and allowing more species to co-occur.

3 *Isolation*. Higher elevations are, for most taxa, much more isolated from other areas of similar habitat (e.g. other mountain peaks) than those at low to intermediate elevations. This may make immigration less likely, increase the likelihood of speciation, and increase the likelihood of local extinction because of the reduced connectivity of populations. In consequence, higher elevations may have lower species richness, but commonly have higher levels of endemicity (although the pattern of endemism may be highly variable depending on the taxon considered; Kessler 2002). This does not explain, however, why intermediate elevations may be most species rich.

4 *Zonation*. Peaks in species richness at intermediate elevations may result from interactions and feedback among zonal communities, the transitions between which serve to inflate species numbers. This assumes elevational zonation in community structure, with marked changes in species composition occurring at some altitudes, rather than a continuous pattern of structural change.

As with latitudinal gradients, there is no necessity that these mechanisms be mutually independent, and present evidence suggests some role for each of them, at least, for different taxonomic groups and regions.

Below the Earth's surface

Life occurs beneath the Earth's surface as well as above it, for example in caves occurring at different depths. Little is known of the effect of this depth gradient on biodiversity. Certainly, the exciting discovery of endemic cave communities reliant on chemosynthetic (as opposed to photosynthetic) energy production, similar in function to those occurring in the deep sea at hydrothermal vent sites, is likely to prove of tremendous interest (Sarbu et al. 1996). However, life also occurs at even greater depths. Bacterial assemblages have been recovered from up to 4000 m underground, which has been noted as a cause of some concern regarding safety in the development of deep repositories for nuclear waste (Pedersen 1993). While their 'species' richness is not related to depth, such assemblages can consist of up to 62 different 'types' at any one depth (Flierman & Balkwill 1989).

Depth

In some sense, depth can be regarded as the marine equivalent of altitude. However, plainly there are limitations to this parallel because few species are able to achieve a purely aerial existence (although a few do spend the bulk of their lives airborne (e.g. swifts and some oceanic seabirds), no species is known to complete its life cycle in the air). Distinction must therefore be drawn between the effects of depth on benthic and pelagic marine assemblages. The oceans average c. 3.8 km in depth, but reach down more than 10 km. From the surface downwards, mean temperature and variability in that temperature decrease, hydrostatic pressure increases, and light and nutrient fluxes decline.

As it does with altitude, species richness tends to decline towards extreme depths, but again linear and hump-shaped relationships have been documented (Fig. 3.22). However, in both the pelagic and benthic realms, the species richness–depth relationship is generally held to be a hump-shaped one; richness commonly peaks at depths of 1000–1500 m for pelagic assemblages, and in many taxa increases with increasing depth to a maximum at 1000–2000 m for megabenthos and 2000–3000 m for macrobenthic infauna (Rex 1981; Etter & Grassle 1992; Angel 1993, 1994b; Rex et al. 1997; Pineda & Caswell 1998) (but cf. final section of Section 3.3.2). Indeed, a hump-shaped pattern of richness with depth may have been a persistent feature of life, with palaeontological examples having been documented (Tokeshi 1999). Whilst the same mechanisms as proposed to explain relationships between species richness and altitude may in modified form also explain those between species richness and depth, for benthic assemblages trends with depth may also be associated with changes in sediment characteristics, particularly particle-size diversity (Etter & Grassle 1992). For samples taken from the western North Atlantic from depths of 250–3029 m, species diversity of macrofauna was found to be positively related to sediment particle-size diversity, and when this effect was statistically controlled for there was no longer any relationship between species richness and depth.

The interplays between the various spatial patterns are important in generating the global landscape of biodiversity that is observed. Macpherson and Duarte (1994) examined the effect of both depth and latitude on (amongst other things) the species richness of benthic fish (Fig. 3.23). They found that species richness declined towards higher latitudes (Section 3.4.1) but at most latitudes species richness also varied with depth; species richness tended to peak at depths of 150–300 m.

3.4.3 Peninsulas and bays

The shapes of land masses and water bodies can have profound effects on the levels of biodiversity associated with them, by affecting environmental conditions and likelihoods of colonization and extinction, leading to gradients in that diversity. Thus, terrestrial species richness is often observed to decline towards the tips of peninsulas (the 'peninsula effect') and marine species richness to decline across bays with distance from the open sea (the 'bay effect') (Fig. 3.24). Exceptions to both patterns are,

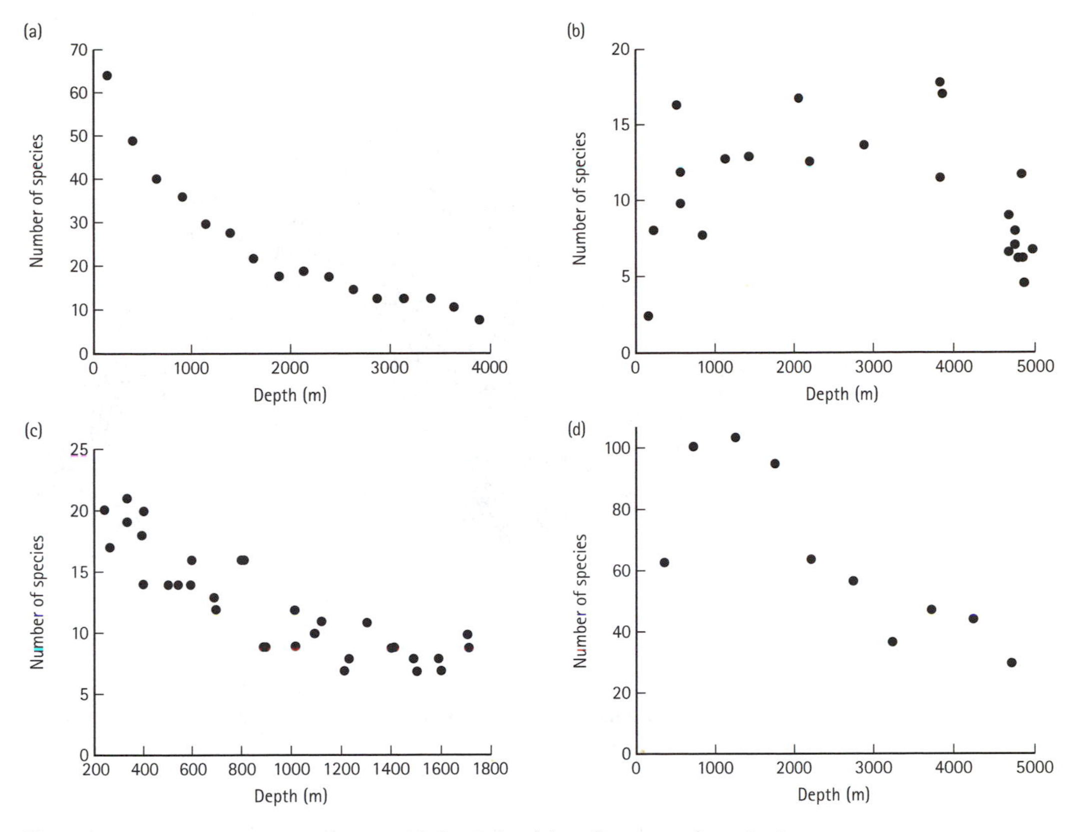

Fig. 3.22 Variation in species richness with depth for: (a) asellote isopod species in the northern seas; (b) gastropod species in the North American basin; (c) fish species on the continental slope of the Balearic Islands; and (d) megabenthos (summing fish, decapods, holothurians and asteroids) in the Porcupine Seabight region to the southwest of Eire. (a, From Svavarsson et al. 1993; b, from Rex et al. 1997; c, from Morenta et al. 1998; d, from Angel 1994b.)

however, not unusual (e.g. Seib 1980; Due & Polis 1986; Brown 1987; Tackaberry & Kellman 1996). Where they do exist, these trends may result from the effects of systematic changes in area or isolation.

3.5 Congruence

Most major terrestrial and freshwater groups are more speciose in tropical than in temperate regions, at low elevations than at high, and in forests than in deserts. Likewise, most major marine groups are more speciose in tropical than in temperate regions, at intermediate than at extreme depths, and in coral reefs than in the pelagic zone. One might, therefore, expect that within biological realms the regional richness of different groups of organisms would be positively correlated (areas in which they

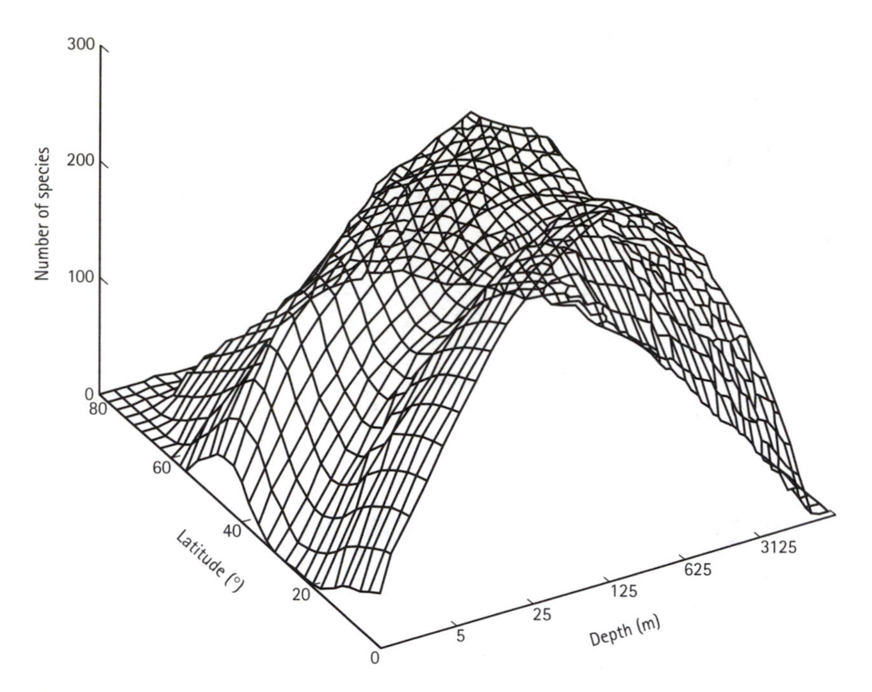

Fig. 3.23 Three-dimensional relationship between species richness, latitude and depth for benthic fish in the eastern Atlantic. (From Macpherson & Duarte 1994.)

are species poor coinciding and areas in which they are species rich coinciding) and, because of the positive local–regional richness relationship, local richness would do likewise. This would be important because it would greatly simplify the development of an understanding of global patterns in biodiversity.

In practice, mismatches between the spatial occurrence of peaks in the richness of different taxonomic groups have often been observed (e.g. Flather et al. 1997; Kerr 1997; Virolainen et al. 2000). Thus, whilst for the taxonomic groups trees, tiger beetles, amphibians, reptiles, birds and mammals, the 5% of land area across the USA and southern Canada in which the highest levels of species richness are attained do overlap between some pairs of taxa, this pattern is not a general one (Flather et al. 1997). Likewise, although the numbers of species in different, large, similar-sized areas for two groups are often significantly correlated, and may enable a very general impression of the patterns in richness of one group to be obtained from those of another, these correlations are frequently weak, of rather limited predictive value, and in some cases substantially explained by latitudinal gradients in diversity (Fig. 3.25; Currie 1991; Flather et al. 1997; Ricketts et al. 1999). These conclusions seem to hold at finer resolutions over more constrained areas. Thus, at a scale of 10×10 km squares, species rich areas for different taxa in Britain

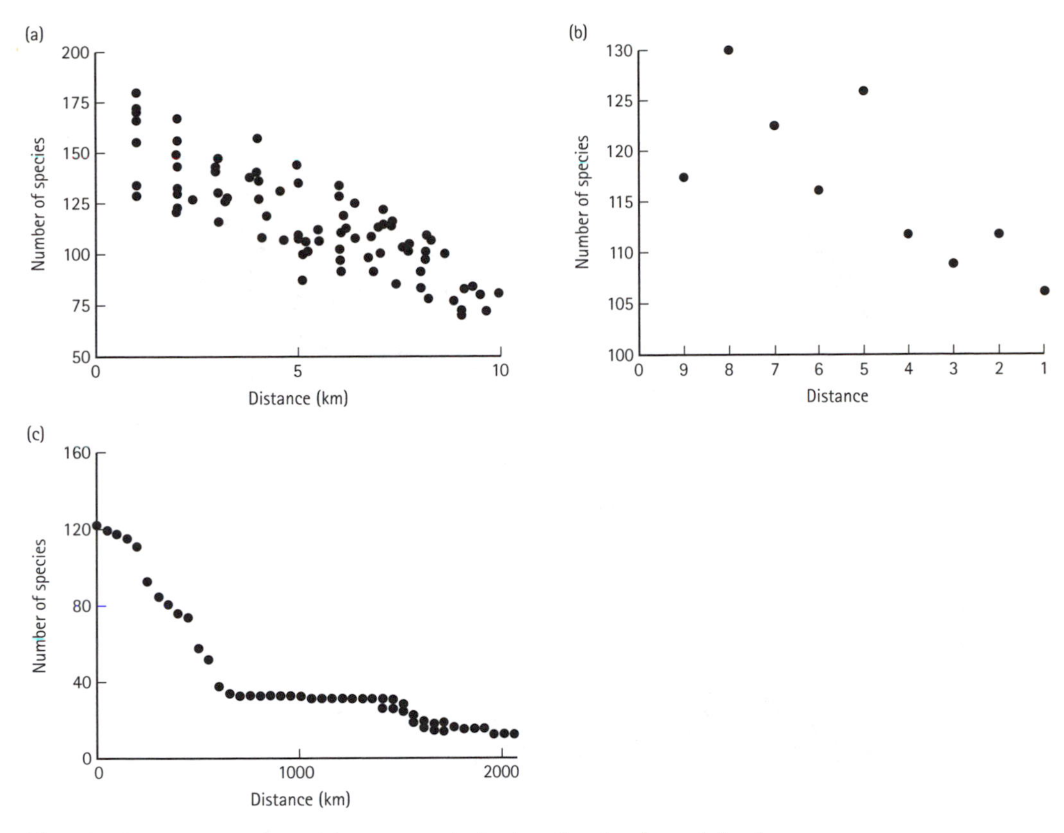

Fig. 3.24 Variation in species richness towards the tips of peninsulas and the shores of bays for: (a) butterflies on the Iberian peninsula, at different distances from the Pyrenees; (b) birds at different distances from the tip of Cornwall; and (c) fish in the Baltic Sea, at different distances from the Atlantic-Skagerrak mouth. (a, From Martin & Gurrea 1990; b, from Gaston & Blackburn 2000; c, from Rapoport 1994.)

frequently do not coincide (Prendergast et al. 1993). These areas are not distributed randomly, overlapping more often than expected by chance, but still at a rather low level. Likewise, different taxa are species poor or species rich in different areas of the northern region of South Africa (van Jaarsveld et al. 1998).

Where positive relationships are found between the species richness of two or more groups, this may reflect patterns of sampling effort (a complication plaguing many biodiversity studies), rather than any underlying covariance. More species of two groups may be recorded in some areas, and fewer in others, simply because greater efforts were made for both groups in the former. If the positive relationships are real, then this does not necessarily imply any direct linkage between the richness of those groups. Covariance can occur because of trophic or other relations, but might also result from random effects (if there is a greater overall number of species in an area, then by chance there are likely to be more species of

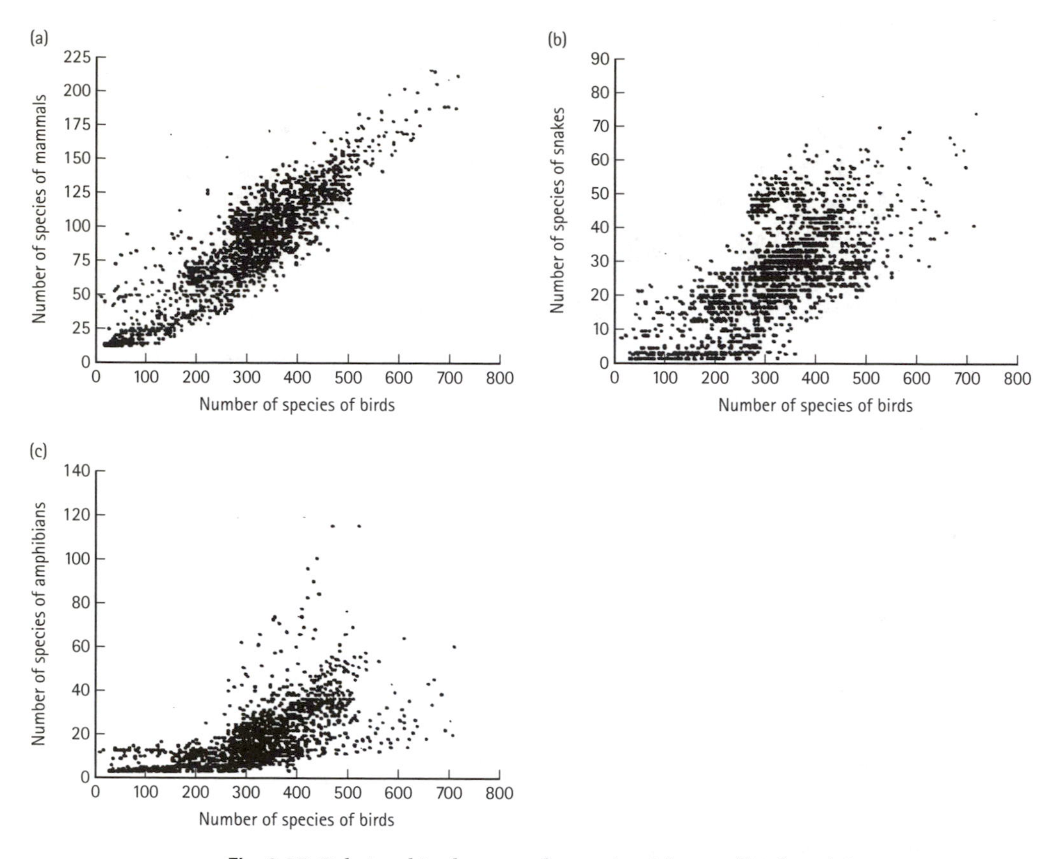

Fig. 3.25 Relationships between the species richness of birds and the species richness of: (a) mammals; (b) snakes; and (c) amphibians across 1962 1° grid cells in sub-Saharan Africa. (From Balmford 2002.)

each of the constituent groups), because groups share common determinants of richness (e.g. energy availability), or even because groups differ in determinants of richness but these determinants themselves exhibit spatial covariance (Gaston 1996b,c).

The frequent lack of strong positive covariance in the species richness of different higher taxa is significant in that it constrains the extent to which observed patterns in biodiversity can be extrapolated from one group to another, and from exemplar groups (like birds and mammals) to biodiversity at large. The latter is particularly important given that only c. 13% of the total number of species estimated to be extant have been formally taxonomically described, the distributions of the majority of these remain largely unknown (a high proportion are known from only a single locality; Andersen et al. 1997; Stork 1997), that species whose distributions are well documented are strongly biased with respect to their higher taxonomic affinities, and that they belong to groups whose potential for indicating patterns of biodiversity at large may in some cases be particularly poor (Ricketts et al. 1999). Such outcomes are, however, inevitable, because of the multiple forces at work in structuring global patterns of biodiversity, and because the particular outcomes observed rest fundamentally on the balance of those forces. Indeed, even where two groups exhibit similar spatial gradients in biodiversity there is substantial variation around those trends, and the details are seldom similar. In the extreme, some groups exhibit patterns of biodiversity that are entirely contrary to the norm (e.g. Section 3.4.1). Which particular patterns are and are not expressed by a given taxon rests on contingencies (e.g. physiology, dispersal ability, resource requirements, evolutionary history; Lawton 1999).

3.6 Summary

1 On average, as the size of a geographical area increases, so too does the number of species that it contains (the species–area relationship).
2 Local species richness tends to be positively correlated with regional species richness (the local–regional richness relationship).
3 There are more higher taxa in the marine realm than in the terrestrial one, but more species in the latter than in the former.
4 The tropical regions contain at least two-thirds of all extant terrestrial species, with the Neotropics containing the greatest overall levels. Marine biodiversity is thought to be highest in the Indo-western Pacific.
5 The distribution of terrestrial biodiversity between provinces is uneven, with 17 mega-diversity countries possessing 66–75% of the world's species.
6 The proportion of endemic taxa present tends, on average, to increase with the size of an area and with higher species richness, and the number of endemics increases towards lower latitudes.
7 Species richness in both marine and terrestrial realms tends to increase from temperate to tropical latitudes, although the generality of the pattern is more uncertain in the former. Latitudinal gradients in richness have been a persistent feature through much of the history of biodiversity.
8 In the terrestrial realm, species richness declines towards high elevations, often with a peak at intermediate elevations, whilst in the marine realm the relationship with depth is typically hump-shaped.
9 Mismatches in the spatial occurrence of peaks in the richness of different taxonomic groups have often been observed, and correlations between the numbers of species in different groups are frequently rather weak.

Further reading

Begon, M., Harper, J.L. & Townsend, C.R. (1996) *Ecology: Individuals, Populations and Communities*. Blackwell Science, Oxford. (*A superb treatment of ecology, including the ecological issues touched on in this chapter.*)

Brown, J.H. (1995) *Macroecology*. University of Chicago Press, Chicago, IL. (*An introduction to macroecology, by its chief proponent.*)

Brown, J.H. & Lomolino, M.V. (1998) *Biogeography*, 2nd edn. Sinauer Associates, Sunderland, MA. (*The best text on biogeography.*)

Gaston, K.J. (1994) *Rarity*. Chapman & Hall, London. (*A synthesis of what is known about rarity, much of it related to the patterns of biodiversity.*)

Gaston, K.J. & Blackburn, T.M. (2000) *Pattern and Process in Macroecology*. Blackwell Science, Oxford. (*A demonstration of how regional-scale processes influence local patterns of biodiversity and community structure.*)

Groombridge, B. & Jenkins, M.D. (2002) *World Atlas of Biodiversity: Earth's Living Resources in the 21st Century*. University of California Press, London. (*Lots of useful maps of patterns of biodiversity.*)

Hubbell, S.P. (2001) *The Unified Neutral Theory of Biodiversity and Biogeography*. Princeton University Press, Princeton, NJ. (*A development of island biogeography theory to explain biodiversity – a thought-provoking read.*)

Lawton, J.H. (2000) *Community Ecology in a Changing World*. Ecology Institute, Oldendorf/Luhe. (*An authoritative exploration of the determinants of community structure and the likely consequences.*)

Mittermeier, R.A., Myers, N., Gil, P.R. & Mittermeier, C.G. (1999) *Hotspots: Earth's Biologically Richest and most Endangered Terrestrial Ecoregions*. CEMEX/Conservation International, Mexico City. (*Impressive, but in our experience it is difficult to obtain a copy.*)

Myers, A.A. & Giller, P.S. (eds.) (1988) *Analytical Biogeography: An Integrated Approach to the Study of Animal and Plant Distributions*. Chapman & Hall, London. (*Remains perhaps the best single-volume treatment of many of the primary issues in biogeography.*)

Ormond, R.F.G., Gage, J.D. & Angel, M.V. (eds.) (1997) *Marine Biodiversity: Patterns and Processes*. Cambridge University Press, Cambridge. (*One of the only volumes dedicated to this topic.*)

Ricklefs, R.E. & Schluter, D. (eds.) (1993) *Species Diversity in Ecological Communities: Historical and Geographical Perspectives*. University of Chicago Press, Chicago, IL. (*A landmark text exploring the roles of large-scale spatial and temporal processes in generating and maintaining diversity.*)

Rosenzweig, M.L. (1995) *Species Diversity in Space and Time*. Cambridge University Press, Cambridge. (*An important overview, with a particular take on the processes that structure patterns of diversity.*)

Tokeshi, M. (1999) *Species Coexistence: Ecological and Evolutionary Perspectives*. Blackwell Science, Oxford. (*A wide-ranging treatment of the patterns and processes of species diversity and coexistence, unusually blending palaeobiological and contemporary perspectives.*)

Whittaker, R.J. (1998) *Island Biogeography*. Oxford University Press, Oxford. (*An up-to-date overview of a topic that has fascinated biologists for generations.*)

4 Does biodiversity matter?

4.1 Introduction

The variety of life is manifestly complex (Chapter 1), has changed dramatically through time (Chapter 2), and is unevenly distributed through space (Chapter 3). For some these observations may be interesting in their own right, and the study of biodiversity may be largely a heuristic exercise. Certainly, exploring such issues has attracted the attentions of generations of natural historians, palaeobiologists and ecologists. But this ignores a fundamental question that demands both an intellectual and a practical response. Does biodiversity matter? In this chapter we address this issue. We discuss the sorts of things that might be valued about biodiversity and why. In so doing, we use 'value' in the broadest sense and not simply as a shorthand for monetary worth. The values of biodiversity can be divided into two broad and largely self-explanatory groups: use values and non-use values. These categories are not always clear-cut, but they are still helpful as long as one is mindful of their limitations. We begin by considering the use value of biodiversity, taking in turn its two major components of direct-use and indirect-use value (Sections 4.2 & 4.3) and the relationships between biodiversity and ecosystem function (Section 4.3). We then move on to address non-use values, including option, bequest, existence and intrinsic values (Section 4.4).

The sequence in which these values are presented is not indicative of our perceptions of their relative importance. Nor are observations that will be made on the form and level of some kinds of use intended to imply any endorsement of their appropriateness. Plainly, some of the examples of the exploitation of biodiversity that we will discuss are distressingly unsustainable at present levels (see Section 5.4.1 for further discussion), and others would be regarded by some, and perhaps a substantial proportion, of the human population as unethical.

4.2 Direct-use value

Direct-use value derives from the direct role of biological resources in consumption or production. It essentially concerns marketable commodities. The scale of the direct-use exploitation of biodiversity is enormous and extremely multifaceted. To date it has eluded comprehensive evaluation. Under some broad headings, selected types of the direct-use value of biodiversity are for food, medicine, biological control, industrial materials, recreational harvesting and ecotourism. We will address each of these in turn.

4.2.1 Food

Biodiversity provides food for humans, and hence is the foundation of all our food industries and related services. This food takes forms that include vegetables, fruit, nuts, meat, and adjuncts to food in the form of food colourants, flavouring and preservatives. These may derive from wild or cultivated sources, but for the bulk of the human population the latter are, of course, predominant (in 1997, global agriculture provided 95% of all plant and animal protein and 99% of energy consumed by humans; United Nations Development Programme et al. 2000). The development of and subsequent improvements in agriculture enabled the continued expansion of the human population, from a global total of perhaps 4 million hunter–gatherers to the present 6 billion people (Cohen 1995). Current agricultural technology enables one person to be fed from the food grown on $\leq 2000\ m^2$ (Trewavas 2002), although inequities mean that some of the human population is obese, and much is malnourished or at or below the level of starvation.

Of the 300,000 or more species of flowering plants, about 12,500 are considered to be edible to humans, although occasional use may embrace a much larger number (Rapoport & Drausal 2001). Around 200 plant species have been domesticated for food. However, at present more than 75% of the food supply (in terms of energy intake) of the human population is obtained, directly or indirectly, from just 12 kinds of plants (bananas/plantains, beans, cassava, maize, millet, potatoes, rice, sorghum, soybean, sugar cane, sweet potatoes, wheat). Average global annual production of major food crops in 1996–98 totalled 2.7 billion tonnes (2.07 billion tonnes of cereals and 0.64 billion tonnes of roots and tubers; United Nations Development Programme et al. 2000). The total number of wheat stalks alone grown in 1994 exceeded 450 trillion, probably a record at that time (Myers 1997).

The diversity of animals that are exploited for food is more difficult to enumerate, although again whilst a wide range of species is consumed or provides products for consumption (e.g. milk), most consumption is concentrated on just a small proportion of these species. Animals of which use is made directly or indirectly include groups of insects (moths, beetles, wasps and bees), crustaceans (lobsters, crabs, shrimp), molluscs (bivalves, gastropods, squid), echinoderms (sea urchins, sea cucumbers) and vertebrates (fish, amphibians, reptiles, birds, mammals). The vast scale of the exploitation is readily apparent from just a few figures: (i) 3.39 billion livestock are maintained worldwide (1996–98) (1.33 billion cattle, 1.76 billion sheep and goats, 0.12 billion equines, 0.18 billion buffaloes and camels; United Nations Development Programme et al. 2000); (ii) average global annual meat production for 1996–98 was 215 million tonnes (United Nations Development Programme et al. 2000); and (iii) global fisheries land more than 80 million tonnes per year.

Whether of plants or animals, the diversity of organisms exploited for food remains rather narrow when compared with their overall diversity, leaving significant potential for further exploitation (although the characteristics necessary for domestication may be exhibited by a surprisingly small proportion of species; Diamond 2002). This gap is chiefly being closed indirectly, through the use of wild species and varieties to supply genes for the improvement of cultivated and domesticated species (increasing yields, tolerances, vigour and disease resistance); industrial-scale agriculture led to the loss of much of the previous local genetic variation in crops and livestock and their replacement by uniform varieties over often vast areas. Indeed, broadening the genetic base of some food species may perhaps be the only way in which our heavy reliance upon them can be maintained. Some of the most valuable genetic material may reside in particular wild populations of species that are exploited for food, or in their close relatives.

4.2.2 Medicine

As well as providing sustenance, biodiversity plays other vital direct roles in maintaining the health of the human population. Natural products have long been recognized as an important source of therapeutically effective medicines, and more than 60% of the world's human population relies almost entirely on plant medicine for primary health care (Harvey 2000). Of 520 new drugs approved between 1983 and 1994, 39% were natural products or were derived from them. Moreover, of the 20 best-selling non-protein drugs in 1999, nine were derived, directly or indirectly, from natural products, with combined annual sales of more than US$16 billion (simvastatin, lovastatin, enalapril, pravastatin, atorvastatin, augmentin, ciprofloxacin, clarithromycin, cyclosporin; Harvey 2000). Plant species that have proven of medical importance include willow trees (from which salicylic acid was originally obtained, and of which aspirin is a simple derivative), foxglove (digitoxin), belladonna (atropine) and poppy (codeine).

Animals also are extensively used in traditional remedies (with international trade in association with Oriental and other customary forms of medicine being substantial), as a source of a range of products in modern medicine (e.g. anticoagulants, coagulants, vasodilatory agents) and for models on which to test potentially useful drugs or techniques.

Examples of recently developed drugs (see Chivian 2001; Mateo et al. 2001 and references therein) include:

- *Taxol*. The Pacific yew tree *Taxus brevifolia* was routinely discarded by logging operations as being of no commercial value. However, it was found to contain the compound taxol, which kills cancer cells in a manner unlike that of other chemotherapeutic agents and has been shown to be one of the most promising drugs for the treatment of breast and ovarian cancer. It has become the best-selling anticancer agent ever (with sales exceeding US$1 billion annually). The taxol molecule, which has now been detected in other species, has been used as the basis for several synthetic compounds that are even more effective.
- *Cone snail venom*. A wide diversity of peptide compounds have been found to occur in the venoms of tropical reef cone snails. These compounds have been found to block a variety of ion channels, receptors and pumps in neuromuscular systems. One, omega-conotoxin, a calcium-channel blocker, has been found to be a potent analgesic and to provide a means of keeping nerve cells alive following ischaemia (insufficient flow of blood and oxygen to an organ). Advanced clinical trials are being conducted on its synthetic form for the prevention of nerve cell death following coronary artery bypass surgery, head injury and stroke, and for the treatment of chronic intractable pain associated with cancer, AIDS, and peripheral neuropathies. This synthetic form has 1000 times the analgesic potency of morphine, but does not lead to the development of tolerance or addiction, or to a clouding of consciousness.
- *Acetylcholinesterase (ACE)-inhibiting drugs*. ACE-inhibiting drugs such as enalapril, captopril, lisinopril and perindopril have been derived based on a peptide in the venom of the fer-de-lance (*Bothrops athrox* or *B. jararaca*), a Neotropical pit viper that kills its prey by causing a drop in blood pressure. These drugs have played a significant role in the decline of human deaths from stroke and heart attack.

The proportion of species that have been investigated for the potential derivation of drugs is quite small. For example, as of 1995, whilst about 37,500 species of plants had been studied phytochemically, only about 14,000 had been studied for at least one type of biological activity (Verpoorte 1998), and the number studied in detail for their medicinal properties is at best in the low thousands (Dobson 1995).

Despite advances in computer-assisted drug design, in molecular biology and in gene therapy, there remains a pressing need for new drugs to counteract drug-resistant pathogens, multidrug-resistant cancers, the emergence of new human diseases (particularly HIV/AIDS), the resurgence of older diseases such as tuberculosis, changes in the geographical distribution of diseases resulting from increased human movement and global climate change, and conditions associated with an aging population in much of the developed world (Dobson 1995; Munro et al. 1999). Perhaps the most efficient way to find them is to exploit the millions of generations of trial and error by natural selection that have given other creatures the means to healthy lives (Beattie & Ehrlich 2001). It has been suggested that one out of every 125 plant species studied has produced a major drug, whilst for synthesized chemicals the potential for finding major new drugs is of the order of one in 10,000 compounds tested (Dobson 1995). Thus, the search for useful compounds from biological material goes on (perhaps the most conspicuous example of what has come to be known as bioprospecting). For example, in the area of cancer treatment, clinical trials have been conducted using compounds derived from tunicates and a bryozoan, and preclinical trials on compounds from a sponge and a mollusc (Munro et al. 1999).

Clues to solutions to other medical problems faced by humans may also lie in other species. Thus, for example, new ways of preventing and treating osteoporosis may perhaps be found in bears, which are the only mammals in which the problem is thought not to occur (Chivian 2001). During the 3–7 months that black bears *Ursus americanus* den, they do not eat, drink, urinate or defecate, and yet they can deliver and nurse young, maintain their bone density and lean body mass, and do not become ketotic or uraemic.

4.2.3 Biological control

The use of natural enemies to control species regarded as problems is increasingly widespread and is often seen as an environmentally friendly alternative to the use of pesticides (but see Section 5.4.3). Biocontrol programmes have been attempted against several hundred species of plants and insects, with approximately 30% of weed biocontrol and 40% of insect biocontrol programmes being successful (Kunin & Lawton 1996). Biological control has included introductions of agents to control populations of pests in or on crops, populations of disease vectors (e.g. mosquitoes) and populations of invasive species.

The economic returns of biological control programmes can be huge, with the monetary values of annual gains in food or other crop production perhaps exceeding by many times the entire investment in control programmes. For example, the cost–benefit ratio for the control of cassava mealybug *Phenacoccus manihoti* by the encyrtid wasp *Epidinocarsis lopezi* in Africa was estimated to be 1 to 149 with annual savings as high as US$250 million (Norgaard 1988).

4.2.4 Industrial materials

A wide range of industrial materials, or templates for the production of such materials, have been derived directly from biological resources. These include building materials, fibres, dyes, resins, gums, adhesives, rubber, oils and waxes, agricultural chemicals (including pesticides) and perfumes. For wood alone, in 1989 the total worldwide value of exports was estimated to be US$6 billion (World Conservation Monitoring Centre 1992), and more than 3.8 billion cubic metres are estimated to be harvested annually worldwide, for fuel, timber and pulp (Kunin & Lawton 1996). Including agriculture, food processing, industrial chemical and pollution control sectors, the biotechnology industry made sales of US$10–12 billion in 1993 in the USA alone (these are projected to reach US$100 billion by 2035; Colwell 1997).

Biological materials have provided the models (biomimicry) for many industrial materials and structures. Thus, inspiration for the dome of the Crystal Palace in London came from the Amazonian water lily *Victoria amazonica*, for air-conditioning systems from the mounds constructed by termites, for Velcro fasteners from the seeds of burdock *Arctium* spp., for the echo-sounder from bats, and for infrared sensors from the thermosensitive pit organ of the rattlesnake (Beattie & Ehrlich 2001; Mateo et al. 2001). As is the case for food and medicine, the scope for exploitation of a far greater diversity of organisms for industrial materials is vast. Plants and other animals have already solved many of the problems and challenges facing humankind, often in what appear to us to be ingenious ways. The reasons that the potential for exploitation is so much greater than presently realized probably have as much to do with cultural factors (the devil you know) as they do with ignorance of natural products.

4.2.5 Recreational harvesting

Examples of recreational harvesting are multifarious but include hunting and fishing, the harvesting of animals (e.g. fish, reptiles, birds, mammals) for display and as pets, and the harvesting of plants for personal and private gardens.

Thus, for example, in the British Isles alone, 25,000 plant species are grown in botanic gardens, and some 65,000 named plant taxa are sold for horticulture, of which 14,000 represent distinct species grown out of doors (Crawley et al. 1996). Likewise, an estimated 14–30 million fish may be traded each year for aquaria, about two-thirds of the species of which are from coral reefs (Groombridge & Jenkins 2002).

The global international legal net trade in wildlife and wildlife products reported by the Convention on International Trade in Endangered Species of Wild Fauna and Flora (CITES) in 1997 included 26,000 live primates, 235,000 live parrots, 76,000 live tortoises, 948,500 live lizards, 259,000 live snakes, 344,000 wild orchids, 22,000 cat skins, 850,000 crocodile skins, 1,638,000 lizard skins and 1,458,000 snake skins (United Nations Development Programme et al. 2000). Species traded legally within national borders and illegal trade are not included in these figures, but run to billions of dollars annually. Recreational harvesting is of huge commercial value, both because of the scale of the trade, and because individual specimens of rare and otherwise sought after species can attract large sums (with the value often increasing as the species become progressively rarer). The illegal trade in wildlife has been argued to rank second in value only to the clandestine arms and drugs markets (Juniper 2002). In the late 1990s an illegally smuggled pair of Lear's macaws *Anodorhynchus leari* were gram for gram more valuable than heroin, fetching c. US$75,000 (Juniper 2002).

4.2.6 Ecotourism

Ecotourism is by definition founded on biodiversity, and has developed into a massive industry. Indeed, tourism as a whole is one of the fastest growing industries in the world. In 1988 an estimated 157–236 million people took part in international ecotourism (i.e. in countries of which they were not nationals), contributing between US$93 and US$233 billion to national incomes (Filion et al. 1994). However, international tourism is also estimated to account for perhaps only 9% of global tourism receipts (the rest is domestic), suggesting that these figures represent only a fraction of the scale and economic impact of ecotourism (Filion et al. 1994). In 1998, an estimated 9 million people went whale-watching alone, with expenditures on just this activity of US$1 billion (Hoyt 2000).

At a regional and local scale, ecotourism can be of economic significance. For example: (i) in Britain, at least US$7.5 billion is spent each year by urban visitors to the countryside in the course of more than 650 million day-visits (Pretty 1998); (ii) bird-watching contributes more than US$1500 million per annum to the economy of South Africa (Turpie &

Ryan 1999); and (iii) marine wildlife tourism contributes US$14 million per year to the Scottish Highlands and Islands (Everett 1998).

A single male black-winged stilt *Himantopus himantopus* that since 1993 has been resident at the Royal Society for the Protection of Birds (RSPB) reserve at Titchwell, UK has been argued to be the most watched bird in Britain, and is estimated to have been seen by more than half a million people.

4.3 Indirect-use value

The biota annually cycles gigatonnes (10^{15} g) of elements such as carbon, hydrogen, nitrogen, oxygen, phosphorus and sulphur, and teragrams (10^{12} g) of aerosols and particles among the atmosphere, hydrosphere (the waters) and lithosphere (the solid matter forming the Earth's crust; Naeem 2002). Such biogeochemical cycling modifies physical and chemical conditions, creating an environment that sustains life. Indeed, in the absence of life, Earth would be a very different place. In particular, it has been estimated that the atmospheric gas composition would be radically altered, and surface temperatures and pressures dramatically heightened (Table 4.1).

The indirect-use value of biodiversity derives from the many functions that it performs in providing services that are crucial to human wellbeing (Table 4.2; Westman 1977; Ehrlich & Ehrlich 1992; Chapin et al. 1997; Daily 1997). These services can in some sense be regarded as being 'free', in that they tend not to be the subject of direct trading in the marketplace, although such a perception has proven detrimental to their maintenance. Alongside those that are perhaps more readily recognized, such as nutrient cycling and soil formation, there are numerous other ecosystem

Table 4.1 Differences between the atmospheric gas composition, surface temperature and pressure of Venus, Earth as it is, and Mars, and estimations of what these would be like if Earth was without life. (From Lovelock 1989.)

	Venus	Earth as it is	Mars	Earth without life
Carbon dioxide	96.5%	0.03%	95%	98%
Nitrogen	3.5%	79%	2.7%	1.9%
Oxygen	Trace	21%	0.13%	0.0%
Argon	70 ppm	1%	1.6%	0.1%
Methane	0.0	1.7 ppm	0.0	0.0
Surface temperature (°C)	459	13	−53	240–340
Total pressure (bars)	90	1.0	0.0064	60

Table 4.2 Some ecosystem services provided by biodiversity.

Atmospheric regulation
Climatic regulation
Hydrological regulation
Nutrient cycling
Pest control
Photosynthesis
Pollination
Soil formation and maintenance

services. For example, many non-commercial species of marine molluscs and crustaceans may not be used directly themselves, but may nonetheless constitute an essential food source for many economically important fish species. The value of these invertebrates is indirect as they derive their value (in an economic sense) from the fish. Likewise, declines in the diversity and numbers of wild bees in many areas (often as a product of habitat destruction) have drawn attention to their agricultural significance as pollinators, and to the adverse effects on crop yields of these losses (O'Toole 1993).

Some natural environments have both a direct and an indirect value. Take, for example, a tropical forest. This may provide a number of direct-use values, including those of timber, medicinal plants, other forest products, hunting and fishing, recreation and tourism. It may also provide indirect-use values, including soil conservation and soil productivity, and watershed protection (with consequences for water supply and storage, flood control, climate, and carbon sequestration; Perrings 1995). The value of the forest for its indirect uses tends, however, vastly to exceed that for direct uses, giving it greater global than local value, and tending to make it more vulnerable to clearance by local people (Godoy et al. 2000). In practice, of course, ecosystem services are essential for the maintenance of all direct-use values.

Indirect-use values are more difficult to quantify or cost than direct-use values and in some cases it may be difficult to recognize, let alone explain, them. There have nonetheless been some, inevitably extremely contentious, attempts to estimate the aggregated annual value of nature's services (Costanza et al. 1997; Pimentel et al. 1997; see also Pimm 1997). These suggest figures similar in magnitude to, larger than, or a large proportion of, the global total annual gross national product, albeit there is nowhere one could purchase a replacement set of such services. The overall benefit : cost ratio of an effective programme for the conservation of remaining natural ecosystems has been estimated at, at least, 100 : 1 (Balmford et al. 2002).

The need to maintain biodiversity because of the services it provides was graphically illustrated in the Biosphere 2 experiments (Cohen & Tilman 1996). Biosphere 2 is the world's largest closed-environment facility, a 3.15 acre area, containing soil, air, water, plants and animals. Roughly US$200 million was invested in its design and construction, millions more in its operation (annual energy investments exceeded US$1 million), and it drew on immense technological resources and expertise. Nonetheless, it proved impossible to create a materially closed system that could support eight humans with adequate food, water and air, for 2 years. Surprise changes in the environment included a dramatic fall in oxygen levels and rise in carbon dioxide, a rise in nitrous oxide (N_2O) concentrations, overloading of water systems with nutrients, and the extinction of all pollinators. In short, with all human technology, ingenuity and unlimited (compared with normal science budgets) financial resources, a system could not be built that will provide eight humans, let alone humankind, with the life-supporting services that natural ecosystems provide for free.

Humans do not live within glasshouses, however large. But, a high proportion lives in cities. These draw on ecosystem services over large areas. Thus, the 29 largest cities in the Baltic Sea region have been estimated to draw ecosystem support services from areas at least 500–1000 times larger than the areas of the cities themselves (Folke et al. 1997). Average residents of North America, Europe, Japan and Australia require the biophysical output (an 'ecological footprint') of 5–10 ha of biophysically productive land and water each to support their consumer lifestyles (Rees 2001).

4.3.1 Biodiversity and ecosystem function

Whilst the importance of biodiversity for ecosystem functions is evident, it is less obvious how much biodiversity is required to provide those functions. Indeed, the relationship between levels of biodiversity and ecosystem functioning has emerged as a dominant issue in ecology (Chapin et al. 1998; Loreau et al. 2001). Numerous hypothetical ways have been identified in which varying levels of biodiversity may influence ecosystem functioning (Martinez 1996; Schläpfer & Schmid 1999). However, in addition to the null hypothesis of no effect, there are three principal ways in which ecosystem processes might respond to reductions in species richness (Lawton 1994; Johnson et al. 1996).

1 *Redundancy*. Beyond some minimum number of species necessary to carry out basic ecosystem processes, most species are equivalent and their loss of little significance (Fig. 4.1a).

2 *Rivet-popping*. Likening the species in an ecosystem to the rivets holding together an aeroplane, the loss of a few species may have no apparent effect, but beyond some threshold losses, the ecosystem processes will fail (Fig. 4.1b; Ehrlich & Ehrlich 1981).

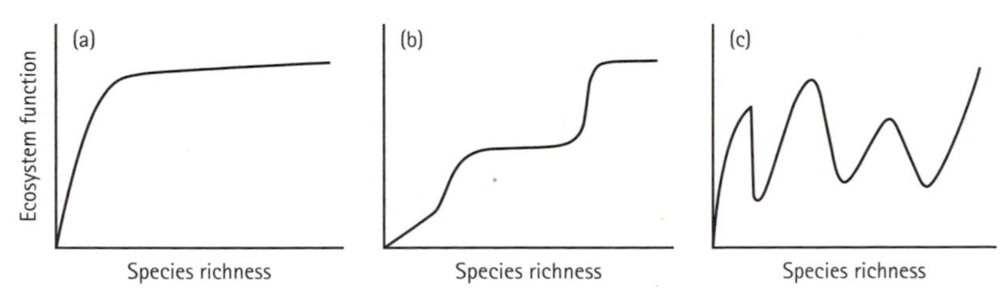

Fig. 4.1 Three possible relationships between species richness and ecosystem function: (a) redundancy; (b) rivet-popping; and (c) idiosyncrasy. (From Naeem 1998.)

3 *Idiosyncrasy*. As diversity changes so does ecosystem function, but the magnitude and direction of change is unpredictable because individual species have complex and varied roles (Fig. 4.1c; Lawton 1994).

There have been a large number of experiments conducted (in the laboratory and in the field) to differentiate amongst these possibilities, with the most common approach being to create replicate assemblages of different numbers of species and to measure the associated ecosystem functioning (Naeem et al. 1994, 1995; Tilman et al. 1996; Schwartz et al. 2000; Díaz & Cabido 2001). The design and the interpretation of the results of some of these studies have been extremely contentious. Although other outcomes have also been reported, a number of experiments have found that ecosystem functioning increases from assemblages of very small to small numbers of species, with the effect diminishing as species numbers increase further (Fig. 4.2), suggesting some degree of ecological equivalency amongst species (redundancy).

Three mechanisms have been proposed to explain why there should be a relationship between biodiversity and ecosystem functioning (Naeem 2002).

1 *Sampling effect*. If in a regional pool of a large number of species some have strong impacts on ecosystem processes, then the more species that are drawn from this pool to form a local assemblage the greater the probability that some of these strongly impacting species will be included.

2 *Species complementarity*. If species differ in their resource use, then the more species that are included in a local assemblage the more thoroughly will the available set of resources be exploited, with the actions of different species complementing one another.

3 *Positive interactions*. Increasing numbers of species in a local assemblage could result in increases in the number of mutual, facultative or positive indirect effects among them, increasing ecosystem functioning.

In practice, all three of these mechanisms may often be operating, with the research challenge being to find ways to determine their relative contribution to ecosystem functioning. Understanding the relationship between biodiversity and ecosystem functioning is, however, further

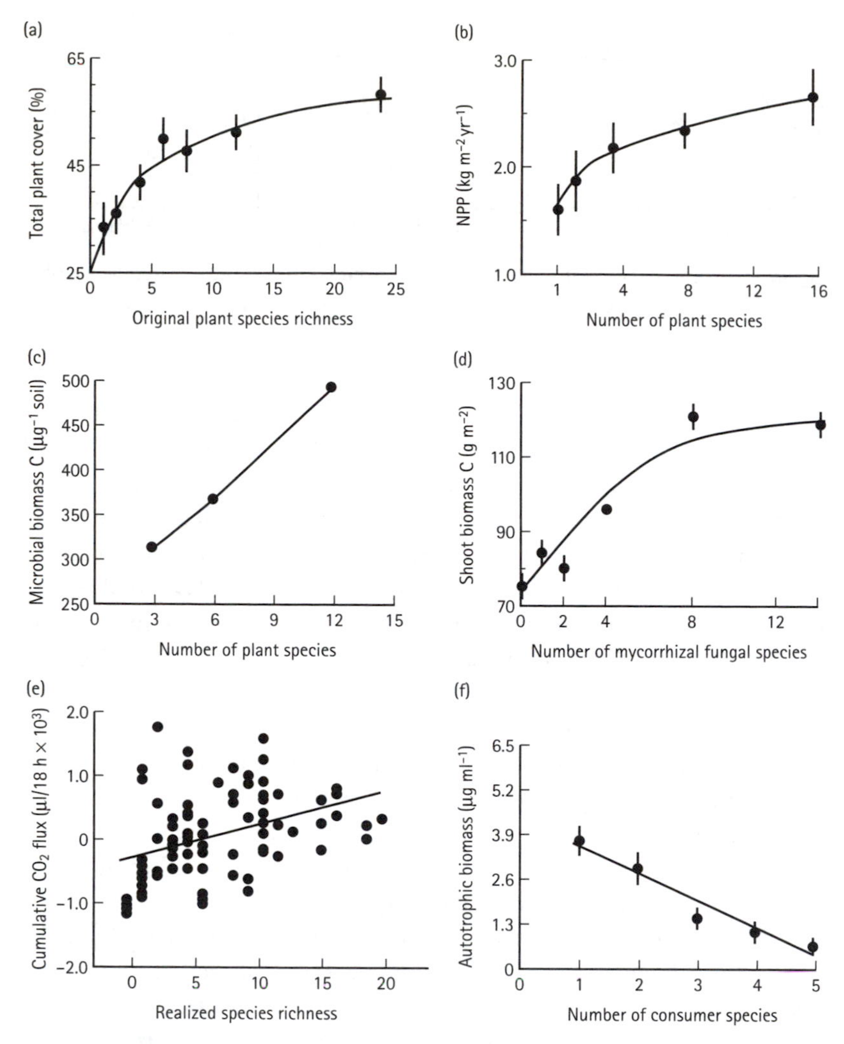

Fig. 4.2 Experimental evidence that biodiversity affects ecosystem processes. Relationships between: (a) plant species richness of experimental grassland plots in Minnesota and percentage of the ground covered with vegetation, a proxy for plant production; (b) plant species richness of experimental old-field ecosystems and net primary production (NPP); (c) plant species richness in Mediterranean herbaceous ecosystems and microbial biomass, a proxy for microbial production; (d) mycorrhizal fungal species richness and shoot biomass, a proxy for plant production; (e) microbial species richness in microcosms and carbon dioxide flux; and (f) heterotrophic protist richness (bacterivores, algavores, omnivores) in microcosms and autotrophic (green alga) biomass, a proxy for production. (From Naeem 2002; based on studies by Tilman et al. 1996, McGrady-Steed et al. 1997, Naeem & Li 1997, Chapin et al. 1998 and Van der Heijden et al. 1998.)

complicated by the temporal dynamics of ecological systems. This may mean that as conditions change different species become more or less important contributors to ecosystem functioning, with the importance of biodiversity lying not simply in how many species are present at a given time but in the maintenance of a pool of species that can buffer a system against the vagaries of an uncertain world (an insurance effect; McGrady-Steed et al. 1997). There seems little doubt that higher species richness increases both species redundancy and temporal resilience of ecosystem functioning, thereby increasing the reliability of that functioning (Naeem 1998).

4.4 Non-use value

Non-use value is that associated with biological resources even if they are not directly or indirectly exploited. Non-use value can be divided into at least four components: (i) option value; (ii) bequest value; (iii) existence value; and (iv) intrinsic value.

4.4.1 Option value

In addition to the necessity that biodiversity be maintained for its current direct- and indirect-use value, one might equally argue that it should be retained for the options for future use or non-use that it provides (Weisbrod 1964). There is, for example, huge unexploited potential for the use of biodiversity, particularly with the possible medicinal and industrial uses of much of the variety of life remaining unexplored. This potential should be valued, and may be vital as the problems faced by humanity change in nature and magnitude. Option value may include the knowledge (of practical or heuristic significance) embodied in organisms, in as much as the loss of a species represents the loss of information (Morowitz 1991).

4.4.2 Bequest value

Closely related, but distinct from option value, is bequest value. This is the value of passing on a resource, in this case biodiversity, intact (or as near as possible) to future generations (Krutilla 1967). The philosopher John Locke suggested that each generation should bequeath 'enough and as good for others' to future generations not just because they should, but because justice demands it. The modern version of this is the slightly more elaborated 'justice as opportunity' view that says we should compensate our children in the future for the loss of wealth, production or ecosystem services for which the present generation is responsible.

This notion is embodied in the final section of the Preamble to the Convention on Biological Diversity, which states that contracting parties are 'determined to conserve and sustainably use biological diversity for the benefit of present and future generations'.

4.4.3 Existence value

All of the values of biodiversity considered thus far in this chapter have been based, in one way or another, on marketable commodities and non-market goods and services. They assume that value is expressed solely in terms of the wellbeing of humanity. However, biodiversity may equally be seen as having value to people irrespective of the uses to which it may or may not be put. That is, value may be placed simply on its existence. For example, the continued persistence in the wild of many species of large-bodied mammals, such as the giant panda *Ailuropoda melanoleuca*, tiger *Panthera tigris* and killer whale *Orcinus orca*, is valued by sectors of the human population, despite the fact that these species are unlikely ever actually to be seen by many of these individuals. Indeed, substantial sums of money are contributed by them towards maintaining populations of such species. Wilson (1984) believes that humankind recognizes and has empathy with other bearers of life ('biophilia'), and that this naturally predisposes them to an appropriate care of, and for, biodiversity in all its multifaceted forms.

4.4.4 Intrinsic value

Direct- and indirect-use values, and option, bequest and existence non-use values rest on human judgements of worth. Whether from a philosophical perspective values can exist independently of such judgements is a contentious issue; however if they can, then biodiversity may be seen to have an intrinsic value. The view that such a value exists seems to be deeply rooted in many societies, cultures and faiths. Logically it leads to an absolute moral responsibility to protect other species, our only known living companions (deities aside) in the universe (Ehrlich & Wilson 1991). Indeed, the notion of an intrinsic value to biodiversity (or components thereof) is found in many regional and global treaties for conservation. The opening section of the Preamble to the Convention on Biological Diversity recognizes the 'intrinsic value of biological diversity and of the ecological, genetic, social, economic, scientific, educational, cultural, recreational and aesthetic values of biological diversity and its components'.

To some, listing intrinsic value first is a true reflection of its significance. Placing it last in this chapter is not intended to convey the converse message.

4.5 Summary

1 Direct-use values of biodiversity are concerned with the consumption or production of marketable commodities. These include food, medicine, use in biological control, industrial raw materials, recreational harvesting and ecotourism. Many present patterns of exploitation are not sustainable.

2 Indirect-use values of biodiversity are more difficult to quantify, not being subject to direct trading in the marketplace, but are nonetheless real and important, embracing the services provided by biodiversity which are crucial for human wellbeing.

3 It is not currently possible to build artificial systems that could provide us with the life-supporting systems that natural systems provide us 'for free'.

4 Ecosystem functioning increases from assemblages of very small to small numbers of species, with the effect diminishing as species numbers increase further, suggesting some degree of ecological equivalency amongst species.

5 Higher species richness increases both species redundancy and temporal resilience of ecosystem functioning, thereby increasing the reliability of that functioning.

6 Apart from present-day use values, biodiversity may have a variety of non-use values, including option value (for future use or non-use), bequest value (in passing on a resource to future generations), existence value (value to people irrespective of use or non-use) and intrinsic value (inherent worth, independent of that placed upon it by people).

Further reading

Barbier, E.B., Burgess, J.C. & Folke, C. (1994) *Paradise Lost? The Ecological Economics of Biodiversity*. Earthscan, London. (*An important topic that we scarcely touch upon.*)

Beattie, A. & Ehrlich, P. (2001) *Wild Solutions: How Biodiversity is Money in the Bank*. Yale University Press, New Haven, CT. (*A fascinating exploration of both the services that biodiversity provides, and the solutions it may harbour for many practical problems faced by humankind. Lots of great examples.*)

Berry, R.J. (ed.) (2000) *The Care of Creation. Focusing Concern and Action*. Inter-Varsity Press, Nottingham. (*Christian response to the environmental crisis for Christians and non-Christians alike.*)

Daily, G.C. (ed.) (1997) *Nature's Services: Societal Dependence on Natural Ecosystems*. Island Press, Washington, DC. (*A landmark text.*)

Johnson, N.C., Malk, A.J., Szaro, R.C. & Sexton, W.T. (eds.) (1999) *Ecological Stewardship. A Common Reference for Ecosystem Management*, Vol. 1. *Key Findings*. Elsevier Science, Oxford. (*Together with its two sister volumes – this first volume is the summary of the other two – this constitutes an impressive and authoritative overview of both the science and practice of ecosystem management. A number of key management themes are covered: changing public perception and values, social, economic, legal and cultural dimensions, the role of people as agents of ecological change and the ecological implications themselves.*)

Jones, C.G. & Lawton, J.H. (eds.) (1995) *Linking Species and Ecosystems*. Chapman & Hall, London. (*The time has come to break down the barriers between these fields of study, and this is a major assault.*)

Kinzig, A.P., Pacala, S.W. & Tilman, D. (eds.) (2001) *The Functional Consequences of Biodiversity: Empirical Progress and Theoretical Extensions*. Princeton University Press, Princeton, NJ. (*An important review of the relationship between biodiversity and ecosystem functioning.*)

Kolstad, C.D. (2000) *Environmental Economics*. Oxford University Press, Oxford. (*One of the first textbooks devoted exclusively to environmental economics, with some good real-life examples.*)

Loreau, M., Naeem, S. & Inchausti, P. (eds.) (2002) *Biodiversity and Ecosystem Functioning: Synthesis and Perspectives*. Oxford University Press, Oxford. (*Another significant review of the relationship between biodiversity and ecosystem functioning.*)

Orians, G.H., Brown, G.M., Kunin, W.E. & Swierbinski, J.E. (eds.) (1990) *The Preservation and Valuation of Biological Resources*. University of Washington Press, Seattle, WA. (*Good on valuation of biodiversity, including genetic resources.*)

O'Riordan, T. & Stoll-Kleeman, S. (eds.) (2002) *Biodiversity, Sustainability and Human Communities*. Cambridge University Press, Cambridge. (*Advocates that the protection of biodiversity is only really successful with involvement of, and co-operation with, the local communities involved.*)

Pearce, D. (1998) *Economics and Environment. Essays on Ecological Economics and Sustainable Development*. Edward Elgar, London. (*Interesting, engaging and provocative view of environmental economics, even if you will not always agree with the views expressed.*)

Pearce, D.W. & Moran, D. (1994) *The Economic Value of Biological Diversity*. Earthscan, London. (*A clear and readable account of how cost–benefit analysis techniques might be applied to problems of species loss and even to estimating the efficiency of conservation efforts.*)

Samson, P.R. & Pitt, D. (1999) *The Biosphere and Noosphere Reader: Global Environment, Society and Change*. Routledge, London. (*Gaia, social evolution, deep ecology, environmental change – this book has it all.*)

Schulze, E-D. & Mooney, H.A. (eds.) (1993) *Biodiversity and Ecosystem Function*. Springer-Verlag, Berlin. (*A landmark volume in this area, but already being overtaken by events?*)

Sexton, W.T., Malk, A.J., Szaro, R.C. & Johnson, N.C. (1999) *Ecological Stewardship. A Common Reference for Ecosystem Management*, Vol. 3. *Public Expectations, Values and Law; Social and Cultural Dimensions; Economic Dimensions; Information and Data Management*. Elsevier Science, Oxford. (*See Johnson et al. 1999.*)

Suzuki, D. (1999) *The Sacred Balance: Rediscovering Our Place in Nature*. Bantam, London. (*Ethics for life and the ecological crisis, by a famous geneticist.*)

Szaro, R.C., Johnson, N.C., Sexton, W.T. & Malk, A.J. (1999) *Ecological Stewardship. A Common Reference for Ecosystem Management*, Vol. 2. *Biological and Ecological Dimensions; Humans as Agents of Ecological Change*. Elsevier Science, Oxford. (*See Johnson et al. 1999.*)

Wilson, E.O. (1984) *Biophilia*. Harvard University Press, Cambridge, MA. (*The exposition of an important idea.*)

Wilson, E.O. & Peter, F.M. (eds.) (1988) *BioDiversity*. National Academy Press, Washington, DC. (*Many contributions address issues of use and value.*)

5 | Human impacts

5.1 Introduction

Although it is essential to humankind, brings innumerable benefits, and has other important values, humans have had strong negative impacts on biodiversity. Indeed, whilst over geological time the general trend has been towards an overall net increase in biodiversity, the late Quaternary has been a period of marked decline, as both a direct and indirect consequence of human activities. This decline comprises all those changes that are associated with reducing or simplifying biological heterogeneity, from genes to ecosystems.

In this chapter we consider the negative human impacts on biodiversity, concentrating particularly on the loss of species. First, we address the level of those losses (Sections 5.2 & 5.3). Second, we examine the four principal proximate causes of the losses, namely overexploitation, habitat loss and degradation, introduced species, and extinction cascades (Section 5.4). Third, we consider the ultimate causes of the impacts of humans on biodiversity, namely the size of the human population, the growth in that population, and the scale of the human enterprise (Section 5.5).

5.2 Species extinctions

The best-known and most widely discussed impact of human activities on biodiversity has been that of the extinction of species. The loss of species seems to capture the public imagination, perhaps because of its irreversibility and the extraordinary nature of some of those species that have met their demise. In addition, species extinctions constitute the obvious, as well as a genuinely useful, barometer of change in biodiversity when this is measured in terms of species richness.

5.2.1 Prehistoric times

The impacts of humankind on other species have lasted for a long time, probably for much of the 100,000–200,000 years for which anatomically modern humans have existed. Although there remains some important debate on the issue, early humans may well have contributed significantly to the extinction of many large-bodied species of birds and mammals, and perhaps other groups, during the late Pleistocene (by some 10,000 years before the present (BP), all the major land masses except Antarctica had been colonized, some for a considerable period, and humans were exerting significant environmental effects). Apparently, broadly coincident with the arrival of humans in different major land masses, much of the megafauna disappeared, suggesting that they were either hunted to extinction (or perhaps close to the brink, with other factors finally tipping them over) or were brought to extinction by anthropogenic ecosystem disruption (Martin 1984, 2001; MacPhee 1999; Miller et al. 1999; Flannery 2001; R.G. Roberts et al. 2001; but see Grayson 2001; Brook & Bowman 2002). Doubtless, these extinctions were accompanied by many others, of which we remain unaware because of the inadequacies of the subfossil record.

The effects of early human activities on the biota are perhaps most graphically demonstrated by the large numbers of avian (and some other) extinctions that followed the colonization of tropical Pacific islands by prehistoric peoples, an expansion that began perhaps 30,000 years BP and was almost complete by 1000 years BP. The combined effects of resource exploitation, deforestation and the introduction of alien species led to roughly half the land bird species on each island group being exterminated (Milberg & Tyrberg 1993; Pimm et al. 1995b; Steadman 1995). The proportion of the avifauna on selected Pacific island groups that has recently become extinct, or is now endangered or in immediate danger of extinction, is less where human occupancy has been longest. This suggests that those areas colonized first have already lost most of the species that are sensitive to human activities (Fig. 5.1), although the time-lapse between human arrival and major extinction events was highly variable on oceanic islands (Steadman et al. 2002). A conservative estimate may be that an average of 10 sea- or land bird species or populations were lost from each of the approximately 800 islands of Oceania alone, giving an overall loss of 8000 species or populations (Steadman 1995). With one to

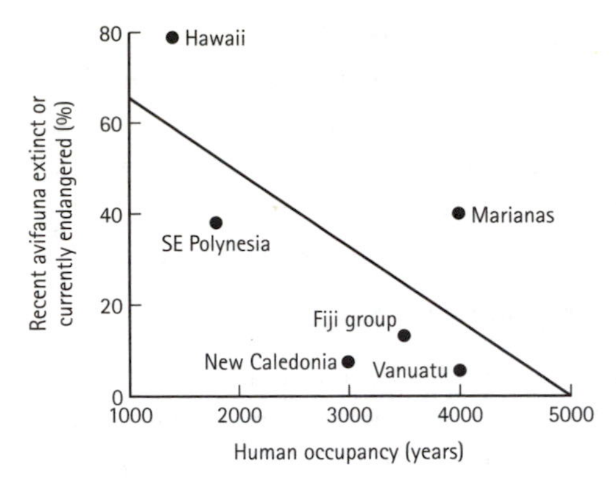

Fig. 5.1 Relationship between the percentage of the recent avifauna of Pacific islands that is extinct or currently endangered and the duration of human occupancy of those islands. The Marianas have an unusually high number of modern losses, as a result of recent colonization by the brown tree snake. (From Pimm et al. 1995b.)

four endemic rail species per island, 2000 species of rails may have been lost alone, which contrasts with the 133 extant species, a number of which are regarded as being highly threatened. It is not difficult to conceive that globally, perhaps a half of all recent bird species have already been driven extinct, at least in part as a consequence of human activities.

It is difficult to comprehend how differently the biota of Earth would have looked when all of these species were still extant. The diversity that we now find so impressive is, at least in terms of the vertebrates that attract so much attention, but a pale shadow of what it would have been without the losses that early humans directly and indirectly wrought. Some of these extinct species, and those which have subsequently been lost, doubtless contributed much to the shaping of environments and the communities associated with them, begging the question of what would truly natural assemblages have looked like? Whether terrestrial or marine, big animals, for example, may consume large quantities of vegetation or large numbers of smaller animals, and may physically disturb the habitat in profound ways. In terrestrial systems many of these big animals have been lost, and in marine ones they are now often 'ecologically extinct' (e.g. species of large sharks and rays, turtles, manatees and dugongs), in as much as their numbers have been reduced to the point where they no longer have major ecological impacts (Jackson & Sala 2001; Jackson et al. 2001).

5.2.2 1600 onwards

Species losses did not end when the primary phase of human colonization of the planet was largely complete. Since 1600 (a date after which the availability of contemporary information improves markedly) there have been over 1000 recorded extinctions of plant and animal species (see Table 5.1 for numbers in some groups). Roughly a half of these took place in the last century. There has been a significant rise in the rate of recorded

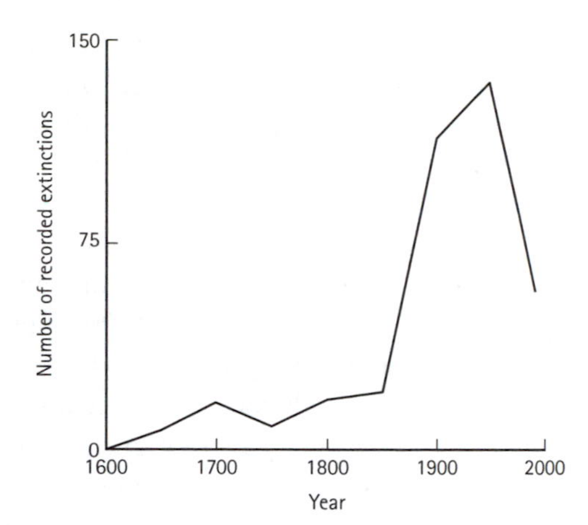

Fig. 5.2 The number of recorded global extinctions of animal species since c. 1600, for which a date is known. (From Smith et al. 1993.)

species extinctions for well-known groups of animals over the past 400 years, with a sharp increase in the 19th century coinciding with European colonial expansion (Fig. 5.2). A global decline in the recorded rate since about 1950 may perhaps in part reflect the growth of conservation activities, but more likely is due to the introduction of more stringent criteria for deciding that a species is genuinely extinct (rather than that it has simply gone unrecorded). For example, the present IUCN (The World Conservation Union) (1994) criteria define a species as extinct 'when there is no reasonable doubt that the last individual has died' and as extinct in the wild when the species is 'known only to survive in cultivation, in captivity or as a naturalised population (or populations) well outside the past range. A taxon is presumed extinct in the wild when exhaustive surveys in known and/or expected habitat, at appropriate times (diurnal, seasonal, annual) throughout its historic range have failed to record an individual'. Thus considerable time and effort is required to substantiate an extinction, particularly where the potential habitat for a species is extensive or difficult to access.

Interesting as the data on recorded extinctions may be, they undoubtedly underestimate the true levels of species losses. There are several reasons for believing this to be so.

1 Available information on extinctions is strongly biased towards higher plants, birds and mammals, which have been better studied, and away from groups such as fungi, lower plants and invertebrates, which have been more poorly studied. For example, most extant species of birds and mammals have host-specific lice and fleas, and probably in many cases also specific microbial symbionts. Thus, presumably the extinction of every avian and mammalian species has been accompanied by the loss of at least one other species. However, these so-called coextinctions have tended to pass undocumented (Stork & Lyal 1993), and despite the recognition of 128 bird and 83 mammal species extinctions, the IUCN

2000 Red List (Hilton-Taylor 2000) includes no extinct lice or flea species. Whilst different taxa may genuinely have suffered rather different recent rates of extinction, the wide disparities that are observed in numbers of recorded extinctions represent an artefactual distortion (McKinney 1999).

2 Available information on extinctions is strongly biased towards islands (71.6% of mammalian species extinctions since 1500 are for island species; MacPhee & Flemming 1999) and developed nations. In both cases this is in part because such extinctions have been easier to document, given the high levels of endemism commonly associated with islands and the longer period of formal study of the biotas of developed nations. It is also because island biotas may be more vulnerable to processes that drive extinctions (in the face of threatening processes, island endemic species may have no refuges), and the biotas of developed nations tend to be relatively species poor and to have experienced the consequences of that human development (extant species may simply be those that were more resilient to extinction).

3 Available information on extinctions is strongly biased towards terrestrial and freshwater species, and away from marine ones. Few marine species have been documented as having been lost. On the one hand, the paucity of documented extinctions of marine species could be because they are genuinely less likely to become extinct, perhaps because of the greater contiguity of the oceans compared with the continents and the resultant larger geographic ranges of marine species. On the other hand, this could be because extinctions in the oceans are hard to document. Both explanations are probably true, as evidenced by the longer average duration of marine species in the fossil record compared with terrestrial ones (McKinney 1998).

4 It is almost invariably assumed that a described species is extant unless sufficient evidence is accrued to show that it is extinct. Museum collections, for example, contain specimens of many species that have not been seen since they were originally collected or at least for a number of decades, and yet because no active search has been made to find them it is assumed that they are extant. Presumably, many of these have actually been lost, given that often the original habitat in the areas they were collected has entirely disappeared. Diamond (1987) observed that at that time (doubtless things have changed a little since), if one followed the assumption 'extant unless proven extinct' then one bird species has recently gone extinct in the Solomon Islands, but if one followed the assumption 'extinct unless proven extant' then up to 12 species may be extinct or endangered, with the latter figure likely to be closer to the real one.

5 Unless a species is known to science, then its extinction will pass unrecorded. Because the majority have remained undescribed (Section

2.4) and much severe habitat loss has taken place in regions for which biological inventories were previously poorly developed, then it follows that many particularly localized species may have become extinct without us being aware even of their existence (Hughes et al. 1997; Prance et al. 2000).

5.2.3 The future

Merely recording numbers of extinctions that have thus far occurred may underestimate the effects of past human activity on species losses, through a process known as extinction debt. Individuals of large-bodied species, for example, may persist after the populations to which they belong have ceased to be viable (they can no longer be self-sustaining), because they are long-lived. The species is effectively extinct; it just doesn't know it yet! Brooks and Balmford (1996) document an example of extinction debt in the Atlantic forests of South America. Here, whilst nearly 90% of the forest has been cleared, no bird species has so far been shown to have become extinct as a result, contrary to the predictions of species–area relationships (Section 3.2.1). However, the number of species presently recognized as being highly threatened with extinction is similar to that predicted to become extinct from deforestation. It would seem that without immediate conservation action these species will inevitably soon be lost.

More generally, information on the numbers of species that have been listed as being threatened with global extinction in the near future provides one of the bases for estimating the scale of impending extinctions (although given the time required for sufficient evidence of extinction to accumulate, some of these species are certainly already extinct). The most recent figures for plants and animals are given in Table 5.1. These are again highly biased, and in much the same ways as are those of recorded extinctions. Only for birds and mammals has the threat status of virtually all extant species been evaluated. In the former case, more than 10% of species have been identified as at threat of global extinction; in the latter case, about 25% have been recognized as such. An estimate for plants has suggested that as many as a half of extant species may qualify as threatened with extinction were it possible to evaluate them (Pitman & Jørgensen 2002).

As discussed earlier (Section 2.3.3), the average life span of any species in the fossil record is estimated to be around 5–10 Myr. For birds and mammals, rates of documented extinction over the past century correspond to species life spans of around 10,000 years (May et al. 1995). Although the calculations are inevitably very rough and ready, projection of impending extinctions, if current trends continue, suggest a life span for bird and mammal species of 200–400 years! These figures may

Table 5.1 Summary of the numbers of species in each of the plant and animal taxonomic classes which are listed as extinct, extinct in the wild (the species has been extirpated from its natural habitat), or globally threatened with extinction. (Adapted from Hilton-Taylor 2000.)

	Extinct	Extinct in the wild	Threatened
Plants			
Bryopsida	2	0	36
Anthocerotopsida	0	0	2
Marchantiopsida	1	0	42
Coniferopsida	0	1	140
Ginkgoopsida	0	0	1
Magnoliopsida	69	14	5099
Liliopsida	1	2	291
Total	**73**	**17**	**5611**
Animals			
Anthozoa	0	0	2
Turbellaria	1	0	0
Enopla	0	0	2
Gastropoda	260	12	846
Bivalvia	31	0	92
Polychaeta	0	0	1
Oligochaeta	0	0	5
Hirudinoidea	0	0	0
Onychophora	3	0	6
Merostomata	0	0	0
Insecta	72	1	555
Crustacea	8	1	408
Chilopoda	0	0	1
Arachnida	0	0	10
Echinoidea	0	0	0
Sarcopterygii	0	0	1
Actinopterygii	80	11	709
Elasmobranchii	0	0	39
Cephalaspidomorphi	1	0	3
Amphibia	5	0	146
Reptilia	21	1	296
Aves	128	3	1183
Mammalia	83	4	1130
Total	**693**	**33**	**5435**

perhaps be regarded as representative of a broad range of organisms, in which case impending extinction rates are at least three to four orders of magnitude faster than background rates seen in the fossil record. To put this into perspective, consider the following analogy (modified from Dunning 1997). Human death rates in populations not subject to war or famine are often in the range of 10–20 deaths per 1000 individuals per annum (in a stable population, average life span = 1/death rate, so this equates to life spans of 50–100 years). If that rate were increased by 1000 times, then everyone would die in the first year.

By comparison with most of those species that have been driven extinct or to the brink of extinction, *Homo sapiens* is a rather recent addition to the Earth. Species that have existed for millions of years are being erased by one that has existed for a fraction of that time.

5.3 Populations, individuals and genetic diversity

The listing of a species as having a significant risk of extinction in the near future is commonly associated with it having suffered a decline in population or geographic range size. In other words, it has undergone a loss of local populations, a decline in the numbers of individuals in remaining populations, or both. Such losses and declines are being experienced by huge numbers of species, whether these are sufficient for them to be listed as threatened by global extinction or not. For example, amphibian population declines are a global problem, with causes that may include ultraviolet radiation, predation, habitat modification, environmental acidity and toxicants, diseases, changes in climate or weather patterns, and interactions among these factors (Alford & Richards 1999; Houlahan et al. 2000). Concerns have similarly been expressed about declines in the abundances of species in a wide range of groups, such as trees (Oldfield et al. 1998), sharks (Manire & Gruber 1990) and birds (Terborgh 1989). Hughes et al. (1997) estimate that in tropical forests, 1800 populations may be being destroyed per hour, 16 million annually. Gaston and Blackburn (2003) estimate that land-use change alone may have caused the overall global bird population to decline by a fifth to a quarter from pre-agricultural levels.

The extinction of individual local populations and declines in species' local abundances both represent potentially insidious forms of erosion of biodiversity (Ehrlich & Daily 1993; Ehrlich 1995; Ceballos & Ehrlich 2002). Population losses, in particular, will tend to reduce the taxonomic, genetic and functional diversity of sites (see Table 1.1), and perhaps the performance of ecosystems (Section 4.3), without initially necessarily contributing to the global species extinctions that attract the bulk of attention.

5.4 Threats to biodiversity

Species losses, and other declines in biodiversity, result from four main causes, namely: (i) direct exploitation; (ii) habitat loss and degradation; (iii) introduced species; and (iv) extinction cascades. These have been termed 'the evil quartet' (Diamond 1984). Whilst reasonably well characterized, the patterns and rates at which these drivers are changing are less well understood.

5.4.1 Direct exploitation

The most obvious way in which humans can cause the extinction of species is by exploiting their populations, either down to the last individual or down to such low numbers that they have a very high likelihood of becoming extinct by chance. The scale of human exploitation of some species is incredibly high, and is not sustainable. Here we give three examples.

1 *Bush meat*. Hunting of wildlife in tropical forests, principally for subsistence or commerce, is ubiquitous (Redford 1992). Indeed, for many species it is difficult to ascertain what their natural abundances would be in the absence of such pressure, because places without the pressure do not exist. For example, 9.6–23.5 million reptiles, birds and mammals, or 67–165 thousand tonnes, have been estimated to be consumed per annum in the Brazilian Amazon (Peres 2000). Demand is increasing as tropical forests become more accessible to hunters, effective human population densities increase, people become more sedentary, traditional hunting practices change, the meat trade becomes more commercial, and demand increases from urban centres for wild meat (Robinson & Bodmer 1999). The use of mathematical models demonstrates that this harvest is not sustainable, particularly because of the low annual production rates of large mammals in tropical forests. Fa et al. (2002) estimate that the mammal production rates in the Congo Basin and the Amazon Basin are about 2.1 and 1.8 million tonnes per year, with extraction rates being 4.9 and 0.15 million tonnes per year respectively. This means that Congo Basin mammals must annually produce 93% of their body mass to balance current extraction rates, whereas Amazonian mammals must produce only 4%. 2 *Fuelwood*. More than 2 billion people (about a third of the present total) are estimated to depend directly for their primary or sole source of energy on biomass fuels, including woodfuels (fuelwood, charcoal, etc.), agricultural residues, and animal wastes (United Nations Development Programme et al. 2000). Of these, fuelwood is the dominant form of biomass energy in many, predominantly developing, countries. Supplies have decreased significantly in many areas in recent decades, with members of some communities having to travel substantial distances to obtain material. Although globally this has to some degree been offset by pro-

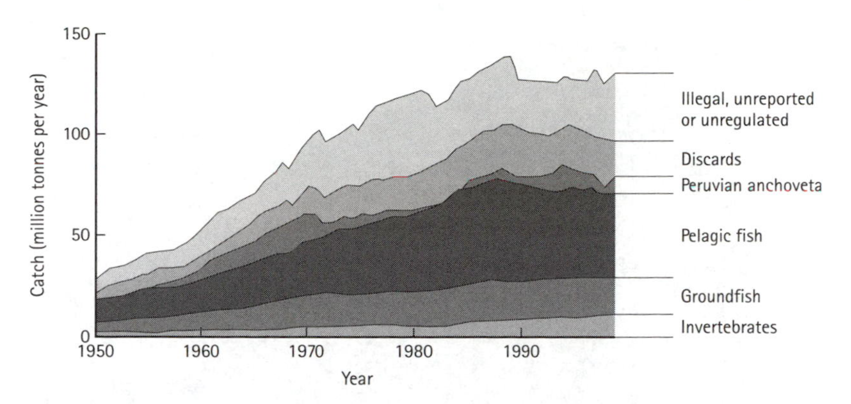

Fig. 5.3 Estimated global fish landings for 1950–99. (Note that the estimates for illegal, unreported or unregulated fish landings are very tentative.) (From Pauly et al. 2002.)

grammes of tree planting, woodfuel demand by 2010 is forecast to be 2.4–4.3 billion m^3 compared with an estimated availability of 2.3–2.4 billion m^3 of fuelwood and charcoal combined.

3 *Marine fisheries*. The 1950s and 1960s saw a huge increase in global fishing effort, fuelled in large part by its industrialization, which gave rise to rapid increases in catches (Fig. 5.3). The first major stock collapse was that of the Peruvian anchoveta *Engraulis ringens* in 1971–72, which was accompanied by declining catches elsewhere, which accelerated in the late 1980s and early 1990s when cod *Gadus morhua* stocks off New England and eastern Canada collapsed (Pauly et al. 2002). Global fishing effort, nonetheless, continued to expand, such that by the mid-1990s a high proportion of stocks had collapsed or were being exploited beyond sustainability (Fig. 5.4). Reported world fisheries landings have been declining slowly since the late 1980s by about 0.7 million tonnes per annum (Watson & Pauly 2001; Pauly et al. 2002). Fisheries have increasingly been 'fishing down marine food webs', as large long-lived predatory fish have been removed and those at lower trophic levels exploited (Pauly et al. 1998). They have changed the evolutionary characteristics of populations through size-selective harvesting (Conover & Munch 2002) and have placed the future persistence of some target species at risk (Hilton-Taylor 2000). Evidence suggests that although the effects of overfishing may be reversible, the time for stocks to recover may be considerable (Hutchings 2000). With declines of fisheries stocks in shallow waters, increasing emphasis has been directed towards deep-water fisheries, which are even less robust to such impacts (Roberts 2002). In addition to those on the stocks of target species, fishing has wider impacts, through: (i) the wholesale reorganization of the structure of remaining species assemblages as trophic interactions are disturbed; (ii) the huge amounts of by-catch of non-target species that are typically simply discarded (by-catch is

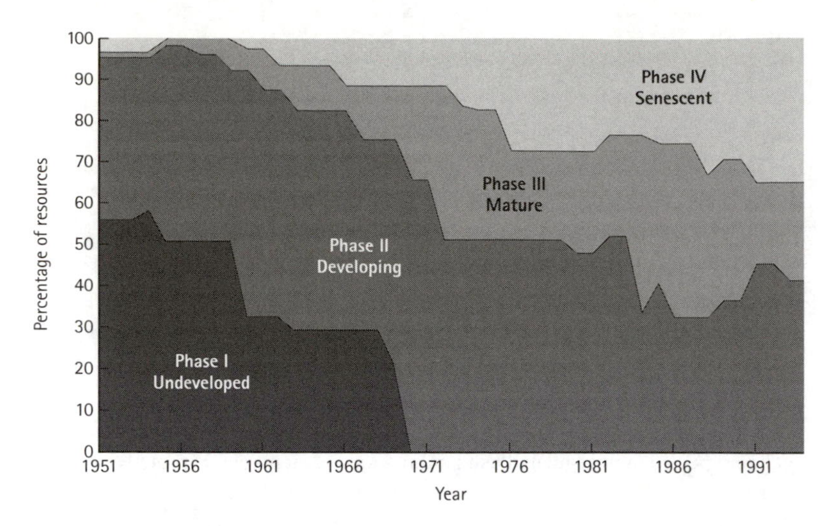

Fig. 5.4 Percentage of major marine fish resources in various phases of fishery development. In 1994 (the last data point shown), about 35% of the 200 major fishery resources were 'senescent' (showing declining yields), about 25% were 'mature' (plateauing at a high exploitation level), 40% were 'developing', and none remained undeveloped (at a low exploitation level). (From Grainger & Garcia 1996.)

in excess of 25 million tonnes per annum); (iii) the incidental capture and killing of other species (including seabirds, turtles, sea snakes, marine mammals, many of which are particularly vulnerable because they are long-lived and have low reproductive rates); (iv) the habitat destruction generated by some of the techniques employed (e.g. bottom-trawling); and (v) the environmental consequences of fishing debris (e.g. lost nets; Dayton et al. 1995).

Perhaps above all, the history of human exploitation of resources teaches us that the populations of even initially extremely abundant species can be reduced to low levels remarkably rapidly, and that the ease with which this can be achieved has grown with the march of technology. Unfortunately, in the short-term, from a strictly economic standpoint ('knowing the cost of everything and the value of nothing'?), non-sustainable use can in some cases still be regarded as a viable option. For example, from this perspective, the best harvesting strategy for biological populations with relatively low growth rates (e.g. whales) may be to exploit them to extinction. The revenue generated by this harvest when invested could conceivably yield a greater cash return than that generated by the sustainable harvest from the population (Clark 1981; Lande et al. 1994; May 1994c). Of course, this ignores both the direct- and indirect-use value (which may both be vital to sustain human populations) and the non-use value of biological resources, both in the short- and the long-term (we cannot conceive of the value that the continued existence of particular species may have in the future).

5.4.2 Habitat loss, fragmentation and degradation

Dramatic reshaping of the distribution of habitats or vegetation types has been a feature of much of the history of humankind, with habitat change as a consequence of the activities of prehistoric populations having been reported on numerous occasions (McGlone 1983; Kershaw 1986; McGlone & Basher 1995; Diamond 1998; Krech 1999; Pudjoarinto & Cushing 2001). Indeed, it has repeatedly been discovered that what had been held to be 'natural' landscapes had actually been much transformed by earlier human activities (for discussion see e.g. Isenberg 2000; Wilcove 2000).

At a broad scale, compared with an estimation of their extent before significant human disturbance, forest/woodland has declined in area by 29%, steppe/savannah/grassland by 49%, shrubland by 74%, and tundra/hot desert/ice desert by 14% (Fig. 5.5; Klein Goldewijk 2001). Cropland now covers 11% of the land surface, and pasture 23%. Human disturbance is evident in every biome on Earth, and in terrestrial systems is most marked in temperate broadleaf and evergreen sclerophyllous forests (< 6.5% relatively undisturbed; Table 5.2). Perhaps some of the most graphic evidence of such changes comes from contrasting the extent of the most speciose terrestrial environment, tropical forest, at different times, in particular areas of the world (Fig. 5.6). Most such forest clearance arises from pressures that are external to the ecosystem, particularly an undervaluing of the forest resource that encourages liquidation of the

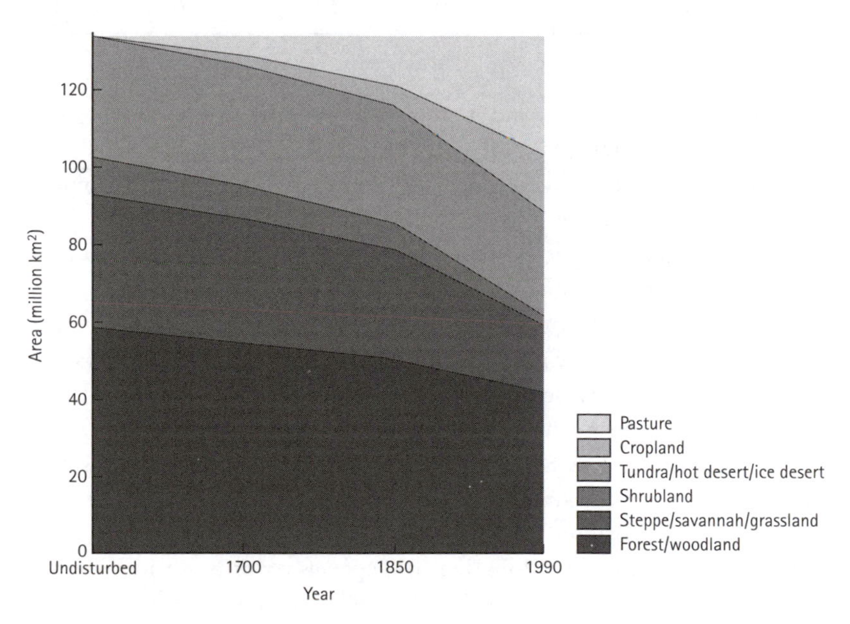

Fig. 5.5 Changes in the area of different land-use types from before significant human impact ('undisturbed') to the present. (Data from Klein Goldewijk 2001.)

Table 5.2 The pattern of human disturbance amongst biomes. Undisturbed areas have a record of primary vegetation and no evidence of disturbance, combined with a very low human population density. Partially disturbed areas have a record of shifting or extensive agriculture, evidence of secondary vegetation, livestock over carrying capacity or other evidence of human disturbance. Human dominated areas have a record of permanent agriculture or urban settlement, removal of primary vegetation or record of desertification or other permanent degradation. (From Hannah et al. 1995.)

Biome	Total area (km^2)	Percentage of undisturbed areas	Percentage of partially disturbed areas	Percentage of human dominated areas
Temperate broadleaf forests	9,519,442	6.1	12.0	81.9
Evergreen sclerophyllous forests	6,559,728	6.4	25.8	67.8
Temperate grasslands	12,074,494	27.6	32.0	40.4
Subtropical and temperate rain forests	4,232,299	33.0	20.9	46.1
Tropical dry forests	19,456,659	30.5	41.1	28.4
Mixed mountain systems	12,133,746	29.3	45.0	25.6
Mixed island systems	3,256,096	46.6	11.6	41.8
Cold deserts/semi-deserts	10,930,762	45.4	46.1	8.5
Warm deserts/semi-deserts	29,242,021	55.8	32.0	12.2
Tropical humid forests	11,812,012	63.2	11.9	24.9
Tropical grasslands	4,797,090	74.0	21.3	4.7
Temperate needleleaf forests	18,830,709	81.7	6.4	11.8
Tundra and Arctic desert	20,637,953	99.3	0.7	0.3

natural capital it provides and its replacement with agricultural systems that yield quicker returns (Noble & Dirzo 1997). This situation is acute in regions where immediate needs predominate, and future income is discounted at a high rate.

As predicted from species–area relationships (Section 3.2.1), land-use changes have brought about the loss of many species, and are the primary cause of species being listed as at high risk of extinction in the near future. Thus, globally 71% of freshwater fish species (excluding Lake Victoria cichlids, because of the complexity of their situation) that have recently become extinct have apparently done so for this reason (Harrison & Stiassny 1999), and 85% of bird and 47% of mammal species (not including most of the small mammals, because of insufficient data) are listed as being at risk on the same grounds (BirdLife International 2000; Mace & Balmford 2000). More than 100 species of birds are at threat as a result, at least in part, of each of 13 causes of habitat loss: selective logging/cutting, smallholder farming, plantations, clear-felling, arable farming/horticulture, livestock farming, infrastructure development, human

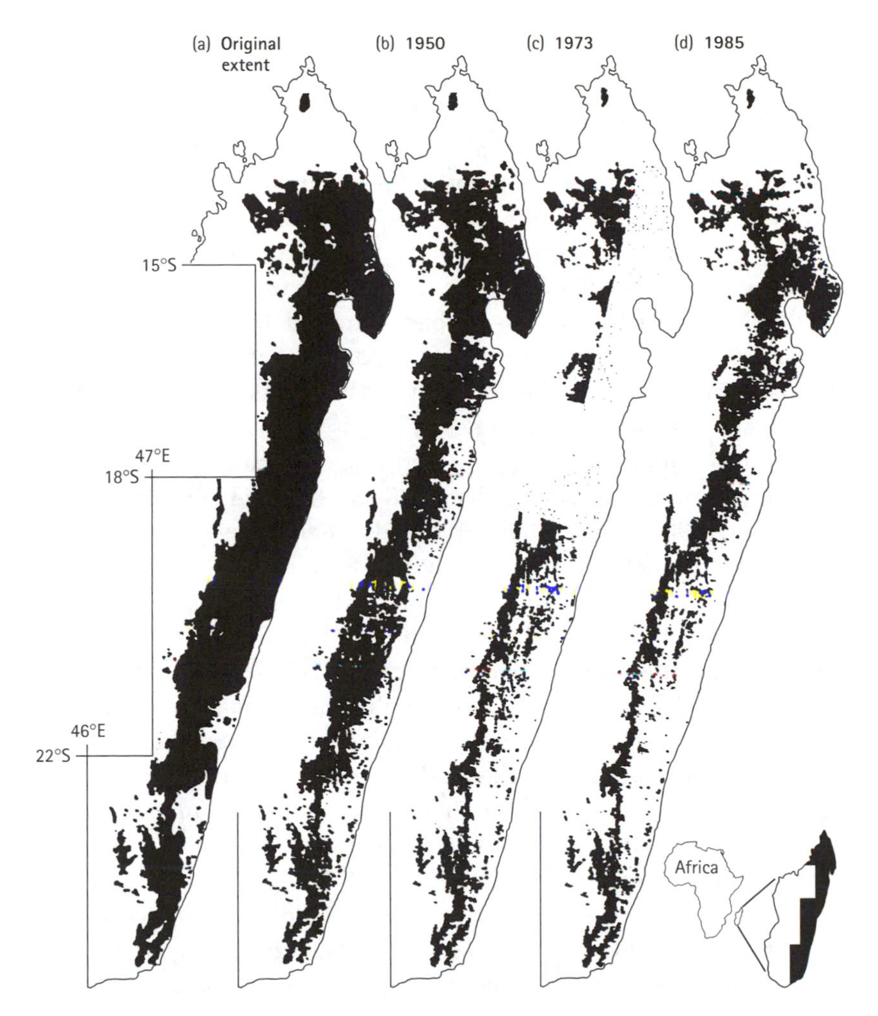

Fig. 5.6 Maps of the distribution of wet tropical forest in eastern Madagascar through time (extensive cloud cover permitted only partial mapping in 1973). The original cover of 11.2 million ha was reduced to 7.6 million ha by 1950, and to 3.8 million ha by 1985 (34% of the original). (From Green & Sussman 1990.)

settlement, grazing, shifting agriculture, deforestation with unknown causes, timber (firewood), and mining (BirdLife International 2000).

Substantial land-use change is predicted to continue into the future, not simply as a consequence of direct human activities, but also as a consequence of anthropogenic global climate change. The global average surface temperature has increased by approximately 0.6°C over the past 100 years, with most of the warming occurring during two periods, 1910–45 and 1976–2000 (Houghton et al. 2001). This temperature is projected to increase by from 1.4°C to 5.8°C over the period 1990–2100, based on a number of climate models, a rate much higher than observed during the 20th century and likely to be without precedent during at least the last 10,000 years (Houghton et al. 2001).

In large part, these changes result because human activities add carbon dioxide (CO_2) to the atmosphere by mining and burning fossil fuels, and by converting forests and grasslands to agricultural and other low biomass ecosystems (Vitousek et al. 1997a). Carbon dioxide is the principal 'greenhouse gas', although others make a contribution, including methane (CH_4), the chlorofluorocarbons (CFCs), ozone (O_3) and nitrous oxide (N_2O). Analysis of air bubbles extracted from ice cores from Antarctica and Greenland reveal that the atmospheric concentration of CO_2 was more or less stable for thousands of years, until about 1800, since when it has increased exponentially.

The distributions of a large number of species currently seem to be shifting in response to climate change (Kozár & Dávid 1986; Frey 1992; Parmesan 1996; Cannon 1998; Hill et al. 1999; Parmesan et al. 1999; Thomas & Lennon 1999; Burton 2001; McLaughlin et al. 2002), and many more are predicted to do so in the future (e.g. Beerling 1993; Huntley 1994; Brereton et al. 1995; Jeffree & Jeffree 1996; Nakano et al. 1996; Rogers & Randolph 2000). Other responses to climate change are also being documented. Thus, although there is regional variation, common shifts in phenology in Europe and North America include earlier breeding or first singing of birds, earlier arrival of migrant birds, earlier appearance of butterflies, earlier choruses and spawning in amphibians, and earlier shooting and flowering of plants (Walther et al. 2002; Root et al. 2003 and references therein).

Many of the changes that humans are making to the landscape involve not simply the reduction of the areas of some vegetation types and the expansion of others, but also the fragmentation of vegetation. This generates a landscape consisting of (often small) remnant areas of native vegetation embedded in a matrix of agricultural and developed land. Fragmentation results in change in the physical environment within patches (e.g. in fluxes of radiation, water and nutrients), in part because the size of areas of vegetation influences local climate, and because of the greater ratio of edge to area for smaller patches of vegetation which increases the potential for penetration by, and influence from, events and processes in the surrounding landscape. Changes in edge to area ratios may also increase pressure from invasive species, and other direct (e.g. hunting) and indirect (e.g. pollution) consequences of human activities. In addition, fragmentation causes biogeographic changes (e.g. in isolation and connectivity), which like its other consequences may be important influences on the size and composition of the biotas of the remnant patches (Saunders et al. 1991).

As well as changes in the pattern of coverage of different vegetation types, those areas that remain may for other reasons be degraded in terms

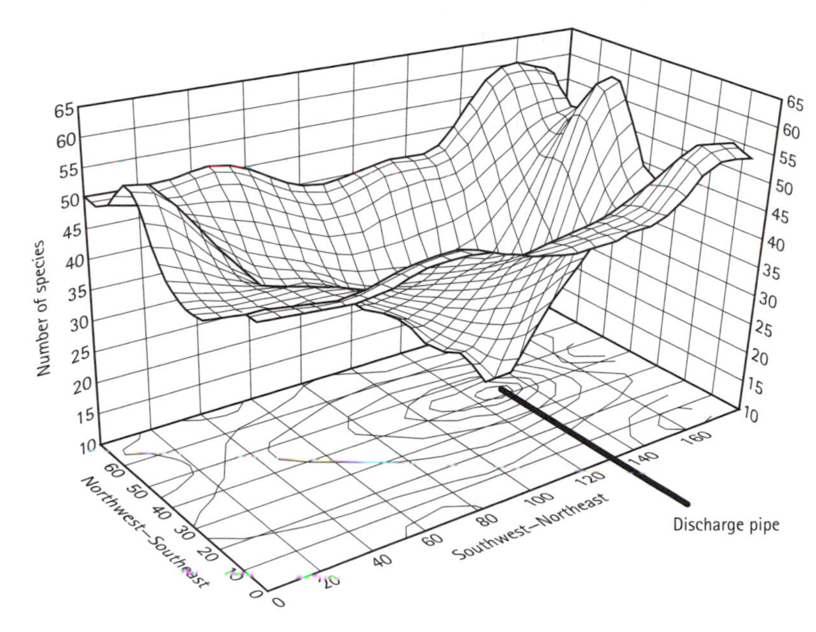

Fig. 5.7 A three-dimensional plot showing the depression of the numbers of microscopic sediment-dwelling species of meiofauna associated with an industrial effluent discharged to the outer reaches of a British estuary. The area shown is approximately 1.7 × 1.7 km. (From Anon. 1994.)

of their capacity to support populations of naturally occurring species (Fig. 5.7). That degradation may take many forms, including changes in the occurrence and abundance of many materials. For example, human activity has markedly altered the global nitrogen cycle, by fixing N_2 (combining it with carbon, hydrogen or oxygen), either deliberately (for fertilizer) or as a by-product of other actions (fossil fuel combustion). Now this activity adds at least as much fixed N to terrestrial ecosystems as do all natural sources combined (Vitousek et al. 1997a). The consequences include increasing atmospheric concentrations of the greenhouse gas N_2O, increasing fluxes of reactive N gases, contribution to acid rain and photochemical smog, increases in productivity of ecosystems where fixed N was in short supply resulting in losses of N and cations from soil, eutrophication of aquatic systems, and loss of biodiversity.

The sheer pervasiveness of such influences is well illustrated by the spread of materials that do not occur naturally. For example, brominated flame retardants are used in electronic equipment, such as computers and television sets, in textiles, cars and many other applications. They have been found to be present in sperm whales *Physeter macrocephalus* that normally stay and feed in deep water, suggesting that these compounds have reached these locations (de Boer et al. 1998).

Table 5.3 The numbers of native and established alien vascular plant species in selected continental and island floras. (Adapted from Vitousek et al. 1997b.)

Region	Native species	Alien species	Percentage of alien species
Russian Arctic	1403	104	6.9
Europe	11,820	721	5.7
USA	17,300	2100	10.8
Southern Africa	20,573	824	3.9
Australia	15,638	1952	11.1
British Isles	1225	945	42.9
Hawaii	1143	891	43.8
New Zealand	2449	1623	39.9

5.4.3 Introduced species

Since prehistoric times, human actions have served, intentionally or accidentally, to introduce non-domesticated species to areas in which they would not naturally have occurred, breaching many natural barriers to their dispersal. Ignoring domesticated species, the earliest known instance involves the introduction of a marsupial, the gray cuscus *Phalanger orientalis*, to New Ireland about 19,000 years ago (Grayson 2001). Perhaps some 400,000 species have now been introduced (Pimentel 2001). Often these constitute a high proportion of the species that occur in a given area (Table 5.3), and they continue to grow in number (Fig. 5.8). Introduced species are now widespread even in many nature reserves (e.g. Lonsdale 1999; Stadler et al. 2000; Pyšek et al. 2002; Sax 2002).

Such movements of species have been brought about by a multiplicity of routes, including intentional introduction for cultivation or sport, the transport of soil and ballast, the connection of waterways through canals, and the release or escape of pets. They reflect our choices as consumers, travellers, gardeners, and so on (Baskin 2002). Not infrequently, the numbers of introduced species in an area increase with the size of the human population, the duration of human occupation, and the numbers of visitors, all of which tend to increase the levels of such activities, and hence the likelihood and frequency with which individuals of given species arrive (Rapoport 1993; Chown et al. 1998; Lonsdale 1999; McKinney 2001). The numbers of introduced species in an area tend also commonly to be positively related to the number of native species, probably because the successful establishment of species of both groups responds to similar factors (e.g. Pyšek et al. 2002; Sax 2002).

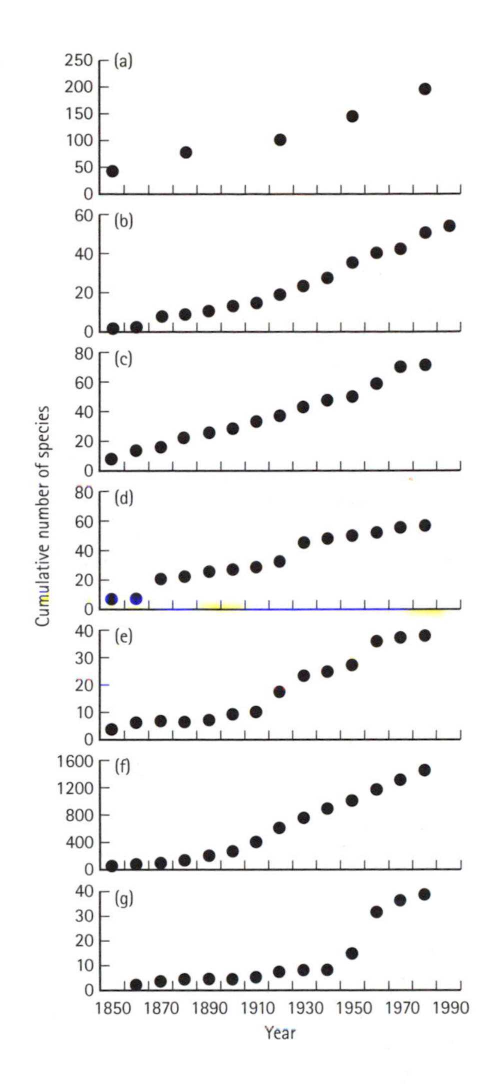

Fig. 5.8 Cumulative numbers of introduced species by decade of introduction for: (a) Illinois plants; (b) Great Lakes animals; (c) Great Lakes plants; (d) San Francisco Bay invertebrates; (e) Hawaiian birds; (f) North American insects; and (g) USA fish. (From Ruesink et al. 1995.)

Some introductions have enriched human existence and most invaders have minor consequences; Williamson (1996) suggests that as a useful rule of thumb, 10% of introduced invaders become established, and 10% of those established become pests. Unfortunately, the negative effects can be very large, and introductions have been described as constituting 'one of the great historical convulsions in the world's fauna and flora' (Elton 1958, p. 31). Introduced species can alter nutrient regimes, fire regimes, hydrology, or energy budgets, change vegetation or habitat, and drive changes in the abundance and distribution of native species, ultimately to extinction (Williamson 1996). Drawn from a wide diversity of groups (Table 5.4), they have thus become major agents of global change. Nearly a half of the threatened species of the USA, for example, are at risk at least in part because of the effects of alien species (Wilcove et al. 1998).

Table 5.4 One hundred of the world's worst invasive alien species. These were chosen according to their adverse effects on biodiversity and/or human activities and their illustration of important issues surrounding biological invasion. (From Baskin 2002.)

Disease agents	
Avian malaria	*Plasmodium relictum*
Banana bunchy top	Banana bunchy top virus
Chestnut blight	*Cryphonectria parasitica*
Crayfish plague	*Aphanomyces astaci*
Dutch elm disease	*Ophiostoma ulmi*
Frog chytrid fungus	*Batrachochytrium dendrobatidis*
Phytophthora root rot	*Phytophthora cinnamomi*
Rinderpest	Paramyxovirus
Aquatic plants	
Caulerpa seaweed	*Caulerpa taxifolia*
Common cordgrass	*Spartina anglica*
Wakame seaweed	*Undaria pinnatifida*
Water hyacinth	*Eichhornia crassipes*
Land plants	
African tulip tree	*Spathodea campanulata*
Black wattle	*Acacia mearnsii*
Brazilian pepper tree	*Schinus terebinthifolius*
Chromolaena (Siam weed, triffid weed)	*Chromolaena odorata*
Cluster pine	*Pinus pinaster*
Cogon grass	*Imperata cylindrica*
Fire tree	*Myrica faya*
Giant reed	*Arundo donax*
Gorse	*Ulex europaeus*
Hiptage	*Hiptage benghalensis*
Japanese knotweed	*Polygonum cuspidatum*
Kahili ginger	*Hedychium gardnerianum*
Koster's curse	*Clidemia hirta*
Kudzu	*Pueraria lobata*
Lantana	*Lantana camara*
Leafy spurge	*Euphorbia esula*
Leucaena	*Leucaena leucocephala*
Melaleuca	*Melaleuca quinquenervia*
Mesquite	*Prosopis glandulosa*
Miconia	*Miconia calvescens*
Mile-a-minute weed	*Mikania micrantha*
Mimosa (giant sensitive plant)	*Mimosa pigra*
Prickly pear cactus	*Opuntia stricta*
Privet	*Ligustrum robustum*
Pumpwood	*Cecropia peltata*
Purple loosestrife	*Lythrum salicaria*
Quinine	*Cinchona pubescens*
Shoebutton ardisia	*Ardisia elliptica*
Strawberry guava	*Psidium cattleianum*
Tamarisk (saltcedar, Athel pine)	*Tamarix ramosissima*

(cont'd)

Table 5.4 *(cont'd)*

Wedelia (Singapore daisy)	*Wedelia trilobata*
Yellow Himalayan raspberry	*Rubus ellipticus*
Aquatic invertebrates	
Chinese mitten crab	*Eriocheir sinensis*
Comb jelly	*Mnemiopsis leidyi*
Green crab	*Carcinus maenas*
Marine clam	*Potamocorbula amurensis*
Mediterranean mussel	*Mytilus galloprovincialis*
Northern Pacific seastar	*Asterias amurensis*
Spiny water flea	*Cercopagis pengoi*
Zebra mussel	*Dreissena polymorpha*
Land invertebrates	
Argentine ant	*Linepithema humile*
Asian long-horned beetle	*Anoplophora glabripennis*
Asian tiger mosquito	*Aedes albopictus*
Big-headed ant	*Pheidole megacephala*
Common wasp	*Vespula vulgaris*
Crazy ant	*Anoplolepis gracilipes*
Cypress aphid	*Cinara cupressi*
Flatworm	*Platydemus manokwari*
Formosan subterranean termite	*Coptotermes formosanus shiraki*
Giant African snail	*Achatine fulica*
Golden apple snail	*Pomacea canaliculata*
Gypsy moth (Asian and European)	*Lymantria dispar*
Khapra beetle	*Trogoderma granarium*
Little fire ant	*Wasmannia auropunctata*
Malaria mosquito	*Anopheles quadrimaculatus*
Red imported (tropical) fire ant	*Solenopsis invicta*
Rosy wolf snail	*Euglandina rosea*
Sweet potato whitefly	*Bemisia tabaci*
Amphibians	
Bullfrog	*Rana catesbeiana*
Cane toad	*Bufo marinus*
Caribbean tree frog	*Eleutherodactylus coqui*
Fish	
Brown trout	*Salmo trutta*
Common carp	*Cyprinus carpio*
Large-mouth bass	*Micropterus salmoides*
Mosquito fish	*Gambusia affinis*
Mozambique tilapia	*Oreochromis mossambicus*
Nile perch	*Lates niloticus*
Rainbow trout	*Oncorhynchus mykiss*
Walking catfish	*Clarias batrachus*
Reptiles	
Brown tree snake	*Boiga irregularis*
Red-eared slider turtle	*Trachemys scripta*

(cont'd on p. 128)

Table 5.4 *(cont'd)*

Birds	
Indian myna	*Acridotheres tristis*
Red-whiskered bulbul	*Pycnonotus cafer*
Starling	*Sturnus vulgaris*
Mammals	
Black or ship rat	*Rattus rattus*
Brushtail possum	*Trichosurus vulpecula*
Cat	*Felis catus*
Crab-eating macaque monkey	*Macaca fascicularis*
European rabbit	*Oryctolagus cuniculus*
Fox	*Vulpes vulpes*
Goat	*Capra hircus*
Gray squirrel	*Sciurus carolinensis*
Mouse	*Mus musculus*
Nutria (coypu)	*Myocastor coypus*
Pig	*Sus scrofa*
Red deer	*Cervus elaphus*
Small Indian mongoose	*Herpestes auropunctatus*
Stoat	*Mustela erminea*

Introduced species have most frequently caused species extinctions through predation/parasitism. Perhaps some of the best-documented examples have concerned the introduction of exotic predators to lakes and islands and the consequent extinction of plants and animals that had evolved no defences against them. Thus, numbers of species of fish, many endemic, from the lakes of the East African Rift Valley may be extinct as a result of the intentional introduction of the Nile perch *Lates niloticus*, a voracious predator (although other factors have also contributed; Harrison & Stiassny 1999 and references therein). Likewise, the accidental introduction of the brown tree snake *Boiga irregularis* to the island of Guam around 1950 resulted, directly or indirectly, in the loss of perhaps 12 species of an original fauna of 22 native birds (three pelagic species and perhaps nine forest ones, some endemic to the island), the reduction of most of the remaining forest species to small remnant populations, and the loss of 3–5 species of an original fauna of 10–12 reptiles (Fritts & Rodda 1998). In both cases, the catholic tastes of the generalist predators involved has been important, enabling them to maintain high abundances even when one of their prey species has been driven scarce.

The potential for introduced species to predate native species highlights the need for great caution in employing biological control of pest species (Section 4.2.3). Whilst this can be exceedingly beneficial in economic terms, potential biological control agents need to be very carefully screened to ensure that they will not have negative impacts on other species. A growing number of cases have been documented in which sufficient caution has not been exercised (Simberloff & Stiling 1996; Henneman & Memmott 2001; Louda & O'Brien 2002).

Introduced species may also cause species extinctions, at least locally, through competition. Thus, the introduction of some ant species, such as the red fire ant *Solenopsis invicta*, the Argentine ant *Linepithema humile*, and the big-headed ant *Pheidole megacephala*, has often caused dramatic reductions in native ant assemblages through aggressive interactions (e.g. Holway 1999; Mack et al. 2000). Likewise, the tropical alga *Caulerpa taxifolia* spread dramatically around the coastline of the Mediterranean, carpeting large areas and excluding many other species (Meinesz 1999).

The economic costs of introductions may be vast. Pimentel et al. (2000) estimate that the approximately 50,000 non-indigenous species in the USA alone result in economic damage and control estimated at US$137 billion per annum.

The net effect of species extinctions and of the introduction of species into areas in which they would not naturally occur is to homogenize biotas across the globe, making them more similar to one another (Lockwood & McKinney 2001); in the extreme we would be left with biota comprising pests and weeds. For example, on average, pairs of states in the continental USA now have 15.4 more fish in common than before European settlement of North America (Rahel 2000).

5.4.4 Extinction cascades

The extinction of one species may lead to the extinction of others. Indeed, this is inevitable where this species provides critical resources for others, such as specialist herbivores, parasites or predators, or perhaps itself acts as a specialist pollinator or dispersal agent. Thus, for example, in New Zealand, the giant eagle *Harpagornis moorei* almost certainly preyed on the large flightless moas, and its extinction likely resulted when these declined in numbers as a result of the hunting by the Maori that led to their demise (Cassels 1984; Worthy 1997; Holdaway 1999; Holdaway & Jacomb 2000). More complex sets of interactions may also result in cascades of extinctions, as evidenced by the dramatic, and often extensive, changes in floral and faunal composition that can result from changes in the abundance and occurrence of key species (e.g. large-bodied predators and herbivores; Terborgh 1988; Owen-Smith 1989; Crooks & Soulé 1999; Jackson 2001; Terborgh et al. 2001). For example, the loss of large-bodied predator species may be accompanied by meso-predator release, in which somewhat smaller predators escape the population controls that were previously imposed on them, and as a result they exert increased predation pressure on their prey species, reducing their abundance and perhaps driving them locally or even globally extinct.

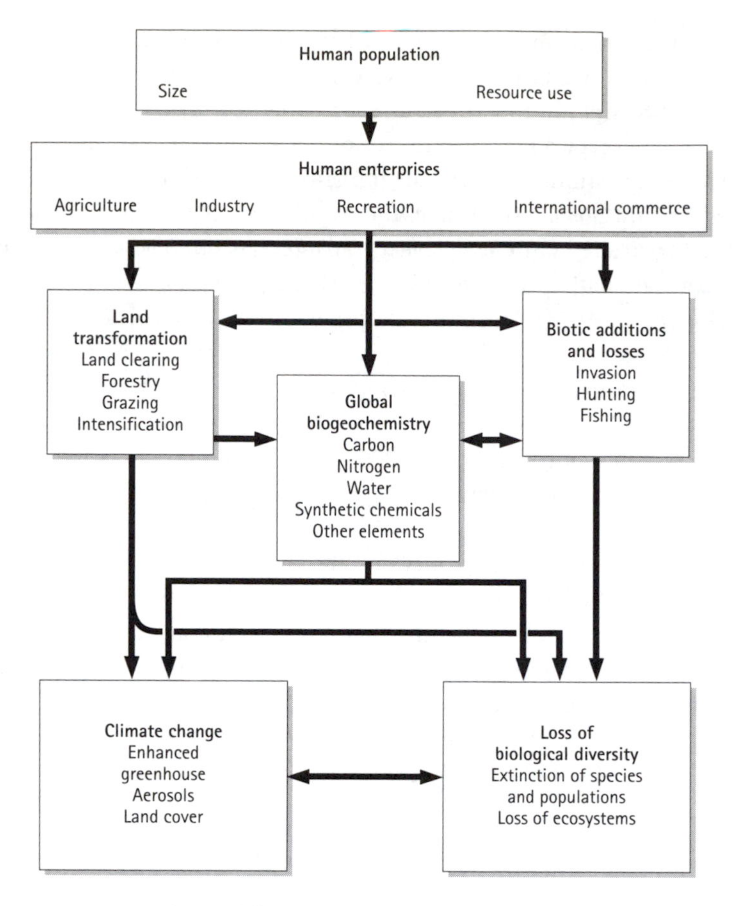

Fig. 5.9 A conceptual model illustrating humanity's direct and indirect effects on the Earth system. (From Vitousek et al. 1997a.)

5.5 The scale of the human enterprise

In some sense all of the above causes of species extinction and threat to biodiversity are proximate. The ultimate causes concern the size of the human population, growth in that population, and what has been termed the scale of the human enterprise (Fig. 5.9; Ehrlich 1995). The facts are stark.

1 *Population size and growth*. The world's human population is estimated to have reached a total of about 6.1 billion individuals in mid-2000. This compares to figures for the other great apes, our closest relatives, of 10,000–25,000 for the bonobo *Pan paniscus*, 100,000–150,000 for the chimpanzee *Pan troglodytes*, 40,000–65,000 for the gorilla *Gorilla gorilla*, and about 38,500 for the orang-utan *Pongo pygmaeus* (Cincotta & Engelman 2000).

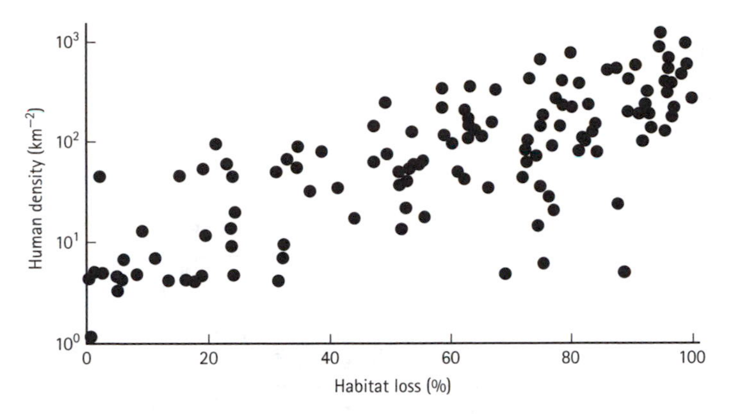

Fig. 5.10 Relationship between human population density and habitat loss for forest ecoregions of the Indo-Pacific. (From Wikramanayake et al. 2002.)

Generally, at a crude spatial resolution, there seems to be a marked positive correlation between the numbers of species found in an area and human density. Balmford et al. (2001) have shown this for sub-Saharan Africa, and it seems to occur because both species numbers and numbers of people show similar relationships with primary productivity, finding similar kinds of areas good for multiplication. Indeed, the human population is distributed such that more than 1.1 billion individuals live within the 25 global biodiversity hotspots (see Section 3.3.3), which constitute some of the most important and threatened areas for other forms of life (Cincotta & Engelman 2000; Cincotta et al. 2000). The density of people in these hotspots is about 73 per km^2, compared with a global average of 42 per km^2.

Levels of habitat loss in areas are commonly correlated with the numbers of people, even at relatively coarse spatial resolutions (Fig. 5.10), but the conflict between people and biodiversity becomes more obvious at finer spatial resolutions (here, of course, positive relationships between numbers of people and species richness tend rapidly to break down – highly urbanized areas may have few native species). Thus, the number of previously native scarce plant species that have not been recorded from areas of Britain since 1970 is an increasing function of the human population density of those areas (Thompson & Jones 1999), and the occurrence and persistence of a number of large-bodied vertebrate species declines with human population density, even when these species are in protected areas and this density is measured in the surrounding areas (Figs. 5.11 & 5.12; Hoare & du Toit 1999; Woodroffe 2000; Parks & Harcourt 2002; Walsh et al. 2003).

The extent of such conflicts will, of course, almost inevitably grow. The human population is currently increasing at an annual rate of 1.2% (about

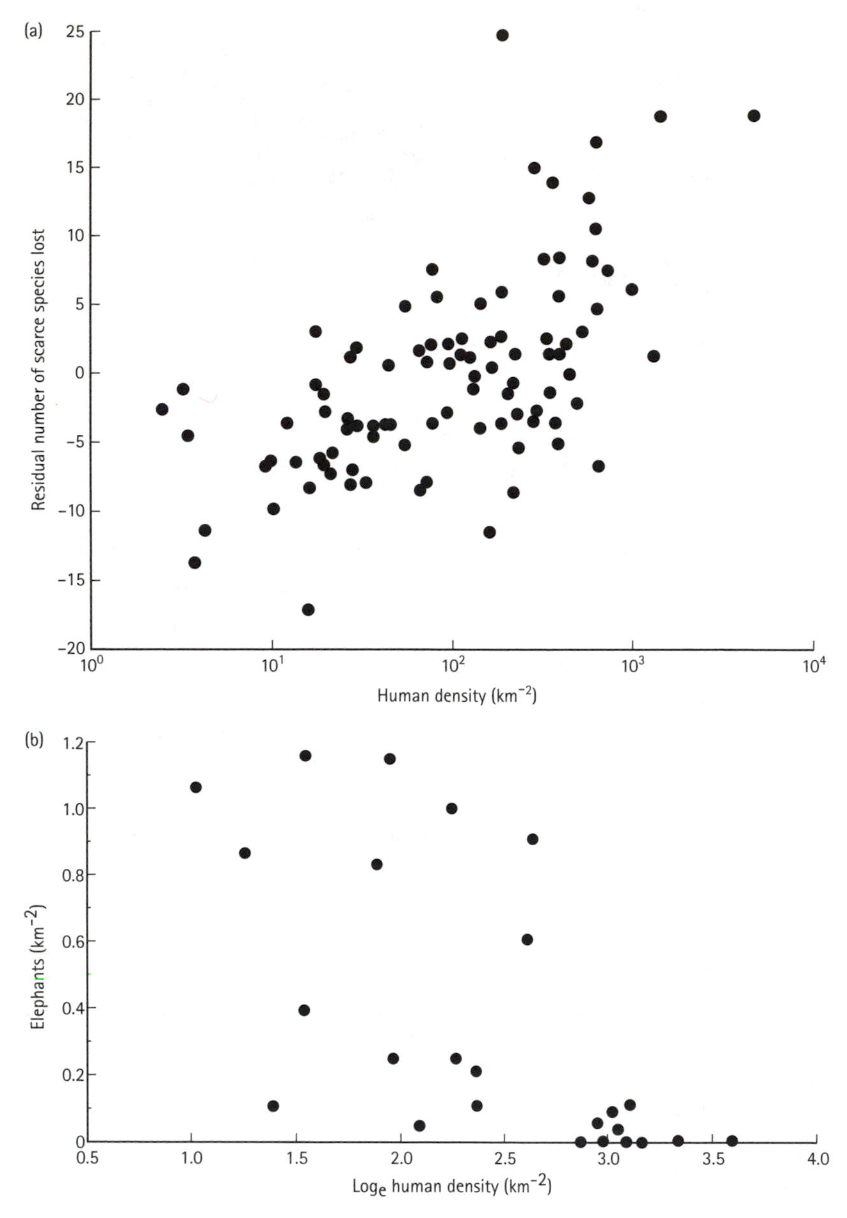

Fig. 5.11 Relationships between human density and: (a) number of scarce plant species lost, after the effects of the original number are corrected for, for vice counties (small geopolitical units) in Britain; and (b) number of elephants for 25 wildlife wards in the Sebungwe region, Zimbabwe. (a, From Thompson & Jones 1999; b, from Hoare & du Toit 1999.)

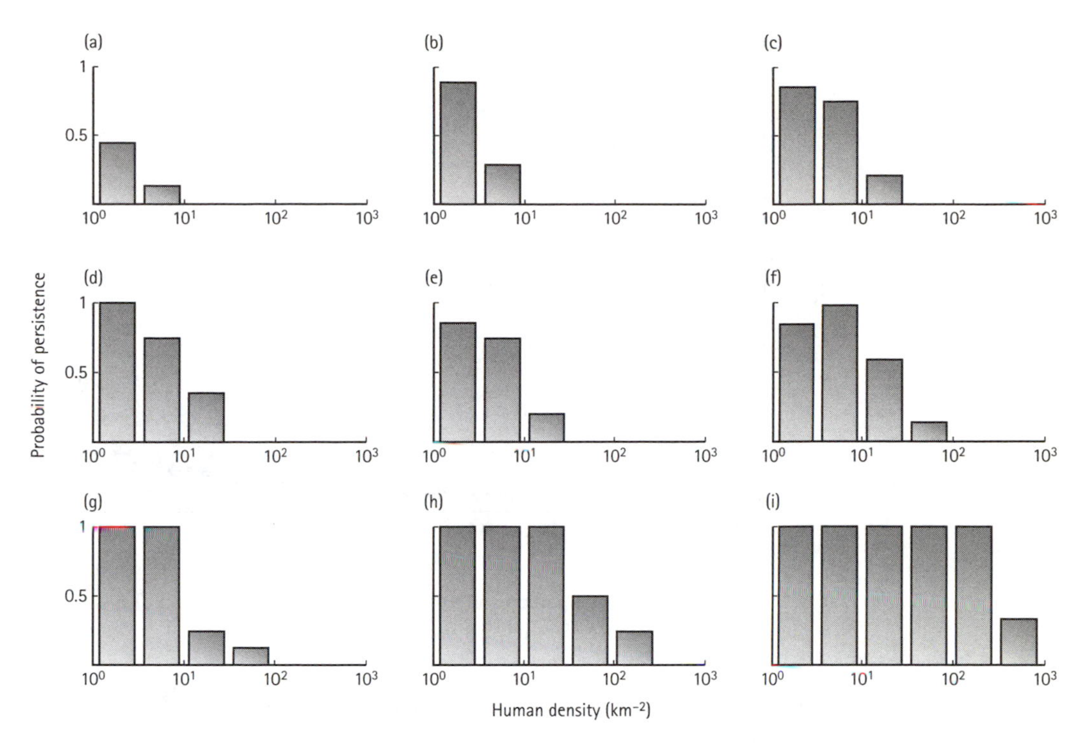

Fig. 5.12 Relationships between human density and probability of persistence for: (a) African wild dog in Southern Africa; (b) grizzly bear in USA; (c) African wild dog in Kenya; (d) mountain lion in USA; (e) wolf in USA; (f) cheetah in Kenya; (g) jaguar in Brazil; (h) spotted hyaena in Kenya; and (i) leopard in Kenya. (From Woodroffe 2000.)

80 million people annually, or nearly a quarter of a million people each day), and by 2050 is expected to be between 7.9 billion and 10.9 billion, with a medium variant of predictions of 9.3 billion (United Nations 2001). Population growth has been slow for most of human existence but over the past 200 years the rate has increased dramatically (Fig. 5.13). In 19 of the global biodiversity hotspots, the human population is growing more rapidly than it is globally, and in most of the hotspots located in developing countries it is projected to grow for several more decades (Cincotta et al. 2000).

The interaction between human population growth and species extinction may perhaps be epitomized by silphion *Ferula historica*, a herb in the carrot family (Riddle & Estes 1992; Cincotta & Engelman 2000). It once grew in abundance in the hills near Cyrene on the coast of what is now Libya, and was apparently highly valued as an antifertility drug in the classical world, in effect an oral contraceptive. It became one of the principal commodities of Cyrene's trade, and became very valuable. Indeed, coupled with the failure of attempts to cultivate the plant, its

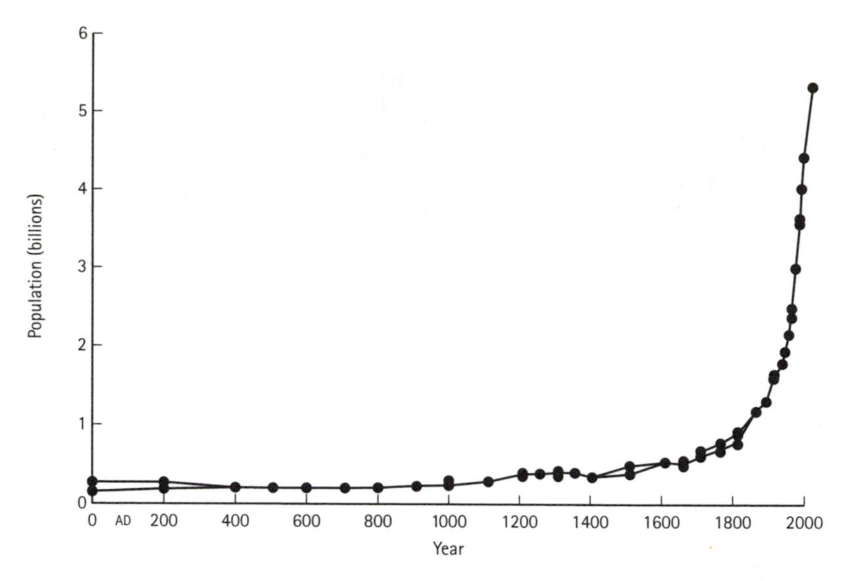

Fig. 5.13 Estimated human population from AD 1 to the present. Different lines represent estimates from different sources. (From Cohen 1995.)

value was such that it was overharvested, and in the 2nd or 3rd centuries AD, it disappeared.

2 *Primary production*. Humans use, co-opt or destroy approximately 35–40% of all potential terrestrial net primary productivity (the net accumulation of organic carbon resulting from the surplus of fixation over respiration; Vitousek et al. 1986; Pimm 2001; but see Rojstaczer et al. 2001 for discussion of the uncertainties in such estimates). The equivalent figure for aquatic systems is 8% of primary production, but with the proportion for nearshore and freshwater systems being much higher and close to that for terrestrial systems (Pauly & Christiansen 1995).

3 *Energy use*. Ehrlich (1995) estimates that from before the agricultural revolution to the present time, total power consumption by humanity multiplied roughly 7000–13,000-fold, from 0.001–0.002 terawatts (1 TW $= 10^{12}$ watts) to 13 TW. Global commercial energy production in 1993 reached 338 exajoules (1 exajoule $= 10^{18}$ joules, or about 163 million barrels of oil), 40% greater than in 1973. Total energy consumption rose to 326 exajoules, 49% greater than 20 years before (World Resources Institute 1996).

4 *Water*. Humanity uses more than a quarter of the 69,600 $km^3\ yr^{-1}$ of terrestrial evapotranspiration and more than a half of the 12,500 $km^3\ yr^{-1}$ of runoff that is geographically and temporally accessible (Postel et al. 1996). Of global water use, 42% is attributable to agriculture and 14% to industry. Freshwater is scarce in many regions, increasing ecological degradation, limiting production of agriculture and industry, impacting on human health, and increasing international tensions.

5 *Global economy*. For many decades global increases in consumption have outpaced increases in the human population. For 1980–97, the global economy nearly tripled to some US$29 trillion, although over the same period the population only increased by a third (United Nations Development Programme et al. 2000). Per capita consumption levels are rising in many nations as their economies develop.

It is inconceivable that an enterprise of this scale would not have major detrimental impacts on biodiversity.

5.6 Summary

1 Biodiversity loss, as epitomized by species extinctions, has been taking place as a consequence of human activities for a long time, initially associated with the colonization of some areas of the world by prehistoric peoples.
2 Since 1600 there have been over 1000 recorded extinctions of plant and animal species.
3 Impending extinction rates are estimated to be orders of magnitude greater than the background rates seen in the fossil record.
4 The principal proximate causes of biodiversity loss are: (i) direct exploitation; (ii) habitat loss, degradation and fragmentation; (iii) the effects of introduced species; and (iv) extinction cascades.
5 The ultimate causes of biodiversity loss concern the size of the human population, the rate of human population growth and the scale of the human enterprise.

Further reading

Baskin, Y. (2002) *A Plague of Rats and Rubbervines: The Growing Threat of Species Invasions*. Island Press, Washington, DC. (*A popular account of the invasions problem.*)

BirdLife International (2000) *Threatened Birds of the World*. Lynx Edicions and BirdLife International, Barcelona & Cambridge. (*The authority on the lamentable state of the global avifauna.*)

Brown, L.R. (2001) *State of the World 2001*. Earthscan, London. (*More applied and environmental slant than the WRI book (United Nations Development Programme et al. 2000) covering the same period.*)

Caughley, G. & Gunn, A. (1996) *Conservation in Theory and Practice*. Blackwell Science, Oxford. (*Includes a useful set of case studies of the decline or extinction of particular species.*)

Cincotta, R.P. & Engelman, R. (2000) *Nature's Place: Human Population and the Future of Biological Diversity*. Population Action International, Washington, DC. (*An interesting analysis of the relationship between biodiversity hotspots and human population.*)

Cohen, J.E. (1995) *How Many People can the Earth Support?* Norton, New York. (*Everything you wanted to know about the human population, and much that you had never thought to ask.*)

Committee on Recently Extinct Organisms. http://creo.amnh.org/. (*Lots of good information on extinctions in recent times.*)

di Castri, F. & Balajii, V. (eds.) (2002) *Tourism, Biodiversity and Information*. Backhuys Publishers, Leiden. (*A lot of interesting information – particularly if you travel a lot.*)

Ehrlich, P. (1997) *A World of Wounds: Ecologists and the Human Dilemma*. Ecology Institute, Oldendorf/Luhe. (*If you don't understand why you should do anything to help maintain biodiversity, read this book.*)

Flannery, T. & Schouten, P. (2001) *A Gap in Nature: Discovering the World's Extinct Animals*. William Heinemann, London. (*Beautiful paintings of many recently extinct species.*)

Fuller, E. (2000) *Extinct Birds*. Oxford University Press, Oxford. (*A fascinating compendium of what is known about recently extinct species of birds.*)

Fuller, E. (2002) *Dodo: From Extinction to Icon*. Collins, London. (*The story of a truly enigmatic species.*)

Hansen, K. (2002) *A Farewell to Greenland's Wildlife*. BæreDygtighed, Klippinge, Denmark. (*A remarkable account of the extermination of the wildlife of Greenland through senseless overexploitation.*)

Hilton-Taylor, C. (comp.) (2000) *2000 IUCN Red List of Threatened Species*. IUCN, Gland. [Also available at http://www.redlist.org] (*The Red List – discover the perilous state of species you thought safe, and others you have never heard of.*)

Houghton, J.T., Ding, Y., Griggs, D.J., Noguer, M., van der Linden, P.J. & Xiaosu, D. (eds.) (2001) *Climate Change 2001: The Scientific Basis*. Cambridge University Press, Cambridge. (*Together with the other two volumes in this three-volume set, the definitive work on climate change.*)

Jennings, S., Kaiser, M.J. & Reynolds, J.D. (2001) *Marine Fisheries Ecology*. Blackwell Science, Oxford. (*An outstanding overview of fisheries exploitation, biology, conservation and management.*)

Kurlansky, M. (1997) *Cod: A Biography of the Fish that Changed the World*. Walker, New York. (*Perhaps not a promising title, until you have read a few pages. . . .*)

Lawton, J.H. & May, R.M. (eds.) (1995) *Extinction Rates*. Oxford University Press, Oxford. (*A landmark volume on extinction.*)

Leakey, R. & Lewin, R. (1996) *The Sixth Extinction: Biodiversity and its Survival*. Phoenix, London. (*Good basic introduction to many of the issues.*)

Levin, S.A. (2000) *Fragile Dominion: Complexity and the Commons*. Perseus Publishing, Cambridge, MA. (*One of the leading mathematical ecologists explains how the natural world is organized, and the consequences.*)

Lockwood, J.L. & McKinney, M.L. (eds.) (2001) *Biotic Homogenization: The Loss of Diversity through Invasion and Extinction*. Kluwer Academic/Plenum, New York. (*A mixed bunch, but includes some good contributions on an important topic.*)

Mackay, R. (2002) *The Atlas of Endangered Species*. Earthscan, London. (*Lots of maps and facts suitable for first-year undergraduates.*)

MacPhee, R.D.E. (ed.) (1999) *Extinctions in Near Time: Causes, Contexts, and Consequences*. Kluwer Academic/Plenum, New York. (*An important text, especially if you are interested in what the extant mammal fauna should look like.*)

McCarthy, J.J., Canziani, O.F., Leary, N.A., Dokken, D.J. & White, K.S. (eds.) (2001) *Climate Change 2001: Impacts, Adaptation, and Vulnerability*. Cambridge University Press, Cambridge. (*Together with the other two volumes in this three-volume set, the definitive work on climate change.*)

Meinesz, A. (1999) *Killer Algae: The True Tale of a Biological Invasion*. University of Chicago Press, Chicago, IL. (*A depressing story of government inaction and failure to prevent the spread of an aggressive introduced species.*)

Metz, B., Davidson, O., Swart, R. & Pan, J. (eds.) (2001) *Climate Change 2001: Mitigation*. Cambridge University Press, Cambridge. (*Together with the other two volumes in this three-volume set, the definitive work on climate change.*)

Moore, P.D., Chaloner, B. & Stott, P. (1996) *Global Environmental Change*. Blackwell Science, Oxford. (*A nice overview of lots of contentious topics.*)

Pimm, S.L. (2001) *The World According to Pimm: A Scientist Audits the Earth*. McGraw-Hill, New York. (*A fascinating, and very accessible, discussion of the scale of appropriation of productivity by humans and its implications.*)

Robinson, J.G. & Bennett, E.L. (eds.) (2000) *Hunting for Sustainability in Tropical Forests*. Columbia University Press, New York. (*Information on human hunting practices, the issues confronting conservationists and the use of tropical rain forests.*)

Safina, C. (1997) *Song for the Blue Ocean: Encounters along the World's Coasts and beneath the Seas*. Henry Holt, New York. (*A well-written, but depressing, account of the state of the oceans.*)

Terborgh, J. (1999) *Requiem for Nature*. Island Press, Washington, DC. (*A depressing lesson on the state of the natural world. Read it!*)

United Nations Development Programme, United Nations Environment Programme, World Bank & World Resources Institute (2000) *World Resources 2000–2001: People and Ecosystems: The Fraying Web of Life*. Elsevier Science, Amsterdam. (*A regular publication, providing valuable appraisals and data on the state of the environment.*)

United Nations Environment Programme (2002) *Global Environmental Outlook 3*. Earthscan, London. (*Comprehensive, but readable, evaluation of environmental trends over the past quarter century.*)

Van Driesche, J. & Van Driesche, R. (2000) *Nature Out of Place. Biological Invasions in the Global Age*. Island Press, Washington, DC. (*A moving although one-sided view of biological invasions.*)

Wilcove, D.S. (2000) *The Condor's Shadow: The Loss and Recovery of Wildlife in America*. Anchor Books, New York. (*You will never look at America the same way again.*)

Williamson, M. (1996) *Biological Invasions*. Chapman & Hall, London. (*Makes sense of a large and bewildering literature.*)

Wilson, E.O. (2002) *The Future of Life*. Little Brown, London. (*What is going to happen if we carry on as we are, and what to do about it.*)

6 Maintaining biodiversity

6.1 Introduction

Use of the term 'biodiversity' arose in the context of, and has remained firmly wedded to, concerns over the loss of the natural environment and its contents. The importance of this connection cannot be overstated. In defining biodiversity in this book, we have relied heavily on the Convention on Biological Diversity (Section 1.2). This was not solely as a matter of convenience. It underscores our belief that, for better or for worse, and with its many flaws, this remains perhaps the single most important international step towards the long-term maintenance of biodiversity. The Convention constituted an historic commitment by nations of the world (though sadly not all of them, including the USA, have ratified or even signed). It was the first time that biodiversity was comprehensively addressed in a binding global treaty, the first time that genetic diversity was specifically covered, and the first time that the conservation of biodiversity was recognized as the common concern of humankind (Glowka et al. 1994). So, having examined the main features and patterns of biodiversity (Chapters 1, 2 & 3), the value placed on it (Chapter 4), and the threats that it faces (Chapter 5), we now turn to the relevant Articles contained in the Convention to provide a useful framework in which to discuss its maintenance into the future (as well as providing a valuable lesson in how such treaties are formulated). Whether or not one regards the Convention as having major significance, this provides a much broader canvas than that obtained by simply focussing on issues traditionally associated with the field of conservation biology. It draws attention to the fact that the maintenance of biodiversity touches on many facets of human activities, and concerns much more than how to prevent individual species from becoming extinct, or the provision of nature reserves and other protected areas for conservation.

The Convention is comprised of 42 Articles (Table 6.1), concerning issues ranging from its objectives, the practical obligations of each signatory, the policies to be followed, and the use of terms. Below we take various Articles in turn, and use these as a starting point to discuss the relationship of particular issues to the maintenance of biodiversity. Each of the Articles chosen is reproduced in full, followed by some commentary. We would encourage readers not to be deterred by the legal language (with its multiple caveats and sub-clauses) of the sections of the Convention that are quoted. This highlights the need to view any serious attempt to maintain biodiversity in a broader societal context; the obfuscation was necessary to achieve a document that so many countries could sign up to. Although at times rather formidable, the underlying ideas remain simple to understand and are amplified in the accompanying text.

6.2 Objectives of the Convention

The objectives of the Convention (Article 1) are threefold:

The conservation of biological diversity, the sustainable use of its components, and the fair and equitable sharing of the benefits arising from the utilization of genetic resources.

(To avoid possible confusion, 'sustainable use' is defined (in Article 2) as 'the use of components of biological diversity in a way and at a rate that does not lead to the long-term decline of biological diversity, thereby maintaining its potential to meet the needs and aspirations of present and future generations' – to many minds, this is unhelpfully vague.)

This is the heart of the Convention, establishing the framework and context for the subsequent Articles, and its overall sense of direction. Indeed, right at the outset the Convention recognizes some of the main strands that must be involved in the future interaction of humanity with biodiversity. Biodiversity must be maintained, if only because to fail to do so would be to imperil human existence through the consequences for direct and indirect use (cf. Chapter 4). This can only be achieved through sustainable use, and only if the benefits arising from the use are fairly and equitably distributed. This reflects a general acceptance that there are social contexts to conservation actions.

Table 6.1 The 42 Articles of the Convention on Biological Diversity.

1	Objective
2	Use of terms
3	Principle
4	Jurisdictional scope
5	Cooperation
6	General measures for conservation and sustainable use
7	Identification and monitoring
8	*In-situ* conservation
9	*Ex-situ* conservation
10	Sustainable use of components of biological diversity
11	Incentive measures
12	Research and training
13	Public education and awareness
14	Impact assessment and minimizing adverse impacts
15	Access to genetic resources
16	Access to and transfer of technology
17	Exchange of information
18	Technical and scientific cooperation
19	Handling of biotechnology and distribution of its benefits
20	Financial resources
21	Financial mechanism
22	Relationship with other international conventions
23	Conference of the Parties
24	Secretariat
25	Subsidiary Body on Scientific, Technical and Technological Advice
26	Reports
27	Settlement of disputes
28	Adoption of protocols
29	Amendment of the Convention or protocols
30	Adoption and amendment of annexes
31	Right to vote
32	Relationship between this Convention and its protocols
33	Signature
34	Ratification, acceptance or approval
35	Accession
36	Entry into force
37	Reservations
38	Withdrawals
39	Financial interim arrangements
40	Secretariat interim arrangements
41	Depository
42	Authentic texts

The emphasis on equitable sharing of benefits arising from the utilization of genetic resources reflects concerns that in the past such resources belonging to one nation have been exploited by one or more others, with no recompense. Although examples usually relate to the exploitation of the genetic resources of developing nations by developed ones, where its consequences are at their most severe, the problem is more widespread. Thus, for instance, Svarstad et al. (2000) relate how the hyphomycete fungus *Tolypocladium inflatum* was collected in soil samples by a biologist during his holiday in Norway in 1969, within an open access regime. Best-selling medicines based on cyclosporin A (an immunosuppressant, and essential in the transplant of human organs), a biochemical produced by the fungus, were subsequently developed by a pharmaceutical company. Two per cent royalties on sales might have been a reasonable claim if there had been benefit-sharing with the source country (although the fungus has subsequently been found to be distributed across many countries), and in 1997 alone these would have amounted to US$24.3 million.

6.3 General measures for conservation and sustainable use

This, Article 6, is perhaps one of the most far-reaching and significant Articles in the Convention, and reads as follows:

Each Contracting Party shall, in accordance with its particular conditions and capabilities:
(a) Develop national strategies, plans or programmes for the conservation and sustainable use of biological diversity or adapt for this purpose existing strategies, plans or programmes which shall reflect, inter alia, *the measures set out in this Convention relevant to the Contracting Party concerned; and*
(b) Integrate, as far as possible and as appropriate, the conservation and sustainable use of biological diversity into relevant sectoral or cross-sectoral plans, programmes and policies.

In short, the conservation and sustainable use of biodiversity are not expected to emerge fortuitously in each nation. Indeed they will not do so, as the recent history of biodiversity testifies. Biodiversity is under great pressure from human activities, with many species being threatened with extinction (Section 5.2.3), and much of the use being unsustainable (Section 5.4.1).

The Convention obliges nations to establish mechanisms for bringing about the conservation and sustainable use of biodiversity, or for developing these mechanisms if they already exist. Strategies, plans and programmes can be seen as a chronological series of steps whereby specific recommendations are turned into methods of achieving those ends and thence into action on the ground (Glowka et al. 1994). They will inevitably have to be dynamic, and under continual refinement and development, in order to respond to the changing circumstances of biodiversity in a particular nation. If they are to be effective, then these national strategies, plans and programmes will not be easy to formulate, as they will have to touch on multiple (perhaps even most) human activities. They will thus have to be integrated with policies in fields as diverse as agriculture, education, employment, energy, health, industry and transport. If they are to be truly effective, then the strategies, plans and programmes for conserving and sustainably using a nation's biological diversity will have to become central to the way in which that nation's affairs are conducted.

A striking example of the ways in which this is not presently occurring concerns so-called perverse subsidies (Myers 1998; Myers & Kent 1998). These are subsidies that are adverse in the long run to both the economy and the environment, and include support for: (i) agriculture – may cause overloading of croplands, leading to soil erosion, pollution from synthetic fertilizers and pesticides, and release of greenhouse gases; (ii) fossil fuels and nuclear energy – may increase pollution, smog and global warming, and creates waste-disposal problems; (iii) road transport – promotes pollution, excessive road-building and resultant habitat loss; (iv) water – encourages greater use and misuse of supplies; and (v) fisheries – support overharvesting. The scale of perverse subsidies is vast, totalling perhaps US$1450 billion per annum, and often exceeding the value in the marketplace of the goods that are generated from a given industrial sector. For example, global subsidies to marine fisheries exceed the market value of the fish that are landed. Myers (1998) observes that a US citizen pays taxes of at least US$2000 a year to fund perverse subsidies and pays almost the same amount through the increased costs of consumer goods and through environmental degradation.

In accordance with Article 6, a number of countries have developed national Biodiversity Strategies (general policy instruments to identify strategic needs) or Action Plans (practical documents that identify what is to be done and who is to do what) (Miller et al. 1995). For example, publication of the UK Action Plan (Anon. 1994) represents such a direct governmental response to Article 6. Its goal, principles and objectives are listed in Table 6.2. At their best, such documents can identify how the ways in which societies operate will be restructured, so as to bring about the conservation and sustainable use of biodiversity. More frequently, they reflect aspirations with little indication of how these will be met, and fail to recognize the fundamental nature of what needs to be done.

Table 6.2 The goal, principles and objectives of the UK Action Plan (Anon. 1994).

Overall goal

To conserve and enhance biological diversity within the UK and to contribute to the conservation of global biodiversity through all appropriate mechanisms

Underlying principles

1 Where biological resources are used, such use should be sustainable

2 Wise use should be ensured for non-renewable resources

3 The conservation of biodiversity requires the care and involvement of individuals and communities as well as Governmental processes

4 Conservation of biodiversity should be an integral part of Government programmes, policy and action

5 Conservation practice and policy should be based upon a sound knowledge-base

6 The precautionary principle should guide decisions

Objectives for conserving biodiversity

1 To conserve and where practicable to enhance:

(a) the overall populations and natural ranges of native species and the quality and range of wildlife habitats and ecosystems;

(b) internationally important and threatened species, habitats and ecosystems;

(c) species, habitats and natural and managed ecosystems that are characteristic of local areas;

(d) the biodiversity of natural and semi-natural habitats where this has been diminished over recent past decades

2 To increase public awareness of, and involvement in, conserving biodiversity

3 To contribute to the conservation of biodiversity on a European and global scale

6.4 Identification and monitoring

In order to know whether strategies, programmes and plans for conservation and sustainable use are appropriate and are working effectively, it will be necessary to gather suitable information. Article 7 places such an obligation on signatories to the Convention (Annex I is given in Table 6.3):

Each Contracting Party shall, as far as possible and as appropriate, in particular for the purposes of Articles 8 to 10:

(a) Identify components of biological diversity important for its conservation and sustainable use having regard to the indicative list of categories set down in Annex I;

(b) Monitor, through sampling and other techniques, the components of biological diversity identified pursuant to subparagraph (a) above, paying particular attention to those requiring urgent conservation measures and those which offer the greatest potential for sustainable use;

(c) Identify processes and categories of activities which have or are likely to have significant adverse impacts on the conservation and sustainable use of

Table 6.3 Annex I of the Convention on Biological Diversity.

Identification and monitoring

1 Ecosystems and habitats: containing high diversity, large numbers of endemic or threatened species, or wilderness; required by migratory species; of social, economic, cultural or scientific importance; or, which are representative, unique or associated with key evolutionary or other biological processes;

2 Species and communities which are: threatened; wild relatives of domesticated or cultivated species; of medicinal, agricultural or other economic value; or social, scientific or cultural importance; or importance for research into the conservation and sustainable use of biological diversity, such as indicator species; and

3 Described genomes and genes of social, scientific or economic importance

biological diversity, and monitor their effects through sampling and other techniques; and

(d) Maintain and organize, by any mechanism data, derived from identification and monitoring activities pursuant to subparagraphs (a), (b) and (c) above.

The combination of the paucity of knowledge of biodiversity and the extraordinary magnitude of the variety of life (see Chapters 2 & 3) make it impossible to identify or monitor all of the components of biodiversity that lie within a nation's borders. The Article and its associated Annex therefore concentrate these undertakings in two directions: first on those components that are considered to be important for the conservation and sustainable use of biodiversity; and second on those activities which are likely to have the most substantial impacts on this conservation and use. Much of this will require the acquisition of entirely new information, while it will be possible to use some existing data (see Chapters 1, 2 & 3), perhaps freshly collated. Combined, this will have benefits far beyond the Convention, serving to improve overall understanding of biodiversity. This will be facilitated by the final clause of this Article.

The ease with which nations can begin to fulfil the requirements of this Article will vary dramatically, on the basis of existing knowledge alone (cf. final comments on Article 8). However, it is important that attempts to improve knowledge are not used as an excuse for failing to undertake action in other spheres of activity. This has been a recurrent problem in the fields of conservation and sustainable use.

6.5 *In-situ* conservation

Article 8 embodies the principal obligations for the conservation of biological diversity. Although it is one of the longer Articles in the Convention, and thus may appear especially daunting, it is so important that we

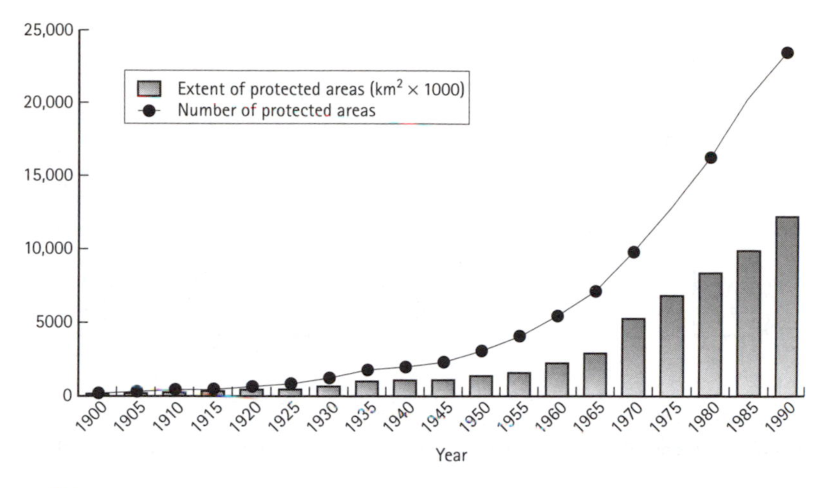

Fig. 6.1 Cumulative growth in the number and extent of protected areas (1900–94). (From Green & Paine 1997.)

must consider all of it. However, to make the task a little less onerous we will divide it into manageable sections.

Each Contracting Party shall, as far as possible and appropriate:
(a) Establish a system of protected areas or areas where special measures need to be taken to conserve biological diversity;
(b) Develop, where necessary, guidelines for the selection, establishment and management of protected areas or areas where special measures need to be taken to conserve biological diversity;

Protected area systems or networks are required to be established as a central plank of a national strategy for conserving biodiversity. More than 20,000 existing protected areas, spread amongst virtually all countries in the world, are recognized by the IUCN (The World Conservation Union) Commission on Parks and Protected Areas, covering an estimated 13.2 million km^2 (Fig. 6.1); marine reserves cover about 1.3 million km^2 of this total. However, this network suffers from a number of severe limitations.

1 Most protected areas are extremely small (Fig. 6.2), typically of a size that is far below that required to maintain viable populations of large vertebrates (Newmark 1987, 1996; Gurd et al. 2001). The severity of this size constraint may be reduced if protected areas are linked by corridors, but in practice with a few notable exceptions this has not happened, and there are both pros and cons to the creation of corridors. Potential benefits include increased immigration rates, and the provision of increased or alternative refugia; potential disadvantages include facilitated transmission of fire, disease and predators, and reduction in between-population

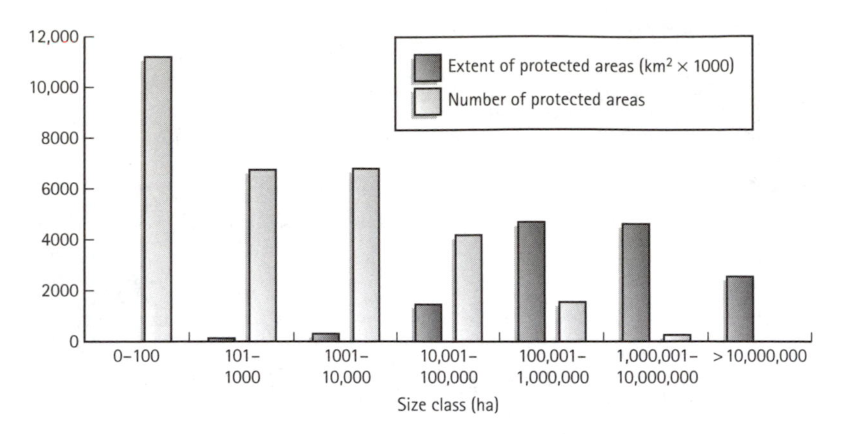

Fig. 6.2 Frequency distribution of protected area sizes. (From Green & Paine 1997.)

genetic variation (Saunders & Hobbs 1991; Newmark 1993; Gaston et al. 2002). The overall number of protected areas continues to increase, but the average size of those declared in any given period has tended to decline through time.

2 Protected areas tend to be biased towards lands of low economic value, experiencing less competition from alternative forms of land use, and towards the limits of geopolitical units (e.g. county, state and country boundaries, where they may serve as buffer zones). In consequence, they do not adequately represent patterns of natural vegetation or species occurrences (Scott et al. 2001; Pressey et al. 2002). Models of the changes in the distributions of species that are likely to result reveal that this situation is likely to be further exacerbated by climate change (e.g. Erasmus et al. 2002).

3 Many areas that have been formally designated for conservation in practice receive no, little or limited protection (and have often been termed 'paper parks'). Thus, for example, Grønne Ejland in Greenland was declared a Ramsar site (a protected area designated under the Ramsar Convention on Wetlands of International Importance) in 1987, with special reference to the presence of the world's largest colony of Arctic terns *Sterna paradisaea* (c. 1950 estimates suggested 50,000–80,000 breeding pairs). This designation never had any practical significance, and in the summer of 2000 not a single breeding pair of terns was recorded as remaining (Hansen 2002). The effectiveness of many other protected areas has been much debated (see Bruner et al. 2001a,b; Vanclay 2001). Ultimately, this will often depend on the level of management activities (e.g. enforcement of park boundaries, anti-poaching patrols). Funds for this are insufficient in much of the world. US$6 billion is presently spent globally on protected areas for conservation (James et al. 1999, 2001). This compares with US$2.1 billion for the cost of a replacement space

shuttle in 1991, US$6 billion spent to resolve property damage following Hurricane Floyd in 1999, US$15 billion agreed in 2002 for a single order of fighter aircraft by the UK government, and US$50 billion spent each year globally on methods of dieting.

4 The overall extent of the existing conservation network is too small. IUCN (1993) advocates that at least 10% of the land area of each nation be set aside for conservation. The expansion of the global network of protected areas to meet a target of 15% has been estimated to carry a global price-tag of US$20 billion–28 billion per annum (Balmford et al. 2002). In practice, even a network covering 15% of different regions is likely to be woefully inadequate to represent all species, especially in the tropics. Substantially larger percentages may be required for ecosystems or nations with higher levels of species richness and/or endemism (Rodrigues & Gaston 2001). The proportion of the land area set aside for conservation may be too small, but the proportion of the marine environment set aside for these purposes is much lower (c. 0.5% of ocean area). Nonetheless, existing evidence strongly supports the notion that designating protected areas of ocean has enormous benefits both for biodiversity within and without those areas, and hence for exploitation of the latter (Dugan & Davis 1993; Bohnsack 1998; Mosquera et al. 2000; C.M. Roberts et al. 2001; Halpern & Warner 2002). Estimates suggest that an initiative to generate a globally effective network covering 30% of the area of the oceans would cost c. US$23 billion per annum in recurrent costs, plus c. US$6 billion per annum (over 30 years) in start-up costs (Balmford et al. 2002).

5 The existing conservation network has been conceived along rather static lines, and is not well equipped to cope with the changes in the distributions of species that are being brought about by global climate changes (Section 5.4.2). These changes would normally cause shifts in the distributions of species, typically with expansions along some range boundaries and contractions along others. However, as protected areas become progressively more like islands of natural vegetation in a matrix of modified environments, often isolated from one another by considerable distances, the possibility for species to respond by such movements becomes increasingly constrained.

There have been a number of attempts to identify priority areas for conservation, to guide thinking in the location of future protected areas and the exercise of other conservation measures. These are based on the principles that biodiversity is unevenly distributed across the planet, that it is under more immediate threat in some areas than others, and that resources for conservation action are limiting. They include approaches based on hotspots of biodiversity, endemism and threat, and on the most outstanding examples of different habitat types, such as Birdlife International's Endemic Bird Areas, Conservation International's Hotspots,

Conservation International's Major Tropical Wilderness Areas, World Resource Institute's Frontier Forests, World Wide Fund for Nature and World Conservation Union's Centres of Plant Diversity, and World Wildlife Fund-USA's Global 200 ecoregions (e.g. Davis et al. 1994, 1995, 1997; Bryant et al. 1997; Olson & Dinerstein 1998; Stattersfield et al. 1998; Myers et al. 2000; Olson et al. 2001). Particularly at regional scales, increasing attention is being paid to maximizing the complementarity between different areas (including the largest number of species in a network of a given total extent, cost, etc.; Pressey et al. 1993).

A key issue in identifying priority areas for conservation is the extent to which areas chosen on the basis of one taxonomic group are also appropriate for the maintenance of the biodiversity of others in a region (this is related to, although not the same as, the issue of how well the patterns of species richness of different groups are correlated; Section 3.5). Whilst there are some important similarities, there are also significant differences, which caution against assuming that planning based on those groups that we know well will suffice for those that we do not (e.g. Brooks et al. 2001).

(c) Regulate or manage biological resources important for the conservation of biological diversity whether within or outside protected areas, with a view to assuring their conservation and sustainable use;
(d) Promote the protection of ecosystems, natural habitats and the maintenance of viable populations of species in natural surroundings;
(e) Promote environmentally sound and sustainable development in areas adjacent to protected areas with a view to furthering protection of these areas;

Of course, whether on land or in the ocean, protected areas, whilst vital, are not sufficient in themselves for the conservation of biodiversity. First, they are not isolated from events beyond their boundaries, and the more degraded conditions become outside, the greater the reduction of population viability within. Second, they are often vulnerable to threats and accidents emanating from outside, such as resource exploitation and chemical contamination. Thus, for example, extinction rates of large mammals in protected areas in West Africa have been shown to increase with human density in the surrounding areas, presumably reflecting the increased hunting pressures that they face (Brashares et al. 2001). Third, much biodiversity will not be contained within protected areas. For example, an unknown but doubtless large proportion of species is unrepresented within protected areas, and large numbers of some flagship species occur outside their boundaries; 80% of Africa's elephants live outside protected areas (Ginsberg 2002). Fourth, many fundamental processes, such as migration and population replenishment (especially in marine systems), occur at scales much larger than those protected areas

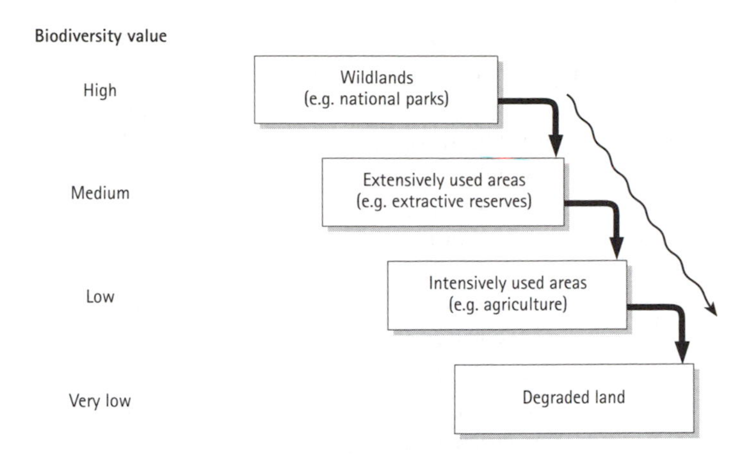

Fig. 6.3 The land-use cascade. (From Terborgh 1999.)

can reasonably attain. Fifth, climate change may make conditions within the boundaries of existing protected areas untenable for some of the species they were intended to conserve. These paragraphs of Article 8 therefore require the management of biological resources both within protected areas and outside of them (i.e. the general protection of ecosystems and populations wherever they occur), and so ensure that development in areas adjacent to protected areas does not undermine the capacity of those protected areas to conserve biodiversity.

Some attempt has been made to estimate what might be the cost of protecting biodiversity in the matrix of landscapes beyond reserves. Thus, it has been suggested that biodiversity remediation costs might be US$34 billion per annum for the forestry sector, US$1 billion for freshwater and US$14 billion for coastal and marine systems (United Nations 1993). Biodiversity conservation in the farming sector would cost far more, with one estimate of US$240 billion per annum, giving an overall annual total of about US$290 billion (James et al. 1999). This is a fraction of the sums presently spent on perverse subsidies (Section 6.3).

(f) Rehabilitate and restore degraded ecosystems and promote the recovery of threatened species, inter alia, *through the development and implementation of plans or other management strategies;*

The conservation of biodiversity is not simply about maintaining things the way they presently are. As we have seen, few (if any) areas are pristine and untouched, directly or indirectly, by human hand, and many are severely degraded (see Table 5.2). A creative approach to restoration is thus also required, which can reverse the slide of lands from wild to degraded (Fig. 6.3). This has given rise to the emergence of the science of restoration ecology (Jordan et al. 1990; Pywell & Putwain 1996; Perrow

& Davy 2002a,b). Many innovative and cost-effective approaches to restoration have been developed, which harness natural ecosystem processes (Dobson et al. 1997). Agricultural and industrial development, whilst it may be curtailed, cannot be stopped, so restoration provides a means of reducing the time for which habitat remains in a degraded state.

(g) Establish or maintain means to regulate, manage or control the risks associated with the use and release of living modified organisms resulting from biotechnology which are likely to have adverse environmental impacts that could affect the conservation and sustainable use of biological diversity, taking also into account the risks to human health;
(h) Prevent the introduction of, control or eradicate those alien species which threaten ecosystems, habitats or species;

The impacts on biodiversity and the environment associated with the introduction of alien species have already been mentioned (Section 5.4.3) and, plainly, actions to ameliorate these effects are a necessary part of an effective conservation strategy. Prevention of invasions is much less costly than is their control once they become established, and so effective quarantine measures are vital, although presently adopted by very few nations. Eradication of established introductions is sometimes possible, particularly from islands and small areas, where action can be taken early in the invasive process, where measures can be persistently applied often over long periods (temptations to reduce efforts in response to initial success in reducing numbers must be resisted), and where there is public support for such campaigns. In some cases the, often high, costs associated with eradication may be more economic than the ongoing year-on-year expenses associated with control programmes that serve solely to contain the distribution or reduce the abundance of an alien species. However, in most cases the latter steps are the only ones that are practical, and may require a great deal of commitment and diligence (Mack et al. 2000).

The need to combat the possible risks associated with the intentional use and release of living 'modified' organisms (which include genetically modified organisms) has been particularly highlighted in this Article. There is, of course, vigorous debate as to how severe these risks are.

(i) Endeavour to provide the conditions needed for compatibility between present uses and the conservation of biological diversity and the sustainable use of its components;
(j) Subject to its national legislation, respect, preserve and maintain knowledge, innovations and practices of indigenous and local communities embodying traditional lifestyles relevant for the conservation and sustainable use of biological diversity and promote their wider application with the approval and involvement

of the holders of such knowledge, innovations and practices and encourage the equitable sharing of the benefits arising from the utilization of such knowledge, innovations and practices;

Intuitively, support for the conservation of biological diversity will be less when necessary changes conflict with present uses (see Section 4.2). The first of these paragraphs requests that Parties to the Convention should minimize these conflicts, although plainly this will often be difficult and, at times, impossible. This issue begs the question of whether it is better to exploit smaller areas intensively, or to exploit less intensively over larger areas. Conventionally, the latter has been viewed as being better for the maintenance of biodiversity. However, evidence from studies both of forestry and fisheries suggests the converse may well be the case (Noble & Dirzo 1997). The long-term sustainability and environmental consequences of intensive agriculture are, however, of great concern. Locally, intensification of agricultural systems can increase erosion, lower soil fertility, and reduce biodiversity; regionally, it may pollute ground waters and cause eutrophication of rivers and lakes; globally, it may change the atmosphere and climate (Matson et al. 1997).

The second paragraph of this part of the Article recognizes that the knowledge, innovations and practices of indigenous and local communities may be pertinent to the conservation and sustainable use of biodiversity, and that this cultural relevance should be promoted, to the benefit of its custodians.

(k) Develop or maintain necessary legislation and/or other regulatory provisions for the protection of threatened species and populations;
(l) Where a significant adverse effect on biological diversity has been determined pursuant to Article 7, regulate or manage the relevant processes and categories of activities; and
(m) Cooperate in providing financial and other support for in-situ *conservation outlined in subparagraphs (a) to (l), particularly to developing countries.*

These paragraphs all concern mechanisms for conserving biodiversity, including the development of appropriate legislation, the regulation and management of processes and activities which from the gathering of suitable information (as outlined in Article 7, above) have been found to be detrimental to biodiversity, and the provision of financial and other support to developing countries. The final paragraph reflects a recurrent theme of the Convention, in recognizing that the resources available for the conservation and sustainable use of biodiversity are not evenly distributed, and that the poorer countries will require support from the richer if these ends are to be achieved.

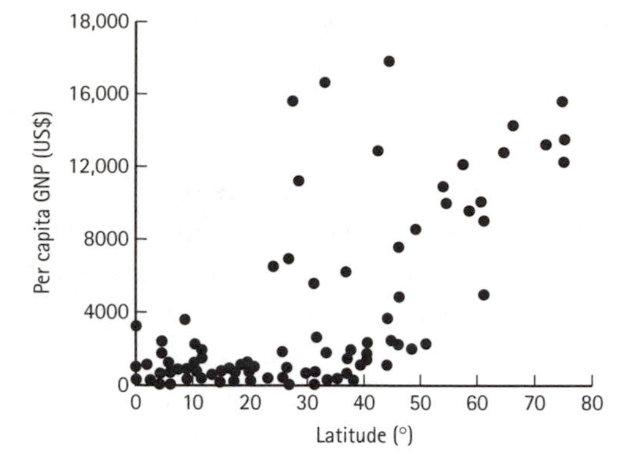

Fig. 6.4 Latitudinal gradient in the per capita gross national product (GNP) of countries of the world in 1986. (From Huston 1994.)

This is particularly so because there is a complex set of interactions between poverty and the environment. First, the majority of biodiversity tends to occur towards low latitudes, and there is also a decline in the wealth of nations (as measured by per capita gross national product, GNP) towards low latitudes (Fig. 6.4), which means that the majority of biodiversity occurs in those nations that have the least resources with which to conduct conservation and sustainable use. Second, damage to ecosystems often impacts most directly on the poor, who suffer the effects of polluted environments, the loss of productive lands, the collapse of fisheries, and the loss of traditional sources of food, fodder, fuel and fibre when forests are cut down (Lean 1998). The poor do not have the financial resources with which to acquire the resources that they need (food, water, etc.) from elsewhere; the large ecological footprint (Section 4.3) of the rich reduces their vulnerability to local environmental degradation. Third, as a consequence, the relative impacts of factors affecting biodiversity are not the same in poorer and richer countries (Fig. 6.5).

6.6 *Ex-situ* conservation

Conservation actions have traditionally been divided into *in-situ* and *ex-situ*, and having dealt with the former in Article 8, the Convention moves on to the latter in Article 9.

Each Contracting Party shall, as far as possible and as appropriate, and predominantly for the purpose of complementing in-situ *measures:*
(a) Adopt measures for the ex-situ *conservation of components of biological diversity, preferably in the country of origin of such components;*
(b) Establish and maintain facilities for ex-situ *conservation of and research on plants, animals and micro-organisms, preferably in the country of origin of genetic resources;*

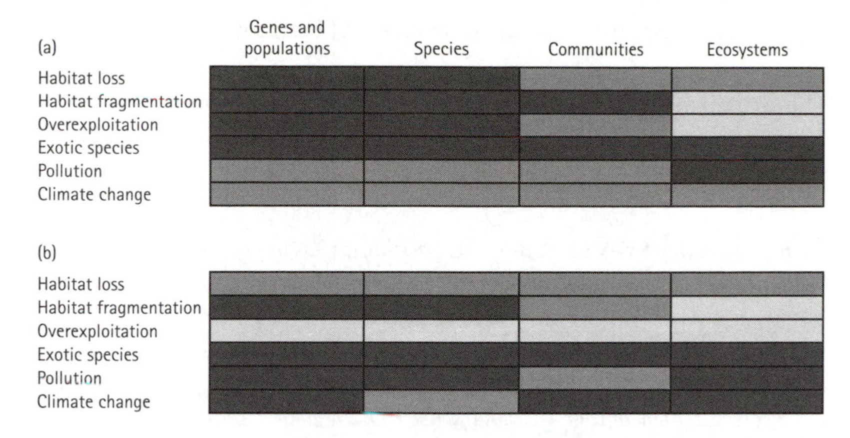

Fig. 6.5 Relative impacts of factors affecting terrestrial biodiversity in: (a) poor; and (b) rich countries. Shading indicates intensity of impact, from black (highest) to light grey (lowest). (From Soulé 1991.)

(c) Adopt measures for the recovery and rehabilitation of threatened species and for their reintroduction into their natural habitats under appropriate conditions;
(d) Regulate and manage collection of biological resources from natural habitats for ex-situ *conservation purposes so as not to threaten ecosystems and* in-situ *populations of species, except where special temporary* ex-situ *measures are required under subparagraph (c) above; and*
(e) Cooperate in providing financial and other support for ex-situ *conservation outlined in subparagraphs (a) to (d) above and in the establishment and maintenance of* ex-situ *conservation facilities in developing countries.*

Ex-situ conservation measures may include seed banks, sperm and ova banks, culture collections (e.g. of plant tissues), artificial propagation of plants and captive breeding of animals. In a growing number of instances, more individuals of given species are held in such facilities than occur in the wild. The relative costs and benefits of *ex-situ* conservation have been much debated (e.g. Tudge 1992; Rahbek 1993; Hurka 1994; Balmford et al. 1995, 1996; Frankel et al. 1995). This is particularly true with regard to large-bodied vertebrates (such as primates, big cats and cetaceans). Key issues here include the ethics of keeping individuals in captivity, whether the resources so used could practically be deployed in other ways (e.g. for *in-situ* conservation), the short- and long-term viability of both captive and wild populations, the relationship between the two (including the use and efficacy of reintroductions of species into areas in which they have become extinct, and to bolster declining natural populations), and other potential benefits of captive populations (e.g. in education of urban human populations). Whatever one's position on these matters, *ex-situ* activities should play only a very secondary role to *in-situ* conservation, as implied by the opening statement of this Article.

6.7 Sustainable use of components of biological diversity

The sustainable use of biological diversity is one of the objectives of the Convention (Article 1). Article 10 embodies the obligations for attaining this goal.

Each Contracting Party shall, as far as possible and as appropriate:
(a) Integrate consideration of the conservation and sustainable use of biological resources into national decision-making;
(b) Adopt measures relating to the use of biological resources to avoid or minimize adverse impacts on biological diversity;
(c) Protect and encourage customary use of biological resources in accordance with traditional cultural practices that are compatible with conservation or sustainable use requirements;
(d) Support local populations to develop and implement remedial action in degraded areas where biological diversity has been reduced; and
(e) Encourage cooperation between its governmental authorities and its private sector in developing methods for sustainable uses of biological resources.

To live sustainably, the human population must do so within the biosphere's regenerative capacity, drawing on its natural capital without depleting the capital stock. Evidence suggests that since the 1980s, human exploitation of the Earth's biological productivity may well have exceeded this capacity, such that the ecological footprint (Section 4.3) of the global population in 1999 was 1.2 times that of the entire Earth (Wackernagel et al. 2002). Issues of sustainability thus extend far beyond the frequent media focus on trade in particular commodities of high economic value, such as wood from mahoganies, horn from rhinoceros, body parts from tigers and ivory from elephants. Put simply, most present use of biodiversity is not sustainable (management approaches have often focussed on maximizing short-term yield and economic gain rather than long-term sustainability).

A major difficulty lies in controlling the level of use. Even where use may be reasonably sustainable at low levels, it may significantly impact at higher levels. This highlights the potential tradeoffs between levels of use, the spatial extent of that use (to obtain the same resource, low levels of use have to be spread over greater areas), and the impacts of use. Such considerations span the extraction of products from natural tropical forests to the planting of genetically modified crops.

In essence, the Convention proposes that sustainable use is to be attained by its integration into national planning. How this can most effectively be done is a complex issue, with debate particularly centred on the most appropriate approach to trade (free-market, highly regulated, etc.).

Sustainable use requires the support of local peoples, and the protection and encouragement of customary use is one way in which to achieve this. However, it is important to distinguish those traditional uses that are compatible with conservation and sustainable use from those that are not. For example, the widespread belief that 'primitive' peoples have no appreciable adverse impact on their environment is, expressed in such a generic fashion, simply a myth (Section 5.2.1; Milberg & Tyrberg 1993). Even when not based on distortions of history, appeals to traditional uses often reflect situations in which human densities were far lower and there was no commercial exploitation (van Schaik & Rijksen 2002).

6.8 Incentive measures

Biodiversity loss is driven in major part by economic forces. Article 11 is an attempt to harness these same forces to its conservation and sustainability.

Each Contracting Party shall, as far as possible and as appropriate, adopt economically and socially sound measures that act as incentives for the conservation and sustainable use of components of biological diversity.

Put simply, the obligation is to adopt measures that encourage conservation and sustainable use (Glowka et al. 1994). In contrast, as exemplified by perverse subsidies, the converse is often the case.

The interactions between society and the environment are complex, requiring careful analysis to determine the full consequences of particular actions. A causal framework for examining these interactions adopted by the European Environment Agency is DPSIR (Fig. 6.6), which provides a useful basis for working through such complexities.

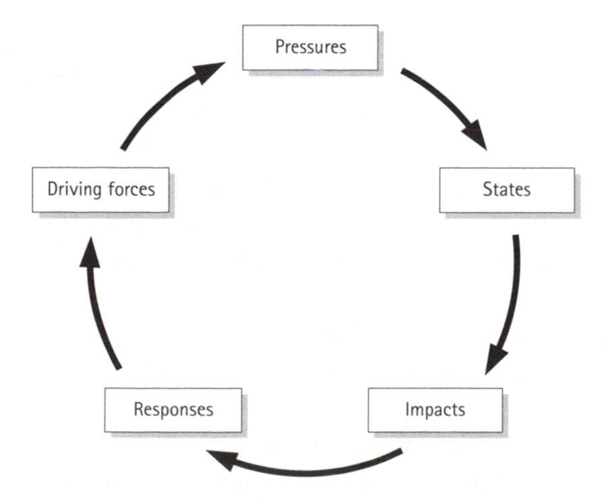

Fig. 6.6 The DPSIR model adopted by the European Environment Agency.

6.9 Responses to the Convention

As has already been mentioned (Section 6.3), a number of Parties to the Convention have produced Biodiversity Strategies and Action Plans. This is, however, a rather easy step in responding to its contents, albeit one which may attract significant media attention. Implementing the changes required to conserve biodiversity effectively and to exploit it in a sustainable fashion is much more difficult, and typically unpalatable to politicians with short-term goals (like re-election and personal financial gain). A number of nations have made small steps in the right direction, but substantial moves are largely wanting.

The obvious way forward, employed by other treaties and agreements, is to establish and agree targets for each party to achieve in fulfilment of the Convention, and protocols for reporting progress so that this can be rigorously assessed. Unfortunately, such an approach has yet to be adopted, despite several Conferences of the Parties (CoPs) and summit meetings; at the time of writing, the most recent summit, the World Summit on Sustainable Development, was held in Johannesburg in 2002. Until significant progress is made in achieving the principles laid down in the Convention, whether by ensuring its application or by some other mechanism (individual nations could make much progress unilaterally), then biodiversity will continue to decline as a consequence of human activities. Whether ultimately this will threaten the existence of humanity is less significant than whether it will threaten the kind of existence people would like to enjoy. For us, it is already doing so.

6.10 Summary

1 The Convention on Biological Diversity is one of the main global attempts to set an agenda for maintaining biodiversity and provides a useful framework for considering these issues.
2 The main objectives of the Convention are the conservation of biological diversity, the sustainable use of its components, and the fair and equitable sharing of the benefits arising from the utilization of genetic resources.
3 The conservation and sustainable use of biodiversity will not emerge fortuitously in each nation, but will require the establishment of explicit mechanisms.
4 In order to know whether strategies, programmes and plans for conservation and sustainable use are appropriate and are working effectively, it will be necessary to gather suitable information.

5 Conservation of biodiversity will require a network of protected areas for *in-situ* protection, measures for its conservation in the wider landscape, and perhaps also the use of *ex-situ* measures.
6 Sustainable use will only be attained by its integration into national planning, to minimize the adverse impacts of use on biodiversity.
7 Whilst there have been moves in the direction of the changes embodied in the Convention, as yet these are wholly inadequate.

Further reading

The Convention on Biological Diversity

Glowka, L., Burhenne-Guilmin, F., Synge, H., McNeely, J.A. & Gündling, L. (1994) *A Guide to the Convention on Biological Diversity*. IUCN, Gland & Cambridge. (*A detailed guide to the Convention on Biological Diversity*.)

Johnson, S.P. (1993) *The Earth Summit: The United Nations Conference on Environment and Development (UNCED)*. Graham & Trotman, London. (*Rio – the official autobiography*.)

McConnell, F. (1996) *The Biodiversity Convention: A Negotiating History*. Kluwer Law International, London. (*A fascinating account of negotiating the Convention by the head of the UK delegation*.)

The Convention on Biological Diversity and all of the material associated with it is accessible at http://www.biodiv.org/.

Conserving and sustainably exploiting biodiversity

Adams, W.M. (1997) *Future Nature. A Vision for Conservation*. Earthscan, London. (*A readable and thought-provoking 'history' of conservation in the UK*.)

Barthlott, W. & Winiger, W. (eds.) (1998) *Biodiversity: A Challenge for Development Research and Policy*. Springer-Verlag, Berlin. (*Another multi-authored, multidisciplinary symposium proceedings, predictably eclectic but with some nice chapters*.)

Byron, H. (2000) *Biodiversity Impact. A Good Practice Guide for Road Schemes*. RSPB, WWF-UK, English Nature and the Wildlife Trusts, Sandy. (*Goes from background theory – what is biodiversity – through to literally where the rubber hits the road*.)

Davidson, E.A. (2000) *You Can't Eat GNP: Economics as if Ecology Mattered*. Perseus Publishing, Cambridge, MA. (*Argues that traditional economic techniques don't work when you're talking about real things such as trees and rubbish*.)

Entwistle, A. & Dunstone, N. (2000) *Priorities for Conservation of Mammalian Diversity. Has the Panda Had its Day?* Cambridge University Press, Cambridge. (*Reviews of recent academic advances and how they can be applied practically*.)

Forey, P.L., Humphries, C.J. & Vane-Wright, R.I. (eds.) (1994) *Systematics and Conservation Evaluation*. Clarendon Press, Oxford. (*An important treatise on methodology, mostly still state of the art*.)

Guruswamy, L.D. & McNeely, J.A. (eds.) (1998) *Protection of Global Biodiversity*. Duke University Press, Durham & London. (*Interdisciplinary approach to formulating policies aimed at protecting biodiversity*.)

Holdgate, M. (1999) *The Green Web: A Union for World Conservation*. Earthscan, London. (*Written by a former director general of IUCN, this book shows how far the conservation movement has come in the last half century.*)

Juniper, T. (2002) *Spix's Macaw: The Race to Save the World's Rarest Bird*. Fourth Estate, London. (*An account of the realities of trying to conserve a magnificent animal, and 'the lethal cocktail of egos, jealousy, law-breaking, suspicion, politicking and greed that has all but wiped them out'.*)

MacDonald, M. (1998) *Agendas for Sustainability: Environment and Development into the Twenty-first Century*. Routledge, London. (*Very practical suggestions for devising global environmental and development agendas.*)

McNeely, J.A., Miller, K.R., Reid, W.V., Mittermeier, R.A. & Werner, T.B. (1990) *Conserving the World's Biological Diversity*. IUCN, Gland; WRI, CI, WWF-US and the World Bank, Washington, DC. (*Authoritative book that champions the view that we 'need to recognise the reasons for the existence of species and ecosystems may be more subtle and inscrutable than simply supporting the economic desires of the current generation of consumers'.*)

Miller, K., Allegretti, M.H., Johnson, N. & Jonsson, B. (1995) Measures for conservation of biodiversity and sustainable use of its components. In: *Global Biodiversity Assessment* (ed. V.H. Heywood), pp. 915–1061. Cambridge University Press, Cambridge. (*More of a book than a chapter, seven lead authors and 39 contributors put together a practical, considered framework for protecting, restoring and managing biodiversity.*)

Milner-Gulland, E.J. & Mace, R. (1998) *Conservation of Biological Resources*. Blackwell Science, Oxford. (*Written by an anthropologist and a biologist, with 10 case studies by invited contributors – that should give you some insight into the book's approach.*)

Moffat, I., Hanley, N. & Wilson, M.D. (2001) *Measuring and Modelling Sustainable Development*. Parthenon Publishing, Lancaster. (*Uses Scotland as a model system – so can't be bad.*)

Norris, K. & Pain, D.J. (eds.) (2002) *Conserving Bird Biodiversity*. Cambridge University Press, Cambridge. (*Not just a book about birds.*)

Oates, J.F. (1999) *Myth and Reality in the Rain Forest: How Conservation Strategies are Failing in West Africa*. University of California Press, Berkeley, CA. (*A clear demonstration that integrated conservation and development projects have failed as a method of maintaining biodiversity in protected areas.*)

Stein, B.A., Kutner, L.S. & Adams, J.S. (2000) *The Precious Heritage. The Status of Biodiversity in the United States*. Oxford University Press, New York. (*With a foreword by E.O. Wilson this is a readable account of the state of biodiversity in the USA.*)

Sutherland, W.J. (2000) *The Conservation Handbook: Research, Management and Policy*. Blackwell Science, Oxford. (*A practical and yet optimistic mixture of information and advice.*)

Swanson, T. (1997) *Global Action for Biodiversity*. Earthscan, London. (*A discussion of the elements of the Convention on Biological Diversity that can only be achieved if there is international agreement, written by an innovative environmental economist.*)

Terborgh, J. (1999) *Requiem for Nature*. Island Press, Washington, DC. (*An account of the realities of trying to conserve tropical forests, and the hard choices that have to be made.*)

Terborgh, J., van Schaik, C., Davenport, L. & Rao, M. (eds.) (2002) *Making Parks Work: Strategies for Preserving Tropical Nature*. Island Press, Washington, DC. (*An account of how and where protected areas work, and what should be done when they don't.*)

Victor, D.G. (2001) *The Collapse of the Kyoto Protocol and the Struggle to Slow Global Warming*. Princeton University Press, Princeton, NJ. (*Makes a strong case that without political action which is both strategic and global, there is no chance of tackling climate change.*)

WRI/IUCN/UNEP (1992) *Global Biodiversity Strategy: Guidelines for Action to Save, Study, and Use Earth's Biotic Wealth Sustainably and Equitably*. World Resources Institute, Washington, DC, World Conservation Union, Gland and United Nations Environment Programme, Nairobi.

Conservation biology

Caughley, G. & Gunn, A. (1996) *Conservation Biology in Theory and Practice*. Blackwell Science, Oxford. (*A great book.*)

Frankham, R., Ballou, J.D. & Briscoe, D.A. (2002) *Introduction to Conservation Genetics*. Cambridge University Press, Cambridge. (*Excellent undergraduate text that covers a lot of ground.*)

Gibbs, J.P., Hunter, M.L. & Sterling, E.J. (1998) *Problem-solving in Conservation Biology and Wildlife Management: Exercises for Class, Field and Laboratory*. Blackwell Science, Oxford. (*Written primarily with a North American audience in mind, this is still a valuable book for an international one, containing 27 practical exercises for use in teaching final-year undergraduates conservation biology.*)

Hunter, M.L. Jr (2002) *Fundamentals of Conservation Biology*, 2nd edn. Blackwell Science, Oxford. (*A well-organized, and wide-ranging, introduction to this subject.*)

Meffe, G.K. & Carroll, C.R. (1997) *Principles of Conservation Biology*, 2nd edn. Sinauer Associates, Sunderland, MA. (*Addresses the major issues in conservation biology, with many helpful examples.*)

Primack, R.B. (2002) *Essentials of Conservation Biology*, 3rd edn. Sinauer Associates, Sunderland, MA. (*A well-organized, and wide-ranging, introduction to this subject.*)

Pullin, A.S. (2002) *Conservation Biology*. Cambridge University Press, Cambridge. (*Simple and clear undergraduate text, but avoids economic and political issues.*)

Spellerberg, I.F. (ed.) (1996) *Conservation Biology*. Longman, Harlow. (*A useful set of reviews of many of the major issues.*)

References

Alford, R.A. & Richards, S.J. (1999) Global amphibian declines: a problem in applied ecology. *Annual Review of Ecology and Systematics* **30**, 133–165.

Alroy, J. (2002) How many named species are valid? *Proceedings of the National Academy of Sciences, USA* **99**, 3706–3711.

Alroy, J., Marshall, C.R., Bambach, R.K., Bezusko, K., Foote, M., Fürsich, F.T., Hansen, T.A., Holland, S.M., Ivany, L.C., Jablonski, D., Jacobs, D.K., Jones, D.C., Kosnik, M.A., Lidgard, S., Low, S., Miller, A.I., Novack-Gottshall, P.M., Olszewski, T.D., Patzkowsky, M.E., Raup, D.M., Roy, K., Sepkoski, J.J. Jr, Sommers, M.G., Wagner, P.J. & Webber, A. (2001) Effects of sampling standardization on estimates of Phanerozoic marine diversification. *Proceedings of the National Academy of Sciences, USA* **98**, 6261–6266.

Altaba, C.R. (1996) Counting species names. *Nature* **380**, 488–489.

Andersen, M., Thornhill, A. & Koopowitz, H. (1997) Tropical forest disruption and stochastic biodiversity losses. In: *Tropical Forest Remnants: Ecology, Management, and Conservation of Fragmented Communities* (eds. W.F. Laurance & R.O. Bierregaard Jr), pp. 281–291. University of Chicago Press, Chicago, IL.

Anderson, S. (1994) Area and endemism. *Quarterly Review of Biology* **69**, 451–471.

André, H.M., Ducarme, X. & Lebrun, P. (2002) Soil biodiversity: myth, reality or conning? *Oikos* **96**, 3–24.

Angel, M.V. (1993) Biodiversity of the pelagic ocean. *Conservation Biology* **7**, 760–772.

Angel, M.V. (1994a) Long-term, large-scale patterns in marine pelagic systems. In: *Aquatic Ecology* (eds. P.S. Giller, A.G. Hildrew & D.G. Raffaelli), pp. 403–439. Blackwell Science, Oxford.

Angel, M.V. (1994b) Spatial distribution of marine organisms: patterns and processes. In: *Large-scale Ecology and Conservation Biology* (eds. P.J. Edwards, R.M. May & N.R. Webb), pp. 59–109. Blackwell Science, Oxford.

Anon. (1994) *Biodiversity: The UK Action Plan*. HMSO, London.

Aptroot, A. (1997) Species diversity in tropical

rainforest ascomycetes: lichenized *versus* non-lichenized; folicolous *versus* corticolous. *Abstracta Botanica* **21**, 37–44.

Armonies, W. & Reise, K. (2000) Faunal diversity across a sandy shore. *Marine Ecology Progress Series* **196**, 49–57.

Arnold, A.E., Maynard, Z., Gilbert, G.S., Coley, P.D. & Kursar, T.A. (2000) Are tropical fungal endophytes hyperdiverse? *Ecology Letters* **3**, 267–274.

Avise, J.C. & Johns, G.C. (1999) Proposal for a standardized temporal scheme of biological classification for extant species. *Proceedings of the National Academy of Sciences, USA* **96**, 7358–7363.

Azovsky, A.I. (2002) Size-dependent species–area relationships in benthos: is the world more diverse for microbes? *Ecography* **25**, 273–282.

Balmford, A. (2002) Selecting sites for conservation. In: *Conserving Bird Biodiversity: General Principles and their Applications* (eds. K. Norris & D.J. Pain), pp. 74–104. Cambridge University Press, Cambridge.

Balmford, A. & Long, A. (1995) Across-country analyses of biodiversity congruence and current conservation effort in the tropics. *Conservation Biology* **9**, 1539–1547.

Balmford, A., Leader-Williams, N. & Green, M.J.B. (1995) Parks or arks: where to conserve threatened mammals? *Biodiversity and Conservation* **4**, 595–607.

Balmford, A., Mace, G.M. & Leader-Williams, N. (1996) Designing the ark: Setting priorities for captive breeding. *Conservation Biology* **10**, 719–727.

Balmford, A., Lyon, A.J.E. & Lang, R.M. (2000) Testing the higher-taxon approach to conservation planning in a megadiverse group: the macrofungi. *Biological Conservation* **93**, 209–217.

Balmford, A., Moore, J.L., Brooks, T., Burgess, N., Hansen, L.A., Williams, P. & Rahbek, C. (2001) Conservation conflicts across Africa. *Science* **291**, 2616–2619.

Balmford, A., Bruner, A., Cooper, P., Costanza, R., Farber, S., Green, R.E., Jenkins, M., Jefferies, P., Jessamy, V., Madden, J., Munro, K., Myers, N., Naeem, S., Paavola, J., Rayment, M., Rosendo, S., Roughgarden, J., Trumper, K. & Turner, R.K. (2002) Economic reasons for conserving wild nature. *Science* **297**, 950–953.

Bartlett, R., Pickering, J., Gauld, I. & Windors, D. (1999) Estimating global biodiversity: tropical beetles and wasps send different signals. *Ecological Entomology* **24**, 118–121.

Baskin, Y. (2002) *A Plague of Rats and Rubber-vines: The Growing Threat of Species Invasions*. Island Press, Washington, DC.

Bates, H.W. (1862) Contributions to an insect fauna of the Amazon valley. Lepidoptera: Heliconidae. *Transactions of the Linnean Society* **23**, 495–566.

Beattie, A. & Ehrlich, P.R. (2001) *Wild Solutions: How Biodiversity is Money in the Bank*. Yale University Press, New Haven, CT.

Beerling, D.J. (1993) The impact of the temperature on the northern distribution limits of the introduced species *Fallopia japonica* and *Impatiens glandulifera* in north-west Europe. *Journal of Biogeography* **20**, 45–53.

Benton, M.J. (1985) Mass extinction among non-marine tetrapods. *Nature* **316**, 811–814.

Benton, M.J. (1995) Diversification and extinction in the history of life. *Science* **268**, 52–58.

Benton, M.J. (1997) Models for the diversification of life. *Trends in Ecology and Evolution* **12**, 490–495.

Benton, M.J., Wills, M.A. & Hitchin, R. (2000) Quality of the fossil record through time. *Nature* **403**, 534–537.

Berra, T.M. (1997) Some 20th century fish discoveries. *Environmental Biology of Fishes* **50**, 1–12.

Bini, L.M., Diniz Filho, J.A.F., Bonfim, F. & Bastos, R.P. (2000) Local and regional species richness relationships in viperid snake assemblages from South America: unsaturated patterns at three different spatial scales. *Copeia* **2000**, 799–805.

BirdLife International (2000) *Threatened Birds of the World*. Lynx Edicions and BirdLife International, Barcelona & Cambridge.

Bisby, F.A. (1995) Characterization of biodiversity. In: *Global Biodiversity Assessment* (ed. V.H. Heywood), pp. 21–106. Cambridge University Press, Cambridge.

Blackburn, T.M. & Gaston, K.J. (1997) The relationship between geographic area and the latitudinal gradient in species richness in New World birds. *Evolutionary Ecology* **11**, 195–204.

Bohnsack, J.A. (1998) Application of marine reserves to reef fisheries management. *Australian Journal of Ecology* **23**, 298–304.

Boucher, G. & Lambshead, P.J.D. (1995) Ecological biodiversity of marine nematodes in samples from temperate, tropical, and deep-sea regions. *Conservation Biology* **9**, 1594–1604.

Bouchet, P. (1997) Inventorying the molluscan diversity of the world: what is our rate of progress? *The Veliger* **40**, 1–11.

Bouchet, P., Lozouet, P., Maestrati, P. & Heros, V. (2002) Assessing the magnitude of species richness in tropical marine environments: exceptionally high numbers of molluscs at a New Caledonia site. *Biological Journal of the Linnean Society* **75**, 421–436.

Boulter, M. (2002) *Extinction: Evolution and the End of Man*. Fourth Estate, London.

Boulter, M.C. & Hewzulla, D. (1999) Evolutionary modelling from family diversity. *Palaeontologica Electronica* **2**. www-odp.tamu.edu/paleo

Bramwell, D. (2002) How many plant species are there? *Plant Talk* **28**, 32–33.

Brashares, J.S., Arcese, P. & Sam, M.K. (2001) Human demography and reserve size predict wildlife extinction in West Africa. *Proceedings of the Royal Society, London B* **268**, 2473–2478.

Brereton, R., Bennett, S. & Mansergh, I. (1995) Enhanced greenhouse climate change and its potential effect on selected fauna of south-eastern Australia: a trend analysis. *Biological Conservation* **72**, 339–354.

Brey, T., Klages, M., Dahm, C., Gorny, M., Gutt, J., Hain, S., Stiller, M., Arntz, W.E., Wägele, J.-W. & Zimmermann, A. (1994) Antarctic benthic diversity. *Nature* **368**, 297.

Briggs, J.C. (1996) Tropical diversity and conservation. *Conservation Biology* **10**, 713–718.

Briggs, J.C. (1999) Coincident biogeographic patterns: Indo-west Pacific ocean. *Evolution* **53**, 326–335.

Brook, B.W. & Bowman, D.M.J.S. (2002) Explaining the Pleistocene megafaunal extinctions: models, chronologies, and assumptions. *Proceedings of the National Academy of Sciences, USA* **99**, 14624–14627.

Brooks, T. & Balmford, A. (1996) Atlantic forest extinctions. *Nature* **380**, 115.

Brooks, T., Balmford, A., Burgess, N., Hansen, L.A., Moore, J., Rahbek, C., Williams, P., Bennun, L.A., Byaruhanga, A., Kasoma, P., Njoroge, P., Pomeroy, D. & Wondafrash, M. (2001) Conservation priorities for birds and biodiversity: do East African Important Bird Areas represent species diversity in other terrestrial vertebrate groups? *Ostrich Supplement* **15**, 3–12.

Brown, J.C. (1987) The peninsular effect in Baja California: an entomological assessment. *Journal of Biogeography* **14**, 359–365.

Bruner, A.G., Gullison, R.E., Rice, R.E. & da Fonseca, G.A.B. (2001a) Effectiveness of parks in protecting tropical biodiversity. *Science* **291**, 125–128.

Bruner, A.G., Gullison, R.E., Rice, R.E. & da Fonseca, G.A.B. (2001b) [Response] *Science* **293**, 1007a.

Bryant, D., Nielsen, D. & Tangley, L. (1997) *The Last Frontier Forests: Ecosystems and Economics on the Edge*. World Resources Institute, Washington, DC.

Burton, J.F. (2001) The response of European insects to climate change. *British Wildlife* **12**, 188–198.

Buzas, M.A., Collins, L.S. & Culver, S.J. (2002) Latitudinal difference in biodiversity caused by higher tropical rate of increase. *Proceedings of the National Academy of Sciences, USA* **99**, 7841–7843.

Caley, M.J. & Schluter, D. (1997) The relationship between local and regional diversity. *Ecology* **78**, 70–80.

Callaghan, T.V., Matveyeva, N., Chernov, Y. & Brooker, R. (2001) Arctic ecosystems. In: *Encyclopedia of Biodiversity*, Vol. 1 (ed. S.A. Levin), pp. 231–247. Academic Press, San Diego, CA.

Cannon, R.J.C. (1998) The implications of predicted climate change for insect pests in the

UK, with emphasis on non-indigenous species. *Global Change Biology* **4**, 785–796.

Cashdan, E. (2001) Ethnic diversity and its environmental determinants: effects of climate, pathogens, and habitat diversity. *American Anthropologist* **103**, 968–991.

Cassels, R. (1984) The role of prehistoric man in the faunal extinctions of New Zealand and other Pacific islands. In: *Quaternary Extinctions: A Prehistoric Revolution* (eds. P.S. Martin & R.G. Klein), pp. 741–767. Arizona University Press, Tucson, AZ.

Ceballos, G. & Brown, J.H. (1995) Global patterns of mammalian diversity, endemism, and endangerment. *Conservation Biology* **9**, 559–568.

Ceballos, G. & Ehrlich, P.R. (2002) Mammal population losses and the extinction crisis. *Science* **296**, 904–907.

Chapin, F.S. III, Walker, B.H., Hobbs, R.J., Hooper, D.U., Lawton, J.H., Sala, O.E. & Tilman, D. (1997) Biotic control over the functioning of ecosystems. *Science* **277**, 500–504.

Chapin, F.S. III, Sala, O.E., Burke, I.C., Grime, J.P., Hooper, D.U., Lauenroth, W.K., Lombard, A., Mooney, H.A., Mosier, A.R., Naeem, S., Pacala, S.W., Roy, J., Steffen, W.L. & Tilman, D. (1998) Ecosystem consequences of changing biodiversity. *BioScience* **48**, 45–52.

Chivian, E. (2001) Environment and health: 7. Species loss and ecosystem disruption – the implications for human health. *Canadian Medical Association Journal* **164**, 66–69.

Chown, S.L. & Gaston, K.J. (1999) Patterns in pelagic seabird diversity as a test of species–energy theory. *Evolutionary Ecology Research* **1**, 365–373.

Chown, S.L. & Gaston, K.J. (2000) Area, cradles and museums: the latitudinal gradient in species richness. *Trends in Ecology and Evolution* **15**, 311–315.

Chown, S.L., Gaston, K.J. & Williams, P.H. (1998) Global patterns in species richness of pelagic seabirds: the Procellariiformes. *Ecography* **21**, 342–350.

Cincotta, R.P. & Engelman, R. (2000) *Nature's Place: Human Population and the Future of Biological Diversity*. Population Action International, Washington, DC.

Cincotta, R.P., Wisnewski, J. & Engelman, R. (2000) Human population in the biodiversity hotspots. *Nature* **404**, 990–992.

Clark, C.W. (1981) Bioeconomics. In: *Theoretical Ecology* (ed. R.M. May), pp. 387–418. Sinauer Associates, Sunderland, MA.

Clarke, A. & Crame, A. (1997) Diversity, latitude and time: patterns in the shallow sea. In: *Marine Biodiversity: Patterns and Processes* (eds. R.F.G. Ormond, J.D. Gage & M.V. Angel), pp. 122–147. Cambridge University Press, Cambridge.

Clarke, A. & Lidgard, S. (2000) Spatial patterns of diversity in the sea: bryozoan species richness in the North Atlantic. *Journal of Animal Ecology* **69**, 799–814.

Cobb, N.A. (1914) *Nematodes and their Relationships*. US Department of Agriculture Yearbook, Washington, DC.

Cohen, J.E. (1995) *How Many People Can the Earth Support?* Norton, New York.

Cohen, J.E. & Tilman, D. (1996) Biosphere 2 and biodiversity: the lessons so far. *Science* **274**, 1150–1151.

Collard, I.F. & Foley, R.A. (2002) Latitudinal pattern and environmental determinants of recent human cultural diversity: do humans follow biogeographical rules? *Evolutionary Ecology Research* **4**, 371–383.

Colwell, R.K. & Hurtt, G.C. (1994) Nonbiological gradients in species richness and a spurious Rapoport effect. *American Naturalist* **144**, 570–595.

Colwell, R.R. (1997) Microbial biodiversity and biotechnology. In: *Biodiversity II* (eds. M.L. Reaka-Kudla, D.E. Wilson & E.O. Wilson), pp. 279–287. Joseph Henry Press, Washington, DC.

Conover, D.O. & Munch, S.B. (2002) Sustaining fisheries yields over evolutionary time scales. *Science* **297**, 94–96.

Convey, P. (2001) Antarctic ecosystems. In: *Encyclopedia of Biodiversity*, Vol. 1 (ed. S.A. Levin), pp. 171–184. Academic Press, San Diego, CA.

Cornell, H.V. (1999) Unsaturation and regional influences on species richness in ecological communities: a review of the evidence. *Écoscience* **6**, 303–315.

Cornell, H.V. & Lawton, J.H. (1992) Species interactions, local and regional processes, and limits to the richness of ecological communities: a theoretical perspective. *Journal of Animal Ecology* **61**, 1–12.

Costanza, R., d'Arge, R., de Groot, R., Farber, S., Grasso, M., Hannon, B., Limburg, K., Naeem, S., O'Neill, R.V., Parnelo, J., Raskin, R.G., Sutton, P. & van den Belt, M. (1997) The value of the world's ecosystem services and natural capital. *Nature* **387**, 253–260.

Couper, A. (ed.) (1983) *The Times World Atlas of the Oceans*. Time Books, London.

Courtillot, V. & Gaudemer, Y. (1996) Effects of mass extinctions on biodiversity. *Nature* **381**, 146–148.

Cowling, R.M. & Samways, M.J. (1995) Predicting global patterns of endemic plant species richness. *Biodiversity Letters* **2**, 127–131.

Cracraft, J. (1992) The species of the birds-of-paradise (Paradisaeidae): applying the phylogenetic species concept to a complex pattern of diversification. *Cladistics* **8**, 1–43.

Crame, J.A. (2000) Evolution of taxonomic diversity gradients in the marine realm: evidence from the composition of Recent bivalve faunas. *Paleobiology* **26**, 188–214.

Crame, J.A. (2001) Taxonomic diversity gradients through geological time. *Diversity and Distributions* **7**, 175–189.

Crame, J.A. (2002) Evolution of taxonomic diversity gradients in the marine realm: a comparison of Late Jurassic and Recent bivalve faunas. *Paleobiology* **28**, 184–207.

Crane, P.R. & Lidgard, S. (1989) Angiosperm diversification and paleolatitudinal gradients in Cretaceous floristic diversity. *Science* **246**, 675–678.

Crawley, M.J. & Harral, J.E. (2001) Scale dependence in plant biodiversity. *Science* **291**, 864–868.

Crawley, M.J., Harvey, P.H. & Purvis, A. (1996) Comparative ecology of the native and alien floras of the British Isles. *Philosophical Transactions of the Royal Society, London B* **351**, 1251–1259.

Crooks, K.R. & Soulé, M.E. (1999) Mesopredator release and avifaunal extinctions in a fragmented system. *Nature* **400**, 563–566.

Culver, S.J. & Buzas, M.A. (2000) Global latitudinal species diversity gradient in deep-sea benthic foraminifera. *Deep-Sea Research I* **47**, 259–275.

Currie, D.J. (1991) Energy and large-scale patterns of animal- and plant-species richness. *American Naturalist* **137**, 27–49.

Curtis, T.P., Sloan, W.T. & Scannell, J.W. (2002) Estimating prokaryotic diversity and its limits. *Proceedings of the National Academy of Sciences, USA* **99**, 10494–10499.

Daily, G.C. (ed.) (1997) *Nature's Services: Societal Dependence on Natural Ecosystems*. Island Press, Washington, DC.

Dauvin, J.-C., Kendall, M., Paterson, G., Gentil, F., Jirkov, I., Sheader, M. & De Lange, M. (1994) An initial assessment of polychaete diversity in the northeastern Atlantic Ocean. *Biodiversity Letters* **2**, 171–181.

Davidowitz, G. & Rosenzweig, M.L. (1998) The latitudinal gradient of species diversity among North American grasshoppers (Acrididae) within a single habitat: a test of the spatial heterogeneity hypothesis. *Journal of Biogeography* **25**, 553–560.

Davis, S.D., Heywood, V.H. & Hamilton, A.C. (eds.) (1994) *Centres of Plant Diversity*, Vol. 1. *Europe, Africa, South West Asia and the Middle East*. IUCN, Cambridge.

Davis, S.D., Heywood, V.H. & Hamilton, A.C. (eds.) (1995) *Centres of Plant Diversity*, Vol. 2. *Asia, Australasia and the Pacific*. IUCN, Cambridge.

Davis, S.D., Heywood, V.H., Herrera-MacBride, O., Villa-Lobos, J. & Hamilton, A.C. (eds.) (1997) *Centres of Plant Diversity*, Vol. 3. *The Americas*. IUCN, Cambridge.

Dayton, P.K., Thrush, S.F., Agardy, M.T. & Hofman, R.J. (1995) Environmental effects of marine fishing. *Aquatic Conservation: Marine and Freshwater Ecosystems* **5**, 205–232.

De Boer, J., Wester, P.G., Klamer, W.E. & Boon, J.P. (1998) Do flame retardants threaten ocean life? *Nature* **394**, 28–29.

de Forges, B.R., Koslow, J.A. & Poore, G.C.B. (2000) Diversity and endemism of the benthic seamount fauna in the southwest Pacific. *Nature* **405**, 944–947.

de Klerk, H.M., Crowe, T.M., Fjeldså, J. & Burgess, N.D. (2002) Biogeographical patterns of endemic terrestrial Afrotropical birds. *Diversity and Distributions* **8**, 147–162.

DeLong, D.C. Jr (1996) Defining biodiversity. *Wildlife Society Bulletin* **24**, 738–749.

Diamond, J. (1998) *Guns, Germs and Steel: A Short History of Everybody for the Last 13,000 years*. Vintage, London.

Diamond, J. (2002) Evolution, consequences and future of plant and animal domestication. *Nature* **418**, 700–707.

Diamond, J.M. (1984) 'Normal' extinctions of isolated populations. In: *Extinctions* (ed. M.H. Nitecki), pp. 191–246. University of Chicago Press, Chicago, IL.

Diamond, J.M. (1987) Extant unless proven extinct? or, extinct unless proven extant? *Conservation Biology* **1**, 77–79.

Díaz, S. & Cabido, M. (2001) Vive la difference: plant functional diversity matters to ecosystem processes. *Trends in Ecology and Evolution* **16**, 646–655.

Dingle, H., Rochester, W.A. & Zalucki, M.P. (2000) Relationships among climate, latitude and migration: Australian butterflies are not temperate-zone birds. *Oecologia* **124**, 196–207.

Dixon, A.F.G., Kindlmann, P., Leps, J. & Holman, J. (1987) Why are there so few species of aphids, especially in the tropics? *American Naturalist* **129**, 580–592.

Dobson, A. (1995) Biodiversity and human health. *Trends in Ecology and Evolution* **10**, 390–391.

Dobson, A.P., Bradshaw, A.D. & Baker, A.J.M. (1997) Hopes for the future: restoration ecology and conservation biology. *Science* **277**, 515–521.

Dodson, P. (1990) Counting dinosaurs: how many kinds were there? *Proceedings of the National Academy of Sciences, USA* **87**, 7608–7612.

Dolan, J.R. & Gallegos, C.L. (2001) Estuarine diversity of tintinnids (planktonic ciliates). *Journal of Plankton Research* **23**, 1009–1027.

Dolphin, K. & Quicke, D.L.J. (2001) Estimating the global species richness of an incompletely described taxon: an example using parasitoid wasps (Hymenoptera: Braconidae). *Biological Journal of the Linnean Society* **73**, 279–286.

Due, A.D. & Polis, G.A. (1986) Trends in scorpion diversity along the Baja California peninsula. *American Naturalist* **128**, 460–468.

Dugan, J.E. & Davis, G.E. (1993) Applications of marine refugia to coastal fisheries management. *Canadian Journal of Fisheries and Aquatic Sciences* **50**, 2029–2042.

Dunning, J.B. Jr (1997) The missing awareness, Part 2: Teaching students what a billion people looks like. *Conservation Biology* **11**, 6–10.

Dworschak, P.C. (2000) Global diversity in the Thalassinidea (Decapoda). *Journal of Crustacean Biology* **20** (Special Number 2), 238–245.

Eggleton, P. (1994) Termites live in a pear-shaped world: a response to Platnick. *Journal of Natural History* **28**, 1209–1212.

Ehrlich, P.R. (1995) The scale of the human enterprise and biodiversity loss. In: *Extinction Rates* (eds. J.H. Lawton & R.M. May), pp. 214–226. Oxford University Press, Oxford.

Ehrlich, P.R. & Daily, G.C. (1993) Population extinction and saving biodiversity. *Ambio* **22**, 64–68.

Ehrlich, P.R. & Ehrlich, A.H. (1981) *Extinction: The Causes and Consequences of the Disappearance of Species*. Random House, New York.

Ehrlich, P.R. & Ehrlich, A.H. (1992) The value of biodiversity. *Ambio* **21**, 219–226.

Ehrlich, P.R. & Wilson, E.O. (1991) Biodiversity studies: science and policy. *Science* **253**, 758–762.

Ellingsen, K.E. & Gray, J.S. (2002) Spatial patterns of benthic diversity: is there a latitudinal gradient along the Norwegian continental shelf? *Journal of Animal Ecology* **71**, 373–389.

Ellison, A.M. (2002) Macroecology of mangroves: large-scale patterns and processes in tropical coastal forests. *Trees* **16**, 181–194.

Elton, C. (1958) *The Ecology of Invasions by Animals and Plants*. Methuen, London.

Enquist, B.J. & Niklas, K.J. (2001) Invariant scaling relations across tree-dominated communities. *Nature* **410**, 655–660.

Erasmus, B.F.N., van Jaarsveld, A.S., Chown, S.L., Kshatriya, M. & Wessels, K.J. (2002) Vulnerability of South African animal taxa to climate change. *Global Change Biology* **8**, 679–693.

Erwin, D.H. (1998) The end and the beginning: recoveries from mass extinctions. *Trends in Ecology and Evolution* **13**, 344–349.

Erwin, D.H. (2001) Mass extinctions, notable examples of. In: *Encyclopedia of Biodiversity*, Vol. 4 (ed. S.A. Levin), pp. 111–122. Academic Press, San Diego, CA.

Erwin, T.L. (1983) Tropical forest canopies, the last biotic frontier. *Bulletin of the Entomological Society of America* **29**, 14–19.

Etter, R.J. & Grassle, J.F. (1992) Patterns of species diversity in the deep sea as a function of sediment particle size diversity. *Nature* **360**, 576–578.

Everett, S. (1998) Marine wildlife tourism. *British Wildlife* **10**, 139.

Fa, J.F., Peres, C.A. & Meeuwig, J. (2002) Bushmeat exploitation in tropical forests: an intercontinental comparison. *Conservation Biology* **16**, 232–237.

Fenchel, T., Esteban, G.F. & Finlay, B.J. (1997) Local versus global diversity of microorganisms: cryptic diversity of ciliated protozoa. *Oikos* **80**, 220–225.

Filion, F.L., Foley, J.P. & Jacquemot, A.P. (1994) The economics of global ecotourism. In: *Protected Area Economics and Policy: Linking Conservation and Sustainable Development* (eds. M. Munasinghe & J. McNeely), pp. 235–252. The World Bank, Washington, DC.

Findley, J.S. & Findley, M.T. (2001) Global, regional, and local patterns in species richness and abundance of butterflyfishes. *Ecological Monographs* **71**, 69–91.

Finlay, B.J. (2002) Global dispersal of free-living microbial eukaryote species. *Science* **296**, 1061–1063.

Finlay, B.J. & Fenchel, T. (1999) Divergent perspectives on protist species richness. *Protist* **150**, 229–233.

Finlay, B.J., Esteban, G.F. & Fenchel, T. (1998) Protozoan diversity: converging estimates of the global number of free-living ciliate species. *Protist* **149**, 29–37.

Fjeldså, J., Lambin, E. & Mertens, B. (1999) Correlation between endemism and local bioclimatic stability documented by comparing Andean bird distributions and remotely sensed land surface data. *Ecography* **22**, 63–78.

Flannery, T. (2001) *The Eternal Frontier: An Ecological History of North America and its Peoples*. Heinemann, London.

Flather, C.H., Wilson, K.R., Dean, D.J. & McComb, W.C. (1997) Identifying gaps in conservation networks: of indicators and uncertainty in geographic-based analyses. *Ecological Applications* **7**, 531–542.

Flessa, K.W. & Jablonski, D. (1995) Biogeography of Recent marine bivalve molluscs and its implications for paleobiogeography and the geography of extinction: a progress report. *Historical Biology* **10**, 25–47.

Flierman, C.B. & Balkwill, D.L. (1989) Microbial life in deep terrestrial subsurfaces. *BioScience* **39**, 370–377.

Folke, C., Jansson, Å., Larsson, J. & Constanza, R. (1997) Ecosystem appropriation of cities. *Ambio* **26**, 167–172.

Frankel, O.H., Brown, A.H.D. & Burdon, J.J. (1995) *The Conservation of Plant Biodiversity*. Cambridge University Press, Cambridge.

Frey, J.K. (1992) Response of a mammalian faunal element to climatic changes. *Journal of Mammalogy* **73**, 43–50.

Fritts, T.H. & Rodda, G.H. (1998) The role of introduced species in the degradation of island ecosystems: a case history of Guam. *Annual Review of Ecology and Systematics* **29**, 113–140.

Fröhlich, J. & Hyde, K.D. (1999) Biodiversity of palm fungi in the tropics: are global diversity estimates realistic? *Biodiversity and Conservation* **8**, 977–1004.

Fuhrman, J.A. & Campbell, L. (1998) Microbial microdiversity. *Nature* **393**, 410–411.

Gaston, K.J. (1994) Spatial patterns of species description: how is our knowledge of the global insect fauna growing? *Biological Conservation* **67**, 37–40.

Gaston, K.J. (1996a) Species richness: measure and measurement. In: *Biodiversity: A Biology of Numbers and Difference* (ed. K.J. Gaston), pp. 77–113. Blackwell Science, Oxford.

Gaston, K.J. (1996b) Biodiversity – congruence. *Progress in Physical Geography* **20**, 105–112.

Gaston, K.J. (1996c) Spatial covariance in the species richness of higher taxa. In: *Aspects of the Genesis and Maintenance of Biological Diversity* (eds. M.E. Hochberg, J. Clobert & R. Barbault), pp. 221–242. Oxford University Press, Oxford.

Gaston, K.J. & Blackburn, T.M. (2000) *Pattern and Process in Macroecology*. Blackwell Science, Oxford.

Gaston, K.J. & Blackburn, T.M. (2003) Macroecology and conservation biology. In: *Macroecology: Concepts and Consequences* (eds. T.M. Blackburn & K.J. Gaston), pp. 345–367. Blackwell Publishing, Oxford.

Gaston, K.J. & May, R.M. (1992) The taxonomy of taxonomists. *Nature* **356**, 281–282.

Gaston, K.J. & Mound, L.A. (1993) Taxonomy, hypothesis testing and the biodiversity crisis. *Proceedings of the Royal Society, London B* **251**, 139–142.

Gaston, K.J., Williams, P.H., Eggleton, P. & Humphries, C.J. (1995) Large scale patterns of biodiversity: spatial variation in family richness. *Proceedings of the Royal Society, London B* **260**, 149–154.

Gaston, K.J., Blackburn, T.M. & Spicer, J.I. (1998) Rapoport's rule: time for an epitaph? *Trends in Ecology and Evolution* **13**, 70–74.

Gaston, K.J., Chown, S.L. & Mercer, R.D. (2001) The animal species–body size distribution of Marion Island. *Proceedings of the National Academy of Sciences, USA* **98**, 14493–14496.

Gaston, K.J., Pressey, R.L. & Margules, C.R. (2002) Persistence and vulnerability: retaining biodiversity in the landscape and in protected areas. *Journal of Bioscience* **27**, 361–384.

Ginsberg, G. (2001) CITES at 30, or 40. *Conservation Biology* **16**, 1184–1191.

Glowka, L., Burhenne-Guilmin, F., Synge, H., McNeely, J.A. & Gündling, L. (1994) *A Guide to the Convention on Biological Diversity*. IUCN, Gland & Cambridge.

Godoy, R., Wilkie, D., Overman, H., Cubas, A., Cubas, G., Demmer, J., McSweeney, K. & Brokaw, N. (2000) Valuation of consumption and sale of forest goods from a Central American rain forest. *Nature* **406**, 62–63.

Gould, S.J. (1989) *Wonderful Life. The Burgess Shale and the Nature of History*. Hutchinson, London.

Gould, S.J. & Lewontin, R.C. (1979) The spandrels of San Marco and the Panglossian paradigm: a critique of the adaptationist programme. *Proceedings of the Royal Society, London B* **205**, 581–598.

Govaerts, R. (2001) How many species of seed plants are there? *Taxon* **50**, 1085–1090.

Grainger, R.J.R. & Garcia, S.M. (1996) Chronicles of marine fishery landings (1950–1994): trend analysis and fisheries potential. *FAO Fisheries Technical Paper* **359**, 1–51.

Grassle, J.F. (1991) Deep-sea benthic biodiversity. *BioScience* **51**, 464–469.

Grassle, J.F. & Maciolek, N.J. (1992) Deep-sea species richness: regional and local diversity estimates from quantitative bottom samples. *American Naturalist* **139**, 313–341.

Grayson, D.K. (2001) The archaeological record of human impacts on animal populations. *Journal of World Prehistory* **15**, 1–68.

Green, G.M. & Sussman, R.W. (1990) Deforestation history of the eastern rain forests of Madagascar from satellite images. *Science* **248**, 212–215.

Green, M.J.B. & Paine, J. (1997) State of the world's protected areas at the end of the twentieth century. Paper presented at IUCN World Commission on Protected Areas symposium 'Protected areas in the twenty-first century: from islands to networks'. Albany, Australia.

Gremmen, N.J.M. (1981) *The Vegetation of the Subantarctic Islands Marion and Prince Edward*. Junk, The Hague.

Griffiths, D. (1997) Local and regional species richness in North American lacustrine fish. *Journal of Animal Ecology* **66**, 49–56.

Groffman, P.M. (1997) Global biodiversity: is it in the mud and the dirt? *Trends in Ecology and Evolution* **12**, 301–302.

Groombridge, B. & Jenkins, M.D. (2002) *World Atlas of Biodiversity: Earth's Living Resources in the 21st Century*. University of California Press, London.

Grytnes, J.A. & Vetaas, O.R. (2002) Species richness and altitude: a comparison between null models and interpolated plant species richness along the Himalayan altitudinal gradient, Nepal. *American Naturalist* **159**, 294–304.

Guégan, J-F., Lek, S. & Oberdorff, T. (1998) Energy availability and habitat heterogeneity predict global riverine fish diversity. *Nature* **391**, 382–384.

Gurd, D.B., Nudds, T.D. & Rivard, D.H. (2001) Conservation of mammals in eastern North American wildlife reserves: how small is too small? *Conservation Biology* **15**, 1355–1363.

Halpern, B.S. & Warner, R.R. (2002) Marine reserves have rapid and lasting effects. *Ecology Letters* **5**, 361–366.

Hammond, P.M. (1995) Described and estimated species numbers: an objective assessment of current knowledge. In: *Microbial Diversity and Ecosystem Function* (eds. D. Allsopp, D.L. Hawksworth & R.R. Colwell), pp. 29–71. CAB International, Wallingford.

Hänel, C. & Chown, S. (1999) *An Introductory Guide to the Marion and Prince Edward Island Special Nature Reserves 50 Years After Annexation*. Department of Environmental Affairs and Tourism, Pretoria.

Hannah, L., Carr, J.L. & Lankerani, A. (1995) Human disturbance and natural habitat: a biome level analysis of a global data set. *Biodiversity and Conservation* **4**, 128–155.

Hansen, K. (2002) *A Farewell to Greenland's Wildlife*. BæreDygtighed, Klippinge, Denmark.

Harrison, I.J. & Stiassny, M.L.J. (1999) The quiet crisis: a preliminary listing of the freshwater fishes of the world that are extinct or 'missing in action'. In: *Extinctions in Near Time* (ed. R.D.E. MacPhee), pp. 271–331. Kluwer Academic/Plenum, New York.

Harvey, A. (2000) Strategies for discovering drugs from previously unexplored natural products. *Drug Discovery Today* **5**, 294–300.

Hawkins, B.A. & Porter, E.E. (2001) Area and the latitudinal diversity gradient for terrestrial birds. *Ecology Letters* **4**, 595–601.

Hawksworth, D.L. (1991) The fungal dimension of biodiversity: magnitude, significance, and conservation. *Mycological Research* **95**, 441–456.

Hawksworth, D.L. & Kalin-Arroyo, M.T. (1995) Magnitude and distribution of biodiversity. In: *Global Biodiversity Assessment* (ed. V.H. Heywood), pp. 107–199. Cambridge University Press, Cambridge.

Hayden, B.P., Ray, C.G. & Dolan, R. (1984) Classification of coastal and marine environments. *Environmental Conservation* **11**, 199–207.

Henneman, M.L. & Memmott, J. (2001) Infiltration of a Hawaiian community by introduced biological control agents. *Science* **293**, 1314–1316.

Hewzulla, D., Boulter, M.C., Benton, M.J. & Halley, J.M. (1999) Evolutionary patterns from mass originations and mass extinctions. *Philosophical Transactions of the Royal Society, London B* **354**, 463–469.

Heywood, V.H. & Baste, I. (1995) Introduction. In: *Global Biodiversity Assessment* (ed. V.H. Heywood), pp. 1–19. Cambridge University Press, Cambridge.

Hill, J.K., Thomas, C.D. & Huntley, B. (1999) Climate and habitat availability determine 20th century changes in a butterfly's range margin. *Proceedings of the Royal Society, London B* **266**, 1197–1206.

Hilton-Taylor, C. (comp.) (2000) *2000 IUCN Red List of Threatened Species*. IUCN, Gland. [Also available at http://www.redlist.org]

Hoare, R.E. & du Toit, J.T. (1999) Coexistence between people and elephants in African savannas. *Conservation Biology* **13**, 633–639.

Hockey, P. (1997a) New birds in Africa. *Africa Birds and Birding* **2**(1), 39–44.

Hockey, P. (1997b) Yet more birds for Africa. . . . *Africa Birds and Birding* **2**(2), 15.

Hogarth, P. (2001) Mangrove ecosystems. In: *Encyclopedia of Biodiversity*, Vol. 3 (ed. S.A. Levin), pp. 853–870. Academic Press, San Diego, CA.

Holdaway, R.N. (1999) Introduced predators and avifaunal extinction in New Zealand. In: *Extinctions in Near Time: Causes, Contexts, and Consequences* (ed. R.D.E. MacPhee), pp. 189–238. Kluwer Academic/Plenum, New York.

Holdaway, R.N. & Jacomb, C. (2000) Rapid extinction of the moas (Aves: Dinornithiformes): model, test, and implications. *Science* **287**, 2250–2254.

Holway, D.A. (1999) Competitive mechanisms underlying the displacement of native ants by the invasive Argentine ant. *Ecology* **80**, 238–251.

Houghton, J.T., Ding, Y., Griggs, D.J., Noguer, M., van der Linden, P.J. & Xiaosu, D. (eds.) (2001) *Climate Change 2001: The Scientific Basis*. Cambridge University Press, Cambridge.

Houlahan, J.E., Findlay, C.S., Schmidt, B.R., Meyer, A.H. & Kuzmin, S.L. (2000) Quantitative evidence for global amphibian population declines. *Nature* **404**, 752–755.

Hoyt, E. (2000) *Whale Watching 2000: Worldwide Tourism Numbers, Expenditures, and Expanding Socioeconomic Benefits*. International Fund for Animal Welfare, Crowborough.

Huber, H., Hohn, M.J., Rachel, R., Fuchs, T., Wimmer, V.C. & Stetter, K.O. (2002) A new phylum of Archaea represented by a nanosized hyperthermophilic symbiont. *Nature* **417**, 63–67.

Hughes, J.B., Daily, G.C. & Ehrlich, P.R. (1997) Population density: its extent and extinction. *Science* **278**, 689–692.

Humboldt, A. & Bonpland, A. (1807) *Essai sur la Géographie des Plantes Accompagné d'un Tableau Physique des Régions Équinoxiales*. [Reprint 1977, Arno Press, New York.]

Huntley, B. (1994) Plant species' response to climate change: implications for the conservation of European birds. *Ibis* **137**, S127–S138.

Hurka, H. (1994) Conservation genetics and the role of botanical gardens. In: *Conservation Genetics* (eds. V. Loeschcke, J. Tomiuk & K. Jain), pp. 371–380. Birkhauser Verlag, Basel.

Huston, M.A. (1994) *Biological Diversity: The Coexistence of Species on Changing Landscapes*. Cambridge University Press, Cambridge.

Huston, M.A. (1999) Local processes and regional patterns: appropriate scales for understanding variation in the diversity of plants and animals. *Oikos* **86**, 393–401.

Hutchings, J.A. (2000) Collapse and recovery of marine fishes. *Nature* **406**, 882–885.

Isenberg, A.C. (2000) *The Destruction of the Bison: An Environmental History, 1750–1920*. Cambridge University Press, Cambridge.

IUCN (1993) *Parks for Life – Report of the 4th World Conference on Natural Parks and Protected Areas*. IUCN, Gland.

IUCN (1994) *IUCN Red List Categories*. IUCN, Gland.

Jablonski, D. (1991) Extinctions: a paleontological perspective. *Science* **253**, 754–757.

Jablonski, D. (1993) The tropics as a source of evolutionary novelty through geological time. *Nature* **364**, 142–144.

Jablonski, D. (1995) Extinctions in the fossil record. In: *Extinction Rates* (eds. J.H. Lawton & R.M. May), pp. 25–44. Oxford University Press, Oxford.

Jablonski, D. (2002) Survival without recovery after mass extinctions. *Proceedings of the National Academy of Sciences, USA* **99**, 8139–8144.

Jackson, J.B.C. (2001) What was natural in the coastal oceans? *Proceedings of the National Academy of Sciences, USA* **98**, 5411–5418.

Jackson, J.B.C. & Sala, E. (2001) Unnatural oceans. *Scientia Marina* **65**, 273–281.

Jackson, J.B.C., Kirby, M.X., Berger, W.H., Bjorndal, K.A., Botsford, L.W., Bourque, B.J., Bradbury, R.H., Cooke, R., Erlandson, J., Estes, J.A., Hughes, T.P., Kidwell, S., Lange, C.B., Lenihan, H.S., Pandolfi, J.M., Peterson, C.H., Steneck, R.S., Tegner, M.J. & Warner, R.R. (2001) Historical overfishing and the recent collapse of coastal ecosystems. *Science* **293**, 629–638.

James, A.N., Gaston, K.J. & Balmford, A. (1999) Balancing the Earth's accounts. *Nature* **401**, 323–324.

James, A.N., Gaston, K.J. & Balmford, A. (2001) Can we afford to conserve biodiversity? *BioScience* **51**, 43–52.

Järvinen, O., Kouki, J. & Häyrinen, U. (1987) Reversed latitudinal gradients in total density and species richness of birds breeding on Finnish mires. *Ornis Fennica* **64**, 67–73.

Jeffree, C.E. & Jeffree, E.P. (1996) Redistribution of the potential geographical ranges of mistletoe and Colorado beetle in Europe in response to the temperature component of climate change. *Functional Ecology* **10**, 562–577.

Johnson, C.N. (1998) Rarity in the tropics: latitudinal gradients in distribution and abundance in Australian mammals. *Journal of Animal Ecology* **67**, 689–698.

Johnson, D.D.P., Hay, S.I. & Rogers, D.J. (1998) Contemporary environmental correlates of endemic bird areas derived from meteorological satellite sensors. *Proceedings of the Royal Society, London B* **265**, 951–959.

Johnson, K.H., Vogt, K.A., Clark, H.J., Schmitz, O.J. & Vogt, D.J. (1996) Biodiversity and the productivity and stability of ecosystems. *Trends in Ecology and Evolution* **11**, 372–377.

Jordan, W.R. III, Gilpin, M.E. & Aber, J.D. (eds.) (1990) *Restoration Ecology: A Synthetic Approach to Ecological Research*. Cambridge University Press, Cambridge.

Juniper, T. (2002) *Spix's Macaw: The Race to Save the World's Rarest Bird*. Fourth Estate, London.

Kaufman, D.M. & Willig, M.R. (1998) Latitudinal patterns of mammalian species richness in the New World: the effects of sampling method and faunal group. *Journal of Biogeography* **25**, 795–805.

Kendall, M.A. & Aschan, M. (1993) Latitudinal gradients in the structure of macrobenthic communities: a comparison of Arctic, temperate and tropical sites. *Journal of Experimental Marine Biology & Ecology* **172**, 157–169.

Kerr, J.T. (1997) Species richness, endemism, and the choice of areas for conservation. *Conservation Biology* **11**, 1094–1100.

Kerr, J.T. & Currie, D.J. (1999) The relative importance of evolutionary and environmental controls on broad-scale patterns of species richness in North America. *ÉcoScience* **6**, 329–337.

Kerr, J.T. & Packer, L. (1997) Habitat heterogeneity as a determinant of mammal species richness in high-energy regions. *Nature* **385**, 252–254.

Kerr, J.T. & Packer, L. (1999) The environmental basis of North American species richness patterns among *Epicauta* (Coleoptera: Meloidae). *Biodiversity and Conservation* **8**, 617–628.

Kerr, J.T., Vincent, R. & Currie, D.J. (1998) Lepidopteran richness patterns in North America. *Écoscience* **5**, 448–453.

Kerr, J.T., Southwood, T.R.E. & Cihlar, J. (2001) Remotely sensed habitat diversity predicts butterfly species richness and community similarity in Canada. *Proceedings of the National Academy of Sciences, USA* **98**, 11365–11370.

Kershaw, A.P. (1986) Climatic change and Aboriginal burning in north-east Australia during the last two glacial/interglacial cycles. *Nature* **322**, 47–49.

Kessler, M. (2002) The elevational gradient of Andean plant endemism: varying influences of taxon-specific traits and topography at different taxonomic levels. *Journal of Biogeography* **29**, 1159–1165.

Klass, K.-D., Zompro, O., Kristensen, N.P. & Adis, J. (2002) Mantophasmatodea: a new insect order with extant members in the Afrotropics. *Science* **296**, 1456–1459.

Klein Goldewijk, K. (2001) Estimating global land use change over the past 300 years: the HYDE database. *Global Biogeochemical Cycles* **15**, 417–433.

Körner, C. (2001) Alpine ecosystems. In: *Encyclopedia of Biodiversity*, Vol. 1 (ed. S.A. Levin), pp. 133–144. Academic Press, San Diego, CA.

Kouki, J. (1999) Latitudinal gradients in species richness in northern areas: some exceptional patterns. *Ecological Bulletins* **47**, 30–37.

Kouki, J., Niemelä, P. & Viitasaari, M. (1994) Reversed latitudinal gradient in species richness of sawflies (Hymenoptera, Symphyta). *Annales Zoologici Fennici* **31**, 83–88.

Kozár, F. & Dávid, A.N. (1986) The unexpected northward migration of some species of insects in Central Europe and the climatic changes. *Anz. Schädlingskde, Pflanzenschutz, Umweltschutz* **59**, 90–94.

Krech, S. III (1999) *The Ecological Indian: Myth and History*. Norton, New York.

Kruckeberg, A.R. & Rabinowitz, D. (1985) Biological aspects of endemism in higher plants. *Annual Review of Ecology and Systematics* **16**, 447–479.

Krutilla, J.V. (1967) Conservation reconsidered. *American Economic Review* **57**, 778–786.

Kunin, W.E. & Lawton, J.H. (1996) Does biodiversity matter? Evaluating the case for conserving species. In: *Biodiversity: A Biology of Numbers and Difference* (ed. K.J. Gaston), pp. 283–308. Blackwell Science, Oxford.

Lambshead, P.J.D. (1993) Recent developments in marine benthic biodiversity research. *Océanis* **19**, 5–24.

Lambshead, P.J.D. (in press) Marine nematode biodiversity. In: *Nematology, Advances and Perspectives* (eds. Z.X. Chen, S.Y. Chen & D.W. Dickson). ACSE-TUP Book Series.

Lambshead, P.J.D., Tietjen, J., Ferrero, T. & Jensen, P. (2000) Latitudinal diversity gradients in the deep sea with special reference to North Atlantic nematodes. *Marine Ecology Progress Series* **194**, 159–167.

Lande, R., Engen, S. & Saether, B.E. (1994) Optimal harvesting, economic discounting and extinction risk in fluctuating populations. *Nature* **372**, 88–90.

Lawton, J.H. (1994) What do species do in ecosystems? *Oikos* **71**, 367–374.

Lawton, J.H. (1999) Are there general laws in ecology? *Oikos* **84**, 177–192.

Lean, G. (1998) It's the poor that do the suffering . . . . *New Statesman* **11**, 10–11.

Lennon, J.J., Greenwood, J.J.D. & Turner, J.R.G. (2000) Bird diversity and environmental gradients in Britain: a test of the species–energy hypothesis. *Journal of Animal Ecology* **69**, 581–598.

Lockwood, J.L. & McKinney, M.L. (eds.) (2001) *Biotic Homogenization: The Loss of Diversity through Invasion and Extinction*. Kluwer Academic/Plenum, New York.

Lomolino, M.V. (2001) Elevation gradients of species-density: historical and prospective views. *Global Ecology and Biogeography* **10**, 3–13.

Lomolino, M.V. & Weiser, M.D. (2001) Towards a more general species–area relationship: diversity on all islands, great and small. *Journal of Biogeography* **28**, 431–445.

Long, A.J., Crosby, M.J., Stattersfield, A.J. & Wege, D.C. (1996) Towards a global map of biodiversity: patterns in the distribution of restricted-range birds. *Global Ecology and Biogeography Letters* **5**, 281–304.

Longhurst, A. (1998) *Ecological Geography of the Sea*. Academic Press, San Diego, CA.

Lonsdale, W.M. (1999) Global patterns of plant invasions and the concept of invasibility. *Ecology* **80**, 1522–1536.

Loreau, M., Naeem, S., Inchausti, P., Bengtsson, J., Grime, J., Hector, A., Hooper, D.U., Huston, M.A., Raffaelli, D., Schmid, B., Tilman, D. & Wardle, D.A. (2001) Biodiversity and ecosystem functioning: current knowledge and future challenges. *Science* **294**, 804–808.

Louda, S.M. & O'Brien, C.W. (2002) Unexpected ecological effects of distributing the exotic weevil, *Larinus planus* (F.), for the biological control of Canada thistle. *Conservation Biology* **16**, 717–727.

Lovelock, J. (1989) *The Ages of Gaia: A Biography of our Living Earth*. Oxford University Press, Oxford.

Lücking, R. & Matzer, M. (2001) High foliicolous lichen alpha-diversity on individual leaves in Costa Rica and Amazonian Ecuador. *Biodiversity and Conservation* **10**, 2139–2152.

Lyons, S.K. & Willig, M.R. (2002) Species richness, latitude, and scale sensitivity. *Ecology* **83**, 47–58.

MacArthur, R.H. & Wilson, E.O. (1967) *The Theory of Island Biogeography*. Princeton University Press, Princeton, NJ.

Mace, G.M. & Balmford, A. (2000) Patterns and processes in contemporary mammalian extinction. In: *Priorities for the Conservation of Mammalian Diversity: Has the Panda had its Day?* (eds. A. Entwistle & N. Dunstone), pp. 27–52. Cambridge University Press, Cambridge.

Mace, R. & Pagel, M. (1995) A latitudinal gradient in the density of human languages in North America. *Proceedings of the Royal Society, London B* **261**, 117–121.

Mack, R.N., Simberloff, D., Lonsdale, W.M., Evans, H., Clout, N. & Bazzaz, F.A. (2000) Biotic invasions: causes, epidemiology, global consequences, and control. *Ecological Applications* **10**, 689–710.

MacPhee, R.D.E. (ed.) (1999) *Extinctions in Near Time: Causes, Contexts, and Consequences*. Kluwer Academic/Plenum, New York.

MacPhee, R.D.E. & Flemming, C. (1999) Requiem Æternam: the last five hundred years of mammalian species extinctions. In: *Extinctions in Near Time* (ed. R.D.E. MacPhee), pp. 333–371. Kluwer Academic/Plenum, New York.

Macpherson, E. & Duarte, C.M. (1994) Patterns in species richness, size, and latitudinal range of East Atlantic fishes. *Ecography* **17**, 242–248.

Major, J. (1988) Endemism: a botanical perspective. In: *Analytical Biogeography: An Integrated Approach to the Study of Animal and Plant Distributions* (eds. A.A. Myers & P.S. Giller), pp. 117–146. Chapman & Hall, London.

Manire, C.A. & Gruber, S.H. (1990) Many sharks may be headed toward extinction. *Conservation Biology* **4**, 10–11.

Manokaran, N., La Frankie, J.V., Kochummen, K.M., Quah, E.S., Klahn, J.E., Ashton, P.S. & Hubbell, S.P. (1992) Stand table and distribution of species in the 50-ha research plot at Pasoh Forest Reserve. *Forest Research Institute Malaysia, Research Data* **1**, 1–454.

Margulis, L. & Schwartz, K.V. (1998) *Five Kingdoms: An Illustrated Guide to the Phyla of Life on Earth*, 3rd edn. W.H. Freeman & Co., New York.

Marmonier, P., Vervier, P., Gibert, J. & Dole-Olivier, M.-J. (1993) Biodiversity in ground waters. *Trends in Ecology and Evolution* **8**, 392–395.

Martin, G. (1996) Birds in double trouble. *Nature* **380**, 666–667.

Martin, J. & Gurrea, P. (1990) The peninsular effect in Iberian butterflies (Lepidoptera: Papilionoidea and Hesperioidea). *Journal of Biogeography* **17**, 85–96.

Martin, P.S. (1984) Prehistoric overkill: the global model. In: *Quaternary Extinctions: A Prehistoric Revolution* (eds. P.S. Martin & R.G. Klein), pp. 354–403. University of Arizona Press, Tucson, AZ.

Martin, P.S. (2001) Mammals (Late Quaternary), extinctions of. In: *Encyclopedia of Biodiversity*, Vol. 3 (ed. S.A. Levin), pp. 825–839. Academic Press, San Diego, CA.

Martinez, N.D. (1996) Defining and measuring functional aspects of biodiversity. In: *Biodiversity: A Biology of Numbers and Difference* (ed. K.J. Gaston), pp. 114–148. Blackwell Science, Oxford.

Mateo, N., Nader, W. & Tamayo, G. (2001) Bioprospecting. In: *Encyclopedia of Biodiversity*, Vol. 1 (ed. S.A. Levin), pp. 471–488. Academic Press, San Diego, CA.

Matson, P.A., Parton, W.J., Power, A.G. & Swift, M.J. (1997) Agricultural intensification and ecosystem properties. *Science* **277**, 504–509.

May, R.M. (1988) How many species are there on Earth? *Science* **241**, 1441–1449.

May, R.M. (1990) How many species? *Philosophical Transactions of the Royal Society, London B* **330**, 293–304.

May, R.M. (1992a) How many species inhabit the Earth? *Scientific American* (October), 18–24.

May, R.M. (1992b) Bottoms up for the oceans. *Nature* **357**, 278–279.

May, R.M. (1994a) Conceptual aspects of the quantification of the extent of biological diversity. *Philosophical Transactions of the Royal Society, London B* **345**, 13–20.

May, R.M. (1994b) Biological diversity: differences between land and sea. *Philosophical Transactions of the Royal Society, London B* **343**, 105–111.

May, R.M. (1994c) The economics of extinction. *Nature* **372**, 42–43.

May, R.M., Lawton, J.H. & Stork, N.E. (1995) Assessing extinction rates. In: *Extinction Rates* (eds. J.H. Lawton & R.M. May), pp. 1–24. Oxford University Press, Oxford.

Mayr, E. & Diamond, J. (2001) *The Birds of Northern Melanesia: Speciation, Ecology, and Biogeography*. Oxford University Press, New York.

McGlone, M.S. (1983) Polynesian deforestation of New Zealand: a preliminary synthesis. *Archaeology in Oceania* **18**, 11–25.

McGlone, M.S. & Basher, L.R. (1995) The deforestation of the upper Awatere catchment, Inland Kaikoura Range, Marlborough, South Island, New Zealand. *New Zealand Journal of Ecology* **19**, 63–66.

McGowan, J.A. & Walker, P.W. (1993) Pelagic diversity patterns. In: *Species Diversity in Ecological Communities: Historical and Geographical Perspectives* (eds. R.E. Ricklefs & D.

Schluter), pp. 203–214. University of Chicago Press, Chicago, IL.

McGrady-Steed, J., Harris, P.M. & Morin, P.J. (1997) Biodiversity regulates ecosystem predictability. *Nature* **390**, 162–165.

McKinney, M.L. (1997) Extinction vulnerability and selectivity: combining ecological and paleontological views. *Annual Review of Ecology and Systematics* **28**, 495–516.

McKinney, M.L. (1998) Is marine biodiversity at less risk? Evidence and implications. *Diversity and Distributions* **4**, 3–8.

McKinney, M.L. (1999) High rates of extinction and threat in poorly studied taxa. *Conservation Biology* **13**, 1273–1281.

McKinney, M.L. (2001) Effects of human population, area, and time on non-native plant and fish diversity in the United States. *Biological Conservation* **100**, 243–252.

McKinney, M.L. (2002) Why larger nations have disproportionate threat rates: area increases endemism and human population size. *Biodiversity and Conservation* **11**, 1317–1325.

McLaughlin, J.F., Hellmann, J.J., Boggs, C.L. & Ehrlich, P.R. (2002) Climate change hastens population extinctions. *Proceedings of the National Academy of Sciences, USA* **99**, 6070–6074.

McLennan, D.A. & Brooks, D.R. (2002) Complex histories of speciation and dispersal in communities: a re-analysis of some Australian bird data using BPA. *Journal of Biogeography* **29**, 1055–1066.

Medellín, R.A. & Soberón, J. (1999) Predictions of mammal diversity on four land masses. *Conservation Biology* **13**, 143–149.

Meinesz, A. (1999) *Killer Algae: The True Tale of a Biological Invasion*. University of Chicago Press, Chicago, IL.

Milberg, P. & Tyrberg, T. (1993) Naïve birds and noble savages – a review of man-caused prehistoric extinctions of island birds. *Ecography* **16**, 229–250.

Miller, G.H., Magee, J.W., Johnson, B.J., Fogel, M.L., Spooner, N.A., McCulloch, M.T. & Ayliffe, L.K. (1999) Pleistocene extinction of *Genyornis newtoni*: human impact on Australian megafauna. *Science* **283**, 205–208.

Miller, K., Allegretti, M.H., Johnson, N. & Jonsson, B. (1995) Measurement for conservation of biodiversity and sustainable use of its components. In: *Global Biodiversity Assessment* (ed. V.H. Heywood), pp. 915–1061. Cambridge University Press, Cambridge.

Mitter, C., Farrell, B. & Wiegmann, B. (1988) The phylogenetic study of adaptive zones: has phytophagy promoted insect diversification? *American Naturalist* **132**, 107–128.

Mittermeier, R.A., Gil, P.R. & Mittermeier, C.G. (1997) *Megadiversity: Earth's Biologically Wealthiest Nations*. CEMEX/Conservation International, Mexico City.

Morenta, J., Stefanescu, C., Massuti, E., Morales-Nin, B. & Lloris, D. (1998) Fish community structure and depth-related trends on the continental slope of the Balearic Islands (Algerian basin, western Mediterranean). *Marine Ecology Progress Series* **171**, 247–259.

Morowitz, H.J. (1991) Balancing species preservation and economic considerations. *Science* **253**, 752–754.

Mosquera, I., Côté, I.M., Jennings, S. & Reynolds, J.D. (2000) Conservation benefits of marine reserves for fish populations. *Animal Conservation* **4**, 321–332.

Munro, M.H.G., Blunt, J.W., Dumdei, E.J., Hickford, S.J.H., Lill, R.E., Li, S., Battershill, C.N. & Duckworth, A.R. (1999) The discovery and development of marine compounds with pharmaceutical potential. *Journal of Biotechnology* **70**, 15–25.

Myers, N. (1997) The rich diversity of biodiversity issues. In: *Biodiversity II: Understanding & Protecting our Biological Resources* (eds. M.L. Reaka-Kudla, D.E. Wilson & E.O. Wilson), pp. 125–138. Joseph Henry, Washington, DC.

Myers, N. (1998) Lifting the veil on perverse subsidies. *Nature* **392**, 327–328.

Myers, N. (2001) Hotspots. In: *Encyclopedia of Biodiversity*, Vol. 3 (ed. S.A. Levin), pp. 371–381. Academic Press, San Diego, CA.

Myers, N. & Kent, J. (1998) *Perverse Subsidies: Tax $s Undercutting our Economics and Environments Alike*. International Institute for Sustainable Development, Winnipeg.

Myers, N., Mittermeier, R.A., Mittermeier, C.G., da Fonseca, G.A.B. & Kent, J. (2000) Biodiversity hotspots for conservation priorities. *Nature* **403**, 853–858.

Naeem, S. (1998) Species redundancy and ecosystem reliability. *Conservation Biology* **12**, 39–45.

Naeem, S. (2002) Functioning of biodiversity. In: *Encyclopedia of Global Environmental Change*, Vol. 2 (ed. T. Munn), pp. 20–36. Wiley, New York.

Naeem, S. & Li, S. (1997) Biodiversity enhances ecosystem reliability. *Nature* **390**, 507–509.

Naeem, S., Thompson, L.J., Lawler, S.P., Lawton, J.H. & Woodfin, R.M. (1994) Declining biodiversity can alter the performance of ecosystems. *Nature* **368**, 734–737.

Naeem, S., Thompson, L.J., Lawler, S.P., Lawton, J.H. & Woodfin, R.M. (1995) Empirical evidence that declining species-diversity may alter the performance of terrestrial ecosystems. *Philosophical Transactions of the Royal Society, London B* **347**, 249–262.

Nakano, S., Kitano, F. & Maekawa, K. (1996) Potential fragmentation and loss of thermal habitats for charrs in the Japanese archipelago due to climatic warming. *Freshwater Biology* **36**, 711–722.

Newmark, W.D. (1987) A land-bridge island perspective on mammalian extinctions in western North American parks. *Nature* **325**, 430–432.

Newmark, W.D. (1993) The role and design of wildlife corridors with examples from Tanzania. *Ambio* **22**, 500–504.

Newmark, W.D. (1996) Insularization of Tanzanian parks and the local extinction of large mammals. *Conservation Biology* **10**, 1549–1556.

Nicol, D. (1971) Species, class, and phylum diversity of animals. *Quarterly Journal of Florida Academy of Science* **34**, 191–194.

Niklas, K.J. (1986) Large-scale changes in animal and plant terrestrial communities. In: *Patterns and Processes in the History of Life* (eds. D.M. Raup & D. Jablonski), pp. 383–405. Springer-Verlag, Berlin.

Noble, I.R. & Dirzo, R. (1997) Forests as human-dominated ecosystems. *Science* **277**, 522–525.

Norgaard, R.B. (1988) Economics of the cassava mealybug [*Phenacoccus manihoti*; Hom.: Pseudococcidae] biological control program in Africa. *Entomophaga* **33**, 3–6.

Novotny, V., Basset, Y., Miller, S.E., Weiblen, G.D., Bremer, B., Cizek, L. & Drozd, P. (2002a) Low host specificity of herbivorous insects in a tropical forest. *Nature* **416**, 841–844.

Novotny, V., Basset, Y., Miller, S.E., Drozd, P. & Cizek, L. (2002b) Host specialization of leaf-chewing insects in a New Guinea rainforest. *Journal of Animal Ecology* **71**, 400–412.

Oberdorff, T., Guégan, J.-F. & Hugueny, B. (1995) Global scale patterns of fish species richness in rivers. *Ecography* **18**, 345–352.

Oberdorff, T., Lek, S. & Guégan, J.-F. (1999) Patterns of endemism in riverine fish of the Northern Hemisphere. *Ecology Letters* **2**, 75–81.

Ødegaard, F., Diserud, O.H., Engen, S. & Aagard, K. (2000) The magnitude of local host specificity for phytophagous insects and its implications for estimates of global species richness. *Conservation Biology* **14**, 1182–1186.

Oldfield, S., Lusty, C. & MacKinven, A. (1998) *The World List of Threatened Trees*. WCMC, Cambridge.

Olmstead, K.L. & Wood, T.K. (1990) Altitudinal patterns in species richness of Neotropical treehoppers (Homoptera: Membracidae): the role of ants. *Proceedings of the Entomological Society of Washington* **92**, 552–560.

Olson, D.M. & Dinerstein, E. (1998) The global 200: a representation approach to conserving the earth's most biologically valuable ecoregions. *Conservation Biology* **12**, 502–515.

Olson, D.M., Dinerstein, E., Wikramanayake, E.D., Burgess, N.D., Powell, G.V.N., Underwood, E.C., D'Amico, J.A., Itoua, I., Strand, H.E., Morrison, J.C., Loucks, C.J., Allnutt, T.F., Ricketts, T.H., Kura, Y., Lamoreux, J.F., Wettengel, W.W., Hedao, P. & Kassem, K.R. (2001) Terrestrial ecoregions of the World: a new map of life on Earth. *BioScience* **51**, 933–938.

O'Toole, C. (1993) Diversity of native bees and agroecosystems. In: *Hymenoptera and Biodiversity* (eds. J. LaSalle & I.D. Gauld), pp. 169–196. CAB International, Wallingford.

Øvstedal, D.O. & Gremmen, N.J.M. (2001) The

lichen flora of Marion and Prince Edward islands. *South African Journal of Botany* **67**, 552–572.

Owen-Smith, N. (1989) Megafaunal extinctions: the conservation message from 11,000 years B.P. *Conservation Biology* **3**, 405–412.

Palmer, M.W. & White, P.S. (1994) Scale dependence and the species–area relationship. *American Naturalist* **144**, 717–740.

Parks, S.A. & Harcourt, A.H. (2002) Reserve size, local human density, and mammalian extinctions in U.S. protected areas. *Conservation Biology* **16**, 800–808.

Parmesan, C. (1996) Climate and species' range. *Nature* **382**, 765–766.

Parmesan, C., Ryrholm, N., Stefanescu, C., Hill, J.K., Thomas, C.D., Descimon, H., Huntley, B., Kaila, L., Kullberg, J., Tammaru, T., Tennent, W.J., Thomas, J.A. & Warren, M. (1999) Poleward shifts in geographical ranges of butterfly species associated with regional warming. *Nature* **399**, 579–583.

Paterson, G.L.J. (1993) *Patterns of polychaete assemblage structure from bathymetric transects in the Rockall Trough, NE Atlantic Ocean*. PhD Thesis, University of Wales.

Patterson, B.D. (2000) Patterns and trends in the discovery of new Neotropical mammals. *Diversity and Distributions* **6**, 145–151.

Patterson, B.D., Stotz, D.E., Solari, S., Fitzpatrick, J.W. & Pacheco, V. (1998) Contrasting patterns of elevational zonation for birds and mammals in the Andes of southeastern Peru. *Journal of Biogeography* **25**, 593–607.

Pauly, D. & Christensen, V. (1995) Primary production required to sustain global fisheries. *Nature* **374**, 255–257.

Pauly, D., Christensen, V., Dalsgaard, J., Froese, R. & Torres, F. Jr (1998) Fishing down marine food webs. *Science* **279**, 860–863.

Pauly, D., Christensen, V., Guénette, S., Pitcher, T.J., Sumaila, U.R., Walters, C.J., Watson, R. & Zeller, D. (2002) Towards sustainability in world fisheries. *Nature* **418**, 689–695.

Pedersen, K. (1993) The deep subterranean biosphere. *Earth-Science Reviews* **34**, 243–260.

Peres, C.A. (2000) Effects of subsistence hunting on vertebrate community structure in Amazonian forests. *Conservation Biology* **14**, 240–253.

Perrings, C. (1995) The economic value of biodiversity. In: *Global Biodiversity Assessment* (ed. V.H. Heywood), pp. 823–914. Cambridge University Press, Cambridge.

Perrow, M.R. & Davy, A.J. (eds.) (2002a) *Handbook of Ecological Restoration*, Vol. 1. *Principles of Restoration*. Cambridge University Press, Cambridge.

Perrow, M.R. & Davy, A.J. (eds.) (2002b) *Handbook of Ecological Restoration*, Vol. 2. *Restoration in Practice*. Cambridge University Press, Cambridge.

Petchey, O.L. & Gaston, K.J. (2002) Functional diversity (FD), species richness and community composition. *Ecology Letters* **5**, 402–411.

Pianka, E.R. (1966) Latitudinal gradients in species diversity: a review of concepts. *American Naturalist* **100**, 33–46.

Pimentel, D. (2001) Agricultural invasions. In: *Encyclopedia of Biodiversity*, Vol. 1 (ed. S.A. Levin), pp. 71–85. Academic Press, San Diego, CA.

Pimentel, D., Wilson, C., McCullum, C., Huang, R., Dwen, P., Flack, J., Tran, Q., Saltman, T. & Cliff, B. (1997) Economic and environmental benefits of biodiversity. *BioScience* **47**, 747–757.

Pimentel, D., Lach, L., Zuniga, R. & Morrison, D. (2000) Environmental and economic costs of nonindigenous species in the United States. *BioScience* **50**, 53–65.

Pimm, S.L. (1997) The value of everything. *Nature* **387**, 231–232.

Pimm, S.L. (2001) *The World According to Pimm: A Scientist Audits the Earth*. McGraw-Hill, New York.

Pimm, S.L., Russell, G.J., Gittleman, J.L. & Brooks, T.M. (1995a) The future of biodiversity. *Science* **269**, 347–350.

Pimm, S.L., Moulton, M.P. & Justice, L.J. (1995b) Bird extinctions in the central Pacific. In: *Extinction Rates* (eds. J.H. Lawton & R.M. May), pp. 75–87. Oxford University Press, Oxford.

Pine, R.H. (1994) New mammals not so seldom. *Nature* **368**, 593.

Pineda, J. & Caswell, H. (1998) Bathymetric species-diversity patterns and boundary constraints on vertical range distributions. *Deep-Sea Research II* **45**, 83–101.

Pitman, N.C.A. & Jørgensen, P.M. (2002) Estimating the size of the World's threatened flora. *Science* **298**, 989.

Platnick, N.I. (1991) Patterns of biodiversity: tropical vs temperate. *Journal of Natural History* **25**, 1083–1088.

Platnick, N.I. (1992) Patterns of biodiversity. In: *Systematics, Ecology, and the Biodiversity Crisis* (ed. N. Eldredge), pp. 15–24. Columbia University Press, New York.

Poore, G.C.B. & Wilson, G.D.F. (1993) Marine species richness. *Nature* **361**, 597–598.

Postel, S.L., Daily, G.C. & Ehrlich, P.R. (1996) Human appropriation of renewable fresh water. *Science* **271**, 785–788.

Poulin, R. (1996) How many parasite species are there: are we close to answers? *International Journal of Parasitology* **26**, 1127–1129.

Prance, G.T., Beentje, H., Dransfield, J. & Johns, R. (2000) The tropical flora remains undercollected. *Annals of the Missouri Botanical Garden* **87**, 67–71.

Prendergast, J.R., Quinn, R.M., Lawton, J.H., Eversham, B.C. & Gibbons, D.W. (1993) Rare species, the coincidence of diversity hotspots and conservation strategies. *Nature* **365**, 335–337.

Pressey, R.L., Humphries, C.J., Margules, C.R., Vane-Wright, R.I. & Williams, P.H. (1993) Beyond opportunism: key principles for systematic reserve selection. *Trends in Ecology and Evolution* **8**, 124–128.

Pressey, R.L., Whish, G.L., Barrett, T.W. & Watts, M.E. (2002) Effectiveness of protected areas in north-eastern New South Wales: recent trends in six measures. *Biological Conservation* **106**, 57–69.

Pretty, J. (1998) *The Living Land: Agriculture, Food and Community Regeneration in Rural Europe*. Earthscan, London.

Price, P.W., Fernandes, G.W., Lara, A.C.F., Brawn, J., Barrios, H., Wright, M.G., Ribeiro, S.P. & Rothcliff, N. (1998) Global patterns in local number of insect galling species. *Journal of Biogeography* **25**, 581–591.

Price, T. (1996) Exploding species. *Trends in Ecology and Evolution* **11**, 314–315.

Pudjoarinto, A. & Cushing, E.J. (2001) Pollen-stratigraphic evidence of human activity in Dieng, Central Java. *Palaeogeography, Palaeoclimatology, Palaeoecology* **171**, 329–340.

Purvis, A. & Hector, A. (2000) Getting the measure of biodiversity. *Nature* **405**, 212–219.

Pyšek, P., Jarošik, V. & Kučera, T. (2002) Patterns of invasion in temperate nature reserves. *Biological Conservation* **104**, 13–24.

Pywell, R. & Putwain, P. (1996) Restoration and conservation gain. In: *Conservation Biology* (ed. I.F. Spellerberg), pp. 203–221. Longman, Harlow.

Rabenold, K.N. (1993) Latitudinal gradients in avian species diversity and the role of long-distance migration. In: *Current Ornithology*, Vol. 10 (ed. D.M. Power), pp. 247–274. Plenum Press, New York.

Rahbek, C. (1993) Captive breeding – a useful tool in the preservation of biodiversity? *Biodiversity and Conservation* **2**, 426–437.

Rahbek, C. (1995) The elevational gradient of species richness: a uniform pattern? *Ecography* **18**, 200–205.

Rahbek, C. (1997) The relationship among area, elevation, and regional species richness in neotropical birds. *American Naturalist* **149**, 875–902.

Rahel, F.J. (2000) Homogenization of fish faunas across the United States. *Science* **288**, 854–856.

Rapoport, E.H. (1993) The process of plant colonization in small settlements and large cities. In: *Humans as Components of Ecosystems: The Ecology of Subtle Human Effects and Populated Areas* (eds. M.J. McDonnell & S.T.A. Pickett), pp. 190–207. Springer-Verlag, New York.

Rapoport, E.H. (1994) Remarks on marine and continental biogeography: an areographical viewpoint. *Philosophical Transactions of the Royal Society, London B* **343**, 71–78.

Rapoport, E.H. & Drausal, B.S. (2001) Edible plants. In: *Encyclopedia of Biodiversity*, Vol. 2 (ed. S.A. Levin), pp. 375–382. Academic Press, San Diego, CA.

Raup, D.M. (1994) The role of extinction in evolution. *Proceedings of the National Academy of Sciences, USA* **91**, 6758–6763.

Reaka-Kudla, M.L. (1997) The global biodiversity of coral reefs: a comparison with rain forests. In: *Biodiversity II: Understanding & Protecting our Biological Resources* (eds. M.L. Reaka-Kudla, D.E. Wilson & E.O. Wilson), pp. 83–108. Joseph Henry, Washington, DC.

Redford, K.H. (1992) The empty forest. *BioScience* **42**, 412–422.

Rees, W.E. (2001) Ecological footprint, concept of. In: *Encyclopedia of Biodiversity*, Vol. 2 (ed. S.A. Levin), pp. 229–244. Academic Press, San Diego, CA.

Reid, J.W. (1994) Latitudinal diversity patterns of continental benthic copepod species assemblages in the Americas. *Hydrobiologia* **292/293**, 341–349.

Rex, M.A. (1981) Community structure in the deep-sea benthos. *Annual Review of Ecology and Systematics* **12**, 331–354.

Rex, M.A., Stuart, C.T., Hessler, R.R., Allen, J.A., Sanders, H.L. & Wilson, G.D.F. (1993) Global-scale latitudinal patterns of species diversity in the deep-sea benthos. *Nature* **365**, 636–639.

Rex, M.A., Etter, R.J. & Stuart, C.T. (1997) Large-scale patterns of species diversity in the deep-sea benthos. In: *Marine Biodiversity: Patterns and Processes* (eds. R.F.G. Ormond, J.D. Gage & M.V. Angel), pp. 94–121. Cambridge University Press, Cambridge.

Rex, M.A., Stuart, C.T. & Coyne, G. (2000) Latitudinal gradients of species richness in the deep-sea benthos of the North Atlantic. *Proceedings of the National Academy of Sciences, USA* **97**, 4082–4085.

Ribera, I., Beutel, R.G., Balke, M. & Vogler, A.P. (2002) Discovery of Aspidytidae, a new family of aquatic Coleoptera. *Proceedings of the Royal Society, London B* **269**, 2351–2356.

Richardson, J.E., Pennington, R.T., Pennington, T.D. & Hollingsworth, P.M. (2001) Rapid diversification of a species-rich genus of neotropical rain forest trees. *Science* **293**, 2242–2245.

Ricketts, T.H., Dinerstein, E., Olson, D.M. & Loucks, C. (1999) Who's where in North America? *BioScience* **49**, 369–381.

Ricklefs, R.E. (1987) Community diversity: relative roles of local and regional processes. *Science* **235**, 167–171.

Ricklefs, R.E. & Schluter, D. (eds.) (1993) *Species Diversity in Ecological Communities: Historical and Geographical Perspectives*. University of Chicago Press, Chicago, IL.

Riddle, J.M. & Estes, J.W. 1992. Oral contraceptives in ancient and medieval times. *American Scientist* **80**, 226–233.

Robbins, R.K. & Opler, P.A. (1997) Butterfly diversity and a preliminary comparison with bird and mammal diversity. In: *Biodiversity II* (eds. M.L. Reaka-Kudla, D.E. Wilson & E.O. Wilson), pp. 69–82. Joseph Henry Press, Washington, DC.

Roberts, C.M. (2002) Deep impact: the rising toll of fishing in the deep sea. *Trends in Ecology and Evolution* **17**, 242–245.

Roberts, C.M., Bohnsack, J.A., Gell, F., Hawkins, J.P. & Goodridge, R. (2001) Effects of marine reserves on adjacent fisheries. *Science* **294**, 1920–1923.

Roberts, C.M., McClean, C.J., Veron, J.E.N., Hawkins, J.P., Allen, G.R., McAllister, D.E., Mittermeier, C.G., Schueler, F.W., Spalding, M., Wells, F., Vynne, C. & Werner, T.B. (2002) Marine biodiversity hotspots and conservation priorities for tropical reefs. *Science* **295**, 1280–1284.

Roberts, R.G., Flannery, T.F., Ayliffe, L.K., Yoshida, H., Olley, J.M., Prideaux, G.J., Laslett, G.M., Baynes, A., Smith, M.A., Jones, R. & Smith, B.L. (2001) New ages for the last Australian megafauna: continent-wide extinction about 46,000 years ago. *Science* **292**, 1888–1982.

Robinson, J.G. & Bodmer, R.E. (1999) Towards wildlife management in tropical forests. *Journal of Wildlife Management* **63**, 1–13.

Rodrigues, A.S.L. & Gaston, K.J. (2001) How large do reserve networks need to be? *Ecology Letters* **4**, 602–609.

Rogers, D.J. & Randolph, S.E. (2000) The global spread of malaria in a future, warmer world. *Science* **289**, 1763–1766.

Rohde, K. (1978) Latitudinal gradients in species diversity and their causes. II. Marine parasitological evidence for a time hypothesis. *Biologisches Zentralblatt* **97**, 405–418.

Rohde, K. (1992) Latitudinal gradients in species diversity: the search for the primary cause. *Oikos* **65**, 514–527.

Rohde, K. (1997) The larger area of the tropics does not explain latitudinal gradients in species diversity. *Oikos* **79**, 169–172.

Rohde, K. (1998) Latitudinal gradients in species diversity. Area matters, but how much? *Oikos* **82**, 184–190.

Rojstaczer, S., Sterling, S.M. & Moore, N.J. (2001) Human appropriation of photosynthesis products. *Science* **294**, 2549–2552.

Root, T.L., Price, J.T., Hall, K.R., Schneider, S.H., Rosenzweig, C. & Pounds, J.A. (2003) Fingerprints of global warming on wild animals and plants. *Nature* **421**, 57–60.

Rosa, R., Grenier, J.K., Andreeva, T., Cook, C.E., Adoutle, A., Akam, M., Carroll, S.B. & Balavoine, G. (1999) Hox genes in brachiopods and priapulids and protostome evolution. *Nature* **399**, 772–776.

Rosenzweig, M.L. (1992) Species diversity gradients: we know more and less than we thought. *Journal of Mammalogy* **73**, 715–730.

Rosenzweig, M.L. (1995) *Species Diversity in Space and Time*. Cambridge University Press, Cambridge.

Rosenzweig, M.L. & Sandlin, E.A. (1997) Species diversity and latitudes: listening to area's signal. *Oikos* **80**, 172–176.

Rosenzweig, M.L. & Ziv, Y. (1999) The echo pattern of species diversity. *Ecography* **22**, 614–628.

Roy, K., Jablonski, D. & Valentine, J.W. (1996) Higher taxa in biodiversity studies: patterns from eastern Pacific marine molluscs. *Philosophical Transactions of the Royal Society, London B* **351**, 1605–1613.

Roy, K., Jablonski, D., Valentine, J.W. & Rosenberg, G. (1998) Marine latitudinal diversity gradients: tests of causal hypotheses. *Proceedings of the National Academy of Sciences, USA* **95**, 3699–3702.

Ruesink, J.L., Parker, I.M., Groom, M.J. & Kareiva, P.M. (1995) Reducing the risks of nonindigenous species introductions. *BioScience* **45**, 465–477.

Ruggiero, A. (1999) Spatial patterns in the diversity of mammal species: a test of the geographic area hypothesis in South America. *Écoscience* **6**, 338–354.

Rutherford, S., D'Hondt, S. & Prell, W. (1999) Environmental controls on the geographic distribution of zooplankton diversity. *Nature* **400**, 749–753.

Sanders, N.J. (2002) Elevational gradients in ant species richness: area, geometry, and Rapoport's rule. *Ecography* **25**, 25–32.

Sarbu, S.M., Kane, T.C. & Kinkle, B.K. (1996) A chemoautotrophically based cave ecosystem. *Science* **272**, 1953–1955.

Saunders, D.A. & Hobbs, R.J. (eds.) (1991) *Nature Conservation 2: The Role of Corridors*. Surrey Beatty, Sydney.

Saunders, D.A., Hobbs, R.J. & Margules, C.R. (1991) Biological consequences of ecosystem fragmentation: a review. *Conservation Biology* **5**, 18–32.

Sax, D.F. (2002) Native and naturalized plant diversity are positively correlated in scrub communities of California and Chile. *Diversity and Distributions* **8**, 193–210.

Schläpfer, F. & Schmid, B. (1999) Ecosystem effects of biodiversity: a classification of hypotheses and exploration of empirical results. *Ecological Applications* **9**, 893–912.

Schopf, J.W. (ed.) (1992) *Major Events in the History of Life*. Jones & Bartlett, Boston, MA.

Schwartz, M.W., Brigham, C.A., Hoeksema, J.D., Lyons, K.G., Mills, M.H. & van Mautgem, P.J. (2000) Linking biodiversity to ecosystem function: implications for conservation ecology. *Oecologia* **122**, 297–305.

Scott, J.M., Murray, M., Wright, R.G., Csuti, B., Morgan, P. & Pressey, R.L. (2001) Representation of natural vegetation in protected areas: capturing the geographic range. *Biodiversity and Conservation* **10**, 1297–1301.

Sechrest, W., Brooks, T.M., da Fonseca, G.A.B., Konstant, W.R., Mittermeier, R.A., Purvis, A.,

Rylands, A.B. & Gittleman, J.L. (2002) Hotspots and the conservation of evolutionary history. *Proceedings of the National Academy of Sciences, USA* **99**, 2067–2071.

Seib, R.L. (1980) Baja California: a peninsula for rodents but not for reptiles. *American Naturalist* **115**, 613–620.

Sepkoski, J.J. Jr (1992) Phylogenetic and ecologic patterns in the Phanerozoic history of marine biodiversity. In: *Systematics, Ecology, and the Biodiversity Crisis* (ed. N. Eldredge), pp. 77–100. Columbia University Press, New York.

Sepkoski, J.J. Jr (1997) Biodiversity: past, present, and future. *Journal of Paleontology* **71**, 533–539.

Seymour, C.L., de Klerk, H.M., Channing, A. & Crowe, T.M. (2001) The biogeography of the Anura of sub-equatorial Africa and the prioritisation of areas for their conservation. *Biodiversity and Conservation* **10**, 2045–2076.

Signor, P.W. (1990) The geologic history of diversity. *Annual Review of Ecology and Systematics* **21**, 509–539.

Simberloff, D. & Stiling, P. (1996) How risky is biological control? *Ecology* **77**, 1965–1974.

Slowinski, J.B. & Guyer, C. (1989) Testing the stochasticity of patterns of organismal diversity: an improved null model. *American Naturalist* **134**, 907–921.

Smith, A.B. (2001) Large-scale heterogeneity of the fossil record: implications for Phanerozoic biodiversity studies. *Philosophical Transactions of the Royal Society, London B* **356**, 351–367.

Smith, F.D.M., May, R.M., Pellew, R., Johnson, T.H. & Walter, K.R. (1993) How much do we know about the current extinction rate? *Trends in Ecology and Evolution* **8**, 375–378.

Soulé, M.E. (1991) Conservation: tactics for a constant crisis. *Science* **253**, 744–749.

Srivastava, D.S. (1999) Using local-regional richness plots to test for species saturation: pitfalls and potentials. *Journal of Animal Ecology* **68**, 1–16.

Stadler, J., Trefflich, A., Klotz, S. & Brandl, R. (2000) Exotic plant species invade diversity hot spots, the naturalized flora of northwestern Kenya. *Ecography* **23**, 169–176.

Stattersfield, A.J., Crosby, M.J., Long, A.J. & Wege, D.C. (1998) *Endemic Bird Areas of the World. Priorities for Biodiversity Conservation.* BirdLife International, Cambridge.

Steadman, D.W. (1995) Prehistoric extinctions of Pacific island birds: biodiversity meets zooarchaeology. *Science* **267**, 1123–1131.

Steadman, D.W., Pregill, G.K. & Burley, D.V. (2002) Rapid prehistoric extinction of iguanas and birds in Polynesia. *Proceedings of the National Academy of Sciences, USA* **99**, 3673–3677.

Stevens, G.C. (1989) The latitudinal gradient in geographical range: how so many species coexist in the tropics. *American Naturalist* **133**, 240–256.

Stork, N.E. (1997) Measuring global biodiversity and its decline. In: *Biodiversity II* (eds. M.L. Reaka-Kudla, D.E. Wilson & E.O. Wilson), pp. 41–68. Joseph Henry Press, Washington, DC.

Stork, N.E. & Lyal, C.H.C. (1993) Extinction or co-extinction rates. *Nature* **366**, 307.

Strayer, D.L. (2001) Endangered freshwater invertebrates. In: *Encyclopedia of Biodiversity*, Vol. 2 (ed. S.A. Levin), pp. 425–439. Academic Press, San Diego, CA.

Svarstad, H., Bugge, H.C. & Dhillion, S.S. (2000) From Norway to Novartis: cyclosporin from *Tolypocladium inflatum* in an open access bioprospecting regime. *Biodiversity and Conservation* **9**, 1521–1541.

Svavarsson, J., Strömberg, J.-O. & Brattegard, T. (1993) The deep-sea asellote (Isopoda, Crustacea) fauna of the Northern Seas: species composition, distributional patterns and origin. *Journal of Biogeography* **20**, 537–555.

Tackaberry, R. & Kellman, M. (1996) Patterns of tree species richness along peninsular extensions of tropical forests. *Global Ecology and Biogeography Letters* **5**, 85–90.

Tavaré, S., Marshall, C.R., Will, O., Soligo, C. & Martin, R.D. (2002) Using the fossil record to estimate the age of the last common ancestor of extant primates. *Nature* **416**, 726–729.

Terborgh, J. (1988) The big things that run the world – a sequel to E.O. Wilson. *Conservation Biology* **2**, 402–403.

Terborgh, J. (1989) *Where Have All the Birds Gone?* Princeton University Press, Princeton, NJ.

Terborgh, J. (1999) *Requiem for Nature*. Island Press, Washington, DC.

Terborgh, J., Robinson, S.K., Parker, T.A. III, Munn, C.A. & Pierpont, N. (1990) Structure and organization of an Amazonian forest bird community. *Ecological Monographs* **60**, 213–238.

Terborgh, J., Lopez, L., Nuñez, V.P., Rao, M., Shahabuddin, G., Orihuela, G., Riveros, M., Ascanio, R., Adler, G.H., Lambert, T.D. & Balbas, L. (2001) Ecological meltdown in predator-free forest fragments. *Science* **294**, 1923–1926.

Thomas, C.D. & Lennon, J.J. (1999) Birds extend their ranges northwards. *Nature* **399**, 213.

Thompson, J.N. (2002) Plant–animal interactions: future directions. In: *Plant–Animal Interactions: An Evolutionary Approach* (eds. C.M. Herrera & O. Pellmyr), pp. 236–247. Blackwell Publishing, Oxford.

Thompson, K. & Jones, A. (1999) Human population density and prediction of local plant extinction in Britain. *Conservation Biology* **13**, 185–189.

Tilman, D., Wedin, D. & Knops, J. (1996) Productivity and sustainability influenced by biodiversity in grassland ecosystems. *Nature* **379**, 718–720.

Tokeshi, M. (1999) *Species Coexistence: Ecological and Evolutionary Perspectives*. Blackwell Science, Oxford.

Torsvik, V., Øvreås, L. & Thingstad, T.F. (2002) Prokaryotic diversity – magnitude, dynamics, and controlling factors. *Science* **296**, 1064–1066.

Trewavas, A. (2002) Malthus foiled again and again. *Nature* **418**, 668–670.

Tudge, C. (1992) *Last Animals at the Zoo. How Mass Extinction Can Be Stopped*. Oxford University Press, Oxford.

Tunnicliffe, V. (1991) The biology of hydrothermal vents: ecology and evolution. *Oceanography and Marine Biology Annual Review* **29**, 319–407.

Turner, J.R.G., Lennon, J.J. & Greenwood, J.J.D. (1996) Does climate cause the global biodiversity gradient? In: *Aspects of the Genesis and Maintenance of Biological Diversity* (eds. M.E. Hochberg, J. Clobert & R. Barbault), pp. 199–220. Oxford University Press, Oxford.

Turpie, J. & Ryan, P. (1999) What are birders worth?: the value of birding in South Africa. *Africa Birds and Birding* **4**(1), 64–68.

United Nations (1993) *Agenda 21: Rio Declaration and Forest Principles, Post-Rio Edition*. United Nations, New York.

United Nations (2001) *World Population Prospects: The 2000 Revision: Highlights*. http://www.un.org/esa/population/unpop.htm/.

United Nations Development Programme, United Nations Environment Programme, World Bank & World Resources Institute (2000) *World Resources 2000–2001: People and Ecosystems: The Fraying Web of Life*. Elsevier Science, Amsterdam.

Vanclay, J.X. (2001) The effectiveness of parks. *Science* **293**, 1007a.

van der Heijden, M.G.A., Klironomas, J.N., Ursic, M., Moutogolia, P., Streitwolf-Engel, R., Boller, T., Wiemken, A. & Sanders, I.R. (1998) Mycorrhizal fungal diversity determines plant biodiversity, ecosystem variability and productivity. *Nature* **396**, 69–72.

van Dover, C. (2000) *The Ecology of Deep-sea Hydrothermal Vents*. Princeton University Press, Princeton, NJ.

van Dover, C.L. (2001) Vents. In: *Encyclopedia of Biodiversity*, Vol. 5 (ed. S.A. Levin), pp. 747–753. Academic Press, San Diego, CA.

van Jaarsveld, A.S., Freitag, S., Chown, S.L., Muller, C., Koch, S., Hull, H., Bellamy, C., Krüger, M., Endrödy-Younga, S., Mansell, M.W. & Scholtz, C.H. (1998) Biodiversity assessment and conservation strategies. *Science* **279**, 2106–2108.

van Rootselaar, O. (1999) New birds for the world: species discovered during 1980–1999. *Birding World* **12**, 286–293.

van Rootselaar, O. (2002) New birds for the world: species described during 1999–2002. *Birding World* **15**, 428–431.

van Schaik, C. & Rijksen, H.D. (2002) Integrated conservation and development projects: problems and potential. In: *Making Parks Work: Strategies for Preserving Tropical Nature* (eds. J. Terborgh, C. Van Schaik, L. Davenport & M. Rao), pp. 15–29. Island Press, Washington, DC.

Van Valkenburgh, B. & Janis, C.M. (1993) Historical diversity patterns in North American large herbivores and carnivores. In: *Species Diversity in Ecological Communities: Historical and Geographical Perspectives* (eds. R.E. Ricklefs & D. Schluter), pp. 330–340. University of Chicago Press, Chicago, IL.

Verpoorte, R. (1998) Exploration of nature's chemodiversity: the role of secondary metabolites as leads in drug development. *Drug Discovery Today* **3**, 232–238.

Vincent, A. & Clarke, A. (1995) Diversity in the marine environment. *Trends in Ecology and Evolution* **10**, 55–56.

Virolainen, K.M., Ahlroth, P., Hyvärinen, E., Korkeamäki, E., Mattila, J., Päivinen, J., Rintala, T., Suomi, T. & Suhonen, J. (2000) Hot spots, indicator taxa, complementarity and optimal networks of taiga. *Proceedings of the Royal Society, London B* **267**, 1143–1147.

Vitousek, P.M., Ehrlich, P.R., Ehrlich, A.H. & Matson, P.A. (1986) Human appropriation of the products of photosynthesis. *BioScience* **36**, 368–373.

Vitousek, P.M., Mooney, H.A., Lubchenco, J. & Melillo, J.M. (1997a) Human domination of Earth's ecosystems. *Science* **277**, 494–499.

Vitousek, P.M., D'Antonio, C.M., Loope, L.L., Rejmánek, M. & Westbrooks, R. (1997b) Introduced species: a significant component of human-caused global change. *New Zealand Journal of Ecology* **21**, 1–16.

Voss, R.S. & Emmons, L.H. (1996) Mammalian diversity in Neotropical lowland rainforests: a preliminary assessment. *Bulletin of the American Museum of Natural History* **230**, 1–115.

Wackernagel, M., Schulz, N.B., Deumling, D., Linares, A.C., Jenkins, M., Kapos, V., Monfreda, C., Loh, J., Myers, N., Norgaard, R. & Randers, J. (2002) Tracking the ecological overshoot of the human economy. *Proceedings of the National Academy of Sciences, USA* **99**, 9266–9271.

Wallace, A.R. (1853) On the habits of the butterflies of the Amazon valley. *Transactions of the Entomological Society of London (NS)* **2**, 253–264.

Wallace, A.R. (1878) *Tropical Nature and other Essays*. Macmillan, London.

Walsh, P.D., Abernethy, K.A., Bermejo, M., Beyers, R., De Wachter, P., Akou, M.E., Huijbregts, B., Mambounga, D.I., Toham, A.K., Kilbourn, A.M., Lahm, S.A., Latour, S., Maisels, F., Mbina, C., Mihindou, Y., Obiang, S.N., Effa, E.N., Starkey, M.P., Telfer, P., Thibault, M., Tutin, C.E.G., White, L.J.T. & Wilkie, D.S. (2003) Catastrophic ape decline in western equatorial Africa. *Nature* **422**, 611–614.

Walter, D.E. & Behan-Pelletier, V. (1999) Mites in forest canopies: filling the size distribution shortfall? *Annual Review of Entomology* **44**, 1–19.

Walter, D.E. & Proctor, H.C. (1998) Predatory mites in tropical Australia: local species richness and complementarity. *Biotropica* **30**, 72–81.

Walter, D.E., Seeman, O., Rodgers, D. & Kitching, R.L. (1998) Mites in the mist: how unique is a rainforest canopy-knockdown fauna? *Australian Journal of Ecology* **23**, 501–508.

Walther, G.-R., Post, E., Convey, P., Menzel, A., Parmesan, C., Beebee, T.J.C., Fromentin, J.-M., Hoegh-Guldberg, O. & Bairlein, F. (2002) Ecological responses to recent climate change. *Nature* **416**, 389–395.

Wang, D.Y.-C., Kumar, S. & Hedges, S.B. (1999) Divergence time estimates for the early history of animal phyla and the origin of plants, animals and fungi. *Proceedings of the Royal Society, London B* **266**, 163–171.

Ward, B.B. (2002) How many species of prokaryotes are there? *Proceedings of the National Academy of Sciences, USA* **99**, 10234–10236.

Watson, R. & Pauly, D. (2001) Systematic distortions in world fisheries catch trends. *Nature* **424**, 534–536.

Weisbrod, B. (1964) Collective consumption services of individual consumption goods. *Quarterly Journal of Economics* 77, 71–77.

Welter-Schultes, F.W. & Williams, M.R. (1999) History, island area and habitat availability determine land snail species richness of Aegean islands. *Journal of Biogeography* **26**, 239–249.

Westman, W.E. (1977) How much are nature's services worth? *Science* **197**, 960–964.

Whitman, W.B., Coleman, D.C. & Wiebe, W.J. (1998) Prokaryotes: the unseen majority. *Proceedings of the National Academy of Sciences, USA* **95**, 6578–6583.

Whittaker, J.B. & Tribe, N.P. (1996) An altitudinal transect as an indicator of responses of a spittlebug (Auchenorrhyncha: Cercopidae) to climate change. *European Journal of Entomology* **93**, 319–324.

Whittaker, R.J., Willis, K.J. & Field, R. (2001) Scale and species richness: towards a general, hierarchical theory of species diversity. *Journal of Biogeography* **28**, 453–470.

Wiegmann, B.M., Mitter, C. & Farrell, B. (1993) Diversification of carnivorous parasitic insects: extraordinary radiation or specialized dead end? *American Naturalist* **142**, 737–754.

Wikramanayake, E., Dinerstein, E., Loucks, C.J., Olson, D.M., Morrison, J., Lamoreux, J., McKnight, M. & Hedao, P. (2002) *Terrestrial Ecoregions of the Indo-Pacific: A Conservation Assessment*. Island Press, Washington, DC.

Wilcove, D.S. (2000) *The Condor's Shadow: The Loss and Recovery of Wildlife in America*. Anchor Books, New York.

Wilcove, D.S., Rothstein, D., Dubow, J., Phillips, A. & Losos, E. (1998) Quantifying threats to imperiled species in the United States. *BioScience* **48**, 607–615.

Williams, P.H. & Humphries, C.J. (1996) Comparing character diversity among biotas. In: *Biodiversity: A Biology of Numbers and Difference* (ed. K.J. Gaston), pp. 54–76. Blackwell Science, Oxford.

Williamson, M. (1988) Relationship of species number to area, distance and other variables. In: *Analytical Biogeography: An Integrated Approach to the Study of Animal and Plant Distributions* (eds. A.A. Myers & P.S. Giller), pp. 91–115. Chapman & Hall, London.

Williamson, M. (1996) *Biological Invasions*. Chapman & Hall, London.

Wilson, D.E. & Reeder, D.M. (eds.) (1993) *Mammal Species of the World: A Taxonomic and Geographic Reference*. Smithsonian Institution Press, Washington, DC.

Wilson, E.O. (1984) *Biophilia*. Harvard University Press, Cambridge, MA.

Windsor, D.A. (1998) Most of the species on Earth are parasites. *International Journal of Parasitology* **28**, 1939–1941.

Woese, C.R., Kandler, O. & Wheelis, M.L. (1990) Towards a natural system of organisms: proposal for the domains Archaea, bacteria and Eucarya. *Proceedings of the National Academy of Sciences, USA* **87**, 4576–4579.

Woodroffe, R. (2000) Predators and people: using human densities to interpret declines of large carnivores. *Animal Conservation* **3**, 165–173.

World Conservation Monitoring Centre (1992) *Global Biodiversity: Status of the Earth's Living Resources*. Chapman & Hall, London.

World Conservation Monitoring Centre (comp.) (1994) *Biodiversity Data Sourcebook*. World Conservation Press, Cambridge.

World Resources Institute (1996) *World Resources 1996–97*. Oxford University Press, Oxford.

Worthy, T.H. (1997) What was on the menu? Avian extinction in New Zealand. *New Zealand Journal of Archaeology* **19**, 125–160.

Wright, D.H. (1983) Species–energy theory: an extension of species–area theory. *Oikos* **41**, 496–506.

Wright, D.H., Currie, D.J. & Maurer, B.A. (1993) Energy supply and patterns of species richness on local and regional scales. In: *Species Diversity in Ecological Communities: Historical and Geographical Perspectives* (eds. R.E. Ricklefs & D. Schluter), pp. 66–74. University of Chicago Press, Chicago, IL.

Wright, M.G. & Samways, M.J. (1998) Insect species richness tracking plant species richness in a diverse flora: gall-insects in the Cape Floristic Region, South Africa. *Oecologia* **115**, 427–433.

Index

Page numbers in *italics* refer to figures; those in bold refer to **tables**.

S.E. Davis. MAY '96.

The Normal Chaos of Love

Ulrich Beck and Elisabeth Beck-Gernsheim

Translated by
Mark Ritter and Jane Wiebel

Polity Press

First published in 1995 by Polity Press
in association with Blackwell Publishers Ltd,

This book was published with the financial support of Inter Nationes, Bonn.

Editorial office:
Polity Press
65 Bridge Street
Cambridge CB2 1UR, UK

Marketing and production:
Blackwell Publishers Ltd,
108 Cowley Road
Oxford OX4 1JF, UK

Blackwell Publishers Inc.
238 Main Street
Cambridge, MA 02142, USA

ISBN 0 7456 1071 4
ISBN 0 7456 1382 9 (pbk)

A CIP catalogue record for this book is available from the British Library and the Library of Congress.

Typeset in 10 on 12 pt Sabon
by Graphicraft Typesetters
Printed in Great Britain by T.J. Press, Padstow, Cornwall

This book is printed on acid-free paper.

CONTENTS

AUTHORS' NOTE

We shared the writing of this book between us as follows: the Introduction was written jointly; chapters 1, 5 and 6 were written by Ulrich Beck; and chapters 2, 3 and 4 were written by Elisabeth Beck-Gernsheim.

INTRODUCTION
Individualization and ways of living and loving

'Why did you marry the man you did?' a daughter asks her mother in Michael Cunningham's novel *A Home at the End of the World*. 'You never worried that you might be making some sort of extended mistake, like losing track of your real life and going off on, I don't know, a tangent you could never return from?' Her mother 'waved the question away as if it were a sluggish but persistent fly. Her fingers were bright with tomato pulp. "We didn't ask such big questions then," she said. "Isn't it hard on you, to think and wonder and plan so much?"' (Cunningham 1991: 189–90).

In similar terms in his novel *The Burden of Proof* Scott Turow describes a father perplexed by his daughter's endless doubts about what the future holds for her: 'Listening to Sonny [his daughter], who was twisted about by impulse and emotion – beseeching, beleaguered, ironic, angry – it struck Stern that Clara [his wife] and he had had the benefit of certain good fortune. In his time, the definitions were clearer. Men and women of middle-class upbringing anywhere in the Western world desired to marry, to bear and rear children. Et cetera. Everyone traveled along the same ruts in the road. But for Sonny, marrying late in life, in the New Era, everything was a matter of choice. She got up in the morning and started from scratch, wondering about relationships, marriage, men, the erratic fellow she's chosen – who, from her description, still seemed to be half a boy. He was reminded of Marta, who often said she would find a male companion just as soon as she figured out what she needed one for' (Turow 1991: 349).

What is the 'New Era' all about? This book argues that one of its main features is a collision of interests between love, family and personal freedom. The nuclear family, built around gender status, is falling apart on the issues of emancipation and equal rights, which no longer conveniently come to a halt outside our private lives. The result is the quite normal chaos called love.

If this diagnosis is right, what will take over from the family, that haven of domestic bliss? The family, of course! Only different, more, better: the negotiated family, the alternating family, the multiple family, new arrangements after divorce, remarriage, divorce again, new assortments from your, my, our children, our past and present families. It will be the expansion of the nuclear family and its extension in time; it will be an alliance between individuals as it always has been, and it will be glorified largely because it represents a sort of refuge in the chilly environment of our affluent, impersonal, uncertain society, stripped of its traditions and scarred by all kinds of risk. Love will become more important than ever and equally impossible.

Women and men are currently compulsively on the search for the right way to live, trying out cohabitation, divorce or contractual marriage, struggling to coordinate family and career, love and marriage, 'new' motherhood and fatherhood, friendship and acquaintance. This movement is under way, and there is no stopping it. One could call it the 'status struggle' which comes after the class struggle. In those countries where prosperity and social security have reached a high level, where peace and democratic rights are beginning to be taken for granted, the contradictions between family demands and personal freedom, or between family demands and love can no longer be concealed behind the daily struggle against misery and oppression. As traditional social identities gradually fade, the antagonisms between men and women over gender roles emerge in the very heart of the private sphere. In a whole range of trivial and important questions, ranging from who does the dishes to sex and fidelity and the attitudes which these reveal, these antagonisms are beginning to change society in obvious and less obvious ways. Weighed down by hopes, love seems to slip away because it is idolized by a society focused on the growth of the individual. And it is laden with more hopes the quicker it seems to vanish into thin air, bereft of any social ties.

Just because all this is taking place in the realm of love, it is happening secretly, in a disguised and covert manner. At first it is nothing more than a certain animosity between 'you' and 'me'. The tensions which love has always brought with it, and the great value we ascribe to it, do not make their appearance as contradictory social roles but as direct clashes between the people involved, in their characteristics, mistakes and oversights, resulting in a battleground for recriminations and attempts to escape. To put it more profanely, workers and managers also understand their differences as personal problems, but at least they are not condemned to love one another, start a household, make a marriage work and bring up children together. In the domestic relationships between men and women, on the other hand, sharing a household makes every disagreement personal and painful. The couple's attempt to arrange everything individually, putting aside the demands of the world outside and creating their own world out of their love for one another, transforms the inherent incongruities into personal difficulties. The reason why the quarrels and arguments are so deeply hurtful is that they form part of the security system to which the couple, for want of any other firm emotional base, has entrusted itself.

Love has become inhospitable, and the ever higher hopes invested in it are meant to buttress it against the unpleasant reality of what seems like private betrayal. 'Everything will be better next time round': this consoling cliché combines both aspects: the hopelessness and the hope, elevating both and individualizing them. All this is comical, banal, tragicomic, sometimes even tragic, full of complications and confusions – and it is what the chapters of this book seek to recount. Perhaps people have simply lost track of other issues. Perhaps, however, weighed down by expectations and frustrations, 'love' is the new centre round which our detraditionalized life revolves. It may manifest itself as hope, betrayal, longing, jealousy – all addictions which afflict even such serious people as the Germans. This, then, is what we mean by the normal chaos of love.

Individualization: a new departure, a new society?

But whatever drives people to play off their freedom, their craving to be themselves and their ego trips against their families, of all things? Why this expedition into the most alien (because closest), holiest, most dangerous continent of your very own self? What *explains* this apparently highly individual but actually commonplace pattern, this zeal verging on obsession, this readiness to suffer, this widespread ruthlessness in tearing up one's own roots and ripping them apart to find out whether they are healthy?

In many people's view the answer is obvious. The individualists themselves are the problem, their wants and discontent, their thirst for excitement and diminishing willingness to fit in with others, to subordinate themselves or do without. A kind of universal *Zeitgeist* has seized hold of people, urging them to do their own thing, and its influence goes just as far as their ability to move heaven and earth, to blend their hopes with the reality around them.

The trouble with this explanation is that it raises further questions. How does one explain this simultaneous mass exodus from the family circle, the fact that so many lives are in upheaval? The millions of divorcees did not arrange this, nor do they have a trade union behind them recommending autonomy and the right to strike. As they understand it, they are defending themselves against a force which often threatens to overpower them, and they believe they are fighting on behalf of their own innermost wishes. It all looks and feels like a unique personal drama, clad in a highly individual costume, but in fact the premiere is being performed with very much the same props again and again in the most diverse languages in metropolises all over the world.

Why then are so many millions of people in so many countries deciding individually as if in a collective trance to abandon what used to be marital bliss and exchange it for a new dream, living together in an 'open marriage' beyond the safety net and the security of the law, or choosing to bring up a child single-handed? Why do they prefer to live on their own, pursuing ideas like independence, diversity, variety, continually leafing over new pages of their egos, long after the dream has started to resemble a nightmare? Is this an ego epidemic, a fever to be treated with ethics drops, poultices of 'us' and daily admonitions on the common good?

Or is it a pioneering expedition into new territory, a quest for better, if unfamiliar, solutions? Despite all their dazzling jousting with self-determination, could all these individuals be the agents of a deeper transformation? Are they the harbingers of a new age, a new relationship between individual and society? This would be a different kind of common ground, not based on a guaranteed consensus on the old precepts. It would emerge from individual biographies, from discussing and questioning each step, finding new arrangements, meeting new demands, justifying one's decisions, and would have to be protected from the centrifugal forces, the transience which threatens the order of our lives. This is the view and the theory presented in this book. Its keyword is *individualization*. Let us first explain what is meant by the term by comparing it with an example from the recent past.

Even late in the nineteenth century, when signs of crisis in the family were becoming perceptible, the fathers of the German Code of Civil Law (and it is certainly no coincidence that this child has only fathers) established marriage as an institution justified in and of itself, one which married people in particular have no business criticizing. 'Corresponding to the general Christian view of the German people,' one reads there (as if copied from a functionalist textbook, under the heading 'General value system'), 'the draft is based on the view that in marital law . . .

it is not the principle of individual freedom which should prevail, but rather that marriage is *to be viewed [as] a moral and legal order independent of the will of the spouses.*'[1]

Individualization intends and produces exactly the opposite principle. Biographies are removed from the traditional precepts and certainties, from external control and general moral laws, becoming open and dependent on decision-making, and are assigned as a task for each individual. The proportion of possibilities in life that do not involve decision-making is diminishing and the proportion of biography open to decision-making and individual initiative is increasing. Standard biography is transformed into 'choice biography' (Ley 1984), with all the compulsions and 'shivers of freedom' (von Wysocki 1980) that are received in exchange.

To put our theme another way, it is no longer possible to pronounce in some binding way what family, marriage, parenthood, sexuality or love mean, what they should or could be; rather, these vary in substance, exceptions, norms and morality from individual to individual and from relationship to relationship. The answers to the questions above must be worked out, negotiated, arranged and justified in all the details of how, what, why or why not, even if this might unleash the conflicts and devils that lie slumbering among the details and were assumed to be tamed. Increasingly, the individuals who want to live together are, or more precisely are becoming, the legislators of their own way of life, the judges of their own transgressions, the priests who absolve their own sins and the therapists who loosen the bonds of their own past. They are also becoming, however, the avengers who retaliate for injuries sustained. Love is becoming a blank that the lovers must fill in themselves, across the widening trenches of biography, even if they are directed by the lyrics of pop songs, advertisements, pornographic scripts, light fiction or psychoanalysis.

Thanks to the Reformation, people were released from the arms of the church and the divinely ordained feudal hierarchy and into a social, bourgeois and industrial world that seemed to offer them virtually unlimited space to cultivate their interests and subjugate nature, using the drawing-board of technology. Similarly, in the comfort of normality and prosperity today, individuals are being released from certain duties by modern technology, which however is threatening to take over their lives and leads them to doubt any assertions about prosperity and progress. They are finding themselves in a lonely place, where they have to take over responsibility for themselves, make their own decisions and imperil their own lives and loves, tasks for which they are not prepared and for which their upbringing has not equipped them.

Individualization means that men and women are released from the gender roles prescribed by industrial society for life in the nuclear family. At the same time, and this aggravates the situation, they find themselves forced, under pain of material disadvantage, to build up a *life of their own* by way of the labour market, training and mobility, and if need be to pursue this life at the cost of their commitments to family, relations and friends.[2]

So what appears to be an individual struggle to break free and discover one's true self turns out to be also a general move conforming to a *general imperative.* This dictates that the individual's biography is planned round the labour market; it presupposes that he/she has some qualifications and is mobile, a requirement especially prized by those who invoke the importance of a happy family without allowing for its needs. The sense of freedom, and the actual freedoms which are upsetting the old picture of family life and encouraging the search for a new one, is not an individual invention but a late child of the labour market, buffered by the welfare state. It is in fact *labour market freedom*, which implies that everyone is free to conform to certain pressures and adapt to the requirements of the job market. And it is vital that you internalize these pressures, incorporating them in your own person, daily life and planning for the future, even though they inevitably collide with the demands of your family and the division of labour within it, which by its very nature excludes such imperatives.

Seen from outside or from a historical viewpoint, what appears to be an individual failure, mostly the fault of the female partner, is actually the failure of a family model which can mesh *one* labour market biography with a lifelong housework biography, but not *two* labour market biographies, since their inner logic demands that both partners have to put themselves first. Interlinking two such centrifugal biographies is a feat, a perilous balancing act, which was never expected so widely of previous generations but will be demanded of all coming ones as more and more women strive to emancipate themselves.

This is only one aspect. But it clearly reveals that in this whole cowboys-and-Indians game between the genders an unsuspected, alien, quite unerotic and asexual contradiction is surfacing: *the contradiction between the demands of the labour market and the demands of relationships* of whatever kind (family, marriage, motherhood, fatherhood, friendship). The ideal image conveyed by the labour market is that of a completely mobile individual regarding him/herself as a functioning flexible work unit, competitive and ambitious, prepared to disregard the social commitments linked to his/her existence and identity. This perfect employee fits in with the job requirements, prepared to move on whenever necessary.

The term individualization thus covers a complex, manifold, ambiguous phenomenon, or more precisely a social transformation; the variety of meanings have to be distinguished from one another, but all of them have practical implications which cannot be ignored. Seen from one angle it means freedom to choose, and from another pressure to conform to internalized demands, on the one hand being responsible for yourself and on the other being dependent on conditions which completely elude your grasp. So the very conditions which encourage individualism produce new, unfamiliar dependencies: *you are obliged to standardize your own existence.* The individuals freed of traditional constraints discover that they are governed by the labour market and are therefore dependent on training offers, social welfare regulations and benefits, from public transport to nursery school places and opening times, student grants and retirement plans.

To put it another way, a traditional marriage and family does not represent restriction nor does a modern individual life mean freedom. It is simply that one mixture containing both restriction and freedom is being replaced by another, which seems more modern and attractive. That it is better adapted to the challenges of our times is shown by the fact that hardly anyone wants to go back to the 'good old days', however nerve-racking things may be for oneself. There are of course a fair number of men who want to turn the clocks back, but not for themselves, only *for the women.*

Time-honoured norms are fading and losing their power to determine behaviour. What used to be carried out as a matter of course now has to be discussed, justified, negotiated and agreed, and for that very reason it can always be cancelled. In search of intimacy the actors turn out to be their own critics, directors and audience, acting, watching and discussing it, unable to agree on the rules for achieving it as fast as they are needed. The rules constantly prove to be wrong, unjust and therefore merely provisional. In such circumstances it seems almost like salvation to take refuge in rigidities, in new/old black-and-white thinking, 'period, that's it, enough.'

The resulting variety is full of peculiar and contradictory truths. Prohibitions are tried out and become normality. This is infectious, stirring up doubts even when people thought themselves safe in old certainties. Diversity requires tolerance, no doubt, but from the opposite point of view it can easily appear to be anomie, licence or moral anarchy, which must be halted with an iron hand. In this sense, the longing for traditional certainties should be decoded, both as an answer to fears of losing one's livelihood and social status, and as an answer to deep cultural uncertainties of the type that nestle into every niche, corner and level of everyday life in the wake of the individualization process. This is the overheard faith in standards speaking up, anxiously witnessing how gender roles are crumbling even in everyday life, as it appeals for the salvation of fatherland, nation and the like.

Haven't there always been individualization processes?

Now one may ask, haven't there always been individualization processes? What about the ancient Greeks (Michel Foucault), the Renaissance (Jacob Burckhardt), the courtly culture of the Middle Ages (Norbert Elias), etc.?[3] It is true, individualization in the general sense of the word is nothing new, nothing that is showing up for the first time now in prosperous Germany. Although it seems to be the same, however, it has a different and perhaps not yet fully disclosed significance. One of the most important aspects is its mass character, the scope and systemic character of the current surge of individualization. It occurs in the wealthy Western industrialized countries as a side-effect of modernization processes designed to be long-term. As already mentioned, this is a kind of *labour market individualism* which should not be confused with resurrecting the legendary bourgeois citizen after the latter's well-documented demise. If in the olden days it was small groups, elite minorities, which could afford the luxury of concentrating on their own interests, nowadays the 'risky opportunities' (Heiner Keupp) associated with individualization are being *democratized* or, putting it more tersely, being brought about by the way we live – in the interplay between prosperity, education, mobility and the like.

In Germany the standard of living even of the lower groups in the social scale has improved 'spectacularly, comprehensively and in terms of social history in a revolutionary way' (Mooser 1983: 286), even though there have been severe setbacks in the past decade due to high unemployment. While earlier generations often knew nothing but the daily struggle for survival, a monotonous cycle of poverty and hunger, broad sections of the population have now reached a standard of living which enables them to plan and organize their own lives (accompanied by a widening gap between the rich and the poor). It would be difficult to overestimate the importance of the progress made in the education field since the 1970s, especially in its consequences for women. 'The moment a woman began to read, the woman's issue was born' (Marie von Ebner-Eschenbach, in Brinker-Gabler 1979: 17). Education opens the trap door: it allows the woman to escape from the restrictions of her existence as a housewife; it deprives inequality of its legitimation; it sharpens her sense of self-confidence and willingness to take up the battle for prizes long denied; her own earnings strengthen her position within the marriage and free her from the need to remain married for purely economic reasons. All of this has not really removed the inequalities but it sharpens our awareness of them, and makes them seem unjust, annoying, politically motivated.[4]

Quite rightly you may object that these are generalizations from a few individual examples, and accuse us of exaggerating this minority trend and the likely future it promises. Individualization processes, in the sense used here, should however not be understood as abrupt changes of direction suddenly affecting everybody. In fact they are the outcome of long-term developments which start earlier in some places and later in others, so that a description of them seems like news from a strange far-off country to some, and to others a quite familiar account of their everyday lives. In Munich, Berlin and Frankfurt (to pick out only a few German cities with pronounced tendencies towards individualization as measured by the proportion of single-person households) the situation is completely different from that in rural areas such as East Frisia, Middle Franconia or Upper Bavaria.[5] And just as there are craftsmen and farm workers in late industrial societies, there are still class distinctions, intact marriages and nuclear families in countries, regions and cities where individualization is very advanced. In a certain sense we can talk about the contours of an individualized society just as in the nineteenth century, with feudalism and social rank still omnipresent, one could talk of an industrial society. What is important is the trend and the forces at work which link together these modern developments.

Seen in this light, 'the' present does not exist; what is perceptible is, in Ernst Bloch's words, 'the simultaneousness of the non-contemporaneous' which the observer may sometimes list under one heading and sometimes under another. In the struggle between continuity and upheaval raging around and in us, reality is arming both sides. What Daniel Yankelovich describes for the United States, however, applies equally to Germany in this respect:

> Continuity and far-reaching changes coexist in American life. American culture is so diverse that an observer who wants to emphasize its continuity can easily do so. Conversely, an observer can just as well document the changing nature of American life. The decisive question is always only this: have the important things stayed the same or have they changed? If the important things have changed . . . then they will permeate the boundaries of the culture and flow into our economic and political life. And if they are significant enough they will disrupt the continuity of our life in a decisive way. (In Zoll et al. 1989: 12)

The picture we are drawing is deliberately not balanced. The centre is occupied more by the emerging new than by the old and familiar. Attention is also drawn more to conflicts and crises than to successes. But it is precisely the turbulences which annoy people and drive them forward to face issues. As Heinrich Mann writes, 'An utterly happy age would probably not have any literature at all' (in Wander 1979: 8). And probably no social science either.

Perhaps this book contains two books, two versions of the same 'object' (to the extent that what the book deals with is 'objective' at all). We have not attempted to iron out or unsnarl the differences in what each of us has written separately in the chapters, after many conversations and common experiences. This results in overlaps, circling flows of thought and repetitions, which we have accepted (without wishing to dismiss criticism of them), among other reasons because that way the provisional, hypothetical and risky quality of our discussions remains clearly recognizable. Furthermore, attempting to write about the chaos of love as a couple with a single hand would be rather like trying to study the language of the Eskimos in Bermuda shorts.

The danger is obvious. In quite different circumstances, Ivan Illich tellingly described what we are also expecting of our readers of both genders: 'You may imagine our procedure like six climbs up the same peak or six rides on the broomstick around the big mountain. Some of you may even believe they are descending into the Inferno, the same hole over and over again, but (each time) . . . down a different spiral staircase' (Illich 1985: 18).

1

LOVE OR FREEDOM

Living together, apart or at war

Freedom, equality and love

One can love all sorts of things and people: Andalusia, one's grandmother, Goethe, black fishnet stockings against white skin, cheese sandwiches, the warm smile of a bosomy woman, fresh rolls, the movement of clouds *and* legs, Erna, Eva, Paul, Heinz-Dietrich – and one can do all this simultaneously, successively, excessively, silently, with hands, teeth, words, looks and great intensity. But sexual love (whatever form it takes) is so overwhelmingly powerful, so engrossing that we often reduce the vast range of our loving potential to longing for a caress, a word, a kiss – need I go on?

The everyday battle between the sexes, noisy or muted, inside, outside, before, after and alongside marriage is perhaps the most vivid measure of the hunger for love with which we assault each other. 'Paradise now!' is the cry of the worldly whose heaven or hell is here or nowhere. The cry echoes in the rage of the frustrated and those in pursuit of freedom, knowing that freedom plus freedom does not equal love, but more likely means a threat to it or even its end.

People marry for the sake of love and get divorced for the sake of love. Relationships are lived as if they were interchangeable, not because we want to cast off our burden of love but because the law of true love demands it. The latter-day tower of Babel built on divorce decrees is a monument to disappointed, overrated love. Even cynicism sometimes fails to conceal that it is an embittered late variant of love. People raise the drawbridges of their longings because this seems the only, the best way of protecting themselves against unbearable pain.

A lot of people speak of love and family as earlier centuries spoke of God. The longing for salvation and affection, the fuss made over them, the unrealistic pop-song truisms hidden deep in our hearts – all this smacks of religiosity, of a hope of transcendence in everyday life (see the extensive discussion on this point in chapter 6 below).

This residual and new secular religion of love leads to bitter religious controversies between two sides determined to defend their individuality, fought out in the privacy of the home or in the offices of divorce lawyers and marriage counsellors. In these modern times our addiction to love is *the* fundamentalist belief to which almost everyone has succumbed, especially those who are against fundamentalist creeds. Love is religion after religion, the ultimate belief after the end of all faith (this analogy is elucidated in chapter 6 below). It fits in with our environment about as well as the Inquisition would with an atomic power station, or a daisy with a rocket to the moon. And still love's icons blossom in us, watered by our deepest wishes.

Love is the god of privacy. 'Real socialism' may have vanished with the Iron Curtain, but we are still living in the age of real pop lyrics (see 'Romanticism now: love as a pop song' in chapter 6 below). Romanticism has won and the therapists are raking it in.

The meaning of existence has not been lost; life is not hollow, at least under the lure and pressure of daily life. Some powerful force has pushed its way in and filled up the gap where, according to previous generations, God, country, class, politics or family were supposed to hold sway. I am what matters: I, and You as my assistant; and if not You then some other You.

Love however should on no account be equated here with fulfilment. That is its glowing side, the physical thrill. Even Eros's powerful allure, its hidden promises awakening our lust, suggesting delights both novel and familiar, does not mean fulfilment, or even require it. Achieving the goal often turns the sight of the flesh which seemed so delightful a moment ago into an alien white mass shorn of any appeal with the clothes so perfunctorily stripped off it.

How easily having one's hopes fulfilled can turn into a chilly gaze! Where only a moment ago overwhelming urgency made a knotted tangle of two walking taboos, merging me and you, all boundaries gone, now we are staring at one another with critical eyes, rather like meat inspectors, or even butchers who see the sausages where others see cattle and pigs.

Anyway there is little hope for anyone who confuses storming the heights with living on the plains, surrounded by the bogs and pitfalls of love. Love is pleasure, trust, affection and equally their opposites – boredom, anger, habit, treason, loneliness, intimidation, despair and laughter. Love elevates your lover and transforms him/her into the source of possible pleasures where others only detect layers of fat, yesterday's stubble and verbosity.

Love knows no grace, however, nor does it stick to vows or keep contracts. Whatever is said, intended or done is no more inevitably linked than the movements of mouth or hands are with other parts of the body. In what court can a spurned or misunderstood lover sue for his/her rights? Who says what is just or true or right in matters of love?

Previous generations hoped and believed that if both sexes were given a sense of freedom and equality then true love would blossom in all its radiance, heartbreak and passion; love and inequality are after all as mutually exclusive as fire and water. Now that we seem to have caught hold of at least the tip of this ideal, we find ourselves faced with the opposite problem: how can two individuals who want to be or become equals and free discover the common ground on which their love can grow? Among the ruins of outdated lifestyles freedom seems to mean breaking out and trying something new, following the beat of one's own drum, and falling out of step with the rest.

Perhaps the two parallel lines will eventually meet, in the far distant future. Perhaps not. We shall never know.

The current situation in the gender struggle

It took two thousand years for people to even begin to suspect the consequences of that mighty message, 'all men are equal.' Only a second later in historical terms, after two decades they are beginning to realize to their horror: 'and so are women.'

If only it were just a question of love and marriage. But one cannot any longer define the relationships between the sexes just in terms of what they seem to involve – sex, affection, marriage, parenthood and so on: one has to include everything else such as work, profession, inequality, politics and economics. It is this unbalanced conglomeration of so many disparate elements which makes the issue so complicated. Anyone discussing the family has to include jobs and income, and anyone talking about marriage has to look into education, opportunities and mobility, and in particular into how unevenly these are distributed, despite the fact that by now women often have the same qualifications as men.

Looking at the state of inequality between men and women from various angles, can one discern any changes over the past decade or two? The findings are ambiguous. On the one hand there have been great upheavals, especially where sex, law and education are concerned. On the whole the changes, except the sexual ones, are discernible more as attitudes and on paper than as facts. On the other hand there is a striking *lack of change* in the way men and women behave, particularly on the job market and in their insurance and pension cover. The result is somewhat paradoxical: the more equal the sexes seem, the more we become aware of persistent and pernicious inequalities between them.

This mixture of new attitudes and old conditions is an explosive one in a double sense. Better educated and informed young women expect to be treated as partners in professional and private life but come up against the opposite tendencies in the labour market and their male colleagues. Conversely, men have glibly *preached* equality without matching their words with deeds. The ice of illusion is wearing thin on both sides; the sexes are equally well qualified and enjoy the same legal rights, yet the inequalities are on the increase, all of us realize this, and there is no longer the slightest legitimation for this state of affairs. There is a sharpening contradiction between women's ambitions to live as equals with their mates and colleagues and the actual conditions confronting them, between male slogans on mutual responsibility and their unwillingness to alter their daily routine a jot. We seem to be right at the very beginning of a breakaway from the old feudal patterns, with all the antagonisms, openings and contradictions such a move implies. Women's awareness is far ahead of the actual conditions; it is very unlikely that anyone can turn this clock back. The prognosis is that we are in for a *long and bitter battle*; in the coming years there will be a war between men and women. Here are some data from widely different fields to illustrate the current situation, and some theoretical considerations.

Sex and marriage

In almost all Western countries there are signals in the form of *high divorce figures*. Although Germany still has relatively low figures compared, say, with the USA, even here almost every third marriage ends in divorce (in large cities almost every second marriage, and in small towns and rural areas roughly every fourth). While the statistics for divorce rates show a slight drop since 1985,[1] divorces in long-standing marriages have increased considerably.[2] At the same time the divorce rate for second marriages is rising, as is that for couples with children. The jungle of parental relationships is growing accordingly: my children, your children, our children, with all the different rules, reactions and battlegrounds for everyone concerned.

The official divorce figures are, however, far exceeded by the *sharp rise in 'informal marriages'*. Estimates speak of 2.5 to 3 million people living 'in sin' in (then West) Germany in 1989.[3] The increase in the numbers of illegitimate children points in the same direction; in 1967 they constituted 4.6% of all children; by 1988 this figure had risen to 10% (in Sweden it had reached 46%).[4] There are however no statistics on divorce for such informal unions available. And it is not just that the proportion of people choosing to live together in this way has quadrupled over the past decade. What is astonishing is how widely accepted this 'common law marriage', so vehemently opposed right up to the 1960s, has become. The tempo of change is perhaps indicated less in the phenomenon in itself than in the fact that an unofficial, untraditional living pattern has been established.

In the 1960s family, marriage and job were still regarded as solid cornerstones for constructing a proper biography. In the meantime questions and choices have emerged at every turn. It is no longer clear whether one should get married or live together, whether one should conceive and raise a child inside or outside the family, whether the father is the man one should live with or the man one loves who is living with someone else or whether one should do any of these things before, after or while concentrating on one's career.

All such agreements can be cancelled and therefore depend on both parties legitimating them and the more or less unequal burdens they imply. This can be understood as a *decoupling and differentiation* of behaviours and attitudes which used to belong to marriage and family life. As a result it is becoming more and more difficult to relate the concepts to reality. Using uniform terms such as family, marriage, parenthood, mother, father and so on disguises the growing diversity of the lives concealed behind them (divorced fathers, fathers of only children, single fathers, fathers of illegitimate children, foreign fathers, stepfathers, house-keeping fathers, flat-sharing fathers, weekend fathers, fathers with a working wife, and so on; see Rerrich 1989, and chapter 5 below).

The direction in which society is developing is also shown by the composition of the households; *more and more people are living alone*. The proportion of single-person households in Germany already exceeds *one in three* (35%). In urban centres such as Frankfurt, Hamburg or Munich the proportion is around 50% and still rising. In 1900 there were five or more people in 44% of all private households; that group accounted for only 6% in 1986. By contrast, two-person households increased from 15% in 1900 to 30% in 1986. In the late 1980s, then, in Germany some 9 million people (roughly 15% of the population) were living alone – and the increase continues. Only slightly more than half of these are people who fit the stereotype 'single' – young, unmarried professional. The rest are elderly surviving spouses, mainly women.[5]

It would be a mistake to interpret such tendencies along simple lines as *growing anarchy and fear of commitment* in the relationships between men and women. There is also the opposite trend. The divorce figures of one in three means that *two in three* 'normal marriages' and families still exist (whatever may be concealed behind the term). It is true that there have been astounding changes in sexual behaviour in a single generation, especially among girls and women. It used to be only the young men who were allowed to 'sleep around' and then only unofficially, and accompanied by a smirk. Today well over half of all girls (61%) think it is important for women to try out sex. Half of them see a certain attraction in having two boyfriends at the same time (Seidenspinner and Burger 1982: 30). But these figures should not deceive us; in fact the new codes of behaviour have their own strict norms. The majority of young people – even though they reject marriage and the family as a model for their own lives – *seek emotional commitment*. Even nowadays a stable partnership is their ideal and aim, 'faithfulness often seems to be taken for granted, without the official pressures of laws and religious beliefs' (Allerbeck and Hoag 1985: 105). So it is not clear where all this is leading to, and the answer to that popular question 'Is the family on its way out?' is a mixture of *yes and no*.

Education, the job market and employment

Although the constitution of the Federal Republic of Germany guaranteed women full legal equality with men, some important forms of discrimination against them were removed only in 1977 when the new marriage and family laws came into force. On paper there are now no reasons whatsoever for treating men and women differently. Women are permitted to retain their maiden names; their responsibility for the family and children, previously laid down by law, has been abolished, and who runs the household is a matter of discussion between the spouses. Likewise, both are entitled to work outside the home. Care of the children is the responsibility of both father *and* mother, who 'must attempt to reach an agreement', as the law puts it, in the event that they differ on this matter (see Beyer, Lamott and Meyer 1983: 79).

Alongside these far-reaching reforms on behalf of women's rights probably the most striking change in post-war Germany, an almost revolutionary development, is that girls and young women have *access to all forms of education and training*. Right up to the 1960s discrimination against women in the educational field was self-evident (surprisingly, it was more pronounced in the upper classes). By 1987 the girls had virtually caught up with the boys and were in the majority as secondary school-leavers (53.6%).

Some changes however run counter to this trend. Vocational training still shows a strong gender bias (early in the 1980s 40% of female workers but only 21% of male workers had no official qualifications). The willingness of girls leaving secondary school to go on to university has also declined over the past ten years from 80% to 63% (for young men the figures have declined from 90% to 73%).[6] Female students continue to prefer certain disciplines (almost 70% choose the humanities, languages or pedagogy) and women entering teaching tend to qualify for 'lower' schools.[7]

Nevertheless, compared with circumstances twenty years ago it is no exaggeration to say that the field of education has become *feminized*. The trouble is that this educational revolution has not been followed by one in the labour market or the employment system. On the contrary, the doors opened by better education are 'slammed shut again . . . in the employment and labour market' (Seidenspinner and Burger 1982: 11). The slight rise in the numbers of women in 'male' professions contrasts with their massive displacement in all other areas. The integration of women into careers which was demanded (and encouraged) in the 1970s continues to follow the '*feudal gender pattern' of an inverted hierarchy*: the more central to a society an area is defined to be, the less women are represented in it, and conversely, the more marginal an activity is considered to be and the less influential a group is, the higher the probability that women have taken over positions within it. The relevant data show this to be true in all areas – politics, business, higher education, the mass media and so on.

It is still exceptional to find a woman in a top position in *politics*. While the representation of women in all decision-making bodies has increased since 1970, the proportion of women decreases the closer one gets to the centres of policy-making. The Social Democratic Party's rules on quotas for women aim at circumventing just this phenomenon; it remains to be seen whether it will have any effect. So far women have most easily gained access to party committees (from roughly 14% in 1970 to 20.5% in 1982). The proportion of women in parliaments has increased from top to bottom; it is highest at the municipal level (the proportion of women in provincial parliaments varies between 6% and 15%; women represent between 9.2% and 16.1% of the members of town and county councils).

In *business* there are very few women in positions of real influence, while their representation in less influential jobs (personnel offices, for instance) is much larger. The picture in the *legal system* is quite similar, if at a slightly higher level. The proportion of women is much higher here (in 1979, for instance, 10% of the public prosecutors were women, in 1987 16% (Federal Office of Statistics 1988: 30). But in the federal courts, 'the places where the significant legal decisions are made, where society's course is charted for the next decades, women have (almost) no place' (Wiegmann 1979: 130).

In *higher education* women are still the exception at the top of the salary pyramid; in 1986 out of a total of 9956 top-ranking and highest-paid professorships only 230 were occupied by women. Further down the scale the proportion steadily increases, and is considerably higher in less well-paid teaching posts, the insecure mid-level positions and among academic assistants, especially in 'marginal fields'.[8] The same picture can be found in the *mass media*; the higher one climbs, the less say women have. If they are active in television, then it is primarily as assistants and in light entertainment departments, and less in the important political and economic ones, and hardly ever in the upper echelons where policy is made (Federal Ministry of Youth, Family and Health 1980: 31).

The *professional qualifications* of younger women at least are not the reason for this discrepancy. They are well trained and have mostly reached higher positions than their mothers (and often their fathers!) ever attained. But the impression is misleading. In many areas of professional life *women have taken over the sinking ships*. Women's jobs are typically those with an uncertain future: secretaries, saleswomen, teachers, semi-skilled workers in industry. Precisely in those areas where large numbers of women work there is a strong tendency to reduce the number of jobs, or in proper sociologists' jargon 'considerable rationalization potential'. This applies particularly in industry. Most jobs for women – in electronics, the food, clothing and textiles industries – are difficult to mechanize, fill in gaps between mechanized processes or consist of putting the finishing touches to highly automated products, all of which will probably soon be taken over by microelectronics and fully automated. Large numbers of women have already lost their jobs in this manner, as the *unemployment figures* show. The proportion of women registered as unemployed over the past years has always been higher than that of men, and the numbers are increasing. In 1950 the unemployment rate for women was 5.1% (men 2.6%); in 1989 it had risen to 9.6% (men 6.9%). Of the roughly 2 million unemployed in the Federal Republic (West Germany) in 1988 *more than half* were women, although they represented only a third of the work-force.[9] The number of academics out of work rose between 1980 and 1988 by 14% for men, but by 39% for women. These figures do not include those women who left work, more or less voluntarily, to become housewives. This means that the number of people retreating into 'miscellaneous unemployment', largely housework, has multiplied over the past ten years (1970: 6000, but by 1984 already 121,000). In other words, as far as women are concerned everything is on the rise: participation in the labour market, unemployment and pseudo-unemployment.

This picture of discrimination against women in the work-force is rounded off by, generally speaking, *lower earnings*. Female industrial workers earned DM 13.69 per hour in 1987, 73% of the average wage for men (Federal Office of Statistics 1988: 480). A comparison over the period since 1960 shows that the differences in gross hourly earnings between men and women have diminished, but nevertheless despite equal training and comparable ages men generally still earn more. For instance, female white-collar workers on average managed to make only 64% of the men's gross monthly salary, and in production teams women reached only 73% of the earnings of their male colleagues.[10]

This state of affairs is in clear contrast to what the younger generation of women has come to expect and demand. One of the crucial findings of the study *Mädchen '82* published by Seidenspinner and Burger is 'the fact that for girls between 15 and 19 *the most important thing is reaching their occupational goals*'; this ranks higher than marriage and motherhood (1982: 9). The young women are highly motivated to get professional qualifications and find good jobs, only to be faced with the opposite tendencies in the labour market; it remains to be seen how they cope privately and politically with this rude shock in the short and long term.

Breaking away from the traditional roles for men and women of course does not just affect one side, the women. In fact it is only possible to the extent that *men* also alter their attitudes and their behaviour. This is becoming all too clear in the employment market with its newly erected barriers for women and in that other traditional area of 'women's work', keeping and running the house and looking after the children.

Women's liberation and family work from a male viewpoint

The representative study *Der Mann*, published by Sigrid Metz-Gockel and Ursula Müller in 1985, offers an ambivalent picture, which is no less clear for its contradictions. The contented male view of gender roles as reported by Helga Pross in the mid-1970s looked like this: 'the man is stronger; he wants to have a career and support a family. The woman is weaker; she wants to keep her current role in the family and only wants to engage in a relatively modest career from time to time, and she wants to be able to look up to her husband' (Pross 1978: 173), a bundle of attitudes which has given way to a *verbal openmindedness and rigid behaviour*. 'Men's reactions are divided. They do not practise what they preach; they conceal the actual inequality behind their slogans about common ground' (Metz-Göckel and Müller 1985: 18).

Little or nothing has changed in the last twenty years, especially where responsibilities for the household and children are concerned. 'Fathers do not cook, wash or dust. They content themselves with their financial contribution to running the household and raising children' (1985: 21). Correspondingly, 'the acceptance by the majority of men of the role of househusband only applies to *other* men' (p. 63). It is quite cunning to stick to the old role while remaining apparently (verbally) flexible. Defending their own 'right to a housekeeper' *and* accepting the equality of women does not strike men as a contradiction. Ten years ago most men explained the discrimination against women as employees in terms of their poorer training. Since these arguments are no longer tenable in the wake of recent educational developments, a new defence wall is being erected – the *maternal role*.

> 61% of men regard the women's family duties as the main reason why they cannot climb the career ladder . . . Asked how a family with children (under 10 years old) should best divide up a job, housework and child-rearing, the great majority (80%) of German men advocates an arrangement whereby the woman stays at home and the man has a career . . . In the men's eyes this does not represent a real disadvantage for the women but just an objective fact . . . Turning the women's issue into an issue about children is the most stable bastion against equality for women. (pp. 26–7)

It is one of history's little ironies that simultaneously a tiny but growing group of men – househusbands and single fathers – are undermining even this entrenched position.

The authors wryly sum up the contradictions in the new male image of women as follows:

> Home sweet home is passé. They attribute considerable importance to the right of the woman to make her own decisions. An independent woman who knows what she wants is desirable. This new independent woman is someone who handles her affairs (and those of the rest of the family) in

> a responsible and self-reliant manner, thereby helping to relieve the man of some of his burdens . . . Men are even capable of detecting several positive aspects in this kind of women's lib. They only have problems with emancipation when the woman's 'independence' threatens to turn against themselves, when demands are made of them, and interests asserted which collide with their own. (pp. 22–3)

Initial investigations into the tiny minority of men who have changed roles and become *new fathers* and *househusbands* complete the picture (Strümpel et al. 1988; Hoff and Scholz 1985). According to their own words, this decision was voluntary only in a strictly limited sense. They have 'fitted in with the request or demand of their *partner* to carry on their professional career. In some cases this was made a condition before conceiving a child' (1985: 17). The *househusbands* suffer from the house*wife* syndrome: invisible achievements, lack of recognition and lack of self-confidence. One of them reports:

> The worst is cleaning, that's awful, really disgusting. You only get to know that when you do it every day. If you have cleaned something on, say, Friday, the same dirt will be in the same place at the same time next week. And that's really what seems almost degrading about this occupation, or at least the mind-numbing bit of it . . . You could almost say it's a bit like mopping up the ocean. (pp. 17–18)

Given this experience, even the men who consciously exchanged pursuing an 'alienating career' for housework alter their view and realize that work outside the home is fundamental to their self-esteem and the esteem of others; all of them are now looking for at least part-time employment (pp. 2, 43). Just how socially unacceptable this kind of role reversal still is can be seen from the fact that the men are often praised for taking on domestic tasks whereas the women take the brunt of the criticism and are accused of being 'bad mothers' (p. 16).

To sum up, the contradictions are piling up behind the façade of the ideal relationship cultivated by both sides. Depending on where one looks, one finds advances or setbacks. Certainly compared with their mothers, young women now enjoy *whole new areas of freedom*; they have more rights, more educational opportunities, more choices in their private lives and as employees (Beck-Gernsheim 1983 and in the present volume). A closer look at social developments reveals, however, that these new freedoms are *not safeguarded by society*. Tendencies on the job market and male insistence on excluding women from important positions in politics, business and so on lead one to suspect that the disagreements faced so far were merely friendly skirmishing and that the real struggle lies ahead.

Both the starting-point and future prospects are highly ambivalent. Generally speaking, compared with the past generation, the women come off quite well: better educated and therefore qualified for good jobs. Their husbands, however, who are roughly as well educated, have already overtaken them, and they are still sentenced to a 'life of housework'. The women's interest in being financially independent and having an absorbing job collides with their wish for a loving partnership and motherhood. This is perhaps especially true of those women who understand the implications of giving up their professional lives and being dependent on their husbands. The whole complex process of female individualization is revealed in this uneasy vacillation between 'living one's own life' and 'being there for others'. Of course this new emancipatory spirit cannot just be popped back into the bottle. From the male point of view it was extraordinarily shortsighted and naive to sharpen women's perception through education while still hoping that they would not see through the men's threadbare arguments in favour of the feudal status quo.

There has been some movement on the male side over the past ten years too. The old cliché of the 'tough guy' no longer applies. Most men want to be able to show their feelings and admit to weaknesses (Metz-Göckel and Müller 1985: 139, and chapter 5 below). They are beginning to develop a new attitude towards sex: 'it no longer appears to be an isolated drive, but a natural part of their personalities. Being considerate towards their partners is important to them' (p. 139).

Men are in a different position however. The word equality means something quite different. It does not mean more education, better opportunities, less housework, as it does for women, but the exact opposite: more competition, renouncing a career, more housework for themselves. Most men still bask in the illusion that they can have their cake and eat it. They imagine that equality is quite compatible with the old division of labour (especially in their own case). Following the old line that whenever women's rights turn into a threat one should appeal to nature, they deceive themselves about the contradictions between their own words and deeds by justifying prevailing inequalities on biological grounds. From a woman's ability to give birth they jump to the conclusion first that women are responsible for children, housework and family, and second that they therefore ought to forgo a professional life or remain in a subordinate position.

The quarrels and disagreements which are surfacing affect men in a highly sensitive area. According to the traditional sex stereotype, a man's 'success' is bound up with his economic and occupational achievements. Only a secure income enables him to live up to the male ideal of the 'good provider' and 'caring husband and father'. In this sense, even satisfying his sexual needs within prevailing norms is in the long term dependent on his economic prowess. Conversely, the man must 'do his best' at work, internalize the constraints his job imposes on him, overtax or even exhaust himself to fulfil these expectations.

This pattern behind 'male elbow-grease' is essential if the employers' strategies of reward and punishment to discipline the labour force are to be effective. Someone with a wife and two children to support is likely to do what he is told. On the other hand, overtaxing a man's ability to work presupposes 'a happy home', represented by the woman. The pressure on men to fit in with the job ethos makes them highly emotionally dependent. They commit themselves to a division of labour in which they delegate essential aspects of themselves and their own emotional competence to their spouses. At the same time they feel under growing compulsion to fit in with what is expected of them. Men can develop a marked ability to ignore the conflicts which are brewing, but this makes them highly vulnerable if their partners partially or wholly withdraw their emotional support. If life at home is not happy but tense and angry, they are hit doubly hard; lack of comprehension and helplessness come on top of their spouse's refusal to understand.

Theses

The issues dividing men and women are not only what they seem to be, i.e. issues dividing the sexes. They are rather private signs of the crumbling of a whole social framework. What appears to be a personal problem has a theoretical side sketched here in three theses:

(1) The prescribed gender roles are the *basis* of industrial society, and not some traditional relic which can easily be dispensed with. Without a distinction between male and female roles there would be no nuclear family. Without the nuclear family there would be no bourgeois society with its typical pattern of life and work. The image of bourgeois industrial society is based on an incomplete, or more precisely, a *divided* commercialization of human labour. Total industrialization, total commercialization *and* families in their traditional form and roles are mutually exclusive. On the one hand a wage-earner presupposes a houseworker, and production for the market presumes the existence of the nuclear family. In that respect industrial society is dependent on the

unequal roles of men and women. On the other hand these inequalities contradict modern thinking and give rise to more and more controversy as time goes on. The more equal men and women actually become, the shakier the foundations of the family (marriage, parenthood, sexuality) seem. In other words, during the modernization phase since the Second World War industrial society has both made great advances and begun to dissolve. Market economies have failed to recognize their own no-go areas and weakened women's ties to their compulsory 'status fate' of looking after a household and a husband who in turn supports both with his wages. As a result adapting the couple's biographies to one another – reproduction and production – and dividing up the chores has become more difficult and gaps in women's social safeguards have become more evident. The problems which couples nowadays have to solve are in fact personalized versions of contradictory trends within industrial society shaken in its feudal *and* modern foundations by our craving to 'be ourselves'.

(2) The dynamics of change, making individuals out of members of social classes, do not stop short at the family's front door. With a mysterious force which they do not understand themselves, although they personify it, whatever strange form it takes, people are shaking off rigid gender roles, bourgeois maxims, set ways, or being shaken to the very depths of their being. The belief that comes over them is *I am myself* and after that I am a woman. *I am myself*, and after that I am a man. 'I' and the *expected* woman, 'I' and the *expected* man are worlds apart. Here the individualization process has quite contradictory consequences. While men and women are *released* from traditional norms and can search for a 'life of their own', they are *driven* into seeking happiness in a close relationship because other social bonds seem too tenuous or unreliable. The need to share your inner feelings with someone, as expressed in the ideal of marriage and bonding, is not a primary human need. It *grows* the more individual we all become and notice the losses which accompany the gains. As a consequence the direct route away from marriage and family usually leads, sooner or later, back to them again.

(3) The clashes of interest which mark the twentieth century are apparent in *all* kinds of household, mutual or single, before, during or after marriage. Here they merely show their private face. But the family is *only the setting, not the cause* of events; even if one changes the backcloth the play remains the same. It looks as if the sexes' close and intricate involvement with one another as lovers, parents, partners, wage-earners,

individuals and members of society is beginning to slacken. Quarrels start between married (and unmarried) couples when they realize there are other *options* – taking a job elsewhere, dividing up the chores differently, revising one's family planning, making love to someone else. Deciding on these matters forces us to realize how different the consequences are for men and women and that the two sexes are in *different camps*. Deciding on who looks after the children, for instance, determines whose career has priority and therefore lays down who in future will be economically dependent on whom, with all the consequences involved. There is a personal and a public side to such decisions; without public support (day care, flexible working hours, proper insurance cover) the private battles are aggravated, and conversely, adequate outside help alleviates the tensions at home. Accordingly private and public strategies for finding solutions must be seen as linked.

This seems the right place to look more closely into our three theses – the 'feudal' nature of industrial society, individualist tendencies in both men and women, and an increasing awareness of the mixed blessings of being able to choose.

Industrial society: a modern form of feudalism

One can best define the distinctive features of the sex roles by comparing them with class distinctions. While class warfare broke out because of widespread poverty and misery among the working population, and was fought out in public, the conflicts emerging nowadays mostly erupt in private relationships and are fought out in the kitchen, bedroom and playroom. Their symptoms are endless, circuitous discussions on feelings or silent disapproval, escaping into solitude and back, losing trust in a partner one suddenly no longer understands, going through the distress of divorce, idolizing children, struggling for a little corner to call one's own wrested away from one's partner but still shared with him/her, keeping a sharp eye out for signs of being pressurized among the trivia of everyday life, pressure which really stems from oneself. Call it what you will, 'trench warfare between the sexes', 'retreating into yourself', 'the age of narcissism'. This is exactly how a *social structure* – the feudal core of industrial society – implodes into private lives.

In a sense the class struggles generated by the industrial system are a modern phenomenon, a product of the way industry works. The wars between the sexes fit neither into the pattern of modern class conflicts nor are they a relic of the past. They are a third variety. Just as much as the contrasts between labour and capital, they are both the *product* and *foundation* of our industrial world, in the sense that wage labour presupposes housework, and the production and family sectors came into existence when they were divided into separate realms in the nineteenth century. At the same time men and women are assigned a position at birth and are in that respect a strange hybrid: '*modern estates*', setting up a modern hierarchy – men above, women below – in industrial society. Strife is inevitable in view of the conflicting pulls of modern thinking and old-fashioned patterns. Correspondingly the ascribed gender-cum-status roles did not start to clash in the way class problems did in the early stages of the modernization process but only now, later on in this process, when the social classes have already lost most of their significance and new ideas can infiltrate the family, marriage, parenthood and the whole private sphere.

In the nineteenth century as industrialization gained ground it helped to form the nuclear family, which in its turn is currently losing its traditional shape. Work outside and inside the home is organized on contradictory lines (see Rerrich 1988). Market forces apply outside, while at home *unpaid* work is taken for granted. Relationships involve *contracts* between the partners, whereas family and marriage imply *communal interests*. Individual competitiveness and mobility, encouraged by the job market, run up against the opposite expectations at home where one is expected to sacrifice one's own interests for others and invest in the collective project called family. So two epochs organized on opposite lines and value systems – modernity and counter-modernity, market efficiency and family support – are welded together, complementing, conditioning and contradicting each other.

The day-to-day situation of men and women brought about by separating the work-place from the home is intrinsically different. So there is not just one kind of inequality based on market values: differences in pay and jobs and promotion etc., but also another kind of inequality running across this. Production is regulated via the labour market and the work involved carried out in exchange for money. Taking on such work makes people – no matter how dependent they are on their employer – into *self*-providers. They are the ones who are offered new jobs, new tasks, new viewpoints. Unpaid family work on the other hand is imposed as a natural dowry through marriage, and by its nature implies *dependency*. Those who take it on – and we know who they are – run a household on 'second-hand' money and remain dependent on their spouses as a link to the source of income. How these jobs are distributed – and here lies the feudal heart of industrial society – is not a matter of discussion. In principle one's fate *is decided in the cradle even in industrial society*, lifelong housework or making a living by fitting in with the labour market. These feudal 'gender fates' are mitigated, cancelled out, aggravated or concealed by our commitment to love one another. Love is blind. Since love may seem the only escape from the distress it itself causes, we tend to deny that the inequality concealed behind it is real. But it is real, and that makes love seem stale and cold.

What seems like the threat of 'being terrorised by intimacy' (Sennett) is, in terms of social theory and history, simply the outcome of contradictions which arise when modern ideas apply to only half the population, those involved in working outside the home; the principles of individual freedom and equality are withheld from one gender and ascribed to the other at birth. Industrial society *never* was nor can it ever be solely industrial; it is alway half industrial and half feudal. This feudal side is not a relic but a *precondition* and *result* of splitting up work and home life.

After the Second World War, when the welfare state was organized, two things happened. On the one hand the idea of organizing one's life according to the demands of the job market was expanded to include women. This was in itself not a new move, more an extension over gender lines of the principles governing industrial societies. The result, however, was totally new kinds of division between men and women. Enlarging the work-force to include women meant the *beginning of the end* of family ideals, gender fates, taboos on parenthood and sex, and even led to a partial reunification of home and work-place.

The social structure in our industrial society known as the pecking order relies on many disparate elements: division of labour between home and work-place, with their conflicting rules, roles assigned at birth prescribing how lives should be lived, and the whole lop-sided construction disguised under a thick (or thin) layer of love and pledges to care for and cherish one another as spouses and parents. In retrospect it becomes apparent that this structure was erected in the face of considerable opposition. Modernization is often seen too one-sidedly. In fact it is double-faced; parallel to the industrial revolution in the nineteenth century, the modern feudal gender pattern was introduced, modern steps accompanied by reactionary ones. The momentous differences between productive work outside and family work inside the home were established, justified and transfigured into eternal truths. An alliance of male philosophers, churchmen and scientists wrapped up the whole package by labelling these social phenomena the 'essence' of man and the 'essence' of woman.

In other words, modernization did not just do away with agrarian society; it created feudal rules of its own, which now in the next stage are becoming invalid. In the twentieth century the modernization process has had the opposite effect to that which it had in the nineteenth. Whereas in those days the consequences were a sharp division between wage-earning and housework, now they are a struggle to bind them together again; restrictions to keep women dependent have been superseded by incentives to take up employment, old stereotyped male and female roles have been replaced by chances for both sexes to escape from gender dictates.

But all this only indicates the direction in which we are going. The essential point is that the human problems arising in our market economies cannot be solved as long as society is split in two by contradictory living patterns and job expectations. Both men and women want to and have to be economically independent, an aim which cannot be achieved as long as the traditional nuclear family remains our guideline for employment conditions, social legislation, city planning, school curricula and the like, all of which still assume that the sexes should have different roles.

The 'battle of the century' being waged in countless homes with a mixture of disappointment and a guilty conscience also flares up because both sexes are trying to cast off their gender stereotypes in their private lives while maintaining them outside the home. As a result they just swap one injustice for another. To free women from the burdens of home and housework the men are expected to fit in with 'this modern feudal existence', and take over exactly what the women reject for themselves. Historically speaking it is like trying to turn the nobility into the peasants' serfs. Men are no more willing than women to obey the call 'back to the sink!' (women ought to know that better than anyone). But that is only one aspect. What remains crucial is that equality between the sexes cannot be achieved in institutions which presuppose their inequality. There is no hope of forcing the new round people into the old square holes required by the employment system, town planners, and so-called social security. No one should be surprised if the resulting tensions lead to couples wrangling bitterly over inadequate solutions like 'swapping roles' or 'sharing the dusting'.

Liberation from gender roles?

The point of view just sketched contrasts oddly with the empirical data. They in fact impressively document a counter-trend towards a *renewal* of the gender hierarchy. In what sense can one legitimately talk about freedom at all? Does it apply equally to men and women? Under which conditions is it feasible, and what gets in its way?

There have been significant moves in the past decades, as the data referred to above attest, freeing women at least somewhat from traditional female tasks. Five main lines can be distinguished, not all related to one another.

First of all, because women now have a longer life expectancy, the shape of their biographies has altered. As has been shown in particular by Arthur E. Imhof in his studies of social history, this has led to a 'demographic liberation of women'. While a woman's lifespan in previous centuries was, in statistical terms, just long enough to produce and raise the socially 'desirable' number of surviving childern, her 'maternal duties' nowadays come to an end at about the age of forty-five. 'Being there for the children' has become a transient phase, succeeded on average by three decades of an 'empty nest' beyond the traditional focus of women's lives. 'Today, in Germany alone, there are over five million women in their "best years" living in post-parental relationships . . . often . . . without any real meaningful activity' (Imhof 1981: 181).

Second, modern developments, especially since the Second World War, have revolutionized housework. The social isolation it now involves is not an inherent feature as such but the outcome of changed attitudes towards traditional living patterns; in the wake of the individualization process the nuclear family tends to stress its independence, turning itself into an island and restricting commitments to surrounding families, relations, neighbours and acquaintances. As a result a housewife has become an isolated worker par excellence.

On the other hand automation has taken over innumerable tasks; a variety of appliances, machines and consumer goods unburden the housewife but rob her job of meaning. It becomes an invisible and never-ending series of 'finishing-off jobs' between ready products, paid services and technically perfected gadgets. Taken together, the effect of isolation and automation is to 'de-skill' housework, so that many women seek work outside the home in search of fulfilment.

Third, though it is true that motherhood is still the strongest tie to the traditional female role, it is hard to overestimate the importance of contraception and the legal possibility of abortion in freeing women from traditional obligations.

Children and therefore motherhood (with all its consequences) are no longer 'a natural fate'; at least in principle the children are wanted and motherhood intentional. The data, of course, also show that for many women motherhood without economic dependence on one's husband/

partner or more or less total responsibility for looking after the child remains a dream. But young women, unlike their mothers, can at least co-decide whether, when and how many children they want to have. At the same time their sex lives are no longer inevitably linked with motherhood and can be self-confidently explored and developed in ways which often contravene male norms.

Fourth, the growing number of divorces shows how fragile marital support has become. Women are often just 'a husband away from' poverty, as Ehrenreich put it. Almost 70% of single mothers must make do with less than DM 1200 (roughly $750) per month. With women pensioners they are the most frequent clients in relief agencies. In this sense too women have been freed, i.e. cut off from lifelong support by a husband. The statistically documented rush of women into the labour market shows that many of them have learned this historical lesson and drawn their own conclusions.

Fifth, equal opportunities in education have also helped to motivate young women to enter the job market.

All these factors taken together – demographic freedom, unrewarding housework, contraception, the divorce laws, professional training and opportunities – highlight women's readiness to push aside the restrictions they feel in their modern feudal roles, a move which certainly cannot be halted. It does however mean that their search for individual solutions, being flexible, qualified, mobile and career-conscious, hits the family with double or triple impact.

There are, furthermore, forces at work driving them back into their traditional positions. If our market economies were really properly established, and every man and woman responsible for his or her own living, the unemployment figures, which are already scandalously high, would multiply. As long as there is mass unemployment and job loss women may be released from direct dependence on marriage but do not gain any independence through working away from home. They remain largely dependent on economic protection even after their husband's support has been withdrawn. This intermediate status between being 'free of' their spouse's support and 'free to' take on a job is clinched by the lure of motherhood. As long as women not only bear children but care for them, feel responsible for them and see them as an essential part of their lives, children will remain welcome 'obstacles' in competition for jobs and a tempting reason for avoiding the rat race.

So the women are tossed back and forth, trying to decide between these contradictory choices. Their quandary is reflected in the way they behave. They escape from home to find a job and back again, trying somehow to reconcile the conflicting conditions and expectations they face in different phases of their lives by making contradictory decisions. Their environment helps to increase the muddle; they have to put up with divorce courts inquiring why they have neglected their careers, and social services asking why they have not yet fulfilled their maternal duties. They are accused of spoiling their husbands' already difficult professional lives with ambitions of their own. Divorce law and the reality behind it, lack of social safeguards, closed doors in the labour market and the main burden of family chores: this is how individualization looks to young women.

For men the situation is quite different. While women are supposed to abandon the old role of 'looking after others' and search for a new social identity for economic survival, men's roles as independent earners fit in with the old pattern. According to male stereotypes, a 'career man', financial self-sufficiency and masculine behaviour are all rolled into one. Men have never been supported by spouses (wives) and they take the freedom to work for a living for granted. The accompanying background support traditionally is provided by their wives. The joys and duties of fatherhood could always be taken in small doses as a recreation. Fatherhood has not represented an obstacle to having a career; on the contrary, finding work has been mandatory. In other words, all the factors dislodging women from their traditional role are missing on the male side. In the context of men's lives, fatherhood and career, economic independence and family life are not contradictions that have to be fought for against prevailing social circumstances; in fact their compatibility with the male role is prescribed. But this also means that individualization in the sense of making a living in the job market encourages men to behave along traditional masculine lines.

If men then reject the dictates of their gender role, they do so for other reasons. Being fixated on one's career is also contradictory: sacrificing one's energy and time for something one has neither the leisure, the need nor the ability to enjoy, fighting for promotion, exhausting oneself for professional and organizational goals one cannot but must identify with, coping with 'indifference' which is nothing of the kind, and so on. Nevertheless, there is no inherent impetus to change this until the women exert pressure, and this in a double sense. If women join the labour force, men are freed of the yoke of being the *sole* supporter of the family. This reduces the pressure to subordinate oneself to others in the interests of wife and family, and opens the way to new kinds of commitment to both fields. On the other hand the mood at home is probably shifting, as the side of men's lives run by women takes on a new slant, and they get an inkling of how dependent they are in everyday matters and how emotionally reliant. Both these aspects encourage them to identify less rigidly with the male role and try out new kinds of behaviour.

The more the couples argue, the more the different positions of the sexes become apparent. There are two central 'catalysing' elements, *children* and *economic security*, where conflicts may remain hidden during marriage but will certainly surface if the couple decides to divorce. In making the transition from one earner to two earners the responsibilities and opportunities generally are reshuffled. Putting it bluntly, after divorce the woman is left with the children and without an income, the man with an income and without children.

At first glance the two-earner model does not seem very different from the one-earner one after divorce. The woman has an income and she has the children (according to most divorce judges). But as men and women become more economically equal, either because the woman finds a well-paid job, or the court lays down support payments, or retirement insurance has to be shared out, *fathers become aware that they are at a disadvantage*, both naturally and legally. The woman takes possession of the child as the product of her womb, which we all know belongs to her, biologically and legally. Who owns the ovum and who the sperm is a matter of opinion. The father of the child always remains at the mercy of the woman and her discretion. This is also true, in fact especially true, of all questions involving abortion. As male and female roles increasingly diverge, there is a swing back, and the men who have chosen to renounce career plans to see more of their children come home to an empty nest. The rise (especially in the USA) in the number of cases where fathers have kidnapped their own children after being deprived of them by court decree is a clear sign of this phenomenon.

Individualization may drive men and women apart, but paradoxically it also pushes them back into one another's arms. *As traditions become diluted, the attractions of a close relationship grow*. Everything that one has lost is sought in the other. God went first, or we displaced him. The word 'belief', which once meant 'having experienced', has taken on the rather shabby tones of 'against our better judgement'. As God disappears, so does the chance of going to a priest, so we have nowhere to unload our burden of guilt or sort out our ideas on what is right or wrong. The class system, which at least had its own interpretations for the misery it generated, has evaporated into a fog of statistics and commentaries. Neighbourhoods which flourished on exchanged news and shared memories are dying out because the jobs are elsewhere. One can make new acquaintances, but they tend to revolve around themselves. Or perhaps one should join a club. The range of contacts seems broader and more colourful, but there are too many of them and they remain superficial, so that our proclaimed interest in one another stops short if more is demanded. Even intimacies can be exchanged like this, fleetingly, as if they were mere handshakes.

All this may keep things moving and open up new 'possibilities', but the variety of relationships is no substitute for a stable primary bond which gives one a sense of identity. As studies have shown, both kinds are necessary: a variety of contacts and lasting intimacy. Happily married housewives often suffer from feeling insecure and isolated. Divorced men who have formed self-help groups find their own loneliness hard to bear even if they have large numbers of social contacts.

The direction in which modern developments are taking us is reflected in the way we idealize love. Glorifying it in the way we do acts as a counterbalance to the losses we feel in the way we live. If not God, or priests, or class, or neighbours, then at least there is still You. And the size of the 'You' is inversely proportional to the emotional void which otherwise seems to prevail.

The implication is that it is less material security and affection than the fear of being alone which keeps families and marriages together. Perhaps the most reliable foundation for marriage, despite all the crises and doubts, is the threat of what would face us without it – loneliness.

What can one conclude from all this? First of all that controversies about the family are relative. The bourgeois nuclear family has been sanctified or cursed, people have either focused only on the crises or preferred a vision of the perfect family arising from the ashes of disappointing alternatives. All these views are based on a false premise. Anyone labelling the family all-good or all-evil ignores the fact that it is neither more nor less than the place where long-standing differences between men and women come to the surface. Within the family or outside it the sexes are confronted with their accumulated contradictions.

In what sense can one talk about escaping from the family? Since the dynamics of the individualization process have infiltrated family life, all forms of living together have started to undergo a radical change. The links once joining biography to family are slackening. A lifelong nuclear family which blends together the biographies of a man and a woman as parents is becoming the exception, whereas alternating between various family and non-family settings, depending on what phase of biography one has reached, is becoming the rule. The family roots behind our biographies are gradually being severed as we move from one phase to the next, and are losing their influence. Everybody takes part in several family and non-family phases, and in this sense increasingly lives his/her own life. Only if one looks at biographies longitudinally, rather than statistically or temporarily, can one detect how individualized family life has become, reversing traditional priorities. The extent to which we have shaken off family ties can therefore best be seen in the *synopsis* of biographies represented by data on divorce and remarriage and on pre-, inter- and extra-marital forms of living together. Predictably the findings are contradictory in themselves and in what they reveal about the pros and cons of married life. Faced with the alternative between family and no family, a growing number of people are 'deciding' on a third possibility: a mixture of various forms, trying out what seems to fit the current situation.

So during their whole lives most people are faced with the pain and effort involved in trying out different ways of living with one another, the end and outcome of which cannot be predicted. Despite all the 'mistakes' no one can be deterred from trying again.

Seeing discrepancies, having to decide

The differences between the sexes' situations and prospects did not come about yesterday. Nevertheless right up to the 1960s the huge majority of women accepted them as a matter of course. During the past three decades they have attracted much attention, and political efforts have been made to obtain equal rights for women. Awareness of the inequalities was heightened by the initial successes, so we must distinguish between the real inequalities plus the reasons behind them, and public awareness of them. The discrepancies between male and female roles have two sides, which can vary quite independently of one another: the actual, objective state of affairs and our awareness of and attitude towards it. What has opened our eyes to the new situation?

As modernization proceeds, the number of decisions to be made rapidly increases in all spheres of daily life. With a bit of exaggeration one can say 'anything goes'. Who does the dishes, and when, who changes the nappies, does the shopping and pushes the vacuum cleaner is becoming just as unclear as who brings home the bacon, who decides whether to move and whether nocturnal delights in bed may only be enjoyed with the companion one duly wed to share daily life with. Marriage can be separated from sex, and sex from parenthood; parenthood can be multiplied by divorce and the whole thing given further ramifications by living together or apart with several homes and the ever-present possibility of revising one's decisions. This mathematical operation yields a fairly high, if fluctuating, total on one side of the equation, which hints at the variety of more or less home-based shadowy figures concealed behind the firm and upright terms 'marriage' and 'family'.

Everywhere we look in our private lives we see new openings and find ourselves forced to make decisions. The plans and agreements which are necessary can be altered or revoked, and since they often involve a measure of unfairness, have to be justified. The discussions and quarrels, disappointments and mistakes made here reveal how different the risks and chances are for men and women. Transforming given facts into decisions is, seen from a systematic point of view, double-edged. The option to take no decision at all is vanishing; having the chance to choose puts one under pressure to do so. So there is no evading going through the mills of weighing up our feelings, our problems and the possible consequences. But decision-making in itself becomes a sort of consciousness-raiser; one suddenly sees the implications and contradictions which interfere with possible solutions.

This often begins with a quite ordinary decision to move house. The job market demands that employees are mobile irrespective of their family circumstances. Families want exactly the opposite. Thinking a market economy through to the end, people would not have any family ties. Everybody would be independent and free to fit in with company demands to ensure his/her own economic survival. An employee is ideally an individual unhindered by family bonds. Correspondingly, this would be a society without any children unless they could grow up with mobile single fathers and/or mothers.

This contradiction between the pulls of personal relationships and commercial demands could remain concealed only as long as it was taken for granted that marriage for the woman meant renouncing a career, taking over care of the children, and agreeing to move whenever her husband's work demanded it. Now that both want or have to earn a living, they are faced with this predicament. It would be perfectly feasible for the state to offer solutions or assistance, say in the form of a minimum income for all citizens, or social safeguards not linked to jobs, or removing deterrents to joint employment, or modifying the criteria for certain jobs, and so on. There is however no sign of any such official plans. Accordingly the couple has to find private solutions, which under the options available amount to distributing the risks between them. The crux is: who is prepared to give up his/her economic independence and security, the very things which are considered indispensable in modern society? Anyone who gives up a job to move house with a spouse usually has to cope with disadvantages, if not be thrown completely off course professionally.

As well as the decisive matter of professional mobility there are other vital factors to deal with: agreeing on how many children one wants and timing their arrival, deciding on who looks after them; the perennial problem of dividing up the everyday chores; the one-sidedness of the decision on contraception; finding common ground on abortion or sexual urges; and resisting the onslaught of sexist ads even for margarine. All these issues affect how men and women live together, and in thinking about them one cannot avoid noticing how very different they look from the man's or woman's point of view. Choosing to have children for instance has the opposite repercussions for the potential mother or father. If on top of this marriage is lived as if it were a temporary arrangement – ready-made for divorce, as it were – then the split which both partners fear is simply anticipated and the unjust consequences of all the decisions and arrangements emerge into the open.

If one takes into account all the latest technological advances and the associated breakdown of taboos – subjecting children to special educational or psychological programmes, intervening during gestation, not to mention the science fiction realities of genetic engineering (see chapter 5 below) – then it becomes apparent that what used to be a united family is being divided into different camps, man against woman, mother against child, child against father. Traditional family agreement is breaking down under the pressure of the decisions which have to be taken. It is not that people themselves bear sole responsibility for overloading their families with such problems, as they often fear. Almost all these issues have an impersonal dimension (hassles with child-care for instance are a byproduct of the carefully defended official view that looking after children cannot be combined with professional commitments). This insight is of course not much help, least of all to the children. But it shows how everything affecting the family from outside – the job market, employment system or the law – is bound to invade our private lives in a distorted and foreshortened form. Within the family (and all its alternatives) the systematically produced delusion is fostered that its members are in control and can pull all the strings and levers necessary to reverse any injustices between the partners.

Even the very core of family life, parenthood, is beginning to crumble into its component parts, motherhood and fatherhood. Currently in Germany every tenth child is growing up in a single-parent family, i.e. cared for by single men or women. The number of single-parent families is rising as the number of two-parent families diminishes. Being a single mother is no longer only the result of being 'abandoned' but often a consciously chosen option. It appeals to many women in view of the quarrels they have with the fathers (who are really only needed to make babies and nothing else) as the only way of bringing up the child they so longed for.

Feelings for and commitment to the child vary depending on how far the individualization process has gone. On the one hand a child is regarded as an impediment to one's own progress (Beck-Gernsheim 1989 and chapter 4 below; Rerrich 1988). It is expensive and exhausting, unpredictable, restricting and likely to throw any carefully drawn up plans into hopeless confusion. As soon as it arrives the child takes over its parents' lives with its needs; its biological rhythms are forced on to them by the power of its vocal cords and the warmth of its smile. And that, from another point of view, is what makes it absolutely irreplaceable.

The child becomes the last remaining, irrevocable, unique primary love object. Partners come and go, but the child stays. Everything one vainly hoped to find in the relationship with one's partner is sought in or directed at the child. If men and women have increasing difficulty in getting on with one another, the child acquires a monopoly on companionship, sharing feelings, enjoying spontaneous physical contact in a way which has otherwise become uncommon and seems risky. Here an atavistic social experience can be celebrated and cultivated which in a society of individuals is increasingly rare, although everyone craves it. Doting on children, pushing them on to the centre of the stage – the poor over-pampered creatures – and fighting for custody during and after divorce are all symptoms of this. The child becomes the final alternative to loneliness, a bastion against the vanishing chances of loving and being loved. It is a private way of 'putting the magic back' into life to make up for general disenchantment. The birth-rate may be declining but children have never been more important. Very often there is only one; the effort involved precludes having any more. But those who imagine that the (economic) costs deter people from bringing children into the world are simply the victims of their own profit-and-loss thinking.

The last vestiges of the Middle Ages, the feudal gender roles discussed above, which industrial society needed and preserved, and which seemed natural, are melting away. It is important to recognize the dimensions of this change. Psychologists and psychotherapists who attempt to understand their clients' current misery only in terms of their personal childhood are missing the point. When people are confronted with having to live in ways which are inherently contradictory, and have no precedents for their own lives, it is misleading to focus exclusively on what they went through as children in the search for the roots of their ills. When the sexes shake off their feudal roles, the problems they encounter as lovers, couples and parents have a great deal to do with the inequalities affecting every sphere of their lives. It is time the psychologists tackled this aspect and modified their approach to take account of these dimensions.

The end of the individual, or a renaissance of limitless subjectivity?

In the debate on the death of the individual, what role does the loss of feudal gender stereotypes in an industrial society play? Are our inner lives being revealed only to be taken over by the booming psycho-business, religious sects and political fanatics? Are we losing the last private corners of our selves and turning into tailor-made consumers prepared to agree to everything on offer?

At first glance, but only then, it does seem as if the social drive of the 1970s has foundered in a mire of subjectivity and narcissism:

> As far and as near as one can see, there is a lot of hard labour involved in the everyday realities of relationships and commitments inside and outside marriage and the family, burdened by living in ways quite incompatible with the future. In their totality, the changes which are coming about cannot any longer be regarded as private phenomena. What is gradually piling up is a series of attempts to patch up relations between the sexes within that highly touchy area, the private sphere, irrespective of its form and despite repeated setbacks, and to find a new kind of solidarity based on *shared* and *admitted* oppression, an approach which may get to the roots of society's difficulties better than any strategies worked out by theorists with their heads stuck in the clouds. (Muschg 1976: 31)

The individual has often been pronounced dead and buried. After two hundred years of cultural appraisal and ideological analysis it still haunts our minds and writings but only as 'the subjective factor'. This is the conclusion reached by Theodor Adorno. Under the heading 'Simple Simon' he notes:

> In the midst of standardised and organised human units the individual persists. He is even protected and gains monopoly value. But he is in reality no more than the function of his own uniqueness, an exhibition like the fetuses that once drew the wonderment and laughter of children. Since he no longer has an independent economic existence, his character begins to contradict his objective social role. Just because of this contradiction he is tended in nature reserves, enjoyed in idle contemplation. (Adorno 1978: 135)

This view is contradicted by what happened in the 1970s and 1980s, which has still not been thoroughly understood, the renaissance of a quite unpredictably influential subjectivity.[11] The various little groups and circles which sprang up on all kinds of issues but were not able to stand for long on their shaky organizational legs were the ones which put the themes of an endangered world on the social agenda, against the resistance of the established parties and faculties and against the massive weight of billion-dollar industrial investments. It does not seem an exaggeration to say that ordinary citizens have taken over the initiative in deciding on which themes are important. The steps up the ladder to political acceptance are: persecuted, ridiculed, excluded, that's what we've always said, party programme, government policy. It has happened this way with women's issues, environmental issues and peace issues. Of course these are only words, sometimes intentions, often just friendly noises. But at least on the verbal level the victory is almost too good to be true.

Maybe a lot of this is packaging, opportunism and only occasionally genuine rethinking. Actions and facts are largely left untouched. Yet it remains true: the themes of the future now on everybody's lips did not result from the farsightedness of our rulers or debates in parliament, and certainly did not emerge from the cathedrals of power in business and science. They have been put on the agenda against the resistance of institutionalized ignorance by the efforts of often muddled, moralizing and doubt-ridden splinter groups; democratic subversion has won a very unlikely victory, and that in Germany, of all places, where a long-standing faith in the authorities has resulted in the population meekly fitting in with all kinds of mad and murderous official policies.

Just a sop to battered left-wing bourgeois intellectuals? Blithely reinterpreting a retreat as a revolt? No. After all no one is suggesting that things are getting better, that there is light at the end of the tunnel. Where is this 'new person' who writes poetry in the morning, manufactures pins in the afternoon and goes fishing in the evening? Anyone interpreting the thematic shifts and changes in public awareness over the past two decades exclusively from the boy scout/class struggle point of view is bound to remain trapped in his/her rigid premises.

Adorno explained the vanishing of the individual with the loss of his independent economic existence. This is exactly where the error lies. Within the welfare state the individual has acquired, in historical terms, a new economic status. He is not primarily an employee in a specific business but a participant in the labour market, organized and buffered by collective bargaining and social safeguards as a reward for his qualifications and mobility. The peculiar result is a social being on his/her own who nevertheless voluntarily adapts to social standards; this is certainly not the resurrection of the recently departed bourgeois individual. Nor is it the delusions of the proletariat deceiving itself about its class role and lured on by the charms of capitalism. Putting it succinctly, and perhaps too simply, this social being is the stage-manager of its own biography condemned at all turns to free choice.

In an individualized society each of us must learn, on pain of remaining at a permanent disadvantage, to conceive of him/herself as the central pivot round which life revolves, a planning office for his/her own abilities, preferences, relationships and so on. If we write our own biographies, 'society' must be seen as a variable which we can manipulate. No doubt the shortage of university places is a problem affecting thousands of others, but how should I go about getting a place for medicine despite my low marks? The social determinants which impinge on one's own life must be processed as 'environmental variables' and ameliorated or overcome by 'creative measures'.

What is demanded is vigorous activity in everyday life, which puts oneself at its centre, selects and opens up opportunities and so enables one to plan and make meaningful decisions about one's own future. Behind the intellectual shadow-boxing we all indulge in, we must develop a self-centred attitude if we want to survive, turning relations between the world and ourselves upside down, so to speak, so that it provides us with the openings we need.

Coupled with this interest in 'the individual solution' there is however considerable pressure to conform and behave in a standardized way; the means which encourage individualism also induce sameness. This applies in every field, the market, money, law, mobility, education and so on, in its own way. The situation for the individual is deeply dependent on the job market; it is so to speak a perfected version of our dependency reaching into the deepest recesses of our lives. This is the outcome when society applies market principles to everyone, with only a few exceptions still relying on traditional support systems (for instance marriage).

The fact that we are under pressure simultaneously to become individuals and adopt standardized strategies does not adequately explain our predicament, for the requirements of the new job market are quite new. They span the separate areas of our private life and our public position. In making our own biographies we have to let the firm, the office, the business, the factory into our private homes. The situations which arise are contradictory because double-faced: individual decisions are heavily dependent on outside influences. What looks like the outside world becomes the inside of an individual biography. So decisions affecting our private existence turn out to be increasingly and obviously predetermined by circumstances and decisions outside our reach. We are confronted by risks, friction and difficulties which we cannot possibly deal with. They encompass more or less every aspect of public life the politicians debate about: the so-called 'holes in the social safety net', wage negotiations and working conditions, fending off red tape, providing education, solving traffic problems, protecting the environment and so on.

To put it another way, our autobiography is increasingly being written by outsiders, our private decisions taken out of our hands. It is true that individual choices and actions or omissions guide people along certain paths in life and assign them the corresponding place in society; such choices could include attending a certain school, passing or failing an exam, choosing this or that career. The point is however that even these apparently free and private decisions and ways of behaving are tied up with political developments and public expectations. Look at education, where decisions at the top have a profound effect on individual lives, either because underprivileged groups are suddenly considered worth supporting and given scholarships or because this assistance is withdrawn and used to encourage elites. The same applies in family matters and the divorce law, tax legislation and pensions which encourage or discourage marriage or remarriage, depending on financial status.

The more dependent people are on such official decisions, the more their biographies become susceptible to crises. The key to making a living lies in employment. Being a suitable employee means finding the right training. Anyone denied access to one or the other faces social and material oblivion. So providing apprenticeships for young people is vital if they are to gain a place in society. At the same time economic or demographic fluctuations can cause entire generations to drift towards the margins of society. In other words, official decisions on who is to be supported or neglected, made according to the needs of the market, can result in a whole generation of individuals, a peer group, being prevented from gaining a foothold. This is also revealed in the inadequate benefits paid by the government, which is expected to compensate whole age groups for the shortage of opportunities in the employment field.

Official thinking and regulations still run along 'standard biography' lines, although this concept is becoming increasingly irrelevant. Social insurance payments for instance depend on criteria which few people can meet in these days of mass unemployment and which fail to correspond with developments within the family and between the sexes. The concept of a 'family bread-winner' has been displaced by a family in which the roles of earner and provider, care-giver and child-rearer are shared and alternated. The place of the 'intact' family has been taken over by a huge variety of 'broken homes'. A growing number of single fathers is faced with discrimination by divorce laws committed to a maternal monopoly on raising children, and so on.

A society departing from the central axes along which industrial society runs – social classes, nuclear family, sex roles – is faced with a system of social services and administrative and political institutions which are taking over these functions as the industrial epoch nears its end. They intervene by laying down norms, dispensing approval or punishment for anyone living in a way which 'deviates' from the official standards, assuming certainties which now apply only to a small proportion of the population. In this way official planning contrasts more and more sharply with real life and the edifice of industrial society threatens to slip into normative legalism.

As a result a new kind of social subjectivity has grown up in which private and political issues are intermingled and augmented. In this sense individualization does not mean individuation, but is a hybrid of consumer consciousness and self-confidence. This self-confidence, which can become life's elixir, flourishes on having to search for personal solutions, cope with uncertainties, acknowledge one's doubts, accept inconsistencies and deal with them with cheerful cynicism. It is as if thousands of Kafkaesque characters were coming to life, quite ordinary, mundane figures prepared to swerve round the hindrances they meet like fish in an aquarium.

And yet it is no exaggeration to say that in the confusion between the sexes, and in initiatives against pollution and for peace some kind of enlightenment seems to be reviving, in a form far removed from high-brow philosophizing and well suited to everyday life. Is it too big a word for such a small shoot? If it is true that being enlightened can include carving out one's own small corner from the mass of everyday commitments, then this little plant called self-awareness, carefully tended in one's own private biographical garden, is like a wild or forgotten cousin of that highly bred orchid 'enlightenment' which is nowadays usually given the prefix 'post-'. There is no need to deny that people are 'dancing around the golden self', or going astray in the jungle of personal growth offers. Nevertheless it would be foolish of us to ignore the new impulses, even if they are often tentative or incoherent, and are trying to express themselves in unsuitable and outworn clichés.

These experiences do not exist at all according to the prevailing theories, indeed cannot exist, and yet they do. We are dealing here with dimensions which for one person may be the most significant and credible experience he/she has ever had, and for another sheer nonsense. Attempting to discuss them implies standing on the boundary between two quite different areas of experience; while in one person's view explanations are entirely unnecessary, in another's they are absolutely ridiculous, and any attempt to convey what consciousness-raising entails would seem inexcusably abstract. What is the point in talking about something one cannot prove exists? This is where the dilemma lies: while a new chance seems to be offering itself for us to understand ourselves and our potential in this world, and is gradually gaining ground, some people think discussing it superfluous, and others find discussion impossible.

In this sense, at least, talking about the 'age of narcissism' (Lasch 1977) is justified, but it is a distorting and misleading label, as it underestimates the scope and effect of the energies which have been unleashed. Largely involuntarily and driven by social changes, individuals are entering a searching and explorative phase. They want to try out and 'experience' (in the active sense of the word) new ways of living to counteract the dominance of roles (man, woman, family, career) which are becoming increasingly irrelevant. They want to express themselves freely and give in to impulses they used to suppress. They allow themselves to enjoy life here and now and not just in the distant future, and to cultivate a conscious delight in the good things in life. They are coming to regard their needs as rights to be defended if necessary against official dictates and obligations. They are developing a feeling for freedom, are highly aware of having to protect their lives against encroachment from outside and ready to become socially and politically active whenever their private territory is endangered, often ignoring the established forms and forums for articulating and organizing political action.

Such experiences are the starting-point for a new ethic based on 'one's duty to oneself' – and not as a solipsistic misunderstanding but as an effort to integrate the individual with the social in a new way which takes account of altering, projective social identities. Casting off standard patterns in one's own life and ideas becomes a permanent habit, an unending personal learning process. Instead of the old fixed images there is a new picture of mankind which specifically includes the possibility of metamorphosis, of personal development and growth. Defining ourselves primarily in terms of our social roles is in this sense nothing but a hypothesis and hangover from the past which we have not yet quite grown out of.

The untrod tracks to be followed here in a loose crowd of fellow individuals lead in exactly the opposite direction to that in which enlightenment has pointed so far. It is no longer a matter of understanding natural laws, developing technologies, building up production, increasing material wealth, altering the economic, social and political circumstances and only after all that finally liberating men and women from their drudgery. Instead the last in the line is brashly pushed to the front: develop your own personality, and this will have a lasting effect on your marriage, family, work colleagues, career, officialdom and the way we all treat our resources and our world. The central problem remains: how can you develop your own potential while remaining a social being, and what kind of society would enable us to take these steps towards freedom?

2

FROM LOVE TO LIAISON

Changing relationships in an individualized society

Pop songs still sing the praises of eternal love. According to recent surveys, living with someone is still regarded as the ideal, as the place where one finds closeness, warmth and affection, an antithesis to the cold concrete wastes outside.

But at the same time there are deep cracks across the picture of the family. On stage and screen, in novels and tongue-tied autobiographies, wherever one turns there is the sound of battle. The battle between the sexes is the central drama of our times; business is flourishing for marriage counsellors, the family courts are booming, divorce figures are high and even in everyday life among very normal families one can hear someone quietly wondering, 'Why, oh why is living together so difficult?'

The way to find an answer is suggested in a remark by Norbert Elias: 'Often enough one cannot understand what is happening today if one does not know what happened yesterday' (1985: viii). So first of all we shall take a look at the past. It will show us that where people gradually cast off the commitments, dictates and taboos of premodern society they began to put new hopes in love, but equally found themselves in new predicaments. The combination of these two factors produced the explosive mixture we know as contemporary love.

Love becomes more important than ever

Severing traditional ties

Comparisons between premodern and modern society always emphasize that human lives used to be determined by a multitude of traditional ties – from family business and village community, homeland and religion to social status and gender role. Such ties always have a double face (as discussed in chapter 3 below).

On the one hand they rigorously restrict the individual's choices, on the other they offer familiarity and protection, a stable footing and certain identity. Where they exist, a person is never alone but integrated into a larger unit. Take religion, for example:

> The fact that our ancestors were bound to Christian beliefs . . . generally meant that their little world, their microcosm, was tied to another, larger world, the macrocosm . . . The result of this bond between microcosm and macrocosm, sheltering hundreds and thousands of little worlds within the unifying greater world, which in turn, according to Christian belief, rested in God's all-encompassing embrace, was not just that even the lowliest person never fought in vain or was left to fend for himself. It also must have given our ancestors an emotional stability which could not be easily thrown off-balance even by the worst ragings of pestilence, famine and war. (Imhof 1984: 23)

With the transition to modern society, changes took place on many levels and they brought about a far-reaching individualization process, cutting people off from their traditional ties, beliefs and social relationships. This process began, as Weber explained in his *Protestant Ethic* (1985), with the teachings of the Reformation, which cancelled any certainty of salvation and dismissed people into a deep inner isolation. This process has continued on many levels over the succeeding centuries; it can be seen in our complex economic system with its intricate infrastructure, and in increased secularization, urbanization, personal mobility and so on. More and more people have been affected by it, and it has reached unique dimensions in the present. As a result each of us is increasingly both expected and forced to *lead our own life* outside the bounds of any specific community or group.

For the individual this severing of traditional ties means being freed of previous constraints and obligations. At the same time, however, the support and security offered by a close-knit society begin to disappear. As secularization gains ground, as new living patterns emerge, as value systems and religions compete for people's minds, many landmarks which previously provided orientation, meaning and a personal anchoring place in a larger universe have vanished. The consequence, so often described by philosophers and historians, sociologists and psychologists, is a profound loss of inner stability. With the 'disenchantment of the world' (Weber 1985) comes a new state of 'inner homelessness', of being all alone in the vastness of the cosmos (Berger, Berger and Kellner 1973: passim). C. G. Jung describes how the relationship between mankind and nature has changed:

> Our world has become dehumanised to the same degree as our scientific understanding has grown. Mankind feels lost in the cosmos because it is no longer bound to nature and has lost its emotional 'subconscious identity' with natural phenomena. These have gradually lost their symbolic content. Thunder is no longer the voice of a wrathful God and lightning no longer his punishing spear . . . No longer do voices speak to people from stones, plants and animals, and people themselves no longer speak to the latter in the belief that they would be understood. Their contact with nature has been lost and with it the powerful emotional energy which this symbolic connection once produced. (Quoted in Imhof 1984: 174–5)

One can call this the initial phase in the individualization process. In the course of centuries traditional forms of interpretation and belief, in brief the socially prescribed *answers*, have gradually been worn away. The next stage starts when the individual is confronted with a range of new *questions*; this is particularly evident in the second half of the twentieth century, largely because there are so many new lifestyles and educational opportunities to choose from. The standard of living in the lower strata of the population improved in the 1950s and 1960s to a degree described as 'spectacular, comprehensive and a revolution in social history' (Mooser 1983: 286). Where earlier generations often knew nothing but the daily struggle to survive, a monotonous cycle of poverty and hunger, nowadays broad sections of the population have sufficient income to take advantage of a whole range of possibilities on how to live their lives. Another factor is the spread of educational opportunities which began in the 1960s, freeing thousands of young people from the need to earn money or wear themselves out physically and mentally from an early age. They have gained access to their youth in the psychological sense, a waiting period and moratorium (Hornstein 1985). And they are free to learn subjects beyond the demands of everyday life, opening their minds to new areas of experience, different traditions and ways of thinking.

The consequence of such structural changes in society is that for the first time large numbers of people are in a position to wonder about matters not directly connected with the daily grind of earning a living. At the very moment when life becomes somewhat easier, questions on the meaning of it all can develop a new urgency. These are the old philosophical themes which now start to enter our private lives: '*Who am I? Where did I come from? And where am I going?*' These questions challenge us to find answers, and turn into a form of stress, indeed sometimes a kind of panic. The old ways of interpreting the world have become very threadbare, and each individual finds him/herself alone with new doubts. Not everybody can find answers, and what remains are anxieties and a sense of insecurity not so much about how to survive but about what lies behind our existence, the meaning of it all.

According to the psychotherapist Viktor E. Frankl, 'leading a meaningless life' is the predominant malady of the present day. We are 'no longer, as in Freud's day, confronted with sexual, but rather with existential frustration. And today's typical patient does not suffer so much from an inferiority complex as in Adler's day as from a deep sense of meaninglessness, coupled with emptiness . . . an existential vacuum' (1984: 11).

Sources of personal stability

In the eighteenth century the prevailing living pattern was not the family in the modern sense but rather a large household covering an 'extended family' which formed an economic unit. Its first commandment was to make a living and ensure the survival of the next generation. Under such conditions there was little room for personal inclinations, feelings or motives. Choosing a spouse and getting married was primarily an economic necessity, with little attention being given to individual compatibility (or incompatibility).

> [For the farmer] 'personal happiness' . . . consisted of marrying a woman with whom he worked, who bore him healthy children and protected him from debt with her dowry. One cannot dispute that this is also a kind of happiness. Love as such, however, linked to the spouse's personality and independent of this working basis, had almost no chance to develop. (Rosenbaum 1982: 76–7)

As research in social history shows, with the transition to a modern society came a far-reaching transformation. What used to be a team sharing the work has turned into a couple sharing emotions. The advent of the bourgeois family brought with it 'a sentimental occupation of the intrafamilial area', introducing privacy and intimacy, the characteristics of our modern image of the family (Weber-Kellermann 1974: 107).

It is probably no coincidence that this occurred in a phase in which traditional ties were beginning to slacken. Life within the family, where feelings and commitments are now concentrated, obviously counteracts and compensates for the other guidelines and social certainties which gradually got lost as society moved on towards its current form. Because people felt increasingly disoriented their longings for a family grew. It became a refuge in which inner homelessness seemed more bearable, a 'haven' in a world which had become strange and inhospitable (see Lasch 1977). Historically speaking this is a new form of identity which has emerged, which one could perhaps best describe as *person-related stability*. As more old-fashioned bonds lose their meaning, those in the immediate vicinity become indispensable in helping us to find our place, subconsciously and consciously, in the world, and to maintain our physical and mental well-being.

To illustrate this empirically, here is one result from a study into the connection between social support and chronic illness. It was shown that having an intimate and trusting relationship with another person provides vital emotional protection and makes any necessary adaptation to new conditions much easier:

> Even if . . . the chances of social contact for a person . . . are considerably reduced by, say, having to withdraw from the world of work, this does not necessarily mean one becomes increasingly susceptible to depression, as long as one keeps a 'confidant'. The quality of this specific relationship to a person whom one can trust completely, whose understanding one can count on and to whom one can turn with personal problems at any time, seems to be a special protective factor. (Badura 1981: 23)

Love and marriage as inner anchors

If our emotional and mental stability depends on the close support of others, then love acquires a new significance as the very heart of our lives. It is an ideal combining romantic and permanent love growing from the close emotional bond between two partners and giving their lives substance and significance. My partner means the world to me, and the sun and moon and all the stars as well. Take a classic love poem, Friedrich Rückert's *Du bist mein Mond*:[1]

> You are my moon and I your earth;
> You say you revolve around me.
> I don't know; I only know I glow
> In my nights because of you [. . .]
>
> You are my soul, you are my heart,
> You are my joy, you are my pain.
> You are the world in which I live,
> The heaven in which I soar,

> O you my grave in which
> I laid my cares to rest forever!
>
> You are calm, you are peace,
> You are heaven granted to me;
> Your loving makes me value mine,
> Your gaze has transfigured me,
> You let me transcend myself,
> My good spirit, my better self!

This exemplifies what we mean by person-related stability based on romantic love. Its inner core can be described as follows. The more other reference points have slipped away, the more we direct our craving to give our lives meaning and security towards those we love. More and more we tend to pin our hopes on another person, this man or that woman. He or she is supposed to hold us upright and steady in a world whirling round faster and faster. Soberly condensed into one sentence by Pfeil, ' "romantic marital love" is a virtual necessity in this world' (in Preuss 1985: 37). Benard and Schlaffer put it more vividly:

> Perhaps it used to be easier. People believed in the church and the state and they believed one would go to heaven if one could only be a good wife and mother. Now that God, if not dead, is at least out of town, only people are left as sources of existential meaning. For most people the work-place is . . . not a really absorbing or satisfying place. What remains is the family, relationships with people one is willing to commit oneself to. Understanding, communicating, caring have shrunk down to the small radius of close relationships. Without them one is reduced to the frosty interactions of office life. Time passes . . . for what? The question of what life means becomes more bearable if one has another person or persons as reference point to help find one's bearings. It is then possible to set up a civilized island for oneself in an empty cosmos. (Benard and Schlaffer 1981: 279)

Against this background marriage also takes on a new meaning, precisely the one we know well. Its basic pattern has been traced by sociologists and psychologists. Marriage has become a central factor in the 'social design of reality' (Berger and Kellner 1965). In living together a man and a woman build up a universe of shared attitudes, opinions and expectations covering everything from trivial day-to-day matters to the great events in world politics. This develops in verbal or non-verbal dialogue, in shared habits and experiences, in a continuous interplay between one's other half and oneself. The shared image of the world is continuously being negotiated, shifted, replaced, questioned and reaffirmed.

The fundamental theme behind marriage is not just the social structure of our lives; it is also increasingly a matter of *identity*. This is the aspect revealed particularly by psychological studies of marriage: in seeking an exchange on many levels with our partner we are also seeking ourselves. We are searching for the history of our life; we want to reconcile ourselves with hurts and disappointments, plan our goals and share our hopes. We mirror ourselves in the other, and our image of a You is also an idealized image of I: 'You are an image of my secret life' (Schellenbaum 1984: 142ff), 'my better self' (Rückert). Marriage is becoming an institution 'specialized in the development and maintenance of the individual self' (Ryder 1979: 365). Love and identity are becoming closely interwoven.

So in the initial stage, falling in love:

> Being in love is the search for one's own destiny . . . a search for one's own self, to the very bottom. This is achieved through the other person, in dialogue with her, in the encounter where each person seeks recognition in the other, in accepting, in understanding, in the confrontation and liberation of what was and of what is. (Alberoni 1983)

And equally in the intimate exchanges of a couple who have been together for years:

> The past with its unsolved questions and sorrows is set free. Or rather the past and the present which everyone is made up of are on the lookout for answers to the question 'Who am I and why am I here?' And what one looks for above all is someone else who wants to hear the questions, as if one can only understand oneself if someone else is listening and as if one's history can only become complete in someone else's ear . . . So the image each partner has of him/herself and the world is born and confirmed, corrected and changed in talking together . . . the question of personal identity is constantly being discussed, 'Who am I and who are you?' (Wachinger 1986: 70–1)

Marriage counsellors, and even more so the divorce figures, can confirm that this dialogue which is sought so passionately at the beginning often falters or dries up, hesitates, is blocked by silent taboos, interrupted or completely cut off. Why does this happen? That is the question to be looked into in the following sections. We shall trace how both phenomena – the growing longing and the frequent failure – have a common root. Simplified into one sentence, the disappointments inherent in our idea of love just as much as the hopes we invest in it are an outcome of our modern concern with being ourselves.

Love is more difficult than ever

The pros and cons of a life of one's own

The old loyalties within premodern society were framed by strict rules and regulations on how to behave. As these have gradually been shed, life has come to seem less confined, with more room to choose and more possibilities to choose from; in many ways it is less restricted and more flexible than before (for an exemplary study of this, see Berger, Berger and Kellner 1973). But this change also implies that each of us is confronted with having to take decisions on numerous levels, from the mundane matters of which resort and which make of car, to long-term matters like how many children and which kind of school. We are expected to be responsible citizens and critical consumers, price-conscious and good to the environment, up-to-date on nuclear energy and the right dosage of the right medicine. As analysts of modern times have noted, 'living with an oversupply of options' (Riesman 1981: 123) often overtaxes the individual.

What has so far been overlooked is the fact that when an individual does not live alone, but with someone else, the stress factors multiply; all the issues which affect the partner directly or indirectly – which television programme, which excursion, which furniture, which routine – have to be fed into the decision-making process as ideas and wishes, habits and norms of *two different* people. The results are predictable: *the more complex the decisions are, the more likely they are to lead to quarrels.*

The likelihood that the couple will disagree is further increased by the fact that on the reverse side of being free to choose one comes up against new restrictions. In one sense everyone is free to plan and decide, and in another the logic of individualism gets in the way. As the family as an economic unit is gradually breaking down, new ways of making a living are emerging which depend on the labour market and the individual. How individuals find jobs depends on the laws of the market – flexibility and mobility, for instance, or competition and career – which give very little consideration to private commitments. Those who do not obey these laws risk their jobs, incomes and social standing.

Here we can see a series of structural developments within society, the effect of which is particularly obvious in post-war Germany. Mobility in all its forms – geographical, social, daily moves between job and family, work and leisure, training, work-place and retirement – continues to force people away from their established ties (to neighbours, colleagues, local customs and so on). Similarly, many people find that their education cuts them off from the milieu in which they grew up. Having achieved a professional qualification means one has more chances on the job market; this pattern of achievement, which of course affects whole groups of people, nonetheless forces each one to plan and decide on his/her own behalf and take personal responsibility for success or failure.

This external description covers only some of the changes involved. The logic behind individualization steers basically adaptable biographies in certain predetermined directions, and therefore has inner consequences for those involved. It leads to a battle over 'space of one's own' in the literal and figurative sense, in a search for oneself and for fulfilling one's own potential. The fact that these words crop up all the time in interviews, therapy and literature does not imply we are all suffering from an outbreak of collective egoism. In fact the talk of finding oneself and doing one's own thing precisely reflects the pressures affecting everyone in their normal lives – demands to be mobile, get educated, find a job – and reaching deep into the innermost recesses of their heart and minds. As a result these themes are now appearing *en masse* in individual biographies in the guise of private problems. When life turns into a 'do-it-yourself biography' (Berger, Berger and Kellner 1973: passim), discovering your own potential is 'not just a new shining star at the zenith of our value system but a cultural answer to new challenges in life' (Baden-Württemberg Provincial Government 1983: 32) or, in succinct form, a social must.

The question immediately arises: how much room is there left in a do-it-yourself biography with all its pressures and restrictions for a partner with his/her own plans and problems? How can the other person avoid becoming an additional hindrance, if not a disruptive factor? To what extent is it possible to share one's life if social circumstances compel one to concentrate on one's own interests? Situations are bound to arise in which, despite the very best intentions, two monads who instead of building up a shared universe have to defend their own separate universes end up arguing, sometimes in a civilized tone, and sometimes bitterly, with no holds barred.

From this viewpoint it is intriguing to compare the new ideas about love, marriage and intimate relationships recommended in self-help books. The trend, presented in all kinds of variations, some mild, some crass, is to give self-assertion top priority, not just in the office and the bus but at home too. The magic formula is known as authenticity. The much-quoted postulates of gestalt therapy, reproduced on countless greetings cards, coffee mugs and posters pinned over beds, put the message most clearly:

> I do my thing, and you do your thing.
> I am not in this world to live up to your expectations
> And you are not in this world to live up to mine.
> You are you and I am me, and if by chance we find each other it's beautiful
> If not it can't be helped.
>
> (Perls and Stevens 1969: 4)

Quite a contrast to love poems like Rückert's! Most self-help books do not go that far, admittedly, but they point in the same direction. Where they used to call for adaptation they now recommend conscious separation. What they teach is constructive disagreement: 'saying no in love' (Schellenbaum 1984). Therapy tries to encourage the view that 'it is not at all desirable for two people who love each other to be *one* heart and *one* soul' (Preuss 1985; emphasis in the original). And they recommend 'laying down as many aspects of daily life together as possible in a marriage contract', from the right to 'personal freedom' all the way to 'arrangements in case of separation' (Partner 1984).

Phrases like these reflect the basic pattern behind individualization applied to living with a partner. It is an attempt to find a way of enabling independent individuals with their own aims and rights to perform the difficult balancing act of living their own lives and yet sharing them with someone else. One cannot help suspecting, however, that this fundamental dilemma is sometimes being treated with remedies which tend to enlarge the problem rather than solve it. If we are told that 'arguing binds people together' (Bach and Wyden 1969), how often is the result the desired creative tension, and how often, to borrow the up-beat title of one such book, 'creative divorce' (Krantzler 1974)?

> Should such negotiations break down, according to a different book, there can be a 'successful divorce', – by no means to be thought of as a failure – but one which 'has been pre-considered in terms of personal upward mobility, with stress laid not nearly so much on what is being left, and may therefore be lost, as on what lies ahead that may be incorporated into a new and better image'. After the successful divorce, this behaviour-modification book tells us, 'Little Affairs' may be useful . . . The person with a 'Positive Self Image' need not worry about promiscuity. *All* these affairs will be 'meaningful' because they will all contribute to the 'self's reservoir of experiences'. (Ehrenreich and English 1979: 276)

If love fails again, if this hope is extinguished, then what you must do is find a new one. The motto is 'How To Be Your Own Best Friend' (Ehrenreich and English: 176). Is that the only remaining hope? Does the individualization which induced our romantic longings necessarily and always lead to a post-romantic world?

> In the post-romantic world, where the old ties no longer bind, all that matters is *you*: you can be what you *want* to be; you *choose* your life, your environment, even your appearance and your emotions . . . The old hierarchies of protection and dependency no longer exist, there are only free contracts, freely terminated. The marketplace, which long ago expanded to include the relations of production, has now expanded to include *all* relationships. (Ehrenreich and English: 276)

It is not only that everyone's life has become more flexible and adaptable; one can choose to live with someone else in a wide variety of ways. Pre-industrial society laid down strict rules for couples to ensure their economic survival. Marriage was teamwork, with men and women having separate spheres and children being welcomed as helping hands and heirs. And nowadays? We have an endless series of questions to answer. Should the wife work outside the home, yes or no, full- or part-time? Should the husband aim straight up the career ladder, or share in the housework or even stay at home as a househusband? Are children a good idea, and if yes, when and how many? If yes, who is going to look after them, if no, who is responsible for contraception? It is becoming increasingly likely that sooner or later, in some respect or another, the partners are going to differ. And this will not necessarily be for personal reasons, unwillingness to compromise or sheer bloody-mindedness. It will be because their biographies as employees face them with clear limits and prevent them from structuring their lives as they might wish if they are to avoid difficulties in their work-places.

As well as all the substantial decisions to be made, there is the time aspect to consider. Every decision can be revoked in the course of a marriage. In fact decisions have to be revocable so that other outside demands can be met. The individualized biography assumes that everyone can update and optimize his/her decisions, and these in turn are affected by the new psychological approach expecting everyone to be open to new challenges, inquisitive and willing to learn. Such postulates are no doubt a great help in warding off the mute indifference which can befall couples trapped in a dreary marital routine. They do, however, have their dangers. What happens if one spouse is quite content with the way things are, while the other is not, or when both want to change but in different directions?

There are couples who both once agreed that it would be best for her to devote herself completely to the family. After a few years, however, bored by the monotony and isolation of domestic life, she wants to go back to work. Her husband, quite happy with the familiar pattern, feels endangered by the change and insists on his customary rights. Or take the example of couples who got married in the 1960s with conventional ideas of fidelity and a few years later read about 'open marriage' as an ideal. What if one of them now wants to hold on to the security of familiar habits, while the other longs to sample the attractions of novelty? Who is in the right?

Sometimes no one is. Right and wrong turn into vague categories as soon as there is no longer a shared standard but just the standards of *two* biographies affected by different expectations and restraints, and on top of all that a rapid change of stereotypes. There is more and more space available for subjective interpretations into which people's wishes can flow, and often both spouses have them, if of different kinds. And the outcome is a huge number of married people feeling misunderstood, injured and betrayed.

Man versus woman

In classic feminist writings the hope was often expressed that the sexes would be able to discover new and better ways of getting on with one another as soon as women were no longer repressed. The assumption was: love is possible only between free and equal partners. Here is an extract from the famous *Vindication of the Rights of Woman*, written in 1792 by Mary Wollstonecraft:

> It is vain to expect virtue from women till they are in some degree independent of men; nay it is vain to expect that strength of natural affection which would make them good wives and mothers. Whilst they are absolutely dependent on their husbands they will be cunning, mean and selfish, and the men who can be gratified by the fawning fondness of spaniel-like affection have not much delicacy, for love is not to be bought . . . Would men but generously snap our chains, and be content with rational fellowship instead of slavish obedience, they would find us more observant daughters, more affectionate sisters, more faithful wives . . . We should then love them with true affection, because we should learn to respect ourselves. (In Rossi 1974: 64 and 71)

Who could honestly say that these proud hopes have been fulfilled? The question is of course why did things turn out so differently? To find out we have to look more closely at the modernization process as it has affected men and women. The general assumption behind debates on modern changes has been that the transition from old-fashioned to modern living has helped to free the individual from outdated duties and bonds. If one compares this idea with research findings in social history and women's studies it proves to be both right and wrong. More precisely, it covers only half the truth, for it ignores the 'other' half of humanity. At the beginning of our modern times individualization remained an exclusive privilege of the men.

This is exemplified in Johann Gottlieb Fichte's natural law (1796), where the relation of the female to the male is described as follows:

> She who surrenders her personality, while maintaining her human dignity, of necessity gives her husband everything she has . . . The least important consequence is that she transfers her fortune and all her rights to him and lives with him. Only in his company, only in his eyes and his affairs does she live or play an active role. She has ceased to lead the life of an individual; her life has become a part of his (as is accurately shown by the fact that she takes on her husband's name). (in Gerhard 1978: 146)

The American historian C. N. Degler sums up as follows:

> The idea of individualism in the West has a long history . . . John Locke and Adam Smith celebrated the principles of individual rights and actions, but the individuals they had in mind were men. On the whole women were not then thought of as anything but supportive assistants – necessary to be sure, but not individuals in their own right. The individual as a conception in Western thought has always assumed that behind each man – that is, each individual – was a family. But the members of that family were not individuals, except the man, who was by law and custom its head. (Degler 1980: 189)

One characteristic of the modernization process is precisely the fact that standard male and female biographies initially develop in quite different directions. During the nineteenth century the range of a woman's life was not broadened, but on the contrary restricted to the interior space offered by home. Providing emotional as well as physical support for the other members of the family became her special task – listening to her husband and his worries, mediating in family quarrels, in short doing what nowadays is called 'the emotional work' or 'caring for the relationship'.

The more the husband had to venture out into the hostile world, the more his wife was expected to remain 'whole and beautiful and pure' to preserve 'within a tranquil and peaceful setting an inner mutual serenity' (Riehl 1861: 60). In a world increasingly run on rational lines, she was supposed to step in as the emotional counterpart, offering him an oasis of calm and affection.

> The charming world of women is to be a fortunate quiet oasis, a source of the poetry of life, a remnant of paradise. And we do not want that to be snatched away by any 'women's issue' or any frustrated blue-stocking or overeducated economist. We want to preserve it . . . as much as possible even for the poor and very poor 'worker', with God's help. (Nathusius 1871; in Lange and Bäumer 1901: 69)

> What attracts us in women is the emotional warmth, the naivety and freshness, where they are superior to precocious and prematurely overworked men, and the attraction they exert on men because of these qualities would be irretrievably lost if their most charming aspects were destroyed by education. (Appelius, Vice-Presidential address to the Weimar Landtag, 1891; in Lange and Bäumer 1901: 94)

> Woman has degenerated through independence and mannish ways; her greatest honour is simple femininity, and that means subordinating herself with an untroubled heart, being modest, wanting to be nothing more than she is meant to be . . . Man was created before woman in order to be independent; the woman was given to him for his sake. (Löhe, nineteenth century; in Ostner and Krutwa-Schott 1981: 25)

Statements like these, found in countless variations throughout the politics and philosophy, religion, science and art of the eighteenth and nineteenth centuries, highlight the real core of the concept of 'contrasting virtues' (Habermas) which was establishing itself. The more self-assertion was demanded of the man outside the family, the more his wife inside it was trained in self-denial. This can be seen in a number of legal statutes which unambiguously establish that a wife is dependent on her husband (Langer-El Sayed 1980: 56). The woman is for instance obliged to use her husband's name, to share his citizenship, to live with him and to fit in with his wishes. The husband has the right to monitor her correspondence and lay down guidelines for housekeeping and expenses; in many cases the right to dispose of the wife's personal possessions was transferred to her husband.

The price of such regulations is high, and obviously to the woman's disadvantage. But their purpose is clear. Since by definition no divergent wishes are permitted between men and women, this arrangement achieves a certain stability, no matter how oppressive it may be for one side. Under such conditions even having a few more options need not disrupt the family harmony. What counts is what he wants. What the woman really wants is to adapt to the man: 'From youth she must be taught the habit . . . of viewing the male sex as the one designed to rule, and of making herself attractive to it by being gentle, patient and submissive'

(Basedow 1770; in Kern and Kern 1988: 51). Agatha Christie writes in her memoirs of her girlhood:

> In one respect, man was paramount: he was the head of the house. A woman, when she married, accepted as her destiny *his* place in the world and *his* way of life. That seems sound sense to me and the foundation of happiness. If you can't face your man's way of life, don't take that job – in other words, don't marry that man. Here, say, is a wholesale draper; he is a Roman Catholic; he prefers to live in a suburb; he plays golf and he likes to go for holidays to the seaside. *That* is what you are marrying. Make up your mind to like it, and like it. It won't be so difficult. (Christie 1977: 122)

Since then change has been rapid. What initially was a prerogative of the men – shaking off old patterns of behaviour – has since the late nineteenth century, and especially since the 1960s, also become feasible for women. This is particularly apparent in education; although new openings became available to them at the turn of the century, the real shift took place fifty years later with offers of education to everybody in the 1960s. The disadvantages for girls, which had long been taken for granted, were now deliberately questioned, and the success of these efforts surpassed all expectations. Within only twenty years the marked differences in levels of schooling gave way to almost equal numbers of girls and boys in state education at every level, all the way up to university.[2]

Working away from home is another example. Although the model of housewife and mother was an ideal of the bourgeois family, women in the lower strata had always been forced to earn money because their husband's wage was rarely enough to support the family. And in the late nineteenth century even in the middle classes, where work within the family gradually lost any links with the production process, more women found themselves forced to look for a source of income; the number of women who had no private means and had to make a living rose. In middle-class society, however, such work was restricted in time, defined only to last until marriage; the woman's place was still in the home.

Really far-reaching changes took place in the 1950s. The first move in Germany, as in other industrial countries, was a marked rise in the number of married women working outside the home.[3] This was followed by a tendency for married women to continue to work until their first child was born, and to return to work after the children had grown up. The second stage, again in all industrial societies, is marked by pronounced shifts in the number of women with children working away from home – working mothers.[4] Nowadays work for them is much more than an interim phase; 'Not working is becoming an exceptional situation for women, increasingly limited to the phase of caring for small children' (Willms 1983a: 111).

Demographic changes also play a role. Since the beginning of the century life expectancy has been rising and has reached an all-time high in the late twentieth century. By contrast, the number of children has drastically sunk, a tendency which began in Europe in the late nineteenth century and has accelerated since the 1960s. The combined effects of these two developments has decisively altered the standard female biography. The task which had become women's main occupation after the extended family had broken up and been replaced by the bourgeois family – raising children – now occupies in purely temporal terms an ever-smaller portion of her life. Now there is a phase which historically speaking is quite new, the 'empty nest' years, where the woman is no longer tied to or needed in her mother role (Imhof 1981: 180f.).

As a result of these changes in education, professional openings, family life, legislation and the like, working women have fewer family commitments, and are coming to expect less support from their husbands; they have to be in some, often contradictory, form independent and able to support themselves. The subjective aspect is of course that women are finding out, in fact having to find out, what they expect of life and making their own plans which are not necessarily focused on the family but on their own personalities. They must plan how to take care of themselves, first of all financially, and to do without a husband if need be. They can no longer consider themselves 'appendages' of the family, but as individual people with corresponding rights and interests, their own futures and their own options.

Here are the classical lines from the final scene of Ibsen's *A Doll's House* (1878–9):

> HELMER: . . . Is this the way you neglect your most sacred duties?
> NORA: What do you consider is my most sacred duty?
> HELMER: Do I have to tell you that? Isn't it your duty to your husband and children?
> NORA: I have another duty, just as sacred.
> HELMER: You can't have. What duty do you mean?
> NORA: My duty to myself.
> HELMER: Before everything else, you're a wife and a mother.
> NORA: I don't believe that any longer. I believe that before everything else I'm a human being – just as much as you are . . . or at any rate I shall try to become one.

What is interesting here is how such changes affect relationships between the sexes. Clearly there is potential here for a new kind of bond no longer restricting man and woman to the daily grind of making a living, as in pre-industrial society, or, as in the bourgeois nineteenth-century model, to antithetical gender roles which complemented one another but presupposed the woman's subordination. Instead there is now the chance of a bond of fellow spirits, or putting it more cautiously, of a partnership between two people who are close to one another in character and attitude to life. This is the bond so longed for in the writings of the women's movement, that 'most wonderful thing' that shines out as a hope at the end of *A Doll's House*:

> HELMER: Nora – can't I ever be anything more than a stranger to you?
> NORA: Oh, Torvald – there would have to be the greatest miracle of all . . .
> HELMER: What would that be – the greatest miracle of all?
> NORA: Both of us would have to be so changed that – Oh, Torvald, I don't believe in miracles any longer.
> HELMER: But I'll believe. Tell me: 'so changed that . . .'?
> NORA: That our life together could be a real marriage.

The striking thing here is of course not so much the high hopes and the possible miracles but the other side, the disappointments and failures which nowadays dog so many marriages and liaisons. Quite obviously, as standard biographies have changed, living together has become more difficult for both sexes. The ideas discussed above on the curbs we all face in choosing how to lead our lives remained imprecise in one crucial respect: they presupposed that both men and women can behave as true partners, sharing the decision-making – a state of affairs which is by no means given.

Now we can complete the picture. The new factor altering love and marriage is not that somebody – meaning the man – has become more himself, more individual in the course of modern times, as the sociologists have traced. What is new is the individual *female* biography, freeing the woman of family duties, and sending her out into the world with an impetus which has been increasing since the 1960s. To put it even more pointedly, as long as it was only the man who developed his potential and the woman was complementarily obliged to look after him and others, family cohesion remained more or less intact – at the cost of her own interests or personality. Now however this 'division of modernity' (see chapter 1 above) cannot be maintained any longer and we are witnessing a new period in the history of women, and therefore in the history of men *and* women. Now for the first time two people falling in love find themselves both subject to the opportunities and hindrances of a biography designed by themselves.

There are already signs of this in the expectations men and women have in living together. As Jessie Bernard has said, every marriage consists of two marriages, the husband's and the wife's (Bernard 1976). This definition focuses attention on an aspect which long remained hidden but has come to the surface in the women's movement and feminist writings: in a number of significant ways the hopes men and women attach to the magic word 'love' are widely divergent. In Lilian Rubin's provocative phrase, they are and remain 'intimate strangers' (Rubin 1983). This applies to their sexual wishes (Ehrenreich, Hess and Jacobs 1986) and erotic dreams (Alberoni 1987) as well as to the division of labour (Metz-Göckel and Müller 1987) and topics to be talked about (Ehrenreich 1984; Fishman 1982), the priorities and modes of communication which are the backbone of everyday life.

This difference in what each expects is probably not new; what is new however is the manner of dealing with it. The more women come to regard themselves as people with wishes of their own, the less they accept the fact that these are not fulfilled. On the contrary, they are increasingly likely to demand satisfaction and if all else fails to take the ultimate consequence, divorce. Studies on the reasons for divorce show that women expect a good, emotionally fulfilling life together much more than men do (Höhn, Mammey and Schwarz 1981; Wagnerova 1982) and are therefore more likely than men to be dissatisfied with their marriage. It was the same with Ibsen's Nora, who leaves a home which her husband thought was a happy one, and is prepared to return only if it becomes 'a marriage', that is to say a marriage according to *her* ideas. The trend hinted at here can perhaps be summed up as follows: if they were disappointed, women used to abandon their hopes; nowadays they cling to their hopes and abandon the marriage.

In a recent survey women were asked why they had left their husbands although the marriage according to all external criteria seemed a good, all-round one. The author describes their reasons as follows:

> They left because they wanted more than what they were able to get from their marriages. What may have qualified as acceptable marriages for our mothers – and indeed for us when we sought to make them – was no longer acceptable. These women wanted more than a roof over their heads, a husband to support them, and children to look after. They wanted emotional intimacy, equality in partnership, and they wanted to exercise control over their own lives. (B. Rabkin, *New Woman*, September 1985: 59)

This is how the conflict potential grows and at the same time the chances of reducing the difficulties diminish. The more women learn to look after themselves, in fact *must* learn to do so in these individualistic times, the less they can swallow the solutions practised by their mothers and grandmothers – adapting to one's husband's wishes while sacrificing one's own. The adhesive which used to guarantee cohesion is vanishing: the old female role, self-denial for the sake of others, willingness to take on the endless and invisible emotional patching up which ensured an at least superficial calm. Who is now supposed to undertake this task? Many women are tired of being the pacifiers, many men are unprepared to step in, and both genders are overtaxed when they find a mountain of emotional labour waiting for them in the evening after the pressure of competition in their job.

The dilemma is exacerbated by the fact that such social upheavals and changes in the rhythm of life inevitably produce friction. Both sexes are trapped between old role models and new facts, faced with unfamiliar claims depending on which area of life or among which group of people they find themselves, and often confused by their own contradictory attitudes. The stage between 'no longer' and 'not yet' produces a volatile mixture, the consequences of which are painfully evident for men and women.

First there is the matter of what might be termed the poverty of the single woman. This applies to women with little education deprived of the traditional protection within marriage but not sufficiently armed to cope with a personally designed biography. These women are 'only a husband away from welfare' and if he is absent, as is the case for the growing group of single and divorced women, the result is known as the 'feminization of poverty' (Pearce and McAdoo 1981). At the other end of the scale, there is another problem emerging, affecting those women who pursue an independent career but must in many cases pay a high price, the loneliness of the professionally successful woman (Bock-Rosenthal, Haase and Streeck 1978; Hennig and Jardim 1977).

Developments of this kind are described by, for instance, the psychologist Jean Baker Miller. In her experience the reasons why women come to therapy have changed markedly within a few years. While in the 1970s the patients were primarily middle-aged women who had married young, raised children and finally realized how much of themselves they had given up in doing so, nowadays those seeking therapeutic help are often professionally successful women of the younger generation, hard-working, single or divorced, who find their emotional needs unsatisfied in the lives they lead. For a woman who dedicates her life to work, there are hardly any househusbands available who are prepared to care for their neglected emotional lives. The consequences are obvious: 'Either both partners are so busy pursuing traditional definitions of success that neither has the energy to nurture the relationship, or the professional woman finds she has no partner at all' (Gordon 1985).

Isidora, the heroine of Erica Jong's novel *Parachutes and Kisses*, fits into this category. Isidora, celebrated author and divorced three times, thinks ruefully:

> accomplished women . . . assume – wrongly – that what holds true for men will also hold true for them: that accomplishment will bring with it fame, fortune, and beautiful lovers . . . But alas, we often get just the reverse. All our accomplishment buys us in the love department is threatened men, soft cocks, abandonment. And we reel backward wondering why we work so hard for professional glory, when personal happiness is the forfeiture we have to pay. (Jong 1985: 113)

At the same time some groups of women are trying out a new role, seeking to escape from the old dependencies by following the motto: every woman for herself, with or without a man. The search for one's own identity means excluding the men, and as a logical reaction, attention is focused only on one's own rights. One good indicator of this trend is the market for women's literature, where relations between the sexes often degenerate into chilly confrontation. The titles, often deliberately provocative, have more than a symbolic value: 'Now It's Time for Me' (Wiggershaus 1985) could serve as a watchword. Instead of 'we' one finds 'Him or Me' (Zschocke 1983) or if in doubt 'I am Myself' (Jannberg 1982). Having been subservient, the women now find the time has come for 'Settling Scores' (Schenk 1979). When two bodies without further ado join for the next sexual encounter while the persons belonging to them remain strangers to one another, the other person is called a 'Misogynist',[5] and the 'Death of Prince Charming' is publicly proclaimed (Merian 1983). The final stage is 'Choosing to be Alone' (Meller 1983).

The repercussions of the women's rejection of their old role for men has not been so well documented, partly perhaps because men still wield more power and have more loopholes through which to escape, but partly also because they find it much more difficult to express their feelings and formulate their frustrations. The diagnosis varies according to the viewpoint and gender of the observer. Some discern 'The Insecure Man' (Goldberg 1979), others note repressed feelings, unwillingness to understand, refusal to give up privileges. Their verdict on men in these uneasy times is 'Worldly but not Wise' (Benard and Schlaffer 1985), the same old patriarchs in new clothes.

It is safe to say that the new signals are confusing and contradictory for men, do not tally with how they were socialized and contain a number of more or less open attacks on their self-esteem. Men from the most varied backgrounds would agree with the plea, 'What Do Women Want?' (Eichenbaum and Orbach 1983). Many of them are on principle willing to concede that the women are quite right, but become reluctant and stubborn as soon as any inconveniences like washing up or looking after the children impinge on their lives. Above all one can find a certain new 'openmindedness' which however proves limited when things begin to become unpleasant for the men (Schneewind and Vaskovics 1991: 171). There is a new kind of ideal woman, someone who is both independent and willing to adapt, depending on what is in the man's interest (Metz-Göckel and Müller 1985: 22f.). As a man in another study put it:

> What you want to do is marry a woman graduate who is intellectual enough to hold a conversation with you, and someone who is confident to help you in your business or help you with your decision-making processes through life, but who is also inclined to family care and household care. If you can find a woman like that, you know you've won. (White 1984: 435)

In view of these disappointments, painful to everyone involved, the women's movement has over the past few years turned to a new theme, the difficult balancing act between being liberated and being committed. No one is yearning to return to the old pattern with all its restrictions, and hopes in a loving partnership between equals do still exist. But more often than before disillusioned people are wondering: *is it possible for equals to love each other? Can love survive liberation? Or are love and freedom irreconcilable opposites?*

On the one hand one realizes that love snatches away one's autonomy: 'the servitude you would inflict on me, making me your Sancho Panza on his nag, and robbing me of my identity, my life. It would be disastrous to accept your love, and to love you' (Fallaci 1980: 156). And on the other one loses a lover because of trying to be free: 'We knew, when we lost our innocence, that we risked the loss of love. But our certainty that enlightenment was always worth the pain was cold comfort when we discovered, more often than not, that we could not apply what we had learned to our private lives without destroying love' (O'Reilly 1980: 219).

Here seems to lie the dilemma. The old kind of relationship involved suppressing the women's initiative, but also gained its resilience from this fact. The new kind has to cater for two separate biographies, or at least the claim to them. Perhaps the resulting squabbles and misery are only the product of an unfortumate interim stage in the course of human gender history, roughly in the way Erica Jong puts it: 'They're still in love, but they can't live together – at least not right now' (Jong 1985: 12). Maybe at this stage becoming an individual is almost impossible and all one can dare is trial and error, picking out which way of life seems best; as the gist of a sociological study goes, 'such temporary measures are becoming increasingly necessary for women. And probably not just for them either' (Brose and Wohlrab-Sahr 1986: 18).

What happens though, the uneasy question remains, if the current difficulties are much more than a phase? What if they are the unavoidable outcome of that epoch-making move towards being oneself which first only involved men but recently has come to include women too? Can two biographies ever be interwoven, or does trying to do it throw so much sand into the works that the shared vehicle can only grind to a halt?

The mid-life crisis

A look into the statistics reveals a striking state of affairs. It is precisely among long-term, seemingly stable marriages that have lasted eighteen or twenty years that the divorce rate is rising sharply.[6] Explanations can be found in psychological self-help literature (Jaeggi 1982; Jaeggi and Hollstein 1985; Wachinger 1986). There is much talk of the mid-life (marriage) crisis, when the couple has built up a solid basis and now starts to develop separate interests which they have to defend against one another. 'Freedom for me!' is the war-cry of this phase and often coupled with long-drawn-out power struggles of various kinds, starting with rejecting the other's advances, fleeing into illness, seeking an accomplice and sometimes ending in open violence. All of these strategies revolve round the question: 'Which of us is going to survive as an independent being?' They are in a sense *attempts to survive within a shared life* which now dominate the marital scene. Here are two descriptions from contrasting viewpoints, first the internal view from Erica Jong's novel *Fear of Flying*:

> And what about those . . . longings which marriage stifles? Those longings to hit the open road from time to time, to discover whether you could still

> live alone inside your own head, to discover whether you could manage to survive in a cabin in the woods without going mad; to discover, in short, whether you were still whole after so many years of being half of something . . . Five years of marriage had made me . . . itchy for solitude. (Jong 1974: 18)

Then the outside view, described by a marriage counsellor:

> Most marriages begin with a kind of passion for togetherness and sharing; the individual is almost extinguished and everything is subordinated to life together. The years spent building up the marriage demand a lot of cohesion, a lot of effort for each other and the children, for the professional positions which are being aimed for . . . But after many years of living together . . . when much of the youthful verve has evaporated, much of the glitter fallen away, when the professional aims have been reached and new goals are hard to find – then an old question crops up again in a new and different guise and more urgently: 'Who am I?' Another kind of passion takes over, to assert oneself, make independent decisions, have a life of one's own . . . The question 'Who am I?' then inevitably becomes a question directed at one's spouse: 'Do you really know who I am?' . . . Breaking up, dissolving the marriage seems less of a threat than giving up oneself and one's own interests. (Wachinger 1986: 80–3)

To explain these patterns one can turn to the laws of psychological development, which show that steps towards maturity always involve some form of separation. The battles and turmoil of adolescence have their analogue in the mid-life crisis with its yearning to escape from marital symbiosis:

> This conflict resembles . . . in many respects the struggles of an adolescent with his parents and indeed serves the same purpose: re-creating one's own identity, swimming away from the depths of symbiotic unity and realizing that the other person will never really be able to share one's loneliness. (Jaeggi and Hollstein 1985: 219)

What seems like the natural course of events from the psychological angle, a predetermined pattern for marriage, shows its special features when looked at from the point of view of social history. To put it very briefly, the mid-life crisis is a *social*, not a natural event. It is first of all a result of the individualization processes we have been describing; more particularly it is the product of an advanced stage of this development, when the context of a woman's life has been included in the process. Finally, it is the product of a demographic development, the huge increase in life expectancy, which is the only thing which enables many couples to reach that stage. In the course of one century there has been 'almost a doubling of the average duration of a marriage (without divorce); a couple that married in 1870 lived together for an average of 23.4 years; by 1900 it was already 28.2 years, in 1930 36 years; couples who said "I do" in 1970 can count on 43 years elapsing until the death of one of them ends their marriage.'[7]

Only where these three factors coincide – individualization in general, female individualization in particular and increased life expectancy – does one find the mid-life crisis en masse. As a historical phenomenon it is a novelty, not reaching broad sections of the population until the second half of the twentieth century. The various steps can be traced as follows: in pre-industrial society there was little room for individual decisions, either in one's own life or in marriage, which essentially consisted of teamwork. It seems reasonable to suppose that at that time the need to discover one's own identity played a minor role.

This changes as soon as the individual person comes to the fore, and changes even further when circumstances force women to look after themselves. Finally, when we realize there are probably many years lying ahead after we have finished establishing a home and a career, our attitudes change. The question which seems more pressing than before is 'Was that all?' In other words a person is confronted with awkward questions, lists the disappointments and shortcomings of life so far and has a vision of a new and better alternative which will compensate for past omissions.

This is the moment when the question occurs to us, what have I given up for my spouse? People recall the grand plans they had in their youth and see the compromises of a shared life. Whether justified or not, many of the omissions get blamed on the other one, and marriage turns into a scapegoat for the life one did not live. Subconsciously people recognize that there are some things they can no longer do, and others they no longer dare to do (one is too old to become a concert pianist, and not brave enough to emigrate to South America).

Even if it is impossible to start again from scratch, one has to do something about the direct monogamous situation while there is time. At least one wants to lay claim to more space and time for oneself, and the more the other resists, because he/she is struggling to find an identity too, the more one insists. So one's partner turns into an enemy, marriage into a place (safety valve, lightning conductor or surrogate) where one struggles to preserve one's identity and self-esteem.

The course of the battles which ensue is often paradoxical, running along the lines 'it's no good with you and no good without you.' Numerous cases have been described where the partners have waged war for many years, in new variations and escalations. At the same time, however, they have never quite managed to separate. They split up and come back again, live together but declare they are really separated, separate but cannot say goodbye, and feel trapped in a dead-end situation. Friends watching such moves over the years can only shrug their shoulders; to anyone not involved it seems incomprehensible, even absurd.

Here again are two descriptions from contrasting viewpoints. The first comes from Oriana Fallaci's novel *A Man*:

> I had gone back . . . to leave you a letter explaining my refusal to continue such a relationship . . . But the leash was broken and there was nothing worse than mending it with lumps in the throat; nothing worse than disturbing my equilibrium, my detachment. There was only one chance of that happening, and it lay in the risk of hearing your voice . . . A phone call would have been enough. Still the fear lasted only one week, and the second week I had already stopped believing in it. Grave mistake. The dawn of the seventeenth day of escape was breaking when the phone rang: 'Hello! It's I! It's me' . . . And a few hours later I was sitting in the plane: I'm coming, Don Quixote, I'm coming; your Sancho Panza is still your Sancho Panza, will always be, you can always count on me, here I am! . . . My problem was insoluble, my survival impossible, and escape achieved nothing. (Fallaci 1980: 246, 362, 264, 357)

Seen from outside, here is an account from a therapist:

> Of course there were constant quarrels, going on holiday separately, few points in common. Despite their endless maundering about a possible separation, however, neither of the two took any steps in that direction, although by all appearances each could easily have lived alone. When I talked to Karin by herself about this, she expressed almost absurd fantasies on the subject, fears that she would be 'all alone' after the separation, that no one would 'care' about her. (Thanks to her career she had more friends and acquaintances than Dieter!) On the other hand I heard Dieter screaming quite hysterically during one of their frequent scenes that he would 'hang himself in the attic' if Karin did not immediately unpack her suitcase. An outsider would have got the impression they were both insane. But of course in their lives outside marriage they were well-adjusted, successful and very well-liked people. This simply showed in unusually vehement form that they 'could not leave each other alone' and in any case neither wanted to be left behind by the other. In calm conversations one could hear from each of them that he or she had 'actually' been ready to separate a long time ago. (Jaeggi 1982: 26)

Such patterns obviously reveal aspects of what is known by psychologists as a symbiotic entanglement, a constellation which produces consequences as hopeless as they seem absurd. Psychologists see the eternal struggle between autonomy and dependency here, between 'closeness and distance' (Jaeggi and Hollstein 1985: 217ff.), 'fusion and resistance' (Schellenbaum 1984: 35ff.). But *why* do such complications come about, why are they insoluble? According to the sociological viewpoint offered here, they did not come about by chance, nor are they genetically determined (or only on the most general level) nor are they part of nature's great plan since Adam and Eve. They are rather an *expression and reflection of the contradictions which came about in the course of individualization.* Behind them lie all the contradictory longings, expectations and obligations which determine our private lives. As described above, as well as becoming more important love is becoming more difficult than ever. On paper one can keep the two strands apart, but in the individual's heart they are inseparably welded together, leading into one set of paradoxes and difficulties after another, whatever labels one gives them – intimacy versus individuality, or symbiosis versus a life of one's own.

The dilemma which is formulated here in theoretical terms has also become a theme in many modern novels, especially in women's literature. Let us again compare two examples. The first is Erica Jong's heroine Isidora again, who expresses her incompatible wishes in an inner monolgue:

> ME: Why is being alone so terrible?
> ME: Because if no man loves me, I have no identity . . .
> ME: But you know that you'd hate to have a man who possessed you totally and used up your breathing space . . .
> ME: I know – but I yearn for it desperately.
> ME: But if you had it, you'd feel trapped.
> ME: I know.
> ME: You want contradictory things.
> ME: I know.
> ME: You want freedom and you also want closeness.
> ME: I know.
>
> (Jong 1974: 251)

Then Fallaci again:

> As long as the beloved oppresses with demands, with bonds, we feel stolen from ourselves and it seems that to give up a job for him or a journey or a romance is unjust; openly or secretly we harbor a thousand resentments, dreams of freedom, we long for an existence without affections, in which to move like the seagulls that fly through the golden dust.

> What an unheard-of torment are the chains with which the beloved one ties us, preventing us from spreading our wings. But when he is no more and that space is flung open, infinite, so we can fly in the golden dust as much as we like, without affections and without ties, we sense a frightful void. And the job or the journey or the romance we sacrificed so reluctantly now appears in all its meaninglessness, we no longer know what to do with our regained freedom, like dogs without masters, sheep without a flock, we wander around in that void weeping over lost slavery, and we would give our own soul to go back to live again in the demands of our jailer. (Fallaci 1980: 378–9)

Obviously the basic dilemma is a built-in feature of our contradictory individualized society. It impinges on all couples but can cause immense upheavals in long-standing marriages because both aspects – being yourself and being close – stand out and crave attention. Think of all the habits and irritations, the rituals and compromises endured for all those years. Who apart from my husband/wife interferes with my life so directly, so relentlessly, so close to home? Think of all the things we have been through, the memories we share, the joys and pains, reaching into the deepest fibres of my being. Who else is so much part of me? In these circumstances the old biblical phrase 'And they became one flesh' takes on a new meaning. It is felt both ways, as a threat and curse, and as a consolation and promise, over and over again, both at once. This explains the hesitation which may last for years, the inability to leave because there is always the other side to remain for.

An outsider merely sees battles without any victors, repetitive arguments, all seemingly to no end. The solution to the riddle lies in our modern longing to be loved tangled up with the idea 'At last there's time for me', each with a logic diametrically opposed to the other. Under such conditions a couple both fears and seeks the quarrels and is prepared to employ all means to maintain them. Each loses a sense of security in the other but each gains a certain confidence from surviving:

> I see now why I wanted my wife to come back.
> It was because of what she had made me into . . .
> When I thought she had left me, I began to dissolve,
> To cease to exist. That was what she had done to me!
> I cannot live with her – that is now intolerable;
> I cannot live without her, for she has made me incapable
> Of having any existence of my own.
> That is what she has done to me in five years together!
> She has made the world a place I cannot live in
> Except on her terms. I must be alone,

But not in the same world. So I want you to put me
Into your sanatorium. I could be alone there?
(T. S. Eliot, *The Cocktail Party*, Act II)

A child as surrogate?

Living with an adult partner under the contradictory rules of a society of individuals often turns out to be deeply painful and insulting. It therefore seems only logical that men and women are developing strategies to protect themselves and reduce the risks of becoming emotionally exhausted. Symptoms of such a move can be found in recent developments on the family and marriage front. The repertoire of possibilities is broad, from premarital therapy (see *New Woman*, July 1985: 44ff.), to drawing up marriage contracts (there is a good example in Partner 1984), to living with someone outside marriage so that, as the pop song says, 'breaking up is not so hard to do' (Schumacher 1981).

Some people are obviously reluctant to make any commitment, reducing their hopes in advance so that they do not have to face disappointment. To put it once again in the terms of current book titles, in the stage 'Beyond Dreams' (Fischer 1983), the 'Fear of Closeness' (Schmidbauer 1985) is growing. A passage from a novel by Erica Jong illustrates this:

> 'You're my fit, my mate,' he said. 'Now that I've found you, I'm never going to let you go.' 'My darling', fighting back the feeling that there might be any truth whatever in his words. After tonight, I'm never going to see him again, she thought. He's a mirage, a dream . . . Passion like this cannot be clung to, cannot last, cannot keep. A man as charming as this could romance his way right into your heart, then leave you flat. She was not ready for that after the recent heartbreak with Josh. She might never be ready for it again. (Jong 1985: 332)

But this cannot solve the problem. If one represses all hope of being close to someone else, what happens to the longings which are so much a part of our age, to find oneself through another? Who can one miss and hug? Perhaps if not a man or a woman then one can love a child. Let us look more closely at this option.

The first stage in the history of individualization weakened the old ties which used to give a person a sense of stability and identity. That was the date in the not very distant past when men and women turned towards one another to find themselves and made love the centre of their existence. By now we have reached the next stage; traditional bonds play only a minor role and the love between men and women has likewise proved vulnerable and prone to failure. What remains is the child. It promises a tie which is more elemental, profound and durable than any other in this society. The more other relationships become interchangeable and revocable, the more a child can become the focus of new hopes – it is the ultimate guarantee of permanence, providing an anchor for one's life.

Seen in this light, recent demographic changes which are rapidly gaining impetus become comprehensible. First there is a marked increase in the number of children born outside marriage.[8] No doubt various causes are at work here but one can assume that among other things we are seeing a new type of unmarried mother. This is the woman who wants to have a child alone, without a man or a traditional kind of partnership.[9] Reduced to a sentence: 'The couple that matters these days is woman and child' (Sichtermann, quoted in Wetterer 1983). Or as Ursula Krechel ironically puts it, 'The new political unit is called motherandchild' (Krechel 1983: 149). In a novel from the new women's literature it is formulated like this:

> I want to have a child when I am thirty-eight . . . I want to do it completely alone. From the sperm bank or a chance lover, without even turning on the light to be able to see him, just let myself get fucked and later find out that I'm pregnant. (Ravera 1986: 138)

Hopes of this kind may gain momentum from recent advances in reproductive technology. There are already reports – from America and Australia – of women who underwent in-vitro treatment during their marriage and now despite an intervening divorce demand that the deep-frozen embryos be implanted. Their ex-husbands are suing them because they reject any paternity role after the marriage has been dissolved. In one case the court has already decided in favour of the woman and granted her the temporary custody of the embryos (*Süddeutsche Zeitung*, 22 September and 31 October 1989). Here are the outlines of a future scenario: where love for the man has evaporated the woman at least wants to keep the embryos for herself.

Now such tendencies are certainly by no means representative of the majority of women. It is however striking that among younger women there has been a dramatic change in attitude about unmarried motherhood. Whereas in the 1960s it seemed important to almost everybody that a woman with a child should be married, by the early 1980s not even half the girls considered this relevant.[10] It is also symptomatic that popular women's books and magazines are offering advice on 'a child alone . . . how to do it.'[11] One title proclaims with defiant self-confidence, 'Single mums, happier without a man' (Heiliger 1985). Here is a motif that recurs again and again in recent women's writing; love for a child replaces love for a man. Here is the report of a woman who is deliberately bringing up her child alone:

> By now I know what kinds of living and loving conditions I have to make for myself in order to feel comfortable with Harpo [her son]. If someone comes along and wants to spoil that for me, I beat it or send him packing . . . That's another way I've changed because of Harpo. Men have lost the importance they used to have in my life. What I've built up for myself – professionally, materially, in private, in my life with Harpo – is independent of any man; no boyfriend is going to tell me what to do or order me around. (Quoted in Häsing 1983: 83)

This is even more marked in the words of Oriana Fallaci from *Letter to a Child Never Born*:

> As for your father, the more I think of it the more I'm afraid I never loved him . . . The same goes for those who came before him, disappointing ghosts in a search that always failed . . . maybe it is true, what my mother has always maintained, that love is what a mother feels for her child when she takes it in her arms and notices how alone, helpless and defenceless it is. As long as it remains helpless and defenceless, at least it doesn't insult you, doesn't disappoint you. (1976: 20–1)

One finds similar sentiments throughout Erica Jong's writing:

> Our children give us more undiluted joy than romantic love ever does . . . Ever since she and Josh had separated she had longed for another baby . . . but who would be the father of her fantasy baby? . . . Well – why not just have a baby and the father be damned? She was likely to end up raising it alone anyway . . . This is the New Family, Mom and kids and lover man (or new husband). At any rate, only the mom and kids are surely linked. The men come and go. (Jong 1985: 68, 296, 107)

Erica Jong is mistaken however; we cannot take it for granted that the New Family consists of 'mom and the kids'. In an increasing number of cases men want the child for themselves after divorce, rather than giving the mother custody. 'Men Fight for their Rights' (*Wiener*, January 1984: 32ff.) and 'The Grief of the Divorced Father' (cover story in *Esquire*, March 1985) is becoming acute. In the words of a counsellor: 'I've seen men crying for fear of losing their children, the way only women used to cry over their children. Young fathers in particular suffer a dramatic sense of loss when they do not get custody. Those are our most difficult cases' (*Eltern*, October 1985: 37). As mentioned above, there is a new kind of kidnapping, with more and more men who have not been granted custody taking their child by force.

But even where matters do not take such an alarming turn one can discern a certain trend, a motif common to men and women. If they feel rejected and unloved by their adult partner, surrounded by indifference and cold silence, people are glad to lavish their love on their child. Peter Handke's *Kindergeschichte* exemplifies this:

> It was a friendless time; even his own wife had become an unkind stranger. This made the child even more real . . . In all this time exchanges between him and his wife were at best matter-of-fact, and in their thoughts they were often only 'he' and 'she' for each other . . . Now, with the infant, she met him almost exclusively in the confined setting of the household, where the sight of her became indifferent to him and even began to displease him as time passed – just as he probably ceased being anyone special for her, now that he had almost stopped presenting himself as 'her hero' with his outstanding work . . . It was also careless of him to transfer to the child the most friendly, intimate and secret wordless gestures and little phrases that had become standard parts of his exchanges with her, without even hesitating or thinking about it . . . It was almost as if the child was finally what was right for him and he now no longer needed a woman. (Handke 1982: 23, 34–5)

There is one significant aspect here which is never registered in the statistics; one discovers it only by working one's way through the numerous autobiographical accounts of 'new' women and mothers that have appeared in recent years. Again and again they describe that they were surprised, overcome, even overwhelmed by the intensity of their feelings for their children (for further details, see Beck-Gernsheim 1989: 31ff.). They experience a bond, so one reads, of a kind quite unknown elsewhere in their lives, so deep and all-embracing, 'a great romantic love' (Dowrick and Grundberg 1980: 74). 'I wondered whether you could get a heart attack from the emotional intensity that you feel as a mother,' writes Jean Lazarre (1977: 96). Or as another woman puts it:

> For the first time in my life I'm really learning about love . . . you [the child] force me to redefine intimacy. Am I close to people with whom I discuss ideas, four times a year? Am I close to friends with whom I can most be myself: by appointment only? Am I close to strangers who thrill

> me with their decency, wisdom and humour, but with whom I don't live? I am not as close to anyone as I am to you. (Chesler 1979: 191, 194)

> In fact she [the child] is the great romantic love of my life. As I strongly disapprove of romantic love, I do not feel complacent about this; but I know that the feelings I have for her correspond more nearly to the women's magazines/medieval poets'/religious mystics' descriptions of love than anything else I have ever felt . . . Emotionally, psychologically, politically, socially my daughter has forced unwelcome changes on me. I feel bullied and victimised – intellectually, emotionally and practically – in precisely the ways I swore I would never be by any man. And I chose that oppression, and do not regret it; indeed I embrace it with love and joy. (Dowrick and Grundberg 1980: 77 and 79)

Statements like these will not astonish anyone who regards motherly love as the essence of womanhood and a natural bond. But since research has shown that in the past the ties between mothers and children were less emotionally tinged than they are today, doubts have arisen whether one can really declare such feelings to be part of our genetic heritage. One can also explain the phenomenon in other terms, more closely linked with the way our society is changing.

From this point of view entering into a bond with a child is highly attractive because the relationship is of a quite different kind than that to another adult. The attraction could be that the child really is innately related to one, not just acquired through the coincidences of biography, and the bond is all-encompassing, lasting, unbreachable, in a sense superior to other liaisons in our barter and throw-away culture. At least as long as it is young, a child permits one to invest all one's love and involvement without risk of disappointment, of being hurt and abandoned.

Searching for utopia?

So far we have been able to trace three stages in the way men and women could relate to one another as society moved from pre-industrial times to the modern day. In the first, where the family consisted of an economic unit, neither partner had an individual biography. In the second, when the 'extended family' began to break up, the men were expected to take the initiative in organizing their own lives. Family cohesion remained intact at the cost of women's rights. And roughly since the 1960s it has been clear that a new stage is with us, where both sexes are faced with the blessings and burdens of making a life of their own.

No doubt there are chances of building up real partnerships in this current situation but equally many hazards which can drive the sexes apart and leave them in opposite lonely corners. The crux of the problem is finding a balance between being yourself and being part of a lasting togetherness with someone who is equally in search of his/her own self. One wonders what is going to happen next; are the quarrels and misunderstandings going to pile up until the only faithful companions we have left are therapists? Or perhaps a pet to cuddle, as in a novel by Elisabeth Plessen: 'His son had been killed on the Eastern Front . . . His wife had run away . . . To console himself he had a cat' (1976: 15). And on the other hand we keep hoping that things will be different, that we can find rules and ways of treating one another that really do enable us to merge two self-made biographies.

But how? The marriage counsellor's insight that 'what [people in] devastated relationships need more than anything else is the chance to talk to one another' (Preuss 1985: 12) may be right but it is certainly no longer enough. What is needed from society is the rethinking of some of its priorities; at the moment there is a tendency to focus too exclusively on the individual person and take private commitments into account only when they can be exploited for market purposes (being mobile and flexible, competitive and career-conscious). Such a change demands the insight from politicians and powers-that-be, organizations and institutions, that our society has reached a critical state where it is neither constructive nor even feasible to apply the prevailing rules any longer; carrying on as before will find us reeling under the gigantic financial and emotional costs of a wholesale war between the sexes, throwing society into private and financial turmoil. On the private level men and women must practise the old female virtues of understanding, tolerance and willingness to compromise, and find the courage to start renegotiating again and again. A mere utopia? We can only try. To quote Beatrice Webb, 'We are at the end of one civilisation; the question is, are we at the beginning of another?' (in Mackenzie and Mackenzie 1984: 291).

3

FREE LOVE, FREE DIVORCE

The two sides of liberation

'Forever yours.' Romantic love is one of the pivots of our society, that delightful feeling of loving and being loved, taking us to the registry office, if not the altar, and helping us all through our lives, 'until death do us part', as the marriage vows put it. The statistics, however, tell another tale. Very many people live alone, and their numbers are rising; others live together without committing themselves and many couples get divorced. Torn between old ideals and attempts to find new solutions, the sexes veer back and forth in and out of togetherness. This has social as well as private consequences:

> So far no one has either considered or worked out what marital problems, misery and separation have cost and continue to cost the state in terms of effort, resources and cash. But even if there are no data available one can conclude that separation has become an economic problem that swallows up a not inconsiderable portion of the gross national product. (Jaeggi and Hollstein 1985: 36)

Individualization, as we can see in this case, always has two sides to it. When marriage turns from being the highly rigid and predetermined arrangement it was in pre-industrial society to being a voluntary union between two individuals, there are bound to be new kinds of irritations and struggles to cope with, however much each loves the other. Or to phrase it more dramatically, *when love finally wins it has to face all kinds of defeat.*

Precisely this is the paradox to be considered next. We shall trace how it came about and try to decode its inner logic, looking at the dynamics forcing people into an endless cycle of hoping, regretting and despite everything trying all over again. None of this is mere coincidence; it is inherent in our modern world and in that ambiguous idea 'freedom'. The difficulties lie in the principle of free choice, which offers us new scope but also lands us with the responsibility for the results, good or bad.

The old days: obligations and certainties

As social historians have consistently shown, marriage in pre-industrial society was not so much the union of two people as of two families or even clans (Rosenbaum 1978, 1982; Schröter 1985; Sieder 1987; Stone 1978, 1979). Accordingly there was no choosing whom one married, in today's sense, no falling in love and following one's own intuitions. The radius of choice was restricted in advance by certain criteria such as status and property, race and religion, and marriage was arranged by a network of family, relatives and the local community. People seldom married for love; the main purpose was to contribute to the family's prosperity and survival as an economic unit, and having children as helping hands and heirs. The British nobility in the sixteenth and seventeenth centuries is a good example:

> The greatest parental pressure was necessarily exerted on the daughters, who were the more dependent and sheltered, were considered members of an inferior sex and who scarcely had any alternative to obedience since being unmarried was even less attractive than an undesirable husband . . . In the early sixteenth century, wills and marriage contracts in which small children were traded in advance like cattle were quite common in all classes and all regions . . . Freedom of choice was almost as limited for the sons as for the daughters. His wish to make use of his guardianship and the financial importance of the contract to prevent the marriage from slipping out of the family's control often prompted the father to marry off his son and heir during his own lifetime to a woman he had chosen. The son was usually under the father's sway because he was . . . financially dependent on him. (Stone 1978: 445–7)

Regulations of this kind contain of course a large element of coercion. The most obvious losers in the traditional marriage system are first of all those at an economic disadvantage – whether because of their position as sibling, their sex, or their lack of social standing. They cannot fit in with the economically determined rules of this system and are therefore excluded in advance from marrying by laws on inheritance, dowry requirements, prohibition on marriage for those without property and the like. Others affected in a negative sense include men and women forced by the family to marry someone who seems suitable. The third group covers those who wish to marry but are forbidden to do so because their chosen partner is incompatible with the family's criteria, in other words the tragedy of 'love and intrigue' so often a theme of world literature:

> Two households, both alike in dignity . . .
> From ancient grudge break to new mutiny . . .
> From forth the fatal loins of these two foes
> A pair of star-cross'd lovers take their life;
> Whose misadventur'd piteous overthrows
> Doth with their death bury their parents' strife.
> (William Shakespeare, *Romeo and Juliet*, Prologue)

There can be no doubt that the traditional rules left little room for personal wishes, and forced them to be rigorously suppressed if the family's wishes differed. But there can also be no doubt that such rules gave marriage a certain stability and permanence. Where a union was arranged by the family and local community, those same persons had an interest in preserving it and could exert their influence via a whole range of social mechanisms. Where choosing a spouse depended on background and status there was a guarantee that in important respects men and women learned the customs and norms, shared the same expectations and understood the rules. Where men and women worked together on the family farm or in the family shop, they were welded together by their mutual efforts and by the setbacks and dangers they faced in their struggle against, say, a failed harvest or a cruel winter.

Imhof describes how it was for a peasant family:

> It was not the particular farm owner and his individual well-being which were decisive, but the well-being and standing of the farm itself; it was not the particular family living there at this or that time, but the succession of families, the lineage. Generation after generation revolved round this centre, farm owner after farm owner, but less as an individual than as someone fulfilling a role. It was an idea, a standard that was central, not an ego. (1984: 20)

Tania Blixen words the position of an aristocratic family in a similar way:

> The relationship between the spouses was no personal one, and strictly speaking they could not personally or directly bring happiness to or

> disappoint each other, but must mutually provide the greatest significance to one another through the relationship they occupied and the importance they had for their mutual tasks in life. For the duc de Rohan there could never be any comparison between his wife and other women; no matter how much more beautiful and gifted and attractive they might be, she still remained the only woman in the world who could give birth to a duc de Rohan. The receptions she held were receptions for the Rohans, and the peasants she supported were the Rohan's peasants and poor people. (1986: 67–8)

Modern times: more freedom, less security

According to the social historians married couples began to behave differently towards one another as agrarian society gave way to modern industrial society. The family clan lost a great deal of its influence, and the rights of those whose lifelong union was at stake were strengthened. 'It is people who choose one another, and no longer families which unite and ally' (Rosenmayr 1984: 113). Such choices were of course not just left to luck; especially during the early years of this change, criteria such as social background, personal estate, upbringing and religious denomination still played a decisive role (e.g. Borscheid 1986; Mayer 1985). Even romantic love keeps its hidden ties to social rules. But seen from the lovers' point of view the balance shifted over the centuries from being told what to do to being free to choose.

> Within the past thousand years ideas on proper match-making have passed through four successive phases. In the first phase marriage was arranged by the parents with little concern for their children's wishes; in the second the parents still prepared the ground but conceded veto power to their children; in the third the children made the choice but the parents could veto it, and in the final, fourth phase, reached only in this century, the children choose their spouses by themselves and do not much care what their parents think. (Stone 1978: 475)

So with the breakdown of the old order it looked as though something wonderful could be found: personal happiness quite untrammelled by outside duties or obligations. It was no longer a union between a man and a woman arranged by outsiders according to prescribed criteria but an intimate, deeply personal encounter between two committed individuals, triumphing over the barriers of class and status and recognizing only one authority – the language of the heart. The story was meant to turn out as beautifully as it does in fairy tales: 'and they lived happily ever after.'

The morning breaks for me! O why could not
Our fathers understand each other just
As easily as we! . . .
The fathers reconciled, I will make bold
To claim thee as my own . . .
Agnes, Agnes!
What joy awaits us! Thou shalt be my wife.
O canst thou grasp the measure of our joy?
(Heinrich von Kleist, *Die Familie Schroffenstein*, V, 1)[1]

What has become of these high hopes? Many of them have been dashed. Life is very different from what fairy tales tell us. Psychologists note that 'the biggest problem people face in their private lives nowadays is how to get on with their partner' (Jaeggi and Hollstein 1985: back cover). Demographers scan the statistics and declare, 'Divorce activity is brisk' (Schmid 1989: 10). There is much talk of 'really relating', of 'talking it through', of 'throw-away loves'. The graver researchers speak of 'serial marriage' and 'monogamy in instalments'.

The situation is indeed paradoxical. Men and women no longer have to obey their families and are freer than ever before to decide for themselves whom they wish to marry (or not). One might have thought that in these circumstances sharing one's life with someone would prove easier and more satisfying, but in fact scores of people are fleeing from exactly this state.

In search of a shared world

One feature of modern life is that each of us has a huge number of often complex and contradictory options to choose from. Various factors play a role, and as time passes their effect becomes increasingly apparent: rapid social change with a whole range of new possibilities, the erosion of traditional ties, new kinds of social and geographic mobility. Someone born in the hills of rural Bavaria is quite likely to move to a city like Hamburg to study and work, spend holidays in Italy beside Lake Garda and plan to retire to Majorca.

This means that each of us has to achieve more than before to find our way through the intricacies of life and establish a sense of identity. Sociologists and psychologists confirm that our love-lives gain enormous significance from this fact; as described above, our view of reality and sense of self-esteem largely rest on how things are at home.

Not surprisingly this means a new kind of strain. If you are free to choose your own partner and build up a world together outside the dictates of family, kinship or clan, this may look like freedom but actually demands a great deal of effort. In the new system the couple is not just expected but *has* to design its personalized life scheme. Berger and Kellner sketch the outlines of this task:

> Marriage and family used to be firmly anchored within a network of relationships linking them to the larger community . . . There were few barriers between the individual family's world and that of the outside community . . . One and the same social life pulsated through house, street and town. To put it in our terms, both the family and the marital relationship were embedded in a much broader network of contacts. In present-day society, by contrast, each family constitutes a segregated sub-world of its own, with its own exclusive rules and concerns.
>
> This fact places far more commitment on the couple's shoulders. In the past setting up a new marriage only meant adding a further variation to an already established social pattern, whereas nowadays couples have to face the often strenuous task of creating their own private world . . . The monogamous aspect of marriage makes investing in this undertaking particularly risky, for the success or failure of it depend on the idiosyncrasies of only two people and the barely predictable future development of these idiosyncrasies . . . according to Simmel the least stable of all social relationships . . . In a relationship which consists of only two people and depends on their efforts, both have to invest more and more in their own realm to counteract the lack of other relationships. This only increases the drama and risk involved. (1965: 225)

Furthermore the same centrifugal forces in society which turn marriage or a close relationship into a fixed star by which to steer one's biography make it very hard for both partners to agree on a common course. The two people who become one by signing the marriage contract (or even without doing so) tend much more than used to be the case to come from different backgrounds, even if they still often obey the laws of endogamy and choose a partner on conventional grounds (social standing, religion, nationality or race). In other words their life histories have provided them with different sets of priorities and hopes, ways of communicating and techniques for making decisions. It is hard work agreeing on a common project. Berger and Kellner comment on this:

> Marriage in our society is a dramatic event in which two strangers get together and redefine one another . . . the concept 'strangers' does not of course [mean here] that the candidates stem from very different social classes – in fact the data show the opposite is the case. The strangeness is rather because, unlike marriage candidates in previous social settings,

> they come from different 'face-to-face' areas. They have no past in common, even though their respective pasts were similarly structured. (1965: 223)

And one step further, if choosing one's own mate used to be primarily directed against the family's wishes, the principle of free choice acquires an updated meaning when the population becomes increasingly socially and geographically mobile. Even though the majority of couples still follow the old rules, there are many who step over local and national boundaries and choose someone quite different in social standing, religion or nationality (e.g. Mayer 1985; Schneider 1989). In Germany nowadays one marriage in twelve is of mixed nationality (Elschenbroich 1988: 364). Here it is particularly obvious that two 'strangers' are getting together. One especially important concern for them is finding how they can help each other to discover themselves, as our modern definition of love demands, although this must entail facing one's own past and roots.

Choosing a partner of a different background in these circumstances means uniting with a different culture, but it also means having to get involved with the fears and hopes, thinking patterns and horizons of an unfamiliar world. An American investigation into marriages between Jewish and non-Jewish partners came to the conclusion:

> Where man and woman share a common group background, a common cultural heritage, a general sense of social similarity, the confrontation with the past can remain a purely personal affair. What each reveals to the other are the personal and family secrets, so to speak. However, when man and woman do not share a common set of ground assumptions about their collective memories, the most minute aspects of self-expression become broad statements about one's cultural history – whether one likes it or not. (Mayer 1985: 70)

The marriages which step beyond the usual radius for choosing a partner show up in sharp relief how the modern person goes about finding a mate. They are a sign that outside influences have little say and that the decision rests with the two people involved. A study of bicultural marriages in Germany noted that they were 'in terms of attitude, very modern marriages; they correspond to the ideal of romantic love and are individualistic.' Furthermore, 'the romantic basis of this relationship is both an opportunity and a problem' (Elschenbroich 1988: 366). The opportunities can be outlined as follows:

> If things go well, if some of the early boldness, optimism and sense of experimenting is preserved, then bicultural marriages are particularly lively and interesting. If the problems posed by communicating across cultures can be integrated into the family, that can encourage a feeling of solidarity and give the family a wide horizon. (Ibid.)

There are, however, typical drawbacks. Part of the risk potential in such unions is that there are no external support systems which are binding for both partners. The job of keeping the marriage intact is left entirely to the couple, and is more difficult the further apart their two cultures are. While during the early stages differences usually recede into the background, and all that counts is being in love and agreeing with one another, in the course of the marriage the differences stemming from their separate worlds inevitably come to the surface and have to be faced; the dividing lines which seemed to have been wiped away in choosing a mate reveal their staying power as time goes on and have to be accepted and coped with by both partners. The American study on marriages between Jewish and non-Jewish people presents a theoretical picture of this predicament:

> While the nascent moments of falling in love evoke a feeling of an intense and lasting present, in which the past and the future are irrelevant, the maintenance of love seems to have the opposite requirement. It seems to call for the probing of the past and charting of the future. It also brings into its discourse the selfhood of the lovers, which inevitably implicates their cultural heritages. There is simply no self that is not linked in some fashion to an ancestry, a family network and a history . . . The intermarriage conversation is inevitably a conversation also about culture, history, and the personal feeling about tradition. (Mayer 1985: 72)

The German study on bicultural marriages traces the developmental patterns using empirical data:

> In . . . interviews bicultural couples described typical phases of their relationships. In the period of initial infatuation an effusive optimism prevails, a feeling of blissful openness, and . . . a certain pride in one's nonconformism. After going through internal and external strains there is often a phase of retreat and renewed identification with one's own background . . . People discover how firmly their own value systems are anchored, often for the first time. Without this confrontation their own value systems usually remain *inconspicuous*, unconscious – and for that reason appear to be very normal. (Elschenbroich 1988: 366–8; emphasis in the original)

In search of a common cause

Now that marriage has shaken off the ties and obligations it had in the days of the extended family, it seems to float along by itself, a sheltered, private place for emotional companionship and leisure. This means more freedom, but, seen in another light, less support from outside. The 'common cause' which held together generations of families has disappeared (Ostner and Pieper 1980) and instead the individuals involved have to negotiate their own common aims. 'The still "empty mould of privacy" must first . . . be filled with content' (ibid.: 120). No doubt this can mean a new closeness but it also harbours considerable risks.

What do you mean by love?

What is the basis of our companionship? At first sight the answer is easy: the modern definition states that we are together because we love each other, our companionship is above all an emotional one. This is of course a sweeping and vague definition, for the components of love have changed throughout history, in recent centuries and particularly over the recent past. At present there are several versions – traditional, modern and postmodern – which coexist as odd bedfellows. This 'non-simultaneity of the simultaneous' means that all sorts of notions, expectations and hopes, not to mention divergent rules and modes of behaviour, are combined in the term 'love' (see for instance the glib discussions on monogamy versus multiple relationships). Satisfying demands for 'love' is therefore a complicated and delicate matter of mediation and coordination, which can lead to fundamental misunderstandings:

> The common ground for a modern Western marriage, an 'identity shared by both partners', is normally continually being confirmed and renewed in conversation. Whether one verbalizes such matters, however, differs from culture to culture. The bourgeois Western manner of dealing with disagreements – talking about them and trying to understand – is by no means a universal need. If the German spouse of a foreign person insists on it, the method may prove completely futile. In some other cultures a close relationship is not considered a criterion for a 'good' marriage; what counts is rather relying on each other, sharing responsibilitiy and providing for the family, dividing up the labour between the sexes and practical staying power. (Elschenbroich 1988: 368)

There is another factor which further complicates matters: what we mean by 'love' subtly changes as time goes by even within our own private relationships. This is especially true where 'romantic love' is seen as the ideal, for the initial phase is full of excitement and joy fed largely on the fascinating otherness of the other and the unknown. As the years pass, however, people inevitably get to know each other and everyday life sets in. This can mean a new sense of togetherness – durable, familiar, reliable – growing out of a shared history, but many couples cannot cope with the metamorphosis. It is neither luck nor fate but an integral part of this model; the 'trap of romantic love' means that love starts out as infatuation and lingers as an expectation which in this form cannot be met, so that all that is left is disappointment.

The American author Jeffrey Ullmann collected the enraptured effusions of prominent contemporaries in his book *Singles' Almanac* – as well as what remained of them later:

- Richard Burton on Elizabeth Taylor: 'Her body is a miracle of architecture.' Afterwards: 'She's too fat and her legs are too short.'
- Elizabeth Taylor on husband no. 1, Conrad Hilton Jr: 'He understands me as a woman and an actress.' Afterwards: 'After I married him I lost my rose-coloured spectacles – I lost weight and was only able to eat baby food.'
- Rita Hayworth on her third husband, Prince Ali Khan: 'My Prince of princes.' Afterwards: 'Ali can do whatever he wants – I've had it with him.' And on her fourth husband, Dick Haymes: 'I'd follow him anywhere on earth.' Afterwards: 'I don't know where he is – and I don't care.'

What perhaps most complicates the search for common ground is the fact that men and women have diverging views on what living with someone means. Men tend to emphasize the practical aspects like keeping the household running and 'making sure that everything goes well' (*Abendzeitung*, 23 October 1987). Women by contrast focus much more on the emotional side; for them sharing feelings and being close are paramount. This is exemplified in an interview with a husband and wife:

MRS O: I often wish I could spend more time with my husband.
MR O: Yes, but what does that mean in practical terms, what do you want to do when you are with your husband?
MRS O: Well, just do something together.
MR O: Do you want more in bed or something?
MRS O: Just more overall – perhaps more conversation – or – you've got problems after all – sitting down together or, well, talking more

or chatting.

MR O: But about what? about what? . . . the paper, or work or what do you want to talk to me about, it's all crap, what do you want to talk about anyway?

MRS O: We have to talk to each other, about plans, and then here you come, right, if you speak up more, say more, then –

MR O: Well, what about plans, that's all a lot of crap, your stupid gabbing . . .

MRS O: Often I think to myself, you could, well you could ring up and so on and so forth.

MR O: Those days are over, because we only have one telephone, the one that's out of order . . . and besides, what is that anyway, that's all hot air; what comes of it, probably just blah, blah, blah, back and forth and how's the weather . . .

MRS O: Well, oh dear, well but sometimes between us it's some kind of connection or something.[2]

The differences in what the sexes expect are probably not new, but their conflict potential only recently began to surface. As soon as women come to see themselves as autonomous people with wishes of their own they are less ready to accept the solutions offered by previous generations – adjusting to your husband, and sacrificing your own interests. Women used to be expected to dispense comfortable feelings, affection and warmth, and nowadays increasingly want to be the recipients of such feelings. They are becoming tired of being the peace-makers and soothers at home. This trend is unmistakable in best-selling women's literature, where renouncing love is recommended, or at least that sort of love which leaves women drained and exhausted: the diagnosis is 'Women who Love too Much' (Norwood 1985); that is why a new 'Emotional Compact' between the sexes is needed (Hite and Colleran 1989: 44f.). And if it isn't fulfilled? The sober conclusion is 'Don't give up everything for a man' (Hite and Colleran 1989).

Difficult decisions: too many options

Marriage in pre-industrial society was held together by the iron bands of a common cause, the family and its survival. Each spouse had a clearly outlined task and knew exactly what was expected of him/her. As soon as the family is no longer one large economic unit these rules no longer apply. The bourgeois family which succeeded it polarized the gender roles – the man was the bread-winner and the woman the heart of the family. In the waning years of the twentieth century even these standard roles are becoming shaky. What is left is a great deal of scope for decision-making, as a glance into the German Code of Civil Law (BGB) shows (see our table).

	Original version of the BGB of 1896, in force since 1 January 1900	Marital Law Reform Act of 1976, in force since 1 July 1977
§ 1354	The husband is entitled to make decisions in all matters concerning marital life; in particular, he decides on residence and housing.	nullified
§ 1355	The woman takes on the husband's name.	As married name the spouses can choose the name of the husband or the wife.
§ 1356	The wife . . . is entitled and obliged to run the shared household.	The spouses regulate the management of the household by mutual consent.

Certainly the fact that both partners are free to choose how to run their mutual home does much to counteract the notion that the woman's role is subordinate; both she and he can bring their own rights and interests to bear. But once again there are losses with the gains. What looks so simple on paper proves a bitter battlefield in ordinary life, with two people with their own ideas, plans and preferences struggling to find a common approach. There is no law of preordained marital harmony at work guaranteeing that they reach roughly the same conclusions. Put briefly, if you have more scope you may feel liberated from old restrictions but you also run the risk of differing in so many respects from your lover that life becomes one long argument. The agreement the legislators recommend is hard to achieve.

It is not rare for couples to wrangle over the choice of a family name long before they are married. (Of course, as the statistics show, it is usually the men who keep their names, but this says nothing about how many couples differ on the matter beforehand, or how many never get married for just this reason.) Deciding on where to live is a problem when a good job offer somewhere else turns up. And how to organize the daily shared routine, provided there is one, is the worst problem of all, a minefield of disappointments and frustrations which do not just affect the smooth running of the household but often stir up deep personal fears that one's role in life and self-esteem are under attack.

Men and women are currently 'exposed to a whole kaleidoscope of possible interpretations of what "man" or "woman", "love" or "relationship", "motherhood" or "fatherhood" still might or should mean' (Wehrspaun 1988: 165). The way the sexes respond to one another is a bewildering mixture of old habits and new starts, with confusion creeping into the most intimate corners. As someone daubed on a wall: 'We want to love each other, but we don't know how,' summing up the predicament.

Talking it through: love as homework

So what is to be done? If there are no external standards, we have to find internal ones. 'This new society is . . . condemned . . . to generate its own rules which make cooperating and surviving possible *and* to insist on obedience to them' (Weymann 1989: 6). It seems like a new version of old Münchhausen, pulling himself out of the swamp by his own pigtail, except that now this has to be done as a couple. In all events tuning in to each other's ideas is crucial, and there are signs of attempts to 'manage relationships via negotiation' (Swaan 1981). This is happening in a wordy world of winding paths and circular routes, where people bump into each other, sometimes stay together, often part but at least try to discuss what is happening. The results, especially in contemporary literature, fill the bookshelves; literature is no longer 'a discourse on love but at best a discourse on a discourse about love' (Hage 1987). As an illustration, here is the monologue by a man in the thick of it:

> Presumably everybody gets the kind of lover he deserves. I've got Anna and the two of us have been together for five years now. In that period of time others have acquired a shared apartment or at least a child. Not us. Each of us does his own thing – to each his own: bed, telephone bill, car, washing machine – the modalities of our relationship simply aren't cleared up yet. Who worries about what, who plays which role. Is living with someone ever compatible with independence? We still have to work a lot of things out. We're not a proper couple yet, even though a lot of people think we are. But we constantly rack our brains over whether we should become one. The only thing we've really achieved over the past years is a lot of good arguments – we live with them. If I criticize Anna's desire to sit around every night in pubs, she accuses me of possessiveness. If she wants to go on holiday alone and regards my idea of spending the summer together in Tuscany as just a pseudo-romantic impulse, she says I am suffering from childish fears of losing her . . . It seems to me as if our relationship consists of nothing but arrangements – emotional clauses in

> a screwing contract with an extraordinary amount of small print . . . I always tell myself, don't get upset because she again refused to spend the night with you. She always says, 'I just need time for myself. You wouldn't enjoy being with me anyway when I'm brooding like this.' But what matters to me is just being with her. She doesn't understand that. 'It stifles me,' she says. 'Why don't you two just get married?' a friend asked me the other day, 'It's crazy to burden yourselves with two households for years and years.' That might be true. But I read somewhere that the average couple spends only eight minutes a day talking to each other after twenty years. Something like that could never happen to us. (Praschl 1988)

To an outsider the interminable talk about how to treat one another may seem ridiculous, but it is not just a symptom of personal confusion or a kind of ego virus infecting more and more of the population; such an interpretation would be tempting but superficial. What is happening in so many private lives is to a large extent the consequence of modern thinking.

As long as there were strict commandments and prohibitions regulating married life and the daily routine, it was fairly obvious to everyone what was correct, pleasing to God and natural. Why bother with big words, complicated questions and long explanations? Each spouse knew the rules and also knew that the other one knew them. (Even those who chose to disobey knew what they were doing: they were violating custom and moral attitudes and rebelling against the norms.) In this respect there has been a fundamental transformation in recent decades, and especially in recent years. The fewer firm regulations there are, the more we are expected to work them out for ourselves, asking 'What's right and what's wrong?' and 'What do you want and what do I want?' and 'What should we do?'

'A modern couple – lots of words and not much loving' (Hage 1987). Couples have to get involved in a continuing dialogue so that they can invent and pursue their common cause, that is to say, they have to fill up their free private space with compatible definitions of love and marriage. This requires enormous effort, time and patience, exactly the qualities identified with 'relationship work'. And it is very hard work, and often seems almost in vain, for beyond every agreement there lies yet another argument to tackle:

> If the individual is not to fail, he must do something to maintain his happiness. Family claims put high expectations on him. Being a 'good partner' means being active, attentive, and empathic. Rifts in opinions have to be recognized early, while they are still just hairline cracks. Patching them up requires sensitive perception of one's partner's needs. (Vollmer 1986: 217)

In the absence of outside authorities it is increasingly important that the couple finds ways of communicating with one another. It is therefore certainly no coincidence that there has been a boom in all branches of psychology and therapy since the 1960s, focusing particularly on the dynamics of love. The imperatives they often proclaim are called 'openness' and 'honesty'. The partners are supposed to admit their feelings, 'be themselves' and not hide behind anxieties, taboos and conventions. A self-help book published in 1970 states:

> We are firmly convinced that . . . the real problems of true love can only be solved in relationships which are open, free, critical and authentic, that is, which give both partners the chance to start out from themselves and offer themselves to their partner without having to distort themselves or fit in with the other's expectations. (Quoted in Bach and Deutsch 1979: 26)

Being open, which is a byproduct of how people behave when no longer bound by old commitments, has suddenly become a watchword, signalling the advent of a new culture. Pop culture transmits it in trivialized form, the mass media dilute it, but the tendency especially among young people is to tell all. Men and women go through hours of heart-searching either to get closer to one another or to reject one another. Every feeling, every move is dredged up, scrutinized, defined and catalogued – my anxieties, your clinging, his father complex. 'The partners start out from the assumption that they have to be authentic, must not be hypocritical and must learn to get along together while being uninhibitedly frank with one another' (Hahn 1988: 179).

The results are not always particularly helpful to the relationship. Not only lying but insisting on the truth can prove destructive. And self-examination is not just a way of escaping from the sins of the fathers (and mothers) but also a dangerous weapon. 'Let there be truth between us,' says Thoas to Iphigenia in Goethe's drama *Iphigenie auf Tauris* (loosely based on Euripides), but only after they have separated forever. The relative success of traditional modes of self-examination such as religious confession or psychoanalysis has a lot to do with the fact that the priest or analyst is not living with the confessee or patient (Hahn 1988: 179).

The ethics of change: getting it all right

As we have described, one of the essential features of modern life is that we have shrugged off the traditional order. It is striking that once this process gets under way, there is little stopping it and a 'drive to expand', indeed a permanent 'ethics of change', is set in motion (J. Berger 1986:

90–1; Wehrspaun 1988). The old barriers stopping people – the laws of nature, God's word, social customs and class imperatives – are gradually wearing away and as a result there are no rules stating when we have to desist. Instead it becomes the norm to look for more: even faster, bigger, more beautiful!

This 'improving' mentality extends far beyond makes of cars and job conditions; it also intrudes into love-affairs. Research has shown that the standards set on living together today are considerably higher than they used to be. It is no longer enough to just get along with each other. People want more, they are in search of 'happiness and fulfilment', the American dream, 'the pursuit of happiness' in their own little home. Disappointments are inevitable, for the higher the expectations one brings to marriage, the more likely one's own seems drab compared with these grand ambitions. Furthermore the dream turns into a trap, arousing hopes which cannot be satisfied. In any close and lasting live-in relationship there will be angry, disillusioned or guilt-ridden moments to augment the happy ones. As a pupil wrote in an essay, 'family is war and peace' (quoted by Lüscher 1987: 23). Expecting to be happy, and only that, collides with the realities of personal relations, the conflicts, compromises and crises which crop up in all our doings with one another. An experienced therapist puts it like this:

> [The countless books on marriage which recommend personal growth and promise maturity deal] not at all or too little with the other side, which is also a part of growth, the depths of distress and destructive violence and efforts to overcome them. [I] do not [see] the family as a sanctuary, a place where nothing but fun and joy prevail – which of course it can be – but as a place where the human being, the most barbaric creature of all, can learn to share time and space with others in a non-violent and non-destructive way . . . Revealing oneself completely to the person with whom one lives and at the same time getting to know sides of his (her) personality, history, hopes and fears which smash the image one has made into a thousand pieces . . . is a long-drawn-out and very painful experience . . . [In this sense] marriage and family life are wonderful places . . . to face life's cesspits.
>
> So I have reached the conclusion after twenty-six-and-a-half years of married life that happiness is not the goal. Marriage has many wonderful sides; it is a place where one can learn to share life with people who are different in age as well as gender, values and perspectives . . . It is a place where one can hate as well as conquer hate, a place where one can learn to laugh and love and communicate. (Jourard 1982: 177–9)

What is one to do, however, if reality does not live up to the ideal? According to the old model people were tied to one another no matter how incompatible their temperaments and inclinations turned out to be. Now the new belief in improving the situation points in exactly the opposite direction – it's better to end the marriage than put up with shortcomings and tone down one's expectations. Or to put it another way, without any external hindrances to the pursuit of perfect love, ordinary couples find themselves under pressure to be dissatisfied with their 'inferior' unions.

Here lies one of the reasons why the divorce figures are rocketing. 'People are getting divorced in such numbers . . . because their expectations of marriage are so high that they are unwilling to put up with a poor substitute' (Berger and Berger, quoted in Jaeggi and Holstein 1985: 36).

> Since after six weeks her third husband no longer leaps to his feet, but becomes flabby and domestic, has had enough of the physiological side of things and is beginning to think about social life, about his job and the fact that he had better invite the de Vries family for the evening, keeps talking about being promoted and having arthritis, she suddenly realizes, flush with moral righteousness and dignity, that she has deceived herself. This feeling of having deceived oneself never fails to appear. So then she decides to speak to him, quite magnanimously, and in order to make her announcement more impressive she puts on a turban. 'Dear third Mr Spider,' says the spider, and folds her hairy little paws, 'let us treat each other in a dignified manner and separate without any sordid muck-raking. Let us not sully the memory of our past happiness with pointless foul language. I owe you the truth, and the truth, my dear, is that I no longer love you . . . I have deceived myself. I believed with all my soul that you would be Mr Spider forever. I'm sorry, but you should know: there's a fourth Mr Spider in my life and he means everything to me.' (Cohen 1983: 330–1)

This search for new horizons is fuelled from within; the more scope one has the more one feels driven to seek alternatives (Nunner-Winkler 1989). In this context it means the new options – separating and divorcing – have an impact even if they play a minor role in the statistics. The mere fact that they are on people's minds (and the mass media do their best to foster this interest) affects the old ways of living together. Anyone upholding the idea of marriage does so knowing there are real alternatives, and may find themselves compelled to justify what amounts to a conscious choice.

The humorist Chlodwig Ploth describes the situation like this:

> Two friends meet in a pub.
>
> A: Wow, it's nice to be back here again. How are you people getting on. What are the Krögers up to?

B: They split up a long time ago. He's living with another woman in Sachsenhausen and I have no idea where she is.
A: Oh, and what about the Zierfelds?
B: They just had a fight. He left and is living in a commune. She's living in Bornheim with Volker – he's a teacher. Don't know if you know him. And how are things with you?
A: Well, you know, it just didn't work out any more. Susi's living somewhere else with a really nice sort, and I'm back in the old flat with Karin – she's a psychologist. And you two? How's that going?
B: Well, we're still together, but you know we've often thought about it, really. But then there's our son, and besides that, you know, and every so often, I don't know if you understand, but sometimes we get on quite well together. It's weird, but, you know, that is how it is. Do you understand?
A: Hey, there's no need to be ashamed, old fruit. I understand, don't worry about it.

(Quoted in Nunner-Winkler 1989)

The very fact that one has to justify living in an old-fashioned way causes the spiral of change to spin even faster. Sticking to familiar habits is easy enough as long as there are no extreme problems to cope with; optional behaviour, on the other hand, has to be justified using positive arguments. A marriage which is predetermined is accepted as long as it is not intolerable, but a freely chosen one has to be defended as the 'best' solution against all the possibilities. So justifying one's step pushes up one's standards on what constitutes happiness.

Work as the great divider

So far we have seen that present-day couples are bound together by their mutual hope of being loved – which causes problems. These private problems, however, inherent in the idea of a perfect love, are exacerbated by yet another factor. The companionship we seek from one another is not to be found in a social vacuum but in surroundings where impersonal forces are at work which often undermine our efforts. This crucial factor is the way employment is currently organized. Instead of binding the couple together as a team in pre-industrial society, the working conditions we know tend to cut men and women off from one another, to segregate them into different worlds.

There are of course still so-called traditional marriages founded on the old pattern of bread-winner/home-maker, sending one out into the stresses of the job market and leaving the other isolated at home with a monotonous routine. It is hard to find a common language for these two worlds, and where words fail there is only silence and alienation:

> She doesn't notice when you are out of breath; she doesn't suspect that your arm is getting sore; of course she knows that you work hard; of course she knows that he supports the household, fits in with all requests, takes care of all the expenses; of course she knows about his troubles and his bad mood; she has her own troubles and bad moods; she also locks her worries away from him. But one day you stand there and ask yourself, how can it go on? No more verve, no more alarms, no more following or accompanying each other, no more shared discussions on the future, nothing but being taken for granted and a peaceful division of labour . . . That is what the peaceful happiness of a sixteen-year marriage turns into, and life becomes like a pot of curdled milk, sour and thick, in which you drown like a fly, quite soberly. (Wassermann 1987: 93)

Or there is the other kind of marriage favoured especially by young people where both partners work away from home and have to manage their lives accordingly. Most professional positions nowadays are designed on the tacit assumption that they will be filled by

> one person backed by half another person and organized in terms of quantity and quality in ways which completely ignore private commitments; auxiliary work and services are provided by the half person, usually the wife. Women's day-to-day chores are meant to provide the husband and family with food, clothing and a comfortable home and to care for the next generation, freeing the man from everyday worries and stresses so that he can take on his taxing professional role unhindered. (Beck-Gernsheim 1980: 68–9)

Given such premises, what happens when more and more women have careers of their own? It is a matter of simple arithmetic; both spouses now lack the third person to take over the work backstage and dispense affection. This is why in thousands of homes after the exertions of the day there are short-tempered people disagreeing on who cleans the bathroom and who fetches the kids, a widespread feud on the private division of labour which has been thoroughly researched.

In fact this is only part of the problem, for in everyday life just as much as in our theorizing about it we tend to forget that it isn't just housework in the strict sense but emotional work that is needed. The human being, and certainly the working human being, does not live by bread alone; emotional support is also essential. The dictates of the market – speed and efficiency, competition and career – infiltrate into our homes and surface as irritability and tension. (It is not coincidental that the gender roles polarizing working husbands and women in charge of domestic bliss were first found in the nineteenth century.) Life at home becomes difficult if both partners are waiting in vain for emotional support and understanding from one another. This is not pure egotism or individual weakness, but a collective event, the same drama in innumerable kitchens brought about by the person-and-a-half jobs which wear everybody out.

My business, your business: a preference for contracts

Feeling increasingly helpless and cornered, people look for advice, and the market responds with a boom in patent recipes on how to run one's life. The flood of books is almost impossible to keep track of, as broad in range as it is diverse, offering a kind of supermarket of philosophies for living and loving. From our viewpoint it is interesting to ask: what rules do they suggest for making our shared lives easier?

One soon realizes that the question is wrongly put, at least in part. Certainly there are plenty of books on offer which purport to tear down the barriers of disappointment, silence and resignation, but there are just as many self-help books which push the topic of companionship – getting on together – right to the margin, if they mention it at all. The main subject is quite different and found in all kinds of variations, sometimes formulated gently and sometimes very crassly: it is protecting 'me' against 'us'. People are recommended to 'regulate as many aspects of everyday living together as possible in a marriage contract' (Partner 1984: 85ff.).

The prime purpose here is not to organize life in ways which promote togetherness or closeness in a permanent dialogue but to protect one's own interests by means of regulations. More and more couples are taking this advice. In Germany (*Süddeutsche Zeitung*, 13 June 1985) and the USA (*International Herald Tribune*, 24 September 1986) there is a sharp rise in the number of people entering into such agreements:

> The man's fiancée was slim. He liked her that way. He wanted her to stay that way. And he was determined to do everything in his power to ensure her continued slenderness . . . Before the wedding, the groom got his bride to agree to a contract to pay a fine if she gained weight, refundable upon weight loss. That was no idle promise. The couple backed it up in writing in a prenuptial agreement negotiated by a New York attorney.
>
> Welcome to marriage, contractual style, circa 1986, a time when legal documents increasingly are spelling out everything from closet-space allocations after the wedding to who gets to keep the rent-controlled apartment after the divorce. It is not uncommon to find premarital contracts decreeing that spouses will alternate in choosing vacation spots, that the parties will share equally in disciplining children or that the partners have fully disclosed to one another the nature of their prior sexual experiences

> . . . Lawyers say they are seeing a rising demand for all sorts of prenuptial agreements, from the strictly financial to those with unusual lifestyle clauses. (*International Herald Tribune*, 24 September 1986)

And what happens if differences nevertheless arise as time goes by? Even then you can make a contract. Where there is nothing more in common the new philosophy of self-help offers civilized ways of coping with the situation, rediscovering the old principle '*do ut des*', plainly translated as 'what I don't like about you and you don't like about me will be got rid of by exchange.' There are already self-help books recommending 'agreements for mutual behaviour alteration'. A few instructions from one of them read as follows:

> Each partner gets something he/she wants from the other. For instance, you contract to 'wear a nice robe in the morning instead of that torn one'. He agrees to 'come home for dinner on time instead of going drinking with the boys'. You start out with simple behaviours and progress to more complex: ('She should initiate more sex . . .', 'He should kiss me more . . .'). (Baer 1976)

Freed from all outer constraints and able to marry whom you like, it paradoxically turns out that you may need new kinds of mutual control. Where everything is open, everything has to be negotiated, and without a common cause each individual's personal interests have to be protected from incursions by the other. The kind of self-help books mentioned above reflect and even amplify this trend. The question of what will become of the couple's togetherness is again incorrectly put, for that is not what is at stake here, or at least not primarily so.

From the evidence collected so far the following picture emerges. In modern marriage what links the two partners is their feelings for one another; the common ground is almost exclusively emotional and if the good feelings seem to be evaporating, then that is the beginning of the end of the marriage. It is the idea of 'romantic love' which gives marriage this strong emotional bias and has helped to transform our expectations; what used to be 'a lifelong bond has turned into a commitment which is upheld only under certain conditions' (Furstenberg 1987: 30).

The strain of persevering

> The ordeals in the mountains lie behind us,
> Ahead lie the ordeals in the plains.
> (Bertolt Brecht)

The main attraction people see in one another nowadays is not a common aim in life but the prospect of happiness, of finding the 'right' partner, a mixture of dream lover and best friend. But as dreams alter and friends prove less exciting than one thought, happiness turns out to be fugitive. More formally, *the space occupied by each individual in modern society makes close relationships precarious*:

> The family as an open space . . . means that it is in principle open to *any* definition, provided it remains a 'private' one not immediately connected with earning a living. But that also means that it is open to *no* definition, at least no permanent one. (Ostner and Pieper 1980: 123; emphasis in the original)

In the recent past hopes were pinned on self-determination and shaking off traditional obligations. The promise was clear: once all obstacles have been overcome, in whatever form – from family resistance to class considerations to lack of money – then true love will win. And it was also absolutely certain that this love would last forever. As Charlotte Brontë's *Jane Eyre* concludes:

> I have now been married ten years. I know what it is to live entirely for and with what I love best on earth . . . I know no weariness of my Edward's society; he knows none of mine . . . We talk, I believe, all day long: to talk to each other is but a more animated and an audible thinking . . . we are precisely suited in character – perfect concord is the result. (Brontë 1966: 475–6)

The modern discovery is that when love changes and what used to be a community of two helpmates has become a community of two lovers, the emotions themselves become hard work. Love under modern conditions is not an event which takes place once but is a state to be fought for anew every day, not just in good and bad times but all the time against the insecurities and upsets modern society forces on it.

To do this one needs patience and tolerance; such a relationship involves tenacious negotiations, often accompanied by skirmishing and a series of mini summit conferences, with no end in sight and the aggravating difficulty that the participants after years of practice are experts in each other's weaknesses and no-go areas. Love, having cast off its old shackles, finds itself under attack from a new quarter:

> Whether walking, sitting or lying down,
> they are together.

They have said their piece. They have kept silence.
That's it . . .

They speak in silence. And keep silent with words.
Their mouths run empty,
Their silence is of nineteen sorts
(if not more).

The sight of their souls and ties
Makes them angry.
They're like gramophones with three records.
They make you uneasy.

(Erich Kästner, *Gewisse Ehepaare*
(Certain married couples))

Love as a cuddly idyll? If only it were. The freedoms modern times offer are 'risky opportunities' (Keupp 1988). The more intense our feelings are, the more likely we are to suffer from them, from the mistakes, misunderstandings and complications they bring about. (If you can climb a peak you can equally fall into a crevasse, and being heartbroken is more than just a cliché phrase from the hit parade.) The distress men and women suffer in trying to live with one another is not purely their own fault, a byproduct of too much egocentricity. It also has something to do with modern definitions of love and marriage. Our feelings are supposed to be the basis, but feelings as we well know can be fickle: 'The heart is an extremely flexible muscle' (Woody Allen's film *Hannah and her Sisters*, final scene). While the classic literary theme used to be 'they can't get together,' in modern literature it is 'they can't live together.' Or as Dieter Wellershoff writes, 'In the old days lovers ran up against institutional barriers, while nowadays they are wading through a swamp of ideology called happiness' (quoted in Hage 1987).

From this one might conclude that any gain in terms of freedom and independence is quietly leaking away again. 'It rather looks as though the exigencies of the past are being replaced by the exigencies of the present' (Mayer 1985: 87). Nevertheless, if our modern ways of living harbour disappointment and conflict, earlier generations with their rigorous restrictions on personal freedom were hardly better off. There is certainly nothing to be gained from returning to the old ways; what we must find are new ways of living with one another which are both free *and* lasting.

One important step in this direction could be recognizing the 'double-faced' nature of liberation processes, the continuous dialectic between advantages and drawbacks. Perhaps that would make it easier to look for happiness on the other side too, amid the strain of persevering, of fighting for what we have. As it goes in a modern version of *Romeo and Juliet*, 'The love of your life? I believe that is when two people manage to put up with each other for their whole life' (Capek 1985). In the chilly world of independence love is defined as a burden and yet missed as a permanent support. As the epochs and their problems change, love remains a utopia, a design for a better world:

> Those marriages which start off with love are a bad sign. I wonder whether those great lovers in the stories one reads would continue to love their mate if she were ill, bed-ridden, and he, the man, had to take care of her the way one takes care of a baby; you understand all the unpleasantness I'm talking about here. Well, I believe he would not love her any more. True love, let me tell you, is growing old together. (Cohen 1984: 18)

4

ALL FOR LOVE OF A CHILD

'Love, marriage, baby carriage': love leads you to the altar and soon after that the baby arrives . . . that is how simple the world looked in the 1950s. Much has changed since then. It is no longer taken for granted that two people in love will get married, and for those who do decide to marry having children is not taken for granted either.

Are we living in an 'anti-child' society? At least this much is clear: in the highly industrialized countries there has been a marked decline in the birth-rate since the 1960s. Compared with other countries, the former German Federal Republic was long most severely affected, but recently Italy, the traditional 'bambini' country, has shown an even lower birth-rate (see the figure).

During the nineteenth century there were songs and poems about loving children, often linking this with 'woman's nature', idealizing the feelings and giving them a romantic aura. In the late twentieth century it has turned into a subject for magazines on parenting and books on child-rearing, a topic weighed down by instructions and educational tips, ordering parents to adopt the right approach and give their offspring the very best upbringing. Affection is recommended, but only in proper doses; even here one can do the wrong thing by 'terrorizing them with affection' (Gronemeyer 1989: 27).

Love for children – an eternal and natural bond, part of the scheme behind the history of mankind, perhaps even a genetic imprint? In fact it seems rather more complicated; what we have to look into is the relationship between mother and child. What are the dreams and longings it contains, what obligations and burdens? How was parenthood some years ago, how is it now, and what is likely to become of it in the future?

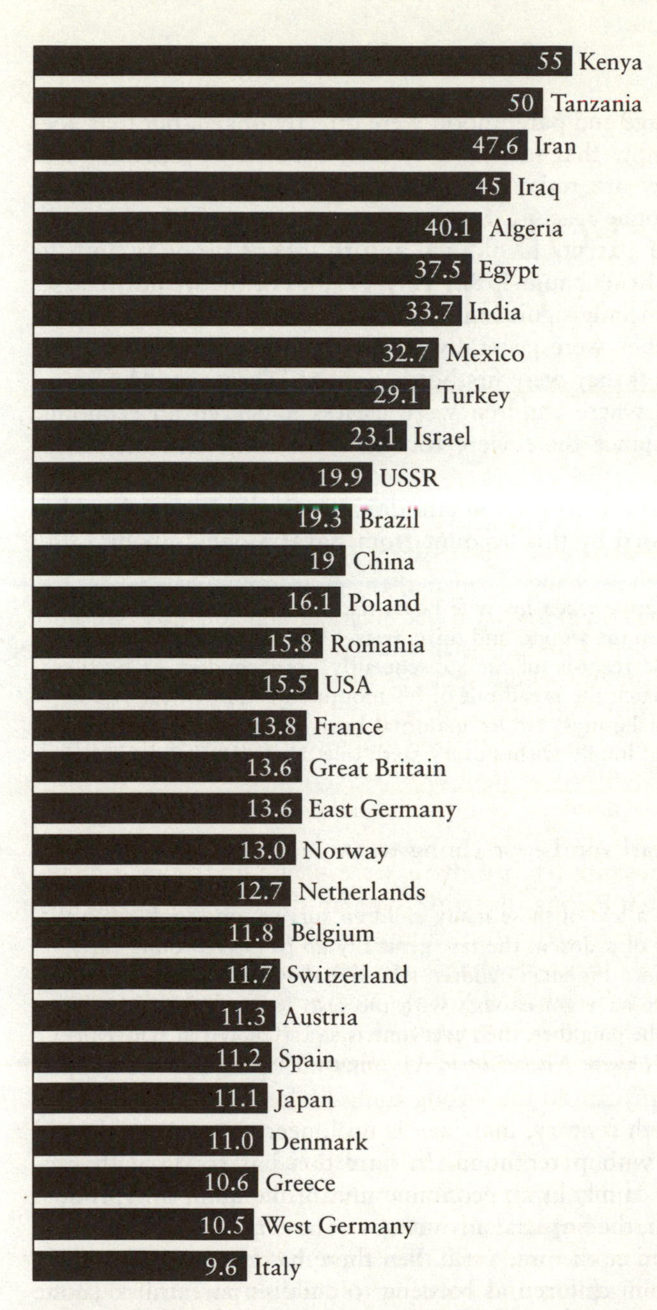

International birth-rates per 1000 inhabitants, with Italy's rate the lowest (UN data, given in *Die Zeit*, 23 December 1988)

Wanting a child

In the past, marriage and parenthood were directly linked, but that does not necessarily imply that men and women used to be more fond of children than they are today. In pre-industrial society children were essential for economic reasons, for their help at home and in the fields, to look after their parents in old age and to inherit property and the family name (e.g. Rosenbaum 1982; Tilly 1978). For the wealthy classes children were financially significant factors as heirs and owners of dowries; no wonder they were generally welcome and sometimes ardently desired, especially if they were firstborns or sons. There were, however, equally situations where children were useless and even an economic burden, if for instance there were too many of them and the family became too large.

No one could afford to get too emotionally involved in his/her children, as is illustrated by this account from Bavaria dated about 1800:

> The peasant is happy when his wife bears the first token of her love; he is still happy when the second and third arrive, but not so much with the fourth one . . . He regards all the subsequently born children as hostile creatures who snatch the bread out of his mouth and those of the rest of the family. Even the most tender maternal heart becomes indifferent to the fifth child and loudly wishes every sixth one dead. (Quoted in Imhof 1981: 44)

The ethnologist Karl von Leoprechting wrote in similar terms in 1855:

> Incidentally only a few of these many children survive, one could expect at most four out of a dozen, the rest generally go to heaven quite early. People rarely mourn for small children who die; they are beautiful angels in heaven and we have got enough with the rest. If an older child who could soon start helping dies, then everyone is sad. (Quoted in *Bad Tölz-Wolfratshauser Neueste Nachrichten*, 11 August 1988: IV)

In the late twentieth century, marriage is no longer so inextricably and inevitably linked with parenthood. In part this has to do with economics. When the family as an economic unit broke up as a byproduct of industrialization, the financial advantages of having children gradually receded and instead costs rose. Since then there has been a drastic shift, summed up as 'from children as blessing to children as burden' (Bolte 1980: 66). Over the past two decades and even more so over the past few years this change has gained enormous momentum, largely because the costs of raising a child have risen steeply, markedly faster than incomes, the inflation rate or the price indexes.

The child as experience of meaning and the self

The men and women who decide to have children today certainly do not do so because they expect any material advantages. Other motives closely linked with the emotional needs of the parents play a significant role; our children mainly have 'a psychological utility' (Fend 1988: 160). The data from other studies confirm this:

> Children do not bring any economic advantages – the exact opposite is the case. Nor can parents today expect practical support and help with difficult problems from their children – our society is too strongly oriented towards individualizing our life styles for that. The real remaining reward is the emotional value children have: the important feeling of being responsible, in charge and emotionally indispensable, and above all seeing oneself embodied in the next generation and represented again in human form. (Hurrelmann 1989: 11–12)

How does this 'psychological utility' express itself? There is a series of well-known motives, perhaps that the child could glue the parents together or fulfil their frustrated hopes of upward mobility. Having children, a demographic study reports, is increasingly connected with hopes of being rooted, of life becoming meaningful, and with a 'claim to happiness', based on the close relationship with the child (Münz 1983: 39):

> the desire for children (is) ego-related and connected with the present: parents want to . . . get something for themselves from giving birth, nursing, raising and providing for the children . . . Hope of discovering oneself through one's children is more widespread . . . it is [typical] of a large number of parents that having children is no longer primarily understood as a service, a kind of devotion or social obligation. Instead it is admitted to be a way of life in which one pursues one's own interests.

Here one can see signs of a parallel in the basic pattern behind a historical transition. The sort of change evident in the marital relationship as society moved from pre-industrial to modern times is also apparent in the relationship between parents and child. In both, the common cause – the survival of the family unit – has disappeared; in both, the relationship between the persons involved is less economic and more personal and private, with all the hopes and interests this involves; in both, the relationship depends largely on the growing, not to say hypertrophic emotional needs of all parties in an individualized world (including all the rewards and horrors inherent in intense feelings). As Jürgen Zinnecker noted in his research into socialization, the more the objective foundation of life crumbles, the more prominent the 'imaginary' becomes in the relationship between the generations. The adults use childhood and youth as 'a projection screen for unrealized and utopian dreams' (1988: 129). This tendency can be seen in the way parents and children interact and also long before that in the hopes linked with parenthood (see Beck-Gernsheim 1988a: 128ff.).

In highly industrialized societies people are always trained to behave rationally, to be efficient, fast, disciplined and successful. A child represents the opposite, the 'natural' side of life, and that is exactly what is so appealing. The child holds out a promise which especially young women, and a few young men, have described vividly in interviews and accounts of their own lives. Being with a child will help them to rediscover some of their gifts and express some of their needs which they sorely miss in high-tech life: being patient or calm, solicitous and sensitive, affectionate, open and close. Motherhood seems to offer the women an alternative refuge from the working world, where it is imperative to behave responsibly and soberly, and emotions are generally considered a nuisance. Committing yourself to a child means contradicting the cognitive side of life, and finding a living counterweight to all that soul-destroying routine. As one woman remarks: 'Where else can you find so much vital energy and joy as in a child?' (Boston Women's Health Collective 1971: II, 644).

'The naturalness of (small) children in a milieu that has become rather "unnatural"' is a theme beginning to appear in surveys (Höpflinger 1984: 104). It is this naturalness which obviously has so much appeal for the 'new women' (and men) who have grown up with the psychological ideas and educational aims introduced into the German school system in the 1970s and are highly sensitized to the price one may have to pay for getting along in our stressful society, the hardened hearts and pent-up feelings which ultimately result in 'an all-round reduced personality'. A child then seems to promise contact with 'genuine people, authentic relationships' (quoted in Häsing and Brandes 1983: 208). An alternative seems to present itself, a way of seeing people and how they grow through nostalgic eyes: 'Children come into the world intact and alive, while our hearts have turned into rubble and dust' (quoted in ibid.). An observer of this generation of 'new parents' writes:

> Mothers and fathers do not pretend to be selfless; they too expect a great deal back from their children. Bringing up a child is a matter of barter . . . They want to be brought up by their children. Sons and daughters are supposed to help the parents achieve their goal of being spontaneous, sensual, uninhibited and creative personalities. It is not the parents raising their children but conversely the children raising their parents. In the truest sense of the word, sons and daughters embody their parents' ego-ideal. (Bopp 1984: 66 and 70)

Another factor here is that, as we have seen, being a free individual has its alarming sides: 'A modern European is condemned to freedom. He is homeless' (Weymann 1989: 2). Having a child, looking after it and providing for it can give life new meaning and significance, can in fact become the very core of one's private existence. Where other aims seem arbitrary and interchangeable, belief in the afterlife vanishes and hopes in this world prove evanescent, a child provides one with a chance to find a firm footing and a home.

Such motives are often directly expressed by people low down on the social scale. A Swiss study on family planning has discovered that the notion of children as the most important thing and main purpose in life is particularly widespread among people with little education (Höpflinger 1984: 146–7). A German study on lower-class families points in the same direction (Wahl et al. 1980: 34–8). In response to the question 'What does having a family and children mean to you?' the answers were:

> 'So that life has some point to it.'
>
> 'You know where you are, what you're working for.'
>
> 'I want to know where I belong.'
>
> 'Life is much nicer if you know someone needs you. If you live alone, day in day out, you have nothing to show for it. With a family you know what you have accomplished. You know what you lived for.'

It is, however, not only the groups at a social disadvantage for whom children are becoming the essence of life. If one goes through the relevant interviews one soon discovers that the 'new women' and men make quite similar statements. One woman writer for instance notes: 'I wanted a child, a family of my own, someone to need and want me' (in Dowrick and Grundberg 1980: 80). Authors describing the new social tendencies remark – sometimes ironically, sometimes caustically – on the vehement search for the meaning of life in the shape of a small child. The new parents are looking for somewhere to anchor, and have children so that 'they have relatives,' to have the feeling of 'belonging somewhere while the world map keeps constantly changing' (Dische 1983: 32). There are cartoons showing 'a weird desire to have children' turning the child into the parent's vehicle in search of faith (Roos and Hassauer 1982: 70).

A woman retrospectively describes her own state when she decided to have a child:

> I had my baby . . . at a time when I was extremely uncertain of myself. My studies at the university were almost over; I had the prospect of being unemployed. The atmosphere in my political circles, the non-dogmatic left, varied between dismal and hopeless. The people I was sharing a house with were going their own ways, my boyfriend was very interested in some blonde, and the no-future mood that flourished later on, in the 'eighties, was already beginning to take hold in the streets and pubs of Frankfurt's Bockenheim district. Losing more and more of my commitments and points of reference made me both happy/light-hearted and dizzy/frightened. I saw that being free was not just beautiful and attractive. On the contrary, it is confusingly two-sided . . . I also had my baby . . . from fear of the void . . . that was opening up in front of me, and of my own uncertain future . . . By starting my family I wanted to create an alternative world for myself. That was it. I had escaped from the freedom which frightened me. (In Häsing and Brandes 1983: 180–1)

Childless for love of children?

Of course there are also strong barriers against having children nowadays. For one thing most people want 'a life of one's own', an aspect of an individualized society which used to affect only men and is now spreading to women as well. It soon becomes all too obvious there is no one in the background, there is no one unconditionally prepared to look after the child. One more telling reason however is that the demands made on parents have risen sharply, a matter which so far has been neglected by researchers and the public authorities. Parenthood has become an increasingly responsible task (see below, under 'Only the best will do', p. 128) and this makes deciding to have a child even more difficult (see Beck-Gernsheim 1988a: 149ff.).

The more one is expected to provide the child with 'optimal conditions' the longer prospective parents wait, even in the planning stage. This applies in all social classes, and no longer just in the middle classes interested in climbing the social ladder. 'The cost of having children and educating them is beginning to be seen from the angle of getting on in life and being successful, particularly in the lower classes' (Fuchs 1983: 348). The list of requirements is long, from pocket money and a room of its own for the child to holidays, toys and sports, and, not to be underestimated, the incidental expenses incurred during the ever-longer period while the child is at school or undergoing training for a job. These standards, transmitted by the mass media, take hold of the minds of broad sections of the population. The phrase 'we can't afford a child' reveals something about the couple's own standard of living but it says just as much about the standard of living they want to offer their child, indeed feel compelled to offer it if they follow the experts' advice. The new rule is 'modern people have only as many children as they can afford financially. They are well aware of their responsibility' (Häussler 1983: 65).

One suspects that the material side is only one aspect, and not the most important. The experts' advice covers much more, and reaches almost everyone, first the education-conscious middle-class women and then more generally via television and magazines. According to these authorities a child needs the right environment, ranging from proper housing and neighbourhood to a stable and affectionate home. And, most important of all, rearing a child is, as the self-help books emphasize, a 'great and responsible assignment' (Boston Women's Health Collective 1971: II, 644).

With so much responsibility around the consequences are obvious. As observers report, the potential mothers and fathers do their best to attain 'a maximum of security . . . in the interest of the children' (Roos and Hassauer 1982: 189). They carry around a list of requirements in their heads, and this list is longer than ever before – safe work-places, good housing, progressive schools and proper nursery care. Even the ecology issue comes in here: many ask themselves whether it is justifiable to have children at all any more, beneath the thinning ozone layer and surrounded by dying forests.

The young women who are up-to-date on (popular) science and highly conscious of their responsibility often subject their love-lives to a rigorous test. Is it good enough to take the strain and provide a child with the stability it needs? More than ever before they cross-examine themselves: if the personality of my child depends on how well I care for it, am I emotionally mature enough to treat it right? This is a new question of conscience, widely found among men and women who are aware of current psychological thinking: am I up to the personal demands of child-rearing? Do I have the inner qualities the child needs to develop properly?

If the answer is no – whether they want children or not – then the consequence must be: no child, or at least not yet. Here are the results of an empirical study on cohabitation:

> Many of them have the feeling there should be a child 'only later' . . . only when the problems in the relationship have been dealt with, or when one personally feels more stable . . . People would like to feel mature enough, for 'if I can't cope with myself, how am I supposed to cope with a child?' . . . For the women this is often linked to feeling anxious about motherhood, which is felt to be a crucial and exceptional test of one's own character. (*Nichteheliche Lebensgemeinschaften* 1985: 77)[1]

As standards for having and bringing up children rise one can discern a new pattern of decision-making. It is known as 'A Responsible Choice: No Children' (Ayck and Stolten 1978), for love of them, as it were. A peculiar spiralling effect gets under way: the fewer the children the more precious each one becomes and the more rights it is given. The more important and expensive a child is, the more people recoil from this huge task and decide to do without. Ayck and Stolten state in their introduction to *Kinderlos aus Verantwortung*:

> This book is not aimed against life with children but against what is done to children nowadays. They need more than care, food and drink. Their psychological needs are often neglected . . . Conscious childlessness is a challenge. Not having children can be an expression of a new moral attitude and a new form of social responsibility. (1978: 12, 18, 25)

Planned children

The decision to have or not to have children is currently affected by a whole series of factors, from the pleasures and deprivations of a life of one's own to the obligations and delights of parenthood. There is always some argument for and another against whatever is decided, keeping hopes and fears alive – 'Wanting a Child: Pros and Cons', as the title of a book by Roos and Hassauer (1982) puts it. Research confirms this: 'In weighing up the pros and cons, typical kinds of insecurity, ambivalence and contradictions become apparent' (Urdze and Rerrich 1981: 94).

So what is thought of as a situation requiring a decision often turns into a long-drawn-out process. This applies particularly to the new women (and sometimes men) who are well informed, aware of their own strengths and weaknesses and anxious to take the right decisions for the right reasons. This again is a characteristic of a society where traditional ideas about class, status and sexual identity no longer direct people down firmly preset paths. We are finding ourselves forced to construct our own biographies, planning the short-term and long-term strategies from what type of schooling we want, what training we undergo, to where we choose to live and who we choose to live with. As the relevant women's literature shows, this need to plan ahead intervenes increasingly in women's lives and their attitudes to motherhood. A handbook for women lays down the correct procedure: a would-be mother should first of all 'think everything through carefully' and then 'make a really certain decision' (Boston Women's Health Collective 1971: II, 640).

A glance into the autobiographies and studies on this topic reveals that the advice is being followed. An empirical survey reports: 'Many of the women interviewed complained of a lack of spontaneity. They have the impression that having children used to be quite natural, whereas nowadays they have to make a conscious decision' (*Nichteheliche Lebensgemeinschaften* 1985: 78). In reflections on their real feelings, in diaries, in conversations with women friends and more than ever with their partners, the new women are trying to track down good reasons for motherhood, and want to 'get informed', to be able to 'prevent' or if necessary 'arm themselves', even 'defend themselves'; they want 'to know all about it' (Sichtermann 1982: 7–11).

This is certainly one reason why they write down their experiences, seeking a way out of the ambivalences and helping each other on the long road to making a decision:

> It was essential for us to do this book. It arose out of a sense of satiation. We talked about having a child for three or four years. The two of us discussed it, and we talked it over with friends, colleagues and other people our age . . . Now the book is done. With it one stage of our biography has come to an end. The child issue has been objectified for us. (A university lecturer, quoted in Bach and Deutsch 1979: 26)

> My boyfriend always said I should write down my reasons for wanting a baby. I did that for three years, but I never came up with a really good reason for it. Just a lot of trivialities. (A graphic designer, quoted in Hahn 1988: 179)

What used to be the most natural thing in the world has now for some groups of the population become highly complicated. Nothing happens spontaneously any more; everything has become cerebral, for the new woman feels compelled to question and problematize what she does. The children, if there are any, are supposed to be welcome, but wishing for them is no longer just a wish but a whole bundle of pros and cons; the children are the result of a plan, 'masterminded births' or 'headbirths', as Günter Grass puts it.

Even the keywords which pop up in interviews and autobiographical accounts are symptomatic. There is talk of 'observing yourself and diagnosing your wants' (Kerner 1984: 153), of 'finding out where you are deceiving yourself' (Dowrick and Grundberg 1980: 100) or 'thinking it through to the very end' (Kerner 1984: 153). Parents expecting twins recall 'immediately of course that there is said to be a higher rate of schizophrenia among twins' (Häsing and Brandes 1983: 152). Perhaps this is an extreme, but let us look further: a dialogue between a blue-collar worker and his saleswoman wife goes into the 'arguments' against having an only child (Urdze and Rerrich 1981: 84). Another saleswoman reports that during the first months of pregnancy she 'had read almost everything' she could find on it, and especially 'the various methods of giving birth' (Reim 1984: 172). A whole network of theories and arguments is woven round the subject of children; as Günter Grass describes:

> A couple to be proud of. A beautiful couple. Out of a modern fairy tale. They have a cat, and no child. Not because they can't or because something does not work, but because when she 'really does' want a child he says 'not yet'. On the other hand when he says, 'theoretically I can imagine it,' she replies as if prompted, 'I can't. Not any longer. Being responsible means looking at things soberly. What kind of future do you want to offer it? There's no future for it. Besides there are already enough of them, there are too many children. In India, Mexico, Egypt, China. Just have a look at the statistics.' (Grass 1980: 12)

Preparing for the baby

How do those fare who – often after lengthy planning – finally decide to have a baby? The pleasure of looking forward is often tinged with other feelings; the 'job of thinking ahead' continues. Even at the first thought of the coming child the couples, and above all the women, are faced with a barrage of popularized scientific information which has taken over a large section of the magazine market in the past few years.

Here are some extracts from a small selection of these guides on how to run one's life as a parent in the late twentieth century.

What she (and sometimes he too) should do before pregnancy

Thanks to the medical scientists a hundred years ago we know that adequate nutrition is important for children's growth. This idea has been perfected in the past century, so that one now knows that proper nutrition begins much earlier, with the prospective mothers, years before they conceive a child. A self-help book from 1969 advises: 'Great stress used to be put on what women ate during pregnancy. Today we go even further and advise women to consider conception only if they . . . are in the best of health' (Schönfeldt 1969: 8). In the advisory manual *ÖKO-TEST: Ratgeber Kleinkinder* (first printed in May 1988, 63,000 copies by April 1989), we read:

> How the mother lives . . . has a decisive effect on the quality of her milk . . . Women on vegetarian diets and organically grown produce have better values. It is not enough to briefly alter one's eating habits during pregnancy . . . because the pollutants accumulate in one's body over many years. (pp. 25–6)

Nor is it enough just to eat properly if you want to do your best for your future baby's health. As medicine strides on towards new horizons, there are new factors to take into account. A health guide suggests: 'It is better if you plan a thorough health check-up before getting pregnant, to make sure you are in the best of health right from the beginning' (Beck 1970: 238). Or even earlier: 'it would be better if you had genetic counselling before even planning your pregnancy' (*Junge Familie: Das Baby-Journal*, 1988/5: 38). To organize a pregnancy in the best possible way it is advisable to take expert advice.

Here are more examples: in a widely read women's magazine there is a detailed programme entitled 'Countdown to Conception'; the motto runs 'Protect your unborn child,' and the first steps are supposed to be taken months before conception, with visits to the dentist and the gynaecologist, including special tests for cat owners because of the risk of toxoplasmosis and for Asian and African-American women, for Jewish women and those from Mediterranean countries because of special genetic susceptibilities (*McCall's*, January 1986: 42). A similar programme, entitled 'Better Babies by Design', recommends 'Pre-pregnancy care' which should ideally start six months before conception. This includes a check-up for both partners, various blood and blood-pressure tests, information on a balanced diet, abstaining from smoking, alcohol and drugs, and avoiding stress. The goal of such efforts is described as follows:

> Why have an ordinary baby – when you could have a better one? Better babies are well-proportioned from head to toe. They have excellent posture – no knock-knees, flat feet or sway backs. They're alert, bright, calm – perfect in every way. They have proper jaws so their teeth grow straight. They have good-shaped skulls with room for their brains to grow properly. (*Observer*, 26 April 1987)

The unborn child: a vulnerable creature

What applies to preparing for pregnancy applies even more when the 'great event' is in the offing: all kinds of precautions and safeguards are required. Here the main driving force is medical advance, in particular in the field of antenatal research. While women in the nineteenth century had very imprecise notions on how and when human life begins, over the last decade the nine months between conception and birth have been explored in ever greater detail. What was once a vague primeval state is now available on colour photos: the image of the unborn child from the very first cell division onwards. One can trace how the embryo grows, how nutrition and metabolism function and which external factors affect events in the mother's body. This is the point: to be able to keep such influences under control the woman carrying the embryo is given a series of instructions. 'Caution! Hazard for pregnant women!' (*Ratgeber aus der Apotheke*, 15 March 1989: 14).

A close look soon reveals, however, that it is not the woman's health that is at stake but that of the baby. Numerous foods are described as harmful for the embryo and therefore end up on the blacklist of forbidden foods for the mother:

> As a matter of course the mother should abstain from alcohol, coffee, black tea and nicotine during the pregnancy. (Bruker and Gutjahr 1986: 54)

> Frequent consumption of meat and sausages has a bad effect. (*ÖKO-TEST: Ratgeber Kleinkinder*: 25)

> Pregnant women should avoid soft cheese, semi-soft sliced cheese and unpasteurised cheese; they should remove the rind from all types of cheese and switch to hard, sliced and processed cheese. Raw meat and pork

> sausage should likewise be avoided . . . and rare meat too. (*Ratgeber aus der Apotheke*, 15 March 1989: 14)

The recommendations do not end when the child is born, for the mother's milk must have all the right nutrients. She is urged to eat fish:

> The metabolites of fish oil contained in the mother's milk . . . are needed for the rapid brain development of the baby in the first months of life. Professor Weber warns: 'A lack of omega-3 fatty acids leads to disorders in the central nervous system and the eyes' (*Eltern*, 1988/4: 15).

A pregnant woman who does not conform willingly is put under pressure and the risks are presented in detail:

> The baby is totally defenceless . . . Pregnant women are harbouring a particularly delicate life within them. Germs which are not dangerous to the mother can bring about severe disorders in the unborn child . . . If an expectant mother is infected by *listeria* she normally only has some flu symptoms . . . the otherwise harmless germs can have disastrous consequences for the unborn child however; nodules may develop in the liver, the spleen, the adrenal gland, the lungs or the stomach, and circulatory or respiratory disorders may occur. *Listeria* can also attack the brain and result in fits, meningitis, premature birth or congenital defects. Roughly 40% of the affected babies die after birth and many have lasting mental retardation . . . [Toxoplasmosis] also generally remains imperceptible for the mother . . . but can harm the baby. The risks run from seizures and retarded growth in mild cases to severe mental retardation, eye problems and even blindness. (*Ratgeber aus der Apotheke*, 15 March 1989: 14)

The ideal mother-to-be orients herself completely on her growing child, and is recommended to alter her own life accordingly. Even watching soaps on television may prove detrimental to the child in future years and is therefore best avoided:

> Babies pick up *Dallas* and *Dynasty* even in their mother's wombs. In later years they cannot do without such series. Even before birth they have been manipulated and programmed for certain films, getting addicted to them. So better avoid TV series if you're going to have a baby. (*Junge Familie: Das Baby-Journal*, 1988/5: 38)

Everyone – community colleges and adult education programmes, churches and ecological groups, regional and national institutions, recognized and self-appointed experts – is offering lectures and courses with tips for expectant mothers and sometimes for the expectant father as well. The themes have proliferated: as a popular magazine mentions: 'Most pregnancy courses are more than just exercises, breathing techniques and medical hints on the course of pregnancy and delivery. Now the unborn child is included, and mother and father become aware of what it needs and how it can be protected.' In the report following these remarks 'three new methods for expectant parents to get in touch with their unborn child' are presented, including 'antenatal foot massage', 'psycho-tactile contact' and the 'antenatal university' (*Eltern*, 1985/9: 15).

If the 'why' of birth has become a special issue, so has the 'how'. In the nineteenth century most children were born at home as a matter of course. Hospital delivery became the norm for our society during the twentieth century, but now at the end of it nothing at all can be taken for granted; experts fervently discuss on television and in the media where the best place is to be born. State hospitals, private gynaecological clinics, practising midwives who will assist at a home delivery or come to the hospital – the range of offers is as broad as it is bewildering, and, as ever, really responsible parents are supposed to know what is best.

What luck that the book market has responded. Sheila Kitzinger, a world-renowned author in the field of birth planning, provides help in 'setting up a birth plan of your own' (1980: 156ff.), taking into account all the relevant details and possible complications, from giving one's consent to electronic heart monitoring (whether and how) and a Syntocinon jab (when and under what conditions) to choosing between epidural and full anaesthesia. (Perhaps one should first study medicine before daring parenthood.) Even a daily newspaper offers a 'comprehensive checklist' to help you 'prepare optimally' (*Starnberger Neueste Nachrichten/Süddeutsche Zeitung*, 21 February 1989: IV). Then there is the suggestion that you 'get your own impression of the atmosphere and services of a clinic'. To do this one can 'arrange an individual tour of the clinic, in which you can visit the maternity ward and the delivery room and interview the doctor or midwife'. Questions you might want to ask are 'what sort of technical equipment for monitoring the delivery do they have (ultrasound, phonocardiogram, scalp electrode) and is it routinely employed?'

Pregnancy may be a natural event, but in the waning years of the twentieth century nature no longer exists in the sense we mean it; nature is usually in the hands of experts. Empirical knowledge tends to be devalued and a woman is not encouraged to listen to experienced friends and neighbours. Rather she should 'immediately ask her doctor for advice and do all the things he suggests and nothing else'; there is no doubt about it, 'the doctor is more important for the expectant mother than the father or the husband' (Schönfeldt 1985: 31).

A digression: entwined in love, responsibility and uncertainty

All these offers represent merely a selection from the repertoire of hints and rules which accompany the arrival of a new child. The fact that they are available does not necessarily mean that they are followed, and so far we do not have any reliable data on actual behaviour. The evidence suggests however that modern parents – especially mothers – orient themselves far more on expert advice than their parents and grandparents did (Rolff and Zimmermann 1985; Schütze 1981; Zinnecker 1988). All the guides and handbooks, lectures and courses make an impact too (see Bullinger 1986; Reim 1984), and there is much caustic comment describing parents nowadays as people smitten with a new virus called 'parenting mania' (e.g. *Kursbuch*, 1983/72 and 1984/76).

This is not to say that everyone catches it. The profile of the target group is roughly as follows: highly susceptible are middle-class women who are well-educated city-dwellers, expecting their first child at a fairly advanced age; other groups of women are also affected, the differences lying in the experts relied on, depending on social class and educational level, from psychological textbooks via feminist writings to evening classes, church pamphlets and magazines for every taste.

So 'new parenting' is not restricted to a small minority, and if one traces the typical features, they seem to be spreading. The better educated our society becomes – more than a quarter of German secondary school pupils qualify to go to university – and the more women there are among them, the stronger this trend becomes. More and more people – especially young people – live in or near a city; fewer than ever before live in small isolated villages or towns. There are also fewer families with large numbers of children, and much preference for the single-child family. And finally many women are delaying motherhood until they too become 'late mothers'.

Though the picture of a widespread 'parenting mania' may seem plausible, it only describes the phenomenon without looking into the reasons behind it. Assuming there is an inner logic to it, we can try to trace why loving and living with a child under modern conditions leads one into a thicket of contradictions. Here are some of the factors which have to be contended with.

A sense of insecurity The certainties which once regulated the relationship between parent and child, defining what each expected from and owed the other, have gradually got lost. Modern people find themselves expelled from that comfortable nest and its safe laws which used to be considered natural and right. The main thrust pushing them along new roads comes from technological advances; the sheer speed with which innovations appear robs the parents of their traditional superior knowledge. Whether the issue is antenatal diagnosis or the toxins in mother's milk, great-grandma's lore (even if it still existed) would not help, nor can one fall back on one's feelings or the voice of nature or even common sense.

The principle of responsibility Emancipation applied to parenthood means being handed the task called parental initiative; one is expected as it were to create the child's life, improving on everything one can. Being a parent comes to be understood as a compensatory form of making the world a better place, or to put it the other way round, the worse the world is, the more parents are expected to protect their children against its hazards (looking for uncontaminated instant milk after Chernobyl, for instance). Dangers to the environment, produced on an international scale, find their way into the family's private kitchens and bedrooms as yet more duties and activities to cram into the day.

Contradictory advice Since people have to bear their feelings of insecurity, their ideals, their responsibility and their endangered environment all at the same time, they turn to whoever seems certain of knowing the right answers and offers convincing explanations to replace the fading traditional ones. This is where scientific research and guidebooks come in. The effect they have, however, is often to increase the reader's insecurity rather than banish it, since opinions boom and die as the experts, the self-appointed authorities and the gurus compete with one another (is mother's milk healthy or not, should one feed on demand or schedule?). This in turn is no accident but a condition of the system, for science as its first principle pleads fallibility, and almost all prior knowledge proves erroneous some time.

Attempts to escape What looks like a way out – reverting to doing as one chooses, going back to nature, rediscovering how to be spontaneous and authentic (another popular recommendation in the handbooks) – tends to lead back to the same dilemma: modern living is characterized by a great deal of uncertainty, so that any attempt to do without knowledge is both understandable and in vain.

Love as an amplifier The very act of bringing up a child is emotionally highly charged. Loving it, the frail little creature, means protecting it, parents are consistently told. This injunction hits them at their weakest spot, the hopes and longings they invest in their progeny. It makes shutting one's ears to what the experts advise very difficult, for they paint lurid pictures of what might happen unless . . . What if something did happen? Could we ever forgive ourselves? It seems safer to follow the instructions.

If one pieces all these components together one gets an idea, at least in outline, of how the feelings of a parent for its child, borne along on love and its handmaidens hope and fear, produce their own paradoxes. Modern thinking says parents are responsible for their children and leaves them no margin for mistakes or revisions. Loving an adult partner usually leaves room for manoeuvre (or if all else fails, for divorce), whereas loving a child is an asymmetrical arrangement with all the decisions one-sidedly on the parents' shoulders and every mistake likely to interfere with the child's chances in life (or so the educationalists tell us). What looks, especially to the childless, like parenting gone mad is the logical outcome when one interlocks loving a child with feeling responsible for its welfare and being uncertain on how to achieve this – a plight rich in poignancy and disasters all its own.

Obligatory antenatal diagnosis

This is a technological age, and pregnancy is no longer considered a natural event; it is a problematic condition requiring precautionary measures and medical monitoring. If the pregnancy is affected by so-called risk factors – there are lots of these, as the books inform us – then antenatal diagnosis is recommended. The cover story in a popular magazine, which flourishes on translating into simple language what the scientists have worked out, earnestly inquires: 'Early tests during pregnancy? Will your baby be born healthy? What kind of test? and when is it necessary? Are there any risks involved?' (*Eltern*, 1989/6: cover story). If some kind of handicap is revealed the parents are faced with a difficult decision: 'In these hard-headed times even slight disorders and handicaps can play a big role in one's development, integration, progress in life and self-esteem' (Roth 1987: 100–1). This sentence was uttered at a conference of human geneticists and specialists in preventive medicine.

So the question becomes: can responsible parents saddle their child with the possibility of a handicap? Is it permissible for them to send their child out into the world starting at a disadvantage? The answer might then be abortion, out of a sense of responsibility, even out of love. Wolfgang van den Daele, a former member of the Commission on Genetic Engineering in the German Federal Parliament describes current reasoning:

> The reactions of the woman (or parents) to antenatal findings are often along 'all or nothing' lines. As a rule they choose abortion even if there is only a risk of a disease, or just the danger of getting one, or if it is not clear whether damage might be severe or minor, so that the probability of a healthy foetus being killed is quite high . . . Even discovering chromosomal abnormalities (XYY for instance), which is almost certainly insignificant, can be taken as a reason for aborting the affected foetus 'as a precaution'. (1985: 145–6)

Antenatal diagnosis induces a new way of thinking about safety. It no doubt takes into account the parents' own interests, their wish to protect themselves from the stresses they would undergo with a disabled child, but it is equally often too 'in the child's interest'. As long as the genetic secrets of the unborn child were kept (and one must remember this was so until only a few years ago) they were beyond human intervention, in short, a matter of fate. Now that genetic technology can discover many of these secrets, they turn into matters to be decided upon and possibly avoided by the parents-to-be.

The more diagnostic measures become available, the more responsibility the parents have to bear. What is discovered in the laboratories redefines (and subtly dictates) how they should behave. Here is an account by a woman who found out after amniocentesis that she was expecting a child with Down's syndrome:

> even if we *did* totally transform our lives to bring up a Down syndrome child, other stark realities confronted us . . . As we ourselves age, to whom could we leave the person [the child] would become? In a society where the state provides virtually no decent, humane services for the mentally retarded, how could we take responsibility for the future of our dependent Down syndrome child? In good conscience we couldn't choose to raise a child who would become a ward of the state. (Rapp 1984: 319)

> pregnancy now is very different from what it was only a decade ago, when once we decided to become pregnant or accept an accidental pregnancy, we did not confront further decisions about whether to carry that particular pregnancy to term. (Hubbard 1984: 334)

The change comes about with antenatal diagnosis; there is now 'a tentative pregnancy' (Rothman). The mother-to-be maintains a certain inner reserve about her pregnancy. Until the laboratory tests have been completed and produced results – for an amniocentesis this means the twentieth week – many women hold back any hopes and keep their feelings in check, 'because no one knows how it will turn out'. Under such conditions pleasurable anticipation can only develop after the lab has signalled 'everything okay, no reason for concern'. From a field study into the effects of antenatal diagnosis:

> Under the conditions imposed by amniocentesis a woman's attitude towards her pregnancy can only be tentative. She cannot ignore it, but nor can she wholeheartedly accept it . . . Most women manage to keep their anxieties at bay, but there is a price to this. The price is gradually forming a bond with the foetus. The woman has to maintain her distance . . . How can she begin to build up a loving relationship to the baby inside her, begin to plan on behalf of it, begin to feel like its mother, if it may not turn out to be a baby at all but just a genetic accident, and ultimately an aborted foetus? (Rothman 1988: 101–3)

Meanwhile genetic research moves on, and new ways of intervening become available. At the moment this is happening before birth, but soon it may be happening before conception. In all likelihood future prospects are roughly as follows (Beck-Gernsheim 1988b). It will be feasible to select, reject or deliberately mix one's offspring's genetic makeup – a kind of building set with genetic bricks in a test tube guaranteeing high-class results. Perhaps one will no longer have to fall back on the old natural ways of conceiving children, and instead just use sperm and eggs which have satisfied stringent criteria for an optimal genetic product. The range of possibilities will be immense, and love will be ready to try them out. Long ago John Locke remarked 'The negation of nature is the path to happiness' (quoted by Rifkin, 1987: 30). What this can mean for parenthood in the age of reproductive technology has been described by Yvonne Schütze in these terms: 'Then love for a child may well be measured by how much parents are willing to do for its genetic endowment' (1986: 127).

Yearning for a child: would-be parents as patients

What happens if you are longing to have a child and no child materializes? According to current research the number of people unsuccessfully and desperately trying to conceive and bear a child is on the rise.

Roughly 10 to 15% of all couples, it is estimated, have fertility problems; it just doesn't work (Michelmann and Mettler 1987: 44). Modern medicine offers them a variety of possible so-called services, ranging from hormone treatment, already a routine part of gynaecology, to in-vitro fertilization or artifical insemination making use of deep-frozen eggs and a sperm bank.[2] Whether the methods are conventional or spectacular they all have a common goal: to produce the child the couple yearns for.

How likely is it that the efforts will be successful? What hindrances and perhaps burdens have to be coped with when medical experts assist in producing pregnancies? Let us consider the prospects and possible side effects more closely.

First of all there are the procedures which are part of the standard repertoire of infertility treatment, measuring your temperature and receiving hormone treatment. Even here your sex life is largely – and in the 'ideal' case completely – under medical control. It turns into a competitive sport and compulsory exercise, to be performed in accordance with instructions (when, or when not, and how, in which position). This reduces sexuality to a merely biological act, and its 'surplus' aspects, the erotic, spontaneous, emotional sides go into hiding. It kills the thrill; your feelings about yourself suffer just as much as your feelings for your partner. Here are two accounts of the problem:

> The main problem of going through infertility is making love to order. It takes all the spontaneity out of it. I went through a stage of only wanting him in the fertile time; it seemed pointless on the other days.
>
> It got to the stage that sex seemed a chore; it really didn't mean anything. It was a bit sticky and not particularly exciting; a bit uptight. I had it all organised. (Pfeffer and Woollett 1983: 28)

Moving on to the more complicated methods of treatment there are other factors to be contended with as well as regulated sex. The procedures are often lengthy and time-consuming, expensive and restricting, not to mention the health risks and emotional strain involved. Here is a vivid account of the various stages of in-vitro fertilization:

> The same routine every day until the seventh day of the cycle, which at least allows one a normal everyday life: take tablets in the morning, venous blood sample to determine oestrogen level and hormone injections in the bottom. Ring the clinic from 3 p.m. on and find out the evening hormone ration. My husband gives me the injections; he's a dermatologist. The IVF team discusses the patients' hormone levels as reported by

the laboratory, and then decides on their fate: stopping treatment or more stimulation . . .

The further treatment progresses, the more of a torture the blood sampling becomes; every jab of the needle seems like a violation of my body . . . But hope gets injected with the hormones. Both my husband and I become more thin-skinned and nervous. From day 10 on we are not allowed to have any more intercourse . . .

A great deal is decided between days 8 and 13 of the cycle. At home we sit and talk about the diameter of the follicle and hormone values and work out the probable date for centesis, the day when the embryo is implanted, and the birth date of our dream child . . . Hope grips us and grows daily in the gloom of the ultrasound cabin. We are completely at its mercy.

Then comes an extremely isolated and tense phase; the IVF treatment completely takes over our lives. We are constantly afraid that all the effort may be for nothing. Before I lie down for my scan in the morning I am always afraid the follicles will have vanished or shrunk. It is a relief each time to see the bubbles show up as black spots on the screen. At last comes the deliverance: 'We will give you the injection to induce ovulation at 11 this evening.' I become calmer but my husband gets more and more nervous. In 36 hours the eggs will be removed, and then it's up to him. He absolutely has to function. In clinical jargon, 'the partner provides a fresh sample of semen.'

In the course of the next two days the removal of the eggs, semen production and embryo transfer all take place, all in the clinic of course, and under continual medical monitoring. Then the patient is sent back home, but not without instructions. She is supposed to live quite normally; only sport, sauna and lifting heavy things are not allowed, and 'please for the next two weeks again no intercourse.' (Fischer 1989: 48–56)

This is an account of quite typical experiences. Whether or not the treatment is successful in the end, first of all it induces a state of permanent tension and permanent apprehension. Whether ovulation will take place, whether fertilizable eggs will be found during centesis, whether there will be any cell division in the fertilized egg, whether the embryo transplantation will go well, whether the hormone levels will remain high enough, whether nidation is successful . . . a series of whethers. What normally happens unseen and unnoticed, inside the woman's body, is broken down into separate visible steps. As studies on how women feel under this treatment show (Hölzle 1989; Klein 1987; Lorber and Greenfield 1987; Williams 1987), this has a very powerful emotional effect; it results in an emotional attachment. As each new step is completed, the couple comes closer to their goal, having a child. From an interview:

> Ever since they allowed John and me to have a look at our embryos in the glass dish through the microscope I really believed it. Yes, we could have our own children, there they were . . . mind you, I don't actually think of them as a baby but these cells have the potential to become a baby . . . our own baby . . . for the first time that abstract hope 'child' becomes real. (Klein 1987: 8)

For the first time hope takes a visible form. This is neither a coincidence nor some irrational reaction on the part of the women affected; on the contrary, it is inherent in the technical procedure itself. It is not easy to forget what one has seen, even if the treatment was not quite successful. Then one thinks, 'We nearly made it, the first stages went well, perhaps next time we'll get further. We can't give up now.' And the next round of treatment begins. The technological possibilities exert a secret seductive power. As one can read in a study on the subject: 'The intensity of the emotions that are part of the inner character of in-vitro fertilisation and of the experience of it . . . directly strengthens the willingness of women to undergo additional attempts at treatment' (Williams 1987: 2). This is illustrated in the interview quoted above. After looking at the contents of the glass dish, which had already aroused such powerful feelings, 'then all you get is this phone call: "Sorry, Mrs M., see you next time." And you ache and ache but then sign on again because it seems you were *so* close, as close as never before in your life . . . so you *had* to give it another try' (Klein 1987: 8).

An emotional roller coaster

In such circumstances many women go through a dizzying jumble of emotions. This too is not incidental but a product of the treatment offered them. Since it consists of distinct steps, the risks and chances of each one have to be weighed up; sober laboratory findings become magic messages. Here is a woman describing what happened to her during ZIFT treatment (ZIFT is a method related to in-vitro fertilization in which zygotes, pre-embryos before the dividing stage, are introduced into the Fallopian tubes):

> [I was] pregnant with optimism throughout the two weeks of fertility drugs before the procedure, and the two weeks after when you hold your breath for fear of dislodging any embryos that might have nestled within . . . There are incredible highs. The process is akin to being in a demonic love affair, when the pull and punishment of the flesh are irresistible. On Day 1 of my ZIFT, when I found they had retrieved 11 eggs

> from my ovaries, I was elated. How could I miss? But by nightfall I was in despair: what if none of the eggs fertilised; what if on the most basic level my husband and I were hopelessly incompatible, our sperm and eggs unwilling to conduct their extra-corporeal courtship; what if by morning we had no zygotes?
>
> The nurse called early to say we indeed had zygotes. Four eggs had fertilised. 'Come get them,' she said, and my heart leaped at the invitation. I dressed carefully and washed my hair, as if I were about to meet somebody special.
>
> Would I be able to hold onto any one of them; would they continue to divide and grow inside me? Knowing the ZIFT odds, I was hopeful. No, that's not strong enough: I was crazed with hope as they put me to sleep, made a tiny split in my navel and through a catheter dropped three of the embryos (the fourth was frozen for a future attempt) into my one good Fallopian tube. All that those embryos had to do was migrate down to my waiting womb. What could stop them now?
>
> Something did, some something. My embryos didn't take hold; they vanished. When that was confirmed, two weeks to the day after the procedure had been performed, I myself vanished for a while into a fetal curl of grief. This was hardly a death, not even a miscarriage, just a non-carriage. But I mourned my embryos as if I'd known them. (Fleming 1989)

Her reaction is neither idiosyncratic nor extreme. Confronted with what seems like the omnipotence of technology women find themselves swinging between euphoria and misery; they feel themselves to be helplessly at the mercy of the doctors if their innermost wish is to be fulfilled. Even the pioneers in the field are beginning to realize that there are certain dangers in this. The less appealing side of advances in treatment is 'the hope and disappointment, the physical and emotional pain of thousands of women and men who had felt they had almost reached their goal when they were accepted as patients for the reproduction programme' (Bräutigam and Mettler 1985: 64).

Still a temptation

The question remains, how successful are all these efforts? The statistics are sobering; a high proportion of the couples treated do not end up with a child. This applies particularly to in-vitro fertilization, the focus of so many desperate hopes. The success rate here is quite low; according to official estimates it amounts to between 10 and 15% – and critics suggest that this figure may be optimistic (summarized in Fuchs 1988). Even the experts in the field admit that, considering current prospects of high failure rates, the rapid spread of laboratories offering such treatment can 'prove fatal for couples affected by childlessness' (Bräutigam and Mettler 1985: 65).

Even where treatment remains unsuccessful, it is not without consequences. The medical intervention does not alleviate the sufferings of the men and women who remain infertile – and they are the majority; on the contrary, if anything these seem to increase. They suffer from what is known as an iatrogenic illness, the strain caused by the medical procedures they have undergone and by always being defined as deficient or in need of treatment. Their self-esteem and self-confidence is often shaken, life with their partner changes for the worse, contacts with friends and acquaintances are reduced, hardly surprisingly, since the elaborate medical routines leave little time for outside interests or other spheres of life. (Pfeffer and Woollett 1983). The child becomes all they think and care about – and does not arrive.

That's all very well, one might object; why don't they just drop out of the cycle of treatments? If, however, one looks at the social as well as the biological implications, this is much more difficult than it appears. Medical advances are presented to the public, and a side-effect of research is that infertility is redefined and extended in time. If there are so many methods of treatment available, why not try out the next one? As the sociologist Barbara Katz Rothman remarks:

> All of the new treatments for infertility have also created a new burden for the infertile – the burden of not trying hard enough. Just how many dangerous experimental drugs, just how many surgical procedures, just how many months – or is it years – of compulsive temperature-taking and obsessive sex does it take before one can now give in gracefully? When has a couple 'tried everything' and can then finally stop? (1988: 28)

While infertility used to be a matter of fate, it is nowadays turning into a deliberate decision, at least in a certain sense. Those who give up without having tried the very latest methods (an endless series) have to take the blame. After all, they could have kept trying. Rothman again:

> At what point is it simply not their fault, out of their control, inevitable, inexorable fate? At what point can they get on with their lives? If there is always one more doctor to try, one more treatment around, then the social role of infertility will always be seen in some sense as chosen. (1988: 29)

The pattern one can see here is a familiar one: technological advances have always offered new chances, new solutions to new problems; at the same time they put people under emotional, mental and sometimes social pressure to make use of the chances they offered.

It is only against this background that one can understand what the interviews often convey: couples for whom the treatment remained unsuccessful nevertheless declare that they do not regret having undergone it. This seems paradoxical when one realizes what a strain such treatment entails. But this very effort justifies their decision and even relieves them a little. They have done what society expected of them, and this is also important to them. They have not backed out of loving a child:

> If I had not gone through all of this I would have had the feeling it was my mistake because I wasn't willing to dare to make an attempt. No one, not even myself, can look me in the eye today and say, 'If you'd really wanted a biological child of your own, you could've had one.' (Interview in *MS.*, January–February 1989: 156)

Parents and children: a whole new realm

Complications of the kind just described are of course the exception. Most couples who want children actually have them. What happens next? What comes after a successful pregnancy and a smooth birth, when yearning to have a child results in having one?

First of all the child turns out to be a source of great joy, opening up new prospects, awakening intense feelings, enhancing the parents' lives with purpose and meaning, providing them with an emotional anchor: all these are not just hoped for but achieved in living with a real child, as many studies have confirmed (see Beck-Gernsheim 1989: 25ff.). Compared with having a family in the old days, an economic community, modern parenthood represents an enormous gain in emotional satisfaction.

This is, however, only one side of the picture. A great deal more is expected of parents than used to be the case, and their tasks have become much more demanding. In everyday life in agrarian societies children simply shared the daily routine and were not given any particular attention or care; they were thought of as unfinished, not quite complete people who scarcely had any needs of their own, and childhood was accordingly an unimportant transitional phase, which did not merit much interest. This is how it was in the Middle Ages:

> Of all the characteristics in which the medieval age differs from the modern, none is so striking as the comparative absence of interest in children . . . On

> the whole babies and young children appear to have been left to survive or die without great concern in the first five or six years. (Tuchmann 1978: 49, 52)

In large sections of the population all the way into the eighteenth and nineteenth centuries

> children just grew up as a matter of course . . . As a rule one could not talk of rearing them in any deliberate way . . . Parents were particularly harsh when inducing the children to work . . . Once the children had done their work, parents generally lacked both the time and the inclination to supervise and instruct them; children were largely left to themselves. (Schlumbohm 1983: 67–72)

Parents in pre-industrial society paid little attention to this role because there were few options open to them; according to the prevailing view of the world, what happened to the child lay largely in God's hands. This attitude changed only when children gradually came to be seen as people in their own right during the eighteenth and nineteenth centuries. Up to the end of the nineteenth century, however, religious beliefs and traditional attitudes remained unshaken so that child-rearing for many people was just a matter of course, following the rules laid down and passed on from one generation to the next. It was only in the course of the twentieth century that religion lost its hold and tradition was pushed aside, breaking up patterns of communal life based on class and status and turning away from something termed the common good. Modern people are meant to take their fates into their own hands – including the fate of their offspring. What is now expected, and recommended by all the experts, is that the child should be given the best possible start.

Only the best will do: modern imperatives

The idea that children need special attention and care to grow up into responsible citizens began its career in the nineteenth century but gained enormous impetus in the 1950s and 1960s. New advances in the fields of psychology, medicine and education showed how a child's future could be shaped. Physical handicaps which once had to be endured as strokes of fate have turned out to be treatable; psychological research in the 1960s focused on the significance of the first years of life, and equated poor care with lost developmental chances. At the same time a large number of people were better off, so that they too could afford to offer their children the special support previously restricted to a very few. And the politicians competed with one another in offering education to those sections of the population which once had to do without it.

All these factors contribute to putting pressure on the parents to do their bit. It is no longer enough to accept the child just as it is, with its physical and mental peculiarities or even deficiencies. The child itself has become the focus of parental effort. It is important to correct as many defects as possible (no more squints, stammering or bed-wetting) and to encourage skills (a boom for piano lessons, learning languages on holiday, tennis schools in the summer and ski schools in the winter). There is a whole new market with enticing offers to increase your child's competence, and soon enough the options begin to look like new obligations. If you can straighten her teeth or lengthen his leg, let them master more than the snow plough and learn some French, you probably will feel obliged to do this.

One can object that these are no more than guidelines for parents and do not represent the reality of bringing up a child. The question then is whether the new standards actually show up in the everyday work of living with children. The available data do not present anything like a coherent picture but they do suggest that parents are converting these models into action in a number of ways. Here are a few details. It is astonishing how much parents know about scientific advances – and not just educated middle-class ones. In a study of lower-class families one reads: 'The parents' knowledge of toilet training, nutritional matters and the various phases of development were generally speaking on a par with scientific discussions' (Wahl et al. 1980: 150). It is particularly important to lower-class families that 'their children should be better off than they were and they work hard to make that a reality' (1980: 41), at considerable material and personal sacrifice. A survey of working-class women sums it up:

> All this – attitudes on early childhood, punishment, empathy with childhood anxieties and wishes – indicates that something has changed in the child-rearing climate of worker families; attitudes and practices have become more child-centred. (Becker-Schmidt and Knapp 1985: 52)

All this may benefit the child – or perhaps not; when does too much attention become a nuisance? It is certainly clear that the parents, and especially the mother, must make a constant effort to meet the new demands. Her first task is to get hold of the latest information; the gap between what one knows about children and what one is supposed to know is always threatening to widen. On the one hand today's young adults generally know very little about raising children, far less than their equivalents did in previous generations. There simply are not so many children around as used to be the norm, and one is less likely to grow up in a large group of siblings; the first encounter with a small baby could well be with one's own firstborn. On the other hand young parents are expected to be mini-experts on their children; with all the knowledge accumulated over the past twenty years on how human beings develop, disseminated in popular form via the media, 'good' parents are considered to be those who make use of these advances for the benefit of their child. This trend, known in pedagogical circles as 'turning child-rearing into a science' implies exactly that: the parents' work involves increasing demands and increasing effort.

Because child-rearing is always a two-way relationship, 'science's conquest of the child' (Gstettner 1981) is also a conquest of the mother (and less often of the father). A net of theories is thrown over the children, and the mothers get caught in it:

> Whether it is a doubt about upbringing or school or what the child should wear or with whom it should go on holiday, when and where, or what it should eat or whether it is too small, too big, too loud, too quiet, too stooped, too straight, or any problem whatsoever, the advice is always the same: better consult your doctor. There is no magazine without a medical page, and periodicals like *Eltern* or *Unser Kind* have huge circulations. Experience becomes unimportant and hints from one's parents or grandparents are no longer up to the level of modern theorists; bringing up a child has been declared a science and can therefore be studied, learned and above all taught. (Sichrovsky 1984: 38–9)

Why don't mothers just go on strike, just stop bothering about what the experts advise? The trouble is they are hedged in, faced by a barrage of imperatives which invade their homes via television, the local newspaper and school reports. The message has a refrain: if you ignore your child's needs you risk damaging it, maybe even ruining its chances of getting on in life. 'Failing to get on in life' is something everyone understands, as getting on is absolutely vital in our mobile society.

A child that is not properly cared for will not be able to cope – this message running through guidebooks and magazines cannot fail to reach the parents. Refusing to take on the load would result in harsh sanctions; only under threat of punishment can they leave all the theories aside. And what makes it even harder, the sanctions would hit what is closest to their hearts, their beloved child. Working on behalf of a child is not just any kind of work but special; work and love are inextricably bound together, and the greater the love the more work seems acceptable. As the paediatrician Sanford Matthews put is : 'Any suggestion that her child will not reach his full potential – emotionally, athletically or intellectually – absolutely sears a woman's soul. And as a consequence her antennae are always up to improve her own performance' (quoted in *McCall's*, November 1983: 196).

In such circumstances only 'heartless' mothers, those 'unfit' to have children, could refuse to conform to the new rules. Culturally prescribed standards are hard to withstand and most mothers would rather do too much than too little, often suffering from the feeling that they could have tried harder. Educational theories suggest one is slacking and this drives the parents back to consult the experts. And so the circle is completed.

Of course it is not only information which is needed; more important is how it is applied. The implication is that the growing child's mother does her 'nurturing work' in several different ways, for the very reason that she believes a child can as it were be 'made'. Let us look more closely at this idea. Who does the making? Far more than ever before specialists are being called in to correct or prevent what nature has offered. These experts do their professional duty, from immunization to prescribing therapeutic exercises. But they can't actually be called in; the patient has to go to them. Can the infant go alone? Who carries out the preparation and follow-up work? Who takes the child to the dentist and physiotherapy, sits in the waiting-room with the child, drives it from one practice to the next, guards over its progress at school by checking on its homework and admonishing its spelling mistakes? In most cases it is the mother.

In fact she does much more, for even during the normal hours of everyday life where no direct intervention by specialists is required, the improving mood prevails – more subtly, but just as pervasively. Under its influence the mother acts as assistant for the child. In the words of an American women's magazine: 'Unstimulated time is a waste of baby time' (Lois Davitz in *McCall's*, July 1984: 126). For the sake of all-round stimulation mothers (less often fathers) trail round zoos and go to the circus, take the baby swimming, organize parties and outings with friends.

In many respects natural childhood is over and is being replaced by 'staged' childhood. Here too it is difficult to resist work because the staging is not just the parents' personal whim. It is an essential part of 'working to preserve status' (Papanek 1979). Where people feel compelled to protect their place in society by their own exertions, this drive is bound to reach the nursery. Having a child is not enough; it has to be brought up, and the parents find themselves contending with fears of sliding down the social scale as well as aspirations to climb up it. In his book entitled *America and Americans* John Steinbeck described this poignantly:

> No longer was it even acceptable that the child should be like his parents and live as they did; he must be better, live better, know more, dress more richly, and if possible change from father's trade to a profession. This dream became touchingly national. Since it was demanded of the child that he or she be better than his parents, he must be gaited, guided, pushed, admired, disciplined, flattered and forced. (1966: 94)

To sum up, one can conclude that life in a highly industrialized society makes the physical job of looking after a child somewhat easier (household gadgets, prepared foods, disposable nappies). But in return new topics keep cropping up which have to be tackled: 'Our times are obsessed with the physical, moral and sexual problems of childhood' (Ariès 1962: 560). These are on a different plane: 'The family today finds itself under *child-care pressure* quite unrivalled in history' (Kaufmann et al. 1982: 530). A child used to be a gift from God or occasionally an unwanted burden, but now it is above all 'somebody difficult to care for' (Hentig 1978: 34).

Love's curriculum

The imperative to give your child the best you can has considerable impact on everyday life together. Bathing and feeding, caressing and cuddling and playing all have an ulterior motive. Instead of just being what it is, each action is defined as a learning event and is meant to stimulate creativity, aid emotional development and encourage the child to learn. As long ago as 1783 a book on bringing up children advised:

> People like to play with infants. But this play could be made more useful than it is . . . Why is the child's attention directed to whatever the mother cares to show and not gradually to one thing or the other with some order? Why do people not lead a child by the hand and teach it in an orderly way to touch something, push it away, draw it closer, grip it, hold it and let it go, etc? Is this not the natural way to help them early to a certain physical dexterity? . . . In short, every game, every joke with infants or children who are not much older must deliberately and knowledgeably be directed to exercises of the speech organs and other parts of the body. (Basedow, quoted in Ostner and Pieper 1980: 112)

Over the past thirty years instructions like these have found their way into every home, thanks to the mass media, which are highly efficient conveyors of parental rules. No one gets left out, even in the most isolated mountain village; the advice columns and advertisements reach all levels of society. The result is a 'widespread tendency to turn childhood into an educational project within the family'. 'A child-centred culture taken for granted in educated and cultivated middle-class families is being recommended to lower- and working-class mothers in a teachable form' (Zinnecker 1988: 124). A favourite magazine for parents declares:

> A variety of sensations foster intelligence and initiative . . . Find ways of letting your child learn. If you offer it all kinds of impressions and chances to move freely you will help it to become an independent and active person. (*Eltern*, July 1988: 150)

It is not only daily life which is being instrumentalized. Even the most spontaneous signs of affection and pleasure get included in the programme:

> The unborn child especially can . . . absorb moods, stimuli, touching at a very early stage . . . Deliberate contact with its parents and their *loving care* act as *a motor to its development* . . . Lay your hands very lightly on your stomach and imagine you are embracing your baby with great *affection*. (*Eltern*, 1985/9: 17; my emphasis)

Maternal love is being changed into something offered by an expert, and in scientific writings just as much as in popular magazines the feeling is declared to be essential. In other words, loving your child is your duty. Here is an extract from a guidebook for young parents:

> [The aim has been] to show how dependent the child is on loving care and attention as the foundation of its intellectual and emotional development . . . To thrive the infant needs . . . the reliable care and love of a person with whom it can form a close bond, preferably its mother. (*Das Baby* 1980: 3, 23)

So maternal love is absolutely necessary but should not be regarded as work, at best a labour of love. It would also be wrong to follow the instructions too strenuously. Here is the paediatrician and psychoanalyst D. W. Winnicott speaking to mothers in 1969:

> Well, enjoy yourself! Enjoy being thought important. Enjoy letting other people look after the world while you are producing a new one of its

> members. Enjoy being turned on and almost in love with yourself, the baby is so nearly part of you . . . Enjoy all of this for your own sake, but the pleasure which you can get out of the messy business of infant care happens to be vitally important from the child's point of view . . . *the mother's pleasure has to be there* or else the whole procedure is dead, useless and mechanical. (Quoted in Schütze 1986: 91; my emphasis)

Because mother love is important but obviously difficult too there is a maze of rules attached to it. There are warnings about mothers loving in a harmful way – 'possessive, sacrificial, hostile, domineering, submissive, hungry for affection and half-hearted' (Schmidt-Rogge 1969, quoted in Schütze 1986: 123). An 'affection index' is being drawn up to enable one to measure the right level and keep its explosive potential under control (Grossmann and Grossmann 1980, quoted in Schütze 1986: 116–17). This means that even the subconscious is being included and prescriptions given for one's deepest feelings. It is a difficult undertaking requiring much preparation. Spontaneous reactions come to seem like archaic relics compared with the complicated task of having the right feelings at the right time in the right dosage. As the title of a book by W. E. Homan (1980) succinctly puts it: 'Children Need Love – Parents Need Advice'.

Rival loves

The expectations are high, and the parents find they do not have unlimited resources of money, patience, time or energy. If their child's needs are to be met, then the adults must scale down their own demands, rights and interests, often making considerable sacrifices. The effect of this is first of all felt by the person in charge of the daily routine, in most cases the mother:

> Our heightened awareness of the requirements children place on their immediate surroundings . . . increasingly leads to exclusive demands being made on at least one parent in the interest of the child, a process by which the interests of the parents, especially the mothers, is postponed for later phases in life, if not suppressed for ever. (Kaufmann et al. 1982: 531)

Since both parents feel the pressure, their relationship changes. 'Children weld a marriage together.' 'Children are a token and pledge of our love for one another.' These are notions commonly associated with wanting to have children. But what really happens? For one thing being a parent has become a complicated task and for another marriage has become a balancing act and a test of resilience. The dilemma is obvious: the more you pour your energy into your child, the less there is left for your partner. The effects of living in a child-centred family have been traced:

> intensive emotional involvement and time spent with the child leads to a cutback in the couple's relationship.
>
> Ideally it looks like this: if both parent have careers, they devote their available free time to the child . . . For working couples, that implies that little leeway is left for the partners to talk to one another. If one of them is detailed to take care of the child, the other one can keep up outside contacts and the like during this time. While this may satisfy one's needs to do something not connected with the child, one's interest in sharing time together which played a role before the child's birth has to be neglected. If only one parent is employed – as a rule the father – then the situation is not very different. Since the woman spends all day with the children, she would like to do something other than concern herself with them in the evening, but her conversation with her husband is more or less reduced to reporting how things went with the children. (Schütze 1988: 107–8)

Among all the books on child-rearing one can now come across a few which look into the dangers of exaggerated parenting. This is how it turns out:

> After the child is born the parents are often so bound up in taking care of it that they have no strength left for looking after one another . . . All expectations have to be reduced for the sake of the child. Quite often there is neither time nor energy left for the partners to talk to each other. Everything has to be subordinated to the needs of the child. All that remains for the parents are the child's leftovers. Over long stretches managing everyday life can be so demanding that the parents do nothing but keep going and drop into bed quite exhausted in the evening . . . Not only the man and woman but their relationship drowns in the daily routine and becomes in a sense just a matter of routine itself. There are no longer any highs. Nothing, or at least very little that is exciting or pleasant happens between them. The intense feelings in the first days after the birth give way to a state of monotony. Some couples cannot even tell whether they still love each other or not. They are together, to be sure, but they have little to do with each other apart from their shared concern for the child. (Bullinger 1986: 57, 39, 56)

From interviews and accounts one can see how the couple's relationship takes a back seat wherever the high-flown ideals of child-rearing experts take over. The refrain is the same: it is enormously enriching to have a child and provides both parents with a new shared role. Then comes the 'but':

> In the first months we were euphoric, everything was stimulating and exciting. We were always so tired that we never got round to talking about ourselves. We thought, though, that things would change. But nothing or hardly anything changed. Having a child is so exacting, we're always so tired and worn out that our relationship is the last thing to get attention. (Quoted in Reim 1984: 101)

So it is not surprising that the strain increases and both become irritable, that tensions rise with the lack of time to talk things over:

> While our child thrived and my husband and I became increasingly certain of ourselves in our roles as parents, our feelings for one another got temporarily left behind ... We only began to think out loud together when our child was eleven months old, about how we could focus on ourselves and were responsible for what happened to us as well as what happened to the child. (Quoted in Reim 1984: 19)

'If marriage changes its meaning and turns into a place for socializing children ... conflicts between the partners are inevitable' (Nave-Herz 1987: 26). The good sides – having time, being patient, finding the energy, sharing feelings – tend to be directed at the child. Under the new conditions it is no longer true that children tie people together, or at least only in part (Chester 1982).

When love hits out

What about the children? What do they get out of the hopes and expectations so fervently directed at them? The answer is disputed or, to put it more elegantly, the topic is still a matter of controversy between the researchers. Most authors acknowledge that the move from pre-modern to modern society has opened up new opportunities for children – individual potential can be discovered and furthered, class, gender and status are no longer such handicaps, wholesale neglect and brutal indifference are things of the past. If one reads descriptions of how childhood used to be in the less developed parts of Europe – monotonous, harsh, repressive, arduous, exhausting – one can hardly regret that these very unidyllic times are over (Ledda 1978; Wimschneider 1987). Nonetheless there has been a growing suspicion that being cosseted also has its disadvantages. The line of thinking runs as follows.

Theories on child-care have tended to make childhood into a programme requiring careful surveillance and monitoring of the various steps and possible deficits. The child is seen as a dependent creature always in need of an adult to define, care for and administer its physical, emotional, current and future needs. Under the cloak of love the parents can hide their delight in wielding so much power: 'Equipped with the appropriate magazines and books, parents plague their children with an effusion of emotion that turns the nursery into a didactic hothouse' (Gronemeyer 1989: 27). Earlier in this century Ellen Key described this effect:

> The child is always supposed to stop doing one thing or do something different, to find something different or want something different from what he is doing or finding or wanting; he is always dragged in a different direction than his own inclinations lead him. And all this is done out of love, attentiveness, delight in judging and helping and advising, to carve and polish the little chunk of human material into a perfect example in the series 'model children'. (Quoted in Liegle 1987: 29)

The current situation is paradoxical; while popular scientific literature on parenting still pours from the presses, bringing new suggestions with each book, the experts are already retreating slowly from positions they used to defend. Some authors admit that they are 'renouncing the pedagogic side' (Honig 1988). Once upon a time it looked as though proper parenting would result in confident and autonomous children. Now the doubts are getting louder: what looked like 'selfless love on the part of the child-rearer today seems remorseless, and partisanship for the child like a perfected form of control and discipline: like training' (ibid.: 71).

This critical viewpoint is backed by the results of empirical research as well as experience with family therapy (e.g. Lempp 1986; Richter 1969). It is by no means always in the children's interest if adults – especially mothers – continually practise self-denial. As psychologists know, a need which has been suppressed does not just vanish but surfaces elsewhere, turning against child and partner in more or less covert resentment. It is very easy to project all one's own expectations on to the child, and bully it with encouragement. Often children are 'pressed into a role in which they are supposed to bolster up the mother's self-esteem' (Neidhardt 1975: 214). All this can mean a stifling climate in the small nuclear family in which hostility as well as love prosper.

If a modern family lavishes a great deal of attention on a child it is not for unselfish reasons; such behaviour shows more than a hint of 'possessiveness' (Ariès 1962: 562). With the future lying ahead the child confronts its parents with their own biographies and ambitions, disappointments and fears, including old dreams of being a huge success and making it to the top. Anyone suggesting that 'my child should have it better than I did' is not just thinking of the child, but mostly of him/herself.

And what if the great expectations prove unfulfillable? Many parents no doubt back down gracefully and continue to love their child. But sometimes this does not happen. There is another side to today's families, one which is often overlooked, forgotten or repressed: attacks on children from members of the family are on the rise. An increasing number of children and young people are being physically maltreated, sexually abused and emotionally rejected. On the basis of recent research on this phenomenon it is estimated that at least 300,000 to 400,000 children and adolescents are affected – that is roughly 3% of the 11 million children and young people under eighteen years of age in Germany.

There are certainly several reasons behind this development. It is, however, clear that it is often the parents' good intentions which end up producing exactly the opposite; disappointed hopes turn into frustration and aggression. Here are the conclusions drawn from one such investigation:

> Parents want 'the best for my child' and often do not notice that for this very reason they fail to recognize what the child really wants or needs. The trend to one-child families . . . hastens this development . . . A large proportion of parents nowadays are pushing their children either openly or (usually) covertly to get high marks at school and start up the professional ladder. In families where the adolescents fail to live up to their parents' expectations, a long battle results over future plans and there is an increased likelihood of tension and strain . . . Parents who fear that low marks or rebellious behaviour could cost their child its chances of finding a foothold in a very tight job market become nervous and irritable, which can quickly lead to aggressive behaviour in both generations. (Hurrelmann 1989: 12)

The same studies look into the special motives behind having children in our society. Let us recall: children are no longer needed as helping hands or as heirs, and the reward for having them lies almost exclusively in their emotional value. As the experts see it, this is an

> intense but equally very uncertain and crisis-ridden kind of reward . . . Compared with pre- and early industrial society today's relationships between parents and children are highly charged and intense. For both

> sides, for parents and children, it is however becoming more and more difficult to deal with this precious asset. (Ibid.)

One could conclude from such findings that the nuclear family is becoming excessively emotional, and the atmosphere in the small family circle dangerously over-heated. There is a similar greenhouse effect in many adult partnerships, but in that case if pressure rises too high there is a safety valve: one can at least consider separation. There is no divorce from a child, and that is the decisive difference; no legitimate escape route offers itself, and society categorically states that 'parents love their children.'

If one thinks this through, it becomes comprehensible that where there is love there is often hostility, an idea that at first seems strange, incongruous and irritating. The two have become linked, not by coincidence but as an outcome of social change: love in conjunction with anxiously high hopes is volatile and can quickly deteriorate into bitter disappointment and cruelty. We mostly prefer to repress such insights. Even family research has long turned a blind eye, but we must be prepared to come to terms with what the police records say. Love is one of our great achievements, the foundation of our relationships between men and women, parents and children – but we cannot have it without its darker sides, which sometimes emerge for a second and sometimes linger for years: disappointment, bitterness, rejection and hatred. The road from heaven to hell is much shorter than most people think.

5

EVE'S LATE APPLE

Or the future of love

Let us now find our way to those private corners where modern fundamentalists worship – euphemized, concealed and sanctified as love, marriage and family. How much easier it would be if we could just escape to other continents and cultures, just turn our backs on the whole issue. But there is no escaping, no shrugging our shoulders and leaving; research into love is like investigating our own secret gods. We are heading for the swirling mists of inwardness, the Platonic caves of the emotions, the furnished rooms of affection and the sacrificial altars of hate and despair. We are aiming for the place where every man and woman assumes he or she can find him/herself – in the palaces and hovels of love designed and built by the welfare state and the job market.

This time it is the future which interests us, as it will probably help us to understand the present as well as offering us a peek round the corner into the next century. What will become of people and the contradictory visions of love which they so ardently project on to one another?

One view claims that seeking happiness in marriage and family life is about as sensible as propping your ladder against a raincloud. The wishes out of which people today and in the future can cobble together their daily lives lead in the opposite direction to what a technological society preaches and expects: an efficient, mobile and market-oriented work-force. Men and women would have to become revolutionarily selfless in a society built from top to bottom on getting on, abiding by contracts, earning money and fitting in with what others expect. They would have to believe in fairy tales, in this case related to a particular person – please insert the name! The stork bringing the babies and Santa Claus bringing the parcels are the guarantors of this family bliss;

happy families are those who spend a large part of the day building castles in the air.

Perhaps it is true that love and family are the place for all the nons – non-commercial, non-calculating, non-exploiting and so forth. Perhaps this non-ness is not an anachronism or a superfluous ornament but a crucial and fundamental statement, a refusal which becomes a form of orientation now that we have lost other signposts like the class system and political utopias. If all this has a core of truth, then the modern nuclear family, seen in historical terms, is an extremely fragile construction likely to disintegrate under the pressure which made it and seemed to give it stability: industrialization, market economies and technological advance (see chapter 1 above, 'Industrial society: a modern feudal society', p. 25).

Of course one can assert that the family is indispensable or possibly even functionally essential. But even this highest accolade awarded by sociologists, perpetuating a male dream of how things should be, is not likely to help much. One does not need second sight to see what will happen to this frail 'essential' weighed down by so many hopes. Just draw a line into the future and take modern developments a step further. What happens if nothing changes and – this is the leading question – the chaos of love is tidied up and properly organized along modern lines: equality, carefully worded contracts, the right approach and the right theories?

Looking at it from the most promising vantage point and peering into the future, it looks as though there would be no great difference between loving and, say, growing apples or book-keeping. The idea behind this scenario is as follows: the secular religion known as love is suffering the fate of other religions; it is losing its mythology and turning into a rational system. The most probable outcome is that (genetic) engineers and legal documents win. What we shall have is a social hybrid of market forces and personal impulses, an ideal of love (or marriage or parenthood) which is safe, calculable and medically optimized. One can already see signs that this is going to happen.

Awakening false hopes: back to the nuclear family

When discussing the future of 'the' family, people often start out from false premises. They compare the familiar pattern father–mother–child with a vague notion of 'no family', or assume that another kind of family is replacing the nuclear one. It is much more likely – assuming the analysis presented here is right – that instead of one kind replacing the other there will be a huge variety of ways of living together or apart which will continue to exist side by side. It will be characteristic that individuals experience several forms in the course of their lives – being single, living together before and during marriage, living with others, various parenthoods after one or two divorces and so on.

One trend, however, which is not difficult to predict is the illusion of returning to the nuclear family, making yesterday into the model for tomorrow. For many people, fleeing from marriage and family is a sign of excessive egotism which has to be fought with targeted regulations to bring especially the women back into the fold. Since it is the women who want to gain 'a life of their own' outside their given roles as house-workers and husband supporters, their private and political efforts naturally meet with scepticism and resistance. The measures to save 'the' family are oriented on the standard domestic norms, with the husband as bread-winner, the wife as home-maker and two or three children – a norm which has existed only since the early nineteenth century. Despite the women's efforts to become liberated and independent there are powerful factors at work backing demands that they go back to the kitchen.

The huge majority of women are a long way from being economically independent and professionally secure. It is true that the sum total of women in work, including married women, has risen continually, so that in 1988 almost every second married woman (in Germany) was employed compared with 57.6% of unmarried women. Among the men more than four in five were employed.[1] Put another way this means that at least half of all women remain dependent on their husband's financial support. Rising unemployment and the shrinking labour market are tending to conserve and restabilize the sexes' traditional roles. Women are being released from wage labour to return to marital support, a move backed by many of them when they want to have children. Both factors stabilizing the traditional female role – being unemployed and wanting to have children – could prove very effective in polarizing biographical patterns, and if the young women are not as well qualified as the men they will again find themselves at the bottom end of the educational and vocational hierarchy.

This political confusion of past and future is aided by successfully dramatizing the mother's role, especially in institutional circles, which stirs up social disapproval for the working mum and gives her a bad conscience. Failing to set up day-care services or arranging nursery school hours so that no mother can coordinate looking after her child with a job have the same result. The battles waged for women's rights in private and in public are really about something else; a man who with male cunning sings the praises of motherhood is not forced to decide between his career and his children or plead to be allowed to accept promotion. Nursery school hours making a career difficult or impossible are an effective little lever in helping to restore the old order even against the mother's will; they become a tool in 'lowering the level of unemployment' by preventing women from looking for work.

But anyone who imagines that the family can be saved by closing the doors to the job market has overlooked what sort of people are involved. It remains completely unclear how young women will respond when they realize that their vociferous interest in having a good job is disappointed and find themselves having to rely on their partners for financial support. It is equally unclear whether a correspondingly large number of young men are willing (or even able, given their own professional problems) to take on the yoke of being the bread-winner. In any case the discrepancies between the women's expectations, systematically awakened by equal educational opportunities, and the cool facts facing them infiltrate into their private worlds and erupt as arguments and frustration. It is not difficult to predict that couples will have to bear a private load of strife and bitterness which modern society has shoved on to their shoulders. At first sight the barriers in the job market seem to shore up the nuclear family, but in fact they fill the corridors of the divorce courts and the waiting rooms of marriage counsellors.

At the same time women are again destined to be poor. Anyone seeking to force women out of jobs and back to the kitchen sink ought to acknowledge that in the face of the rising number of divorces this means reserving the gaps in the social security system for women.

This fact highlights the fundamental error of trying to restore the old status quo for the sexes in private and public life. For one thing this contravenes legal positions in modern democratic society which offer equal rights irrespective of gender and make success dependent on personal achievement. For another the upheavals in family life are misleadingly labelled private problems and all links with social changes ignored or denied.

Look at some common suggestions on how to stick the disintegrating marriages together again: take part in a 'family training' or get professional help in choosing your spouse; all we lack is enough marriage counsellors and the difficulties would vanish; the real threat to married life lies in pornography, or legal abortion or feminism, we must do something to stop them. And so on. Social contexts and historical developments are simply passed over.

To borrow an image from Max Weber, modernization is not a carriage you can climb out of at the next corner if you don't like it. Anyone really meaning to restore family conditions as they were in the 1950s would have to turn the clock back. This would entail not just indirectly keeping women away from jobs by subsidizing motherhood or polishing up the image of housework, but openly denying them opportunities and education. The wage differential would have to be increased, legal rights reversed. Perhaps the real trouble began with universal suffrage; at all events the women would have to be prevented from acquiring information – perhaps a lock on the television, and censored newspapers. In short all the modern achievements shared equally by men and women would have to be redefined as exclusively male property, for ever.

Being equal means being on your own: contradictions between work and family

The other possibility would be for women to be genuine equals in all areas of society. The universal modern principle of equal rights would be vindicated, patriarchal divisions in housework, parliaments, factories and management overcome. In the women's movement discussions often link demands for equal treatment with claims to alter 'the male working world'. The struggle is to become economically secure, to wield power, to share decision-making but also to introduce more 'feminine' attitudes and values into public life. What exactly equality means is not defined. If equality is pursued in the sense that everyone is a mobile member of the labour force, then this implies a society of singles.

The logic behind modern life presupposes a single person (Gravenhorst 1983: 17), for market economies ignore the needs of family, parenthood and partnership. Anyone expecting employees to be flexible and mobile without paying any regard to their lives as private individuals is aiding the break-up of family life by putting the market first. The fact that work and family are incompatible remained concealed as long as marriage was synonymous with woman at home and man at work; it has surfaced with great turbulence now that each couple has to work out its own division of labour. Demanding equality along market lines has the effect of turning the partners into rivals and individuals, competing with one another for the good things in modern life. This is no mere speculation; in Germany and elsewhere the number of single-person households and single parents is rising sharply. It also becomes clear from the sort of life people are expected to lead in such circumstances.

Running one's life alone has several built-in hazards against which one must take precautions. It is important to find and maintain contacts for all kinds of occasions; a web of friendships has to be made and guarded, even if this is one of the pleasures of life alone and the charm of brief encounters is not to be underestimated. But all this presupposes one has a good job as a source of income, self-esteem and social supports, and this too has to be tended and defended. A private cosmos can be created round one's own ego with its idiosyncrasies, strengths and weaknesses.

The more successful this effort proves, the greater the danger that it will prove an insurmountable obstacle to any close partnership, however much one longs for one. Life as a single person generates a deep longing to love and be loved by somebody but at the same time makes it difficult or impossible to integrate this somebody into a life which is really 'one's own'. This life is only possible in the absence of the other; there is no space left for him (or her). Everything is planned round avoiding feeling lonely: all kinds of contacts making different demands on one's time, daily habits, a well-filled calendar and carefully planned moments to recover from social life, all designed to alleviate any fear of being left out which hovers behind the dynamic façade. This delicate balance is imperilled by a real relationship however much one longs for one. Every effort to achieve independence turns out to sabotage intimacy and the prison gates close on a loner, who in wanting to defend 'a life of his/her own' puts another row of bricks on to the surrounding walls.

The kind of existence led by single people is not a peculiar side-effect of social change; it is the archetypal existence behind a full market economy. According to the logic of the market we do not have any social ties, and the more we accept this the less we can maintain close friendships. So here there is a case of paradoxical social behaviour in which a high level of social contacts prevents the formation of deep relationships.

Such reflections are at the moment more speculation than description. There is, however, no denying that the picture applies to a growing section of the population, and is what we have to look forward to if both sexes demand equal rights. Everybody – including parts of the women's movement – has the right to expect that offers once made to men should now be extended to women, and assert that women are as useful as members of the job world as men are. They should however realize that this road does not lead to a happy world of co-operative equals but to separateness and diverging interests.

Post-marital marriage: extended and serial families after divorce

Someone from, say, the twenty-second century looking back at the industrial middle ages we live in as the twentieth century turns to the twenty-first will probably smile and be puzzled: there were so many political pressure groups, and people voted, made suggestions, coalitions and plots. Everything was looked into and chewed over in the major media. What got left out, simply ignored, were the significant changes which heralded a whole new age. They took place surreptitiously, in the normal course of the day, almost unnoticed by politicians hastening busily from committee to constituents' meeting, but had a radical and profound effect. How extraordinary that the population continued to stare at their governments and politicians while the decisive factors slipped in by the back door and turned their world upside down.

Why this happened is difficult to explain, and to find the reasons one would have to put aside some certainties which industrial society has dictated. To use a comparison, people arguing about rearranging the seating in a moving train should not be surprised if they fail to notice how fast it is going and where it is headed.

As products of an industrial and capitalist society we have come to think of change as normal. It is therefore no wonder that in concentrating on what is politically feasible – moving the seats – we tend to forget the larger dimensions; the curious thing, however, is that in reorganizing the seating people assume they are helping to decide the train's route, whom it mows down and where they would like it to halt.

What are the back doors which permit revolutionary ideas to infiltrate normality? One of them was mentioned in the previous section: equality in the labour market, meaning that everybody can participate irrespective of the gender limits imposed by classical industrial society. In the following sections we shall come across some other back-door factors, and here is divorce, seen as a revolving door between an old and a new age.

Divorce as such is nothing new; on the contrary, it typifies modern thinking in that something given and lasting is conceived as being revocable and subject to change like everything else on our horizon. One can go further and say that the contradictory nature of marriage as recommended by the church, a free choice which can never be revoked, has been revealed and marital commitment returned to the partners as a matter of agreement, the way it started. So what?

On the other hand, as divorce becomes normal, the doors are opened to long-drawn-out and painful adjustments which shift and rearrange how the sexes and generations live with one another. During the initial phase this fact remains concealed, with good reason. Establishing the new principle depends first of all on describing it as fairly insignificant, before it can become the most normal thing in the world, one of our modern watchwords disguising the often spectacular consequences of supposedly normal actions. Also, the change takes place in private, as part of an individual fate affecting this and that person and their marriage and families, under a magnifiying glass, as it were, and in slow motion. The macroscopic structural changes cannot be seen or experienced directly; one can find them only through the spectacles of statistics and realize they have been hatched out of normal social eggs a few decades later.

According to social myth and shortsighted therapists the marital relationship ends with divorce (after an appropriate period for dealing with the pain involved). This view falsely equates legal (sexual and spatial) separation with the social and emotional realities of marriage breakdown. Family research[2] is only gradually waking up from its drowsy fixation on the nucleus of the family and discovering to its astonishment the other phenomenon of 'post-marital marriage', while still ignoring its opposite, 'intra-familial divorce'.[3] Like someone who has lost an arm but still tries to use it, divorced people live their marriages long after they have separated, with the ex-spouse still occupying as much mental space as missing and mourning over the loss of him/her leaves behind.

Only someone equating marriage with sex, loving and living together can make the mistake that divorce means the end of marriage. If one concentrates on problems of material support, on the children and on a long common biography, divorce is quite obviously not even the legal end of marriage but transforms itself into a new phase of post-marital 'separation marriage'.

In this phase the divorced couple encounters dimensions which prove impervious to separation. These divorce-resistant sides of marriage, on which the spouses rub their souls raw and bloody, include the indissoluble commonality of the children and a remembered identity as a couple. Such themes and forms of negative cohabitation can occupy people's minds when living apart just as much as when they were together:

> When I saw you last time, you said something that would fit my open wound as well as a manhole cover . . . 'I hope that our relationship will become normal again someday' . . . Good God, the way you talk to me?! I want to reply now, because I couldn't do it when I was sitting opposite you; it was as if I was paralysed. Listen, I don't share your hope. I won't see you again in a cold, extinguished present. It may seem desirable and comfortable to you for us to become serene people who will meet someday like two veterans of a great love battle, the kind that award each other the medal of honour for bravery and forgiveness. Two lucky escapees who once chased each other through heaven and hell, and now sit peacefully in a garden; the lawn-sprinkler revolves like a dragonfly stuck

> in place and I play with your children while you chat a bit about your professional problems and I'm ashamed to add anything about the problems of my loneliness and my poverty. Your wife brings us tea and discreetly disappears . . . You've got to know: this vision horrifies me! I detest the idea that time will conquer us too, just as it overruns everything else. Why does no one stand up against it anyway? It is not as omnipotent as people always think and then do nothing and just leave the battlefield on time without a fight. No grass should ever grow over anywhere I am, was or will be. And if I have to keep on writing like this forever in order to keep you, I wouldn't hesitate for a moment, because I am so close to you; that way I can preserve us and speak to you and enjoy the good life I used to have. (Strauss 1987)

Anyone assuming that the legal act of divorce is a criterion to distinguish between an old and a new marriage fails to realize that marriages overlap and intersect outside family boundaries. Divorced people remained linked to one another on numerous levels, including support payments, children and a shared biography.

Who pays whom: at the latest when one leaves one marriage and enters into another the notion of a bread-winner collapses. What may have been good enough for one marriage is never good enough for two or more, so that – given the same amount of work and same amount of income – after remarrying all one can do is share the shortages (Lucke 1990).

Parenthood is divisible but cannot be terminated. Father and mother live separately after a divorce but they remain parents and have to renegotiate what this means in daily life. Family is thus divided into a marriage, which can break up, and post-marital parenthood which divides into motherhood and fatherhood. Post-marital parenthood (usually) requires help by the courts because otherwise antagonisms seem irreconcilable. Formally shunting child or children between their separated parents presents mother and father with the residue of 'common ground', offering them an attenuated and cryptic kind of family life which cannot be brought to an end. This may mean all sorts of things depending on the individuals involved, but the real impact of being separated parents will make itself felt as soon as one of them decides to move, forcing both to renegotiate.

If one cannot equate social with legal separation for the adults concerned, one can do it even less for the children. Perhaps the divorced parents are at least starting a new life, spatially and legally, but the children begin a double life in which they have to split themselves emotionally and physically between two families now negatively related to one another, with all the ambiguities, forced secrecy and divided loyalties this implies, and their parents' jealousy of one another as a weapon which they can use for their own ends.

However one defines the multi-dimensional commitment of children of divorced parents to different families, and no matter how great the effects on them in the short and long term may be, children symbolize the continuity, the indivisibility of marriage, even if the family no longer has an address. The children after all cannot get divorced from their parents; all they can do is choose with whom they want to spend most of their time, which means rejecting the other parent in this respect, and try to work out a way of living with two interlinked but unfriendly families.

Divorce then is only possible to a limited extent and in certain ways. It is designed for the adults, not the children, and hence not the family as a whole. Seen from below, through the children's eyes, their parents remain the core of their family, although they have nowhere to live out family life. Being parents has to happen somehow outside the range of their new nuclear families or remains of families – sitting for hours in the park or a café (incidentally rather like two-career couples who are both fully mobile and have to arrange where to be together).

This shows that equating divorce with the break-up of the family is a partisan view describing the adults' wishes. Having recognized this bias, one can see that divorce drives a wedge between marriage and parenthood just as it splits up marriage and family. Divorce shatters the combination of marriage and family but does not destroy the family; it remains a reality for the children, if only in the compulsion they feel somehow to stay close to their biological parents despite the antagonisms they may face in their new nuclear families.

While marriages can be cancelled and remade, families cannot; they live on in the persons of the children who move quietly across the boundaries of new partnerships and families. Correspondingly, the image of the family after parents have separated is fundamentally ambiguous for children who find themselves living with one parent or another in a new nuclear family; or at least the child's image of the family does not tally with what other members perceive. Such children belong simultaneously to two different families; as well as almost insoluble emotional tangles, having overlapping families can also mean social and material advantages and support in planning their own lives.

This gaping difference between the realities surrounding marriage and family life becomes even clearer if one looks at the grandparents. If the divorce settlement goes badly, the parents' parents may be robbed of their grandchildren through no fault of their own. This applies particularly to the kind of social contact usually taken for granted. At the same time, however, like the children, they personify the remains of the family which divorce divided up.

Finally, as divorce has become normal, the relations between the members of the small nuclear family have undergone a metamorphosis. This is obvious where the biological and social parents are different people, and it is hard for the onlooker to discern who originally belonged to whom. As the number of divorces rises, children actually growing up with their biological parents become the exception (see Gross and Honer 1990). It is far more common that they grow up in mixed families in which children from different marriages form a new, temporary, no-longer-nuclear family, with 'brothers' and 'sisters' who may well come from other social circles or nationalities. Divorce, then, in the long term systematically loosens the links between biology and society which used to be fused in the archetypal small family. One could even say that just as reproductive medicine with its sophisticated methods for automating non-marital insemination severs the links between social, legal and biological parenthood, widespread divorce automatically does the same.

There are a number of points worth noting where relationships between the sexes and the generations are split up and remixed by multiple divorce. For one thing they make whole networks of interrelated extended families, whose structure is difficult to see through from the outside. In a certain sense divorce can run counter to aspirations of individualism and making it alone. But it is certainly not true, whatever the prevailing view has been up to now, that divorce just means moving from one family to the next and that it therefore has no impact on what happens in private life. Such a view is plausible only if one ignores the various overlapping dimensions inside and between families and insists on peering exclusively at the so-called nucleus of the so-called nuclear family.

It takes quite a lot of empirically fortified wishful thinking to overlook the upheavals in social and family structures being brought about by millions of divorces. Family research which continues to think in terms of nuclear families and suggests by amassing data on them that they are not subject to change will someday find itself on the shelf beside the other curious products of a blind empiricism.

Eve's late apple: the enforced liberation of the male

Whereas women's liberation is on everyone's lips – and, even more than that, is in individual cases capable of erupting into the calmest family circles overnight, one only rarely hears of a man breaking out of his accustomed role. All right, there is the obligatory mid-life crisis and there are the long-haired, the sensitive men, the single fathers' groups and homosexual clubs. The father changing nappies by now plays a prominent role in bank ads. It has also become clear that there is no natural connection between a penis, a career and a rocket. Arguing all this out again would mean duplicating the literature on the subject (Simmel 1985; Ehrenreich 1984; Goldberg 1979; Pilgrim 1986; Theweleit 1987; Brod 1987; Hollstein 1988).

What remains unclear is whether and how this deeply cracked male shell is to be removed and what a man, having thought about himself and his role in life, would be like, apart from either compulsively masculine or the prescribed opposite, an unsuccessful version of a misunderstood female wish. Worse still, little attempt has been made to discuss this, which may be no accident. Perhaps imitating women's liberation or retreating into categorical rejection of its peculiarities and excesses are really signs that men have not yet clarifed their positions for themselves.

The male images that fire the women's movement oscillate between patriarchal oppressor, sex machine and scientifically blinkered threat to the environment, on the one side, and on the other, hen-pecked husband, emotional cripple, semen donor and childish family appendage. In order to clarify these idealized negations a little it makes sense to stress one point: the theory of master and servant, which Hegel developed and Marx refined, and which the women's movement now applies to men and women, is not correct and never has been, for a number of reasons.

According to the traditional gender divisions, the male is only a master in the sense of not having to do work in the house, but he has to become a servant to bring home his wages. In other words, his phantom position in the family presumes he puts up with being a dependent wage-earner. Repressing his own interests and doubts, adapting in advance to the demands of a higher power, was and still is in many cases the bitter price paid by the legendary patriarch, endured tacitly or with a lot of grumbling.

The man's subservience to the organization employing him, his professional egotism, his concern with competition and career represent the other side of his concern for his family. His 'family feeling' does not in traditional terms show in his commitment to the household, but paradoxically in subordinating himself to a career which takes material form in the household budget. His fate is a kind of altruistic self-repression. He swallows hard time after time not for his own benefit but because he has those hungry mouths to feed at home.

The façades of male power and male desires originated in the competitive rat race of the work world. In traditional social structures a man is not permitted to take the direct path to lasting sexual satisfaction; only in the matrimonial bed is he allowed to enjoy in a legal manner the encounters which his none too secret impulses urge upon him. The way to the matrimonial bed used to lead, however, through the factory gate and to the physical and symbolic burdens men had to bear. The ideal male's behaviour consists of resisting and sublimating sexual drives, acquiring skills with which to conquer the world and finding a place in the machinery of an organization which is tailored to faceless, indistinguishable employees; only then can he explore and develop his own alien personality, tenderness, love and sexual needs. Male culture is a repressing and repressed culture, for its prerequisite is abstract, success at work, quite the opposite of male and female interest in one another and the spontaneity of love and loving. In the end there is nothing left except the daily grind. A man is a man. Work is work. That's it.

Just how irrelevant the master–servant idea is in the relations between the sexes is shown by the fact that a master needs a servant, whereas in the age of women's lib a man is no longer dependent on a woman, or more precisely no longer dependent on a wife. In the power struggle which has broken out between the sexes, the men's cards are quite good; sex and love are no longer tied to marriage and material support. If a man wants he can say 'love and/or sex, yes, marriage, no', and in doing so he furthers the women's cause. Someone who has no interest in feeding an unemployed female for the rest of his life must count on his partner having a job, and so advances two things at the same time: the financial and social independence of his girlfriend and his own liberation from the age-old yoke of being used by others to preserve his family.

At this point it becomes clear that men's liberation is a passive affair, and therefore tends to remain silent. It consists of enjoying the renunciation forced on him. A man does not have actively to escape – as women escape from their roles as housekeepers and mothers – to try out another world, of work and science and politics. He has all that behind him; for him it is conformity. But under the auspices of their struggle for sexual freedom and professional acknowledgement the women have freed the men of earlier duties. One probably unintentional result of women's lib is men's lib. They were robbed of the role of being sole earner? Fine, that means the women are no longer entitled to expect financial support. Women discover their sexual side? Fine, that means the protectrix of the marital monopoly on sex abandons her efforts; there are more willing women around. Companionship, sex, love and affection are no long in bondage to a wedding ring – in the interests of the women themselves.

Seen in this light it could well be that men – often of course quite unaware of their objective cleverness – are encouraging the women to liberate themselves not in an arbitrary manner but as proxies for male liberation. Men seem to engage in self-liberation as spectators, stunned and well-meaning, by encouraging the women's rebellion against their traditional roles. Their own liberation – not having to be the sole earner – falls like a ripe apple into their laps. Eve's late apple. Let it be said that the old 'king of the castle' role is being revived in this version of letting the women do the chores. And let it also be said that narrow-minded men who declare their outrage at women's liberation apparently have little insight into their own situation.

This gift to men, who still do not realize what luck they have with their misfortune, of course has the drawback that women's lib is not only happening without the men, as it were, but is also directed against them. It is a hollow kind of freedom, grafted on to something else, not really freedom at all. The men find themselves sitting in the middle of a world which no longer exists. Smoke from the feminists' gunpowder is swirling round their heads. The beams are cracking. The concrete monuments to their masculinity are crumbling away. Their first duty, they think, is to notice nothing and pretend life is as nice as it always used to be. If necessary with force. Hidden force. Perhaps there is still time to adopt countermeasures and pay the women back for treating them so badly.

The fact that their burden as bread-winner has disappeared with the women's revolt does not matter. The women chose to do it themselves. That their obsession with getting on, getting as much as possible, 'let's get on with it', ruins any real pleasure, including their own, also does not matter. That's just the way men are.

Certainly there used to be a point where everything came together – career, put up with it, here's the next step, keep going – and suddenly it has turned into a big empty nothingness. The person you know best and least, that artificially produced numbskull in his office armour, his casual uniform, would have to be stripped bare, discovered, felt. Use your eyes, for instance, for a transcontinental holiday through your own life and your own body.

This might mean of course that men would run wild or get out of hand, upsetting the mechanisms at home and at work. They could turn things upside down, question routines, inquire, interrogate, not give in, become rebellious and insist on running against the grain. Or they might just begin to mould, go bad, become the parasite they always were, among other things. Family work does not mean taking on exaggerated ideas about cleanliness. Should a man go so far as to dust under the bed? Maybe a bit of dirt is nice. Maybe the hole in my sock is becoming. Maybe the misplaced pair of shorts enriched by the remains of a cheese sandwich and a dirty fork has something to do with art, an idea the artist Joseph Beuys would have envied. Maybe his 'Greasy Corner' is merely a weak version of male ideas on beauty and housekeeping. Get started, try it out, let the dirty sheets pile up, fight, laugh, get stuck in the chaos lurking a few inches away from order. But live, simply start living, and never stop again. Wishful thinking in view of the real world which men believe they inhabit, without noticing that it hardly exists any longer.

This much is true: so-called 'young adult males' are increasingly unwilling to enter into marriage with women who have no professional training. It is also true that most men have altered their attitudes and strategies towards women's liberation. Men pretend to be open and broad-minded. If 'Home sweet home' is passé, the new focal point for the old order has already been spotted and fixed: the child, and with it the 'indispensable' mother. By transforming the women's issue into a mother-and-child issue – with the active participation of women – many men believe they can lean back and make themselves comfortable on the sofa again.

The pay-off comes, at the latest, before, during and after divorce when parenthood is split up and motherhood turns against fatherhood. That is when men, who suddenly rediscover their fatherly feelings, are hit by their legally backed absence from the family, which during the marriage seemed perfectly normal. The father becomes the victim of the inverted inequality with which he has hitherto lived quite cheerfully. Now the mother has the say in everything, legally and actually, and the father has to make do with what she grants him, usually as little as the law allows.

Becoming a father is not difficult, but being a divorced father certainly is. At the moment when it is too late, the family personified by the child becomes the centre of all hope and concrete effort; the child is offered time and attention in a manner which during the marriage was allegedly out of the question, 'although I really would like to spend more time with him/her'. Divorce confronts the man with his own feelings as a father; he is the one to mourn for, having realized too late what liberation means, just as its objective slips away.

Now everything turns against him. Step by step he is faced with the costs of a life lived away from his family: enforced loneliness, learned helplessness, legally rationed time with his kids, all bars behind which his newly discovered fatherhood seems unjustly imprisoned. His outrage, pain and bitterness are occasionally shock-waves which herald his own efforts to shake off outdated patterns of thinking and being.

Strictly speaking old Adam has become superfluous in almost every respect. A relic of the old idea of manliness, he could almost be put on display in a museum. The trouble is he is still trying to make himself heard: women should be pushed out of jobs so that men can claim work as the main pillar of their existence. In making babies husbands have to fear being pushed out of the race by a coalition of semen donors, doctors and test tubes. Female interest in his penis-fixated bang-bang sexual repertoire has flown away like a butterfly. A man can continue to live with the fictions, but the collapse of them, their forced and suffered loss, could free him to seek new ways of being. The fact that he has not noticed this or seized the chance offered does not make Eve's late apple more succulent.

Divorce as a wedding guest: marriage contracts

The problems overrunning the nuclear family feel like individual ones but they are also of a general nature. Much has been said about how choosy the population has become, but the opposite applies just as much; nuclear families already exposed to severe strain are also expected to take on a large burden of official obligations. It may seem drastic, but it is quite correct to say that they are misused as the nation's rubbish dump. One could mention, for instance, the fact that they are expected to tutor their children at home to make up for teacher shortages. Or that polluted air and water and toxins in foods greatly increase the parents', or specifically the mother's, job in feeding the family, since she is meant to remove from the menu everything that a legalized conspiracy of authorities, experts and industries have poured, dumped and pumped into her kitchen. Children have to be planned and timed to fit in with career and social insurance regulations. It goes without saying that the family is expected to step in if unemployment benefits run out. And if the members of the family who are willing and able to work are not as mobile as the market demands and refuse to accept jobs far from home, they are officially suspected of shirking and lose some of their rights.

There is something in the modern medicine cupboard to treat these 'minor ailments', treat this 'cold' in the family by having a dose of agreements, contracts, provisions and counselling sessions. The trouble is that uncertainty on this scale just where one hoped to find domestic peace makes planning, stipulations and arguments unavoidable. The medicine turns out to be part of the disease it claims to heal; family is no longer an emotional haven, a place to air one's other qualities, but just as regimented as the world outside. Contracts between lovers devalue their love.

An antenuptial agreement is not a new invention; among the nobility it was the custom to work out complicated treaties on distributing wealth and rights. This was, however, not the partners' concern, as it is nowadays, but was the responsibility of their families, with the bride's father liable for the dowry, and the groom and his family expected to provide property to support the marriage. The meaning and point of those marriage agreements was only distantly related to what is intended in the modern ones. What is now at stake is regulating the consequences of divorce and establishing norms for daily life.

There is currently a boom in premarital contracts, reflecting how uneasy people feel about getting married. The more provisions such a document makes, the greater its signatories' fear of falling into an abyss which the agreement is meant to bridge. Divorce is no longer the exception but has become the rule, and everyone is confronted with the possibility that it could affect them, or their nearest and dearest. Anyone who has lived through it will, like the survivor of a sunken liner, put on a life-jacket next time he/she embarks on a voyage. This life-jacket is the antenuptial agreement, signed by both parties; it does not prevent the ship from sinking but makes its loss at least prospectively less disastrous.

Is it surprising that people who have already gone through the misery of divorce as adults or have survived it as children start negotiations with a new partner just like politicians form coalitions? The likely end is the sponsor of the beginning. Predictable problems are anticipated; all the tricky issues in, during and after marriage are supposed to be included and arranged before the couple even goes to the registry office. Who gets what and who pays whom are the main questions, but even battling over (often as yet non-existent) children in advance is meant to take place painlessly, laying down in advance what rights each partner has if there is a divorce, and agreeing on child-rearing methods to defuse any squabbles in this field. Arrangements are made on sharing hobbies or not, on going on holiday, and, particularly thorny, on developing one's potential. It is not uncommon for the loving contractual partners to agree to back up each other's ambitions along the lines: if I help you with your career you must let me off the housework to get a proper training.

Some go into the greatest detail: how the house is run, from polishing shoes to making breakfast; mores of sexual behaviour about what is acceptable or out of the question; who is prepared to move house; when the children should arrive; who will look after them and who wants to combine doing both. All of this and much more can be laid down in the form of a binding agreement formulated by a notary. In the mind's eye one sees the couple in the midst of a domestic quarrel poring over the document, hoping it can solve their misunderstandings.

It is both poignant and ironic when love soberly regulates how it may end; both partners agree that they will consent to divorce each other, and have insight, and promise not to dramatize the divorce either to themselves or to others, and especially not in front of the children; they want to see it as 'one of life's natural offshoots' and not contest it (Partner 1984: 128). Some even pledge to celebrate their divorce with a party even bigger than the marriage itself. One wonders what feelings are really concealed behind this pseudo-civilized idea of an 'amicable divorce'.

No doubt contractual marriage – 'an emotional contract' – is one answer to the problem, but it also contains elements which speed up its own dissolution. Interests which one never used to be able to barter are now openly offered in exchange for others, providing the partners with weapons against each other which they are likely to use as soon as their disagreements prove hard to solve. As far as I know, there has not yet been any research into the course and duration of marriages which started out under voluntary contracts of this kind, but one can presume that ending such a marriage is easier, and this very fact encourages the participants to consider ending it earlier. Marriage turns into a tenancy for temporarily satisfying mutual needs.

The assortment of means available for 'curing' and 'saving' the family also includes the other offerings with which modern society tries to patch up its self-inflicted wounds. Offer the housewives a glittering wage to compensate for their low-status job. Being married is one of the very few positions in Germany which one can hold without being trained for it; perhaps we should offer training courses, ending with a certificate (this would provide work for unemployed teachers and give quarrels a new quality, in which both quasi-therapists could elegantly hurt one another with psychological half-truths). Anyone who nevertheless really does fall through one of the holes over which family life is constructed can count on the sympathy and bills of a marriage counsellor.

The pattern is always the same: family, the place which was meant to be the opposite of the chilly, hard world outside, gets converted into a predictable and manageable part of it. This has not happened in the course of any political reform of family life but very slowly, step by step, as the security risks in being married have been met by insurances against them. This is quite logical. Neither political commitment nor waiting for utopia clears away the dirty dishes or helps one achieve one's aims despite the protests of one's partner. The more divorces there are, the more contracts, and as a result even more divorces. In the end love turns against the place where it once sought a home and refuge, and is fickle, absorbed only in itself.

Parenthood as a building set: genetic engineering and designing offspring

Until recently one's family was a natural product, a blood relationship determining social and material heredity, establishing kinships and so on. Attention is now turning to this because the natural basis for human nature can be technically altered – through reproductive medicine, organ transplantation and cracking the genetic code. Paradoxically much more attention has been paid to our withering and endangered environment, known as nature, so that the incredible triumph of the biosciences, producing an unnatural world, has gone almost unnoticed. What is happening is that the ancient link between nature and family is being severed and the consequences cannot yet be measured but only guessed at in the form of questions. Taking an overall view, there are two main lines of thinking.

The first is that there is nothing new in the principle of interfering with motherhood and fatherhood. Ever since the Enlightenment people have tried to tame nature; using technology to pursue the same aim is not essentially different, even though we can now influence how human beings are made. Technical advances always contain a risk element which has to be respected but equally opens new possibilities for human development. For its advocates the chances lie mainly in pre-embryonic treatment of congenital disorders and in enabling the increasing number of infertile couples to have children of their own. Furthermore natural parenthood has long been joined by social and legal parenthood, with the probability of a child growing up with its biological parents becoming smaller and smaller.

The other view, which I share, is that fleeing into generalizations, contending that things have always been like this, is just a cloak under which to smuggle in new techniques without having to answer embarrassing questions. It may be that the new dimension remains invisible in a laboratory where substances look indistinguishable, and it makes no difference whether they come from humans or from animals, where one can alter a person's character without anaesthetics and is not forced to explain what one is doing with pre-embryonal cells. But from the sociological angle the new dimension with its social implications is all too apparent. The double helix, genome analysis, genetic corrective measures or heterologous and homologous fertilization suddenly present a whole new range of possibilities of abolishing the anthropological constants of motherhood and fatherhood which have prevailed in all previous societies.

This epoch-making change is perhaps not so visible in the biology and chemistry of the cell and its nucleus, but certainly is in the consequences which these new techniques have or will have for family and kinship systems. Social and biological parenthood, once identical, is breaking up into a series of steps which start out from the natural processes and combine various components like a building set. The essential difference from, say, adoption or divorce, which cancel the link between biological and social parenthood in other ways, lies in the deliberate technical manipulation involved, multiplying and selecting human potential until now firmly enclosed within family units.

For the sociology of the family this development is two-edged. Social parenthood is freed of its biological moorings and can float freely; being a parent and having a child become two separate phenomena which can be organized independently of one another. The biological side is concerned with combining and selecting sperm and ovum, while being a parent exists on its own and has to redefine itself. Technically it would be possible to uncouple reproduction from the family, either by organizing this in the clinics or by delegating delivery to a group of women chosen according to criteria of whatever kind. This may sound like science fiction but it shows the direction in which we are going.

On the other hand parenthood no longer limited to one's own genetic makeup opens up possibilities which make one's imagination seem a dreary hanger-on while reality gallops off into the distance. Soon it will be taken for granted that one can determine the sex of a child or predict its appearance and probable diseases in advance. Embryo transfer, babies in test tubes, swallowing a pill to make twins or triplets, purchasing deep-frozen embryos from a highly specialized store run by experts under governmental supervision – some of these things are already normal and others just a matter of time.

Once babies can be bred in test tubes, what does motherhood mean? What effect will it have on women who have always seen motherhood as part of their existence? Who is really the father, brother, sister, uncle of this newborn? One can already have one's own embryos deep-frozen, so that one can give birth to them later, after the job situation has been settled, or, as has already happened in the USA, implant one in one's own mother and hand the pregnancy and birth over to her, making her mother and grandmother in one and the child its mother's sibling. And why not? Who is going to be able to stop such initiatives (in the long run), if they apparently promise two advantages: women can concentrate on their professions and babies be born to keep up the population figures, satisfy the markets and make sure that there will be enough wage-earners to pay for the pensioners. The mind reels.

This is where matters are beginning to get out of control. The doctors in reproductive medicine cry: 'You're free to choose! It's your decision . . . All we want to do is ease the suffering . . . You don't have to take part . . . There is no coercion . . . Even this technique, in itself, is quite neutral, all that matters is doing things carefully. Abuse must be prevented at all costs; our legal system and responsible scientists will see to that.'

Let us assume for a moment that this highly improbable prediction is true. Let us suppose that there are laws for damming up the technological spring tides (in fact there are none); let us assume that all of a sudden both sides discuss the pros and cons in an unusual atmosphere of mutual goodwill and respect, nobody attempting to browbeat the other. All that this completely unrealistic approach would mean is that the new outline of a post-family society is sketched out, under the pretext of giving the patients the right to choose; the new design for family life would be fuelled by remarkable and unstoppable medical advances and given its blessing by a new set of regulations on genetics. The result would be an age in which parenthood has lost its links with natural processes, and biology would take off on its own, making it increasingly difficult to decide where the line should be drawn and when society should make efforts to protect itself.

In fact this revolution is taking place without any governmental intervention, without any draft laws, without any debates or votes in parliament, simply as a tacit part of medical advance. It is being financed by our public health insurance system which pays for the patient's consultation with the doctor. This much is clear: genetic engineers and researchers are not responsible for the results. It is up to society alone to decide whether it should make use of the broad range of offers becoming available.

> It [society] will want to do this. First those who actually suffer from a congenital illness, then those who have recessive illnesses, then those who might be susceptible, then those who are considered impaired. Finally potentially almost everyone. This corresponds to optimal coverage in all other services and products. Once it gets on the market, enters the minds of the masses and and awakens individual wishes and needs, it becomes a product to demand and use. Ethics has no staying power against consumer wishes. First comes the fear of one's own disease or disability and

> then perhaps fear of eugenics. First comes food, and after that moral considerations.
>
> The great feat, modernization at all levels, will be available only to the next generation – but then unavoidable. The responsibility of one generation for the next cannot be restricted to offering optimal conditions under which to grow up. The parents' duty will start when the fertilized egg settles in the uterus. Because every haemophiliac represents a burden to the community of insurance payers, every incipient baby will undergo genetic screening in the 32 cell stage. If any undesirable tendencies are diagnosed, one can choose between abortion or amelioration, that is embryo therapy. But why stop at congenital illnesses? After all, the parents' wishes can be taken into account and transferred to the embryo. Will the child be blond or brunette, will it be a little podgy or short? All that can be arranged in advance. Whatever happens, a single person who briefly gets together with someone else to go through the traditional reproductive motions can equally well make use of these technical services. (Gabbert 1988: 87, 89–90)[4]

In genetic paradise it is not only the 'crooked sticks', as the elderly Kant once described humanity, which would be straightened out according to people's ideas, beliefs and fears. It might seem more tempting to split up love and reproduction, parenthood and affection, and perhaps even assign each to its own sphere and institution. This is likely to appeal particularly to societies which are unable to solve the 'problem' of a dwindling population by the old take-your-luck method of getting married and having children.

Vanishing points and tentative identities: beyond the male and female roles

Let us assume that both of us, you and I, have one free wish. We could do what we wanted. How can we get out of this embarrassing situation?

Our 'sorrow beyond dreams', our loss of utopia shows up quite clearly in our lack of imagination: we have forgotten how to wish. We have cast off traditions and the hopes they represented, and now even the memories of them, memories of another path, some transcendental aim for the sake of which others set whole caravans and nations in motion. Inquiring about utopias, even positive ones, has become awkward. First, they have faded, second, they have become dystopias, and third, the enlightened average European is much too enlightened to wish for one. So what is there to lose, where the loss that really threatens us overshadows all else?

Why does that pervasive sense of hopelessness and being too late which paralyses so many attempts at thinking nowadays not encourage us to use our imagination? Feeling hopeless presupposes you secretly believe that everything should be useful. For a different, questing kind of thinking hopelessness can have a liberating effect. Just as one can count on people to loot when under martial law, in a state of acknowledged defeatism one can count on the imagination responding with visions of other worlds, uninhibited by stern calls to stick to the facts. But people continue to think small, which is often the death knell for creative ideas.

What would have to happen – and let's answer quite freely, without any reservations about what is feasible – to enable you to share your life with someone else in a way that is good for both of you?

Even wishful thinking has to be organized. Two aspects are worth distinguishing, first of all in this section the external factors which upset our attempts to love each other – being unequal, on the move, in search of ourselves, and then in the next the turbulences which are inherent in post-traditional love (which is the subject of chapter 6, on the secular religion called love).

Let us start out with a simple matter: how to organize two individual biographies which are supposed to run along the same rails. Putting it the other way round, modern society is nomadic, we are on the move in everyday life, on holiday, in our professional lives, and brakes would have to be found to bring us back to a more settled rhythm. One would have to limit mobility parallel to limiting growth in the economy. Rediscovering how to be less hasty and more self-sufficient might be a big step in improving our social lives.

That, however, puts something quite social democratic and quite unrevolutionary at the top of the agenda (alongside throttling the amount of traffic and the like): we should uncouple work from income. A society which has become rich can at least dream of abandoning this imperative from all previous societies and eras, releasing people from having to work to survive. First hints in this direction can be found in the debates on citizens' pensions, benefit payments, uncoupling social security from wage-packets, and allowing people at least sometimes to decide whether to work or not. This would slow down the roundabout forcing people to decide in favour of their jobs and against their families. At least there would be a place to try out living together.

In the private sphere, where both partners often lack any sense of direction, it is often overlooked that gender inequalities are not just a superficial issue which can be ironed out by the people involved. These fundamental inequalities are in fact a built-in feature of industrial society, reflecting its attitude to work inside and outside the family. In fact our society is founded on the contradictions between modern changes and reactionary structures, and they cannot be abolished just by letting people choose between family and career. The sexes will never become equals as long as they are subject to pressures which perpetuate the current hierarchy. The only way out is to rethink the entire structure of industrial society and reorganize it to take account of our need for a satisfying private life, to find a new balance freed of gender barriers. Instead of the pseudo-alternatives 'back to the nuclear family' or 'let everyone have a job' one ought to look into a third possibility, limiting and buffering market requirements so that our needs as social animals are recognized and satisfied.

This principle can be understood as the exact opposite of the interpretation sketched in chapter 1 above. As the family becomes a community of individuals, in what amounts to a second historical step, production and private needs are divided up within the family. The difficulties which are bound to crop up can be solved only if arrangements are made enabling both functions to be combined throughout the couple's life together.

For instance being prepared to move house: first it is conceivable that one could alleviate some of the detrimental effects of moving on. So far it has always been taken for granted that it is the individual (usually male) who moves, and the family, including the wife, trails after him. The only alternative for the couple involved seems to be giving up the wife's career, with all its long-term consequences, or a split family, often a first step towards divorce, and society suggests this is a personal problem. A helpful alternative would be cooperative mobility, on the lines, if you want him/her, you must make his/her spouse a good offer too. The employment offices would have to organize job counselling and referral for whole families. Firms, and the government, would be required not just to keep talking about family values but actually to contribute to them by offering cooperative employment models perhaps encompassing several organizations. At the same time one could investigate whether existing expectations (for instance in the part-time academic job market) cannot be reduced, allowing people to continue living at home. There could be legal clauses recognizing unwillingness to move for family and relationship reasons. In assessing the acceptability of a job, one should also take the risk factors for the family into account.

Of course in view of current mass unemployment, suggesting people should move around less seems even more unrealistic than it already is. Similar effects can perhaps be achieved in other ways, for instance by taking away the pressure to work; this would mean increasing social assistance to provide a minimum income for everyone, and decouple caring for the elderly and those in poor health from the employment market. Loosening the thumb-screws like this has a long tradition (welfare state guarantees, reducing the working week). Since mass unemployment forces women in millions to join the search for jobs, while lean organizations have increased productivity with fewer employees, this topic is bound to be on the government's agenda sooner or later.

But cutting back the dynamism of the market in favour of the family is only one side of the solution. People will have to work out how to live with one another again. There are no rules any more, no guidelines from the past, so that everything has to be agreed by the persons concerned if it has any chance of working. This would include weighing up the relationships one automatically acquires with the ones one personally wants, and discovering what potential they hold as a support system to aid one's search for oneself without the barriers and snares built into traditional family relationships.

Such unexciting notions as friendship must be revived, friendship as a deliberately sought trusting partnership between two people involved in an honest exchange of ideas, not as fascinating and risky as love, and therefore often longer lasting. As Henry Miller said, 'A friend equips you with a thousand eyes, like the goddess Indra. You live countless lives through your friends' (quoted in Schmiele 1987: 162).

Friendship does not just fall into your lap, nor does it come easy if you are young; it has to be carefully protected against the centrifugal forces which threaten all market biographies (and is rather like a two-career marriage in that respect). It has to be renewed again and again by backing one another in difficult moments and being open to constructive criticism, acting as a shared lifeline to take the weight of each other's confusions and weaknesses. Acquaintanceship is the looser form, and interweaving both helps to form a safety net for individual biographies revolving round their own limitations and doubts. In other words, one would have to form and try out what kind of close relationship fits in with living as an individual and can ward off some of its miseries and madnesses. One special feature deserves to be named: being simultaneously close and yet on one's own, allowing for the fact that individuals need their own company more than that of others.

With a society of individuals there is no going back to old forms of communal living. Instead we need new forms allowing us to live separately together, tested by both partners and accepted by town planners, architects and landlords, so that each partner can retreat into his/

her separate corner or seek the other's company in equal measure, doing away with group pressures and standard living patterns.

Perhaps these are the first signs of a certain post-industrial enlightenment, getting rid of some of industrialism's destructive features. The new focus is on values such as self-awareness, sharing, loving people, bodies, nature and other creatures, finding the same wavelength, discovering oneself, spending time alone, arguing, and doing the chores; looking out for friends to accompany, support and criticize one's journey through life. None of these ideas is particularly new, but they do challenge the firmly fixed patterns of family life which industrialization has landed us with. How can one combine the quest for oneself, a projected, tentative identity, with the rigid prescriptions in the old family roles: good husband-and-father, good wife-and-mother, nice child?

On the one hand, forced to be mobile and often up to the eyes in work, we make the family, rather than the neighbourhood, or clan, or community into the centre of our private lives. On the other, however, it is hard to escape from the fixed roles which make family life a stabilizing force and a place where needs can be anticipated and qualities appreciated. In this respect it is hindering our search for who we are, as opposed to where we came from, a search which depends on experimenting and persistence. The family is not a gang of Boy Scouts exploring its new terrain, wandering through the undiscovered continents of the self, searching out the different selves which reside in all of us.

Exchanging one's own family for marriage therefore looks like escaping from one trap only to step into the next, as long as families stop adults from reverting to being like children, shedding their snakeskins, until family life becomes a programme of discovery for all its members. 'We want children's rights! Down with discrimination against stuffy old grown-ups!' are demands pointing in this direction. Opening up the family to let its members live their dreams of being alone and at the same time cultivating a network of friendships that can outlast identity crises and marital upheavals would be two ways of relieving marriage of overblown expectations and toning down the panic and confusion of divorce.

The nuclear family was and is a programme which seems insidiously easy to adopt. It looks like the answer to all the questions, and they wreak their vengeance only later because they have not been posed or properly answered. Society will find a way out of this tangle of possibilities only if it can come up with a new viable model for living together which serves as a good example and is publicly acknowledged.

It would certainly be a mistake to imagine that the bourgeois family could be replaced by a post-bourgeois one. What we already have is a variety of post-bourgeois family, no longer – or only just – families, coming into being as men and women quarrel and reorganize themselves and develop their own dynamics, credos – and sometimes blinkers – over generation lines. This searching phase does not, however, seem to have led to any crystallization; inventing new ways of living suitable for the future still seems to be hampered by the dogged defence of only slightly modified old ways (a bit of shared housekeeping, a little back-pedalling in one's career, with mutual encouragement). Recognizing that if one looks carefully none of the advances people enthuse about have really taken place is the first hard step to maybe someday taking one's life into one's own hands.

We have got caught up in the details of everyday life instead of facing the real questions: wallowing in freedom, jingling tarnished reminders of past joys and trivial triumphs, an orgy of dressing up and dancing and amazement, arguing and fighting over the minor liberated zones and peaks inside and outside oneself. These horizons, these dreams of better ways of living together have nothing to do with any reality that ever existed before industrial society; they are a product of it, and of its insistence that private lives, marital difficulties, parenthood, family, sexuality and gender identity are all just personal matters. Our dreams, ideologies and designs for another world are never just projections or visions suggested by the powers-that-be to motivate us to carry on. It is rather that the mistakes which we individually stage and suffer from always reflect the actual situation in which we live, with our deepest longings and the daily conflicts we simply cannot avoid by any of the escape routes discovered so far. In this sense at least the mistakes are right; glorifying in a nostalgic manner the charms of private life proves useless in the face of so many individuals setting off to write their own biographies.

Love always starts out from the private side of life, is set alight by small details and yet seems to transcend mundanity. Seen from above, or outside, love always remains tied to the trivialities of daily life, habits that have become man and wife, with pictures of me and you and the general attitudes they conceal. Love is bound to an inherited role personified in the beloved, and beyond him/her the forces of history and politics which reappear anew in every one of us.

It starts out by wandering, getting lost, trying out, flirting, making it, waking up in a snakepit of hissing jealousy, being amazed that the flames one walked through left no marks, discovering that solitude provides company, memories, strange worlds in books and the cosy, twinkling reflection of the lake which seems external only as it refracts and reflects the heavens. Such experiences are quite private, individual and hard to share, suggesting a dimension which alters one's perception, sensitivities and the colours of the world. It could at least encourage us to ask what really matters: does this way of seeing things, the uncertainty and significance of maybe loving and being loved help us to find out how to word the vital questions for our time: what to do about technology run wild and nature dying all around us?

6

LOVE, OUR SECULAR RELIGION

What comes after tradition? Nothing?

Nobody should be rash enough to claim they know all about love. To conclude this book it seems worth examining some ideas on what love means in our detraditionalized, non-religious and individualized world:

> Only two things
> Underwent so many guises,
> Through Me and Us and You,
> But everything was suffered
> For the question: why?
> . . .
> Whether roses or snow or oceans
> Whatever bloomed faded away,
> There are only two things: a void
> And a stigmatized self.
> (Gottfried Benn)[1]

Let us assume that is the situation: there are only two things, a void and a stigmatized self. What does this void, this emptiness mean? Does lacking traditions imply that we are really in a vacuum stretching from now into the future and likely to last for ever? That there is a whole assortment of 'essentials' and 'gods'? Or just do-it-yourself beliefs? Maybe taking refuge in consumerism: platters of paté and holidays on distant shores? Or perhaps all these things plus some signs of a post-tradition which we have not grasped, regulating how the stigmatized individuals live with and without one another?

To put the question another way, let us assume for a moment that the churches have become empty shells which it would be unchristian to abolish; does talking about 'emptiness' there not mean simply negating what used to be? Is it a reflection of our lack of imagination when we insist on thinking comparatively in terms of then and now? Or do we really mean there is nothing to replace what has vanished – it's over, that was it, curtains. And then?

Perhaps beneath the nothingness, between the cracks across the emptiness one can glimpse a new kind of small-scale paradise quite unconnected with the old realms and their rules which gave life its meaning, a little utopia which does not depend on tradition and therefore cannot be codified or institutionalized and need not justify itself; it is simply tailored to fit individual needs. In this last chapter we are immodestly and tentatively looking for the meaning of life in a post-Christian modern society, and our discovery is, quite simply and unsociologically, love. Looking into the future one can safely guess that love in all its glory, its loftiest and deepest values, its hells and heavens, in all its human and animal entirety will turn out to be one main source of satisfaction and meaning in life.

A suggestion and a question: perhaps now that the class system, pitting men against women and predetermining family structures, is on the way out, both sexes could begin to long for and expect new ways of friendly coexistence to be the norm? Just as the class struggle paradoxically gave birth to ideas of equality and solidarity, could it be that the battle between the sexes is allowing us to think up new possibilities, to redefine paradise, and awake political and social impulses towards living in a liberated and liberal way together? Are new realities emerging, and with them new neuroses? What effect does it have that our personal lives no longer centre on religious beliefs, social class, filling hungry stomachs, or being the pillars of the nuclear family, but rather on discovering who we are and where we are going, trying out different ways of living and loving. Is it just Sodom and Gomorrah in modern dress? Does its influence reach beyond our private lives and affect other realms, science, politics, the labour market and business? Or does paying so much attention to our own interests and potential prove a dead end, resulting in pseudo-intimacy, in alienated lovers, frustrated because although we find it impossible to live with each other, we still cannot do without one another?

Max Weber (1985) noted how the 'spirit of capitalism' was an unintentional byproduct of Protestant asceticism. Let us suppose that now that the Protestant/professional ethic of doing one's duty is fading away and the accustomed pattern of family life is collapsing, there is a good chance that the next battles will be for love itself, for its own sake. What would be the side-effects, the unwanted genie which could escape from the bottle crammed with love and romantic ideas and therapeutic efforts? Are there any repercussions here for political thinking or action? These questions will be discussed rather than answered, in three steps.

(1) Why is love being elevated to the rank of a latter-day religion? What can be clarified or explained by comparing love and religion? Where is such a comparison apt and where is it irrelevant? To find out we must define some terms which tend to be used in several senses, sometimes apparently describing the disintegration and at others the idolization of family, marriage and loving relationships. Our thesis is that the structure of industrial society which laid down gender, family and occupational roles is crumbling away, and a modern form of archaic anarchy is breaking out, with love on its banner, and a thousand delights and obstacles in its path. It is this quest for personal freedom and satisfaction here and now, which can so quickly revert into hatred, desperation and loneliness, that is leaving its mark on the divorce and remarriage figures, on overlapping and serial families, as millions of people go in search of happiness.

(2) The retort, the antithesis, would be that 'it has always been like that,' a deep conviction that love in this form has always existed even if historians cannot trace it. We intend to show that investing such hopes in love is a modern phenomenon, something specific to our times. It is true that romantic love was invented long before the second half of the twentieth century; loving one another as an ultimate form of self-revelation, for instance, was celebrated in a mixture of realism and fantasy in the eighteenth and nineteenth centuries, spelled out in anguish and ecstasy. The novel aspect of the past few decades is that this poetically heightened love–hate romanticism has been transformed into a popular mass movement adorned with all the accoutrements of modern life and finding its way into all corners of cultural life, therapists' textbooks, divorce laws and people's hearts. Marrying someone for love no longer means setting up a family, material security, parenthood and so on, but discovering and being oneself in all one's facets, having the best of both worlds by venturing ever further along one's personal path but still trusting in the constant support and companionship of one's partner.

(3) For individuals who have to invent or find their own social settings, love becomes the central pivot giving meaning to their lives. In this

world where no one demands obedience or respect for old habits, love is exclusively in the first person singular, and so are truth, morality, salvation, transcendence and authenticity. In accordance with its inner logic, this modern type of love is rooted in itself, in the individuals who live it. Growing out of itself and its own subjective views, it easily turns totalitarian: rejecting any outside authority, and agreeing to take over responsibility, to compromise and be fair only for emotional, spontaneous reasons. The only obligation is to be honest. It is not a crime, not breaking the rules, if one does not love, even if one's behaviour inflicts deeper wounds on others than robbing or assaulting them might. So love is not just a way of finding affection and closeness; it also provides an excuse for attacking one's lover with the sharp knives of intimacy. It is our conjecture, and this will have to be fleshed out and discussed, that love has become a blueprint for hopes and actions untrammelled by old ties and constraints previously enforced by the state, the law and the church, and developing its own inner logic, conflicts and paradoxes. While psychologists usually claim they can best explain all the turbulent relationships by looking at the individuals and how they grew up, and sociologists tend to seek the reasons in external factors like job opportunities and women's rights, we believe the roots lie somewhere else. One fundamental cause of so much emotional upheaval is the inherent contradictoriness of a form of living erected on rapidly changing feelings and the hopes of both partners that they can 'become themselves'.

The disintegration and idolization of marriage, family and close relationships

Women and men reading this book will have been left with a contradiction, more hidden in some chapters and more open in others, which must now be clarified. They will have noticed that convincing illustrations of the disintegration of marriage and family life are countered by equally convincing illustrations of how extremely important these two institutions remain. Rising divorce figures which apparently show the end of marriages are answered by high remarriage rates, proving how attractive marriage still is. Anyone concluding from the declining birthrate that having children and being parents have lost their priority has to think again on seeing the effort made by thousands of women (and men) to escape infertility. Does the collective decision in favour of 'common law marriage' mean people are fundamentally sceptical about family conventions? No, the family researchers reply (they even have to defend their profession): couples living together before or outside marriage do not tend to live wild or unorthodox lives, and there is little to distinguish them from married couples.

Never before has marriage been built on such ephemeral and immaterial foundations (see chapter 3 above). Men and women with good jobs are economically independent of family support. Their union no longer serves any political ends or the maintenance of dynasties or owning property as it did in the feudal hierarchy. Inherited ties, which used to be taken for granted, have slackened, and the couple working as a team becomes the exception; in short everything which used to be firm and preordained is vanishing. Instead one is supposed to seek and find in the macro-microcosm of life with the beloved everything that society previously assigned to various professions and often different parts of town: romantic love, keeping a mistress, comfortable affection, liberation from the shackles of adulthood and a humdrum life, being forgiven one's sins, refuge in family history and future plans, parental pride and pleasure and whatever other incompatibilities – with their enigmatic dragon's features – there may be.

Seen historically, in an era when men and women have lost their old political and economic certainties and moral guidelines one wonders why they are seeking their own private bliss in such a uniform way, marrying for love, of all things, while society in general suggests that differentiating is the answer. Marrying for love has existed only since the beginning of the industrial revolution and was its invention. It is regarded as the most desirable goal although the social realities suggest exactly the opposite. Marriage has lost its stability but none of its attractiveness as a result of its metamorphosis from a means of passing on wealth and power into the airy version we know, nourished only on emotional involvement and the desire to find oneself. Despite and contrary to the 'bad' reality, the family and loving relationships continue to be idealized on every level of society (with slight behavioural differences), irrespective of income, education and age. Here is some evidence from research into working-class attitudes:

Interviewer: 'What does having a family and children mean to you?'
Mr Schiller: 'That there is some sense in life.'
Mrs Schiller: 'You know why you're there, you know what you're working for.'
Mr Xeller: 'To me, family means everything. I'd give up everything but that.'
Mrs Taler: 'Family and children are the main thing and the most important thing.'

There is scarcely anything else in the parents' lives which they describe so

> emphatically as the core of their lives. Only having a family and children gives existence a subjective 'purpose'. (Wahl et al. 1980: 34–5)

This finding is both paradoxical and mysterious: the family is simultaneously disintegrating and being put on a pedestal. If one can draw conclusions about beliefs from how people behave, seventh heaven and mental torment seem to be very close neighbours in our ideal image of a loving couple. Perhaps they just live in different storeys – tower room and torture chamber – in the same castle. Above all some explanation must be found for the fact that so many people are yearning to have children, often to the exclusion of all other interests, while at the same time the birth-rate is declining. Equally, why does family life hold out so much appeal, promising personal salvation in a domestic paradise of companionship, parenthood and love, while there is also a sharp rise in the divorce rate? What induces the sexes to tear at each other's throats and still keep their high hopes of finding true love and personal fulfilment with this partner, or the next, setting standards which are so high that disappointment is almost inevitable?

These two poles, idealizing life as a couple and divorcing in thousands, represent two sides of a new faith quickly finding followers in a society of uprooted loners. Their hope rests in love, a powerful force obeying rules of its own and inscribing its messages into people's expectations, anxieties and behaviour patterns, leading them through marriage and divorce to remarriage.

It is as if love occupies its own different world separate from real life in the family and separate from the person whom it is supposed to help to greater happiness. According to its tenets someone who for the sake of true love sacrifices a marriage, family ties, parenthood, perhaps ultimately even the well-being of those dependent on him/her, is not committing a sin but merely obeying the rules, answering the call of the heart and seeking fulfilment for him/herself and others. He or she is not to blame; it would be wrong to cling to an order which does not value love highly enough:

> Many people believe that one crisis in life is rather like any other. In fact, however, a divorce in a family with children is a disruption which cannot be compared with any other life crisis . . . When else do we have this overpowering urge to kill someone? When else are children used as weapons against their parents? In contrast to other crises, a divorce brings the most elementary human passions to the surface – love, hatred and jealousy . . . In most critical situations – earthquakes, floods, fire – parents instinctively get their children to safety before anything else. In the critical situation of a divorce, however, the children take second place for both

> mother and father; their own problems take priority. While divorce proceedings are under way parents neglect their children in almost every respect; domestic order breaks down and the children are left to themselves. Parents living apart spend less time with their children and have less empathy for their needs. In the panic of the upheaval naked egotism wins. (Wallerstein and Blakeslee 1989: 28–9)

The religious nature of our faith in love is clear in this striking parallel to Calvinism. The congregation was encouraged, in fact urged to make the world subservient to their own desire to please God, a message which implied breaking with tradition. Worshipping love in the modern way takes up this idea again, allowing or forcing us to break with family ties in order not to betray our personal search for genuineness, for true love. Abandoning one's own children for someone else is not a breach of love but a proof of it; idealizing love means pledging to break with all false forms of it. This illustrates the extraordinary power love already exerts over us as well as the contradictions of trying to live up to this ideal while coping with the mundane routine of ordinary life.

Such attitudes, wishing and hoping for the ultimate in love, constitute a belief, a religious state of mind, which must be clearly distinguished from behaviour, or what people actually do. In love as in Christianity there are pharisees, converts, atheists and heretics. And cynics often turn out to be disappointed and embittered adherents of an exaggerated faith in love. Because there are many contradictions between belief and action, it is vital to keep the two levels clearly separate. The assertions made here refer to our knowledge, our belief in love and hardly at all to behaviour which shows the opposite, or no matter how perversely results from it.

In addition there is a phenomenon which one could term the law of the inverse significance of faith and certainty. Anyone who feels comfortable in everyday life with a loving companion forgets how important this belief is to him/herself. Attention always focuses on uncertainties, and only when these crop up and certainty is banished does it become painfully obvious what a role love plays in designing our individual lives, even if we try to deny this.

How does this quasi-religious belief in love as the ultimate answer express itself if not in the ways people behave? Some would say: there are several priorities for me, love included, and then again love comes in so many shapes and sizes from passionate to maternal and companionable after seventeen years of marriage, homo- or heterosexual. One gauge of the intensity and power of love's claims on us, as we have said, lies in the divorce figures which unequivocally reveal what deep commitments are given up (see chapter 1 above). At the same time, however, research unanimously reveals an unshaken hankering for family and marriage, even though the 'Home Sweet Home' sign has been hanging rather crooked for some time. The number of remarriages after (early) divorce is also high (Federal Office of Statistics 1988: 71 and table 3.23). Children of divorced parents strive particularly hard to make a happy family, a goal which they sadly often fail to achieve (Wallerstein and Blakeslee 1989: 38–9).

None of this reflects what actually happens in everyday life, highlighting the differences between how one would like life to be and how living at close quarters with other individuals actually is.[2] While Weber (1985) investigated documents of the Calvinist faith for signs of inner ascetiscism, nowadays we would have to consult self-help books, therapeutic principles and transcripts of divorce proceedings to find signs of faith in true love.

Love as a latter-day religion

The essence of our faith in love can best be shown by comparing it with religion. Both hold out the promise of perfect happiness, to be achieved along similar lines. Each offers itself as a way of escaping from the daily grind, giving normality a new aura; stale old attitudes are tossed aside and the world seems suffused with new significance. In the case of religion all energy is directed towards another infinite reality, understood as the only true one and encompassing all finite life. In love this opening up of normal boundaries takes place both sensually, personally, in sexual passion and also in new perceptions of oneself and the world. Lovers see differently and therefore are and become different, opening up new realities for one another. In revealing their histories they recreate themselves and give their future a new shape. Love is 'a revolution for two' (Alberoni 1983); in overcoming antagonisms and moral laws which stand in their way they really prove their love. Inspired by their feelings, lovers find themselves in a new world, an earthly one but a realm of its own.

Love 'as an archetypal act of defiance' (Alberoni): that is what modern love seems to promise, a chance of being authentic in a world which otherwise runs on pragmatic solutions and convenient lies. Love is a search for oneself, a craving to really get in contact with me and you, sharing bodies, sharing thoughts, encountering one another with nothing held back, making confessions and being forgiven, understanding, confirming and supporting what was and what is, longing for a home and trust to counteract the doubts and anxieties modern life generates.

If nothing seems certain or safe, if even breathing is risky in a polluted world, then people chase after the misleading dreams of love until they suddenly turn into nightmares.

We are always vaulting over the apparently firm boundaries of everyday reality. Memory takes me back to myself when I was young. I wonder about the clouds and imagine a story behind them. I read a book and find myself in a different epoch; my head is full of scenes from someone's life who is now dead and I have never met; voices I have never heard are conversing in my inner ear. Among the extraordinary experiences in life love has a special status. Unlike illness and death it is sought for and not repressed, at least at this moment in our culture; it is immune to conscious or practical manipulation and cannot be produced on order. Those who hope to find it are looking for salvation here and now, and the 'hereafter' is in this world, with a voice, a body and a will of its own. Religion tells us there is a life after death; love says there is a life before death.

Few authors have described the extreme aspects of love so perceptively as Robert Musil, as P. L. Berger pointed out:

> Sexual longings violently disrupt the smooth routine of life by suddenly ripping off the social masks men and women wear, revealing a frightening animal side beneath their decorous behaviour. As Ulrich (the protagonist in Musil's novel *The Man Without Qualities*) observes after one of his wild encounters with Bonadea, love transforms people into 'raving fools', and with this ability sexual experience 'thrusts' itself into normal reality like an 'isle on which another level of consciousness prevails'. It is interesting in this connection that in the same passage Ulrich compares sexuality with other disruptive factors in real life, especially with the theatre, music and religion. (Berger 1983: 235–6)

Love is communism within capitalism; misers give their all and this makes them blissful:

> Falling in love means opening oneself to a new form of existence without any guarantee of achieving it. It is a rhapsody to happiness without any certainty that there will be a response . . . And if the answer does come from the person we love, then it seems something undeserved, a miraculous gift one never counted on getting . . . Theologians have their own term for this gift: grace. And if the other person, our beloved, says he or she loves us too and each is engrossed in the other, this is a blissful moment in which time stands still. (Alberoni 1983: 39–40)

Love is a utopia which is not ordained or even planned from above, from cultural traditions or sermons, but grows from below, from the power and persistence of sexual drives and from deep personal wishes.

In this sense love is a religion unhampered by external meanings and traditions, its values lying in the depth of the lovers' attraction to one another and their subjective mutual commitment. No one has to become a member, and no one needs to be converted.

So our faith in love is linked to its lack of tradition; it comes after all the disappointing credos, and needs neither organizing committees nor party membership to be an effective subjective and cultural force. It is the outcome of sex being partially freed of taboos and wide disillusionment with other prescribed beliefs passed down to us. As befits modern social structures, there is no external moral agency responsible for love, but just the way the lovers feel for one another.

While a religion which lacks firm teaching usually vanishes, love is a religion without churches and without priests, and its continued existence is as certain as the tremendous force of sexual needs now freed of social disapproval. It cannot be organized, which also means it is independent, and its only place, despite all its cultural offshoots, is in the hearts of those involved; this makes it a non-traditional, post-traditional religion which we are hardly aware of because we ourselves are its temples and our wishes are its prayers.

Now that the old law-givers, the church, the state and traditional morality are on the retreat, even love can shed its old standard patterns and established codes. The result is a kind of positivism making norms out of individual preferences and values. This does not however reduce love's status as a force giving life purpose and meaning; on the contrary it confirms it. Here church and bible, parliament and government are merged into one – a matter of conscience guiding each person how to shape and structure his/her life. This is at least the ideal we share, this is how we would like it to be, even though in practical terms the solutions are often standard ones.

Because lovers can only rely on their own intuitions to guide them in matters of love, the whole process is a circular one, and so is any discussion of it. Therapists try to clarify these intertwined personal sufferings and experiences on general lines, but the very basic formula – I am myself – which is supposed to justify and explain everything else is, as Milan Kundera ironically notes in his *Laughable Loves* (1974: 92), a peculiar attempt to define something in terms of itself. In his analysis of the language of love Roland Barthes reveals this circularity:

> *adorable*/adorable
>
> Not managing to name the specialty of his desire for the loved being, the amorous subject falls back on this rather stupid word: *adorable*, ... Herein a great enigma, to which I shall never possess the key: Why

> is it that I desire So-and-so? Why is it that I desire So-and-so lastingly, longingly? Is it the whole of So-and-so I desire (a silhouette, a shape, a mood)? And, in that case, what is it in this loved body which has the vocation of a fetish for me? What perhaps incredibly tenuous portion – what accident? The way a nail is cut, a tooth broken slightly aslant, a lock of hair, a way of spreading the fingers while talking, while smoking? About all these *folds* of the body I want to say that they are *adorable*. *Adorable* means: this is my desire, insofar as it is unique; 'That's it! That's it exactly (which I love)!' Yet the more I experience the specialty of my desire, the less I can give it a name; to the precision of the target corresponds a wavering of the name; what is characteristic of desire, proper to desire, can produce only an impropriety of the utterance. Of this failure of language there remains only one trace: the word 'adorable'.
>
> ... *Adorable* is the futile vestige of a fatigue, a fatigue of language itself. From word to word, I struggle to put 'into other words' the ipseity of my Image, to express improperly the propriety of my desire: a journey at whose end my final philosophy can only be to recognize – and to practice – tautology. *The adorable is what is adorable.* Or again, I adore you because you are adorable, I love you because I love you. (Barthes 1978: 18, 20–1)

In fact those precious, holy sides of love are not just the outcome of our being besotted with ourselves. One has to look further into quite different fields, like education, scientific advances, world markets and technical risks if one wants to grasp why so many people plunge into a frenzy of love as if they were slightly insane. The outside world confronts us with a barrage of abstractions: statistics, figures, formulas, all indicating how imperilled we are, and almost all of them elude our comprehension. Loving is a kind of rebellion, a way of getting in touch with forces to counteract the intangible and unintelligible existence we find ourselves in.

Its value lies in the special, intense experiences it offers – specific, emotional, engrossing, unavoidable. Where other kinds of social contact are losing their hold, politics seem irrelevant, classes have faded into statistics, and even colleagues at work rarely find time for one another because their shifts and flexible working hours forbid it. Love, and especially the clashes it induces – from the 'eternal issue of the dishes' to 'what kind of sex', from parenting to tormenting each other with self-revelations – has a monopoly: it is the only place where you can really get in touch with yourself and someone else. The more impersonal life around you seems, the more attractive love becomes. Love can be a divine immersion in all kinds of sensations. It offers the same relief to a number-cruncher as jogging through the woods does to an office-worker – it makes you feel alive again.

A society short on traditions has produced a whole range of idols: television, beer, football, motorcycles, cordon bleu meals – something for every phase in life. You can join clubs or peace initiatives or keep up long-distance friendships to guarantee you still share some common ground with someone. You can hark back to old gods, or discover new ones, polish relics or read the stars. You can even insist on continuing the class struggle and sing about being free, although you know that such golden days, if they ever existed, are over.

What distinguishes love from these other escape routes is that it is tangible and specific, personal and now; the emotional upheavals cannot be postponed or handed on, and both sexes find themselves forced to react whether they want to or not. No one can decide to fall into or out of love, but might at any moment find themselves falling through the trap door into a new dimension.

Love is therefore not a substitute or a lightning conductor, nor is it a politically desirable export article or just a television advertisement. The boom in love reflects current living conditions and the anonymous, prefabricated pattern forced on people by the market relegating their private needs right to the end of the list.[3]

Taking over from old categories like class and poverty, religion, family and patriotism there is a new theme, sometimes disguised as uncertainty, anxiety, unfulfilled and unfulfillable longings, sometimes sharply outlined and standardized in pornography, feminism and therapy, but gradually developing its own radiance, its own rhythms, opening up prospects much more alluring than the ups and downs of being promoted, having the latest computer or feeling underpaid.

'Being loved means being told "you do not have to die"' (Gabriel Marcel).[4] This glowing hope seems more delightful and irresistible the more we realize how finite, lonely and fragile our existence is. Illness and death, personal disasters and crises are the moments when the vows prove true or merely lies, and in this respect the secular religion of love can claim like other religions to give life sense and meaning. Or put the other way round, the idea of dying shatters normal life, making it seem highly suspect; in moments of pain and fear love acquires a new dimension. The brittle, carefully constructed shell cracks open – at least momentarily – and lets in questions like Why? and What for?, fed on memories of desperately missed togetherness.

As religion loses its hold, people seek solace in private sanctuaries. Loving is bound up with a hope which goes beyond basking in intimacy and sex. Making love in bed is one way, caring for one another in a sick-bed is another. Love's power is proven in its ability to cope with weakness, age, mistakes, oversights and even crime. Whether the promises 'for better, for worse' are actually kept is another question which applies just as much to other religions. Illness can result in a new kind of devotion; hidden behind the hope that we can compensate for our mistakes and shortcomings by lavishing love on the beloved is the belief that love is an act of confession, and often a gesture against a heartless society.

The analogy between love and religion giving our life a purpose comes to an end when love itself dies. The end of a loving relationship remains meaningless in this latter-day religion, or can acquire some meaning only if the lovers part 'for the sake of love', by mutual understanding. Perhaps for future generations changing lovers will be like changing jobs, and love mobility a version of social mobility, but at the moment the wrangling in the divorce courts points in the opposite direction.

Believing in love means being under the sway of the present, here and now, you and me, our mutual commitment, and how we live it. Delay is out of the question and so is asking for God's help or postponing happiness until the next life. There is no merciful heaven waiting where our disagreements and exaggerated expectations of one another are bound to be fulfilled, even if we fail in this world. Love is unrelenting and demands cash down.

Faith in love means you love your lover but not your neighbour, and your loving feelings are always in danger of turning into hate. Ex-lovers lose their home and even their residence permits; they have no right to asylum. Not being loved necessarily implies being rejected, a topic on which psychotherapists, acting as intensive care units for those ravaged by divorce, can write volumes. Faith in love produces two groups which fluctuate considerably; on the one hand there are the current lovers, quantitatively stable but varying in identity. On the other there is a group of ex-lovers which increases as the current lovers swap and change. People find themselves interwoven into networks of insiders and outsiders, the blessed and the no-longer-blessed, once closely related, now tenuously linked, all in search of a final satisfying love.

For all the similarities between love and religion, there are also enormous differences; love is a private cosmos, whereas religion is in alliance with the powers-that-be. Lovers are their own church, their own priests, their own holy scriptures, even if they sometimes resort to therapists to decipher these. They have to create their own rules and taboos; there is an infinite number of private systems of love, and they lose their magic power and disintegrate as soon as the couple ceases to act as priests worshipping their belief in each other.

Love builds its nest out of the symbols lovers use to overcome their unfamiliarity with one another and to provide their relationship with a past. The nest is decorated as the focus of their togetherness, and turns into a flying carpet bearing their shared dreams. In this way the fetishes, the sacrifices, the ceremonies, the incense and the daily rites constitute the visible context within which we love. Instead of being officially sanctified and administered, this private faith is individually styled, invented and adorned: snuggling in Mickey Mouse and teddy symbols, agreeing everything yellow means love, inventing nicknames to use in our secret world, all these are efforts to counteract the nagging fear that it might end and all could be lost and forgotten.

Religion's horizon takes in this world and the next, the beginning and the end, time and eternity, the living and the dead, and is therefore often celebrated as immutable, untouched by time. Love's horizon, by contrast, is narrow and specific, consisting of a small world of you and me and nothing more, exclusive, apparently selfish, somewhere between unjust and cruel in its logic, arbitrary and outside the range of the law. Its imperatives cut across other wishes and its principles withstand any attempt to standardize them.

For these very reasons, however, love is the best ideology to counteract the perils of individualization. It lays stress on being different, yet promises togetherness to all those lone individuals; it does not rely on outdated status symbols or money or legal considerations, but solely on true and immediate feelings, on faith in their validity and on the person they are directed towards. The law-givers are the lovers themselves, phrasing their statutes with their delight in each other.

The history of love: democratized romanticism

The opposite view to this line of thinking is of course that 'things have always been like that', and that love in all its finery and confusion – procreation, sexual desire, repression, passion, intimacy, hate and violence – has been the same human drama since history began. It looks easy to prove. The fact that we exist and are continuing to exist permits one to conclude that the matter of the birds and the bees has been consistently popular throughout the ages. Whether black, yellow, white, eleventh-century Moslem, fifteenth-century Christian or a slave in ancient Greece, under tyranny or democracy, nothing has essentially changed in the way people make other people. Varied witnesses such as biologists, psychologists and dramatists (Plautus, Shakespeare, Kleist, Beckett and Harold Pinter) all speak, for once, the same language: either love was always the secret core of life or it never was. Which implies that our theory is false either way.

This forces us to be more precise. Our focus of interest is not the biological effects of sexual behaviour, nor the mass of social institutions which have grown up round it. Our topic is love as a symbolic world in our culture, and its relation to other symbolic worlds like poverty, careerism, technological hazards and environmental awareness. If in medieval warrior societies or in the class system love played a role but not the leading one, nowadays in our view the opposite applies and will do so even more in the future. In other words, as society becomes more prosperous people's lives are less restricted by class considerations or established authorities and their attention centres on a hectic search for emotional satisfaction.

In sharp contrast to prevalent ideas among sociologists it seems to us that the conviction that love alone gives life purpose and meaning is the logical outcome of modern changes in society. Put rather crudely, which makes this thesis vulnerable and easier to refute, there is a historical succession – religion, class, love – not in any order of rank or suggesting anything like progress but in the sense of shifting principles and horizons, each with its own scope. When life seems to be falling apart individuals do not seek the protection of the church or God or their classes but someone they can trust who shares their world and promises support and understanding. Of course there are numerous asynchronicities and overlapping areas, but the focal point has changed position. There is a corresponding change, in Max Weber's term, in 'the guiding values', the 'light' that picks out or blacks out culturally important or irrelevant elements.

This means that industrial capitalism does not just feed parasitically on traditional values and beliefs[5] but that new attitudes and new goals are establishing themselves as industrialism begins to fade. There is a move against individualism: believing in love.

Here one can link up with competing attitudes, with the way psychologists and psychiatrists interpret the world. Asking what love means is not limited to personal responses and experiences undergone in early childhood but includes the social structures which frame our lives such as working and living conditions, family ideals, gender role stereotypes and values within which people's personal needs and wishes are organized and oriented.

The ideas in this book support the theory that love has undergone a change of meaning in the course of history; they are on the side of Eros. In our culture sex is to erotic love as reality is to potential. The blessing or curse of real life weighs down our longings, and passion seems little more than packaging, the tempting description on the menu rather than the tough bird on the platter. In science's 'realistic' view passionate love has always been assigned a place somewhere close to perversion or just beside extravagance. Both socialists and capitalists easily suspect it of shirking its duty, which may well be true if one insists on this viewpoint; lovers more than anyone else adapt their behaviour to their view of the world, thereby altering reality. It is, however, striking that other centuries and cultures, lacking our scientific wisdom, left such reservations to the rabble and refined the art of loving in ways we can barely imagine.

Even a quick survey proves what diverse forms love can take. Cultural and social history distinguishes between hundreds of forms of passionate love alone (leaving out other loves like roast duck and a really good back-hand). In early India, China and Arabia love was an art form, there was platonic love, the sins of the flesh cultivated by Christian monks, stylized and refined courtly love directed at a usually unreachable noblewoman, the all-consuming passion of the Italian Renaissance, tolerating neither restrictions nor authorities and ultimately becoming a passion for a mistress, accepted at court and imitated in literary circles by the European ruling classes so that its style coloured the erotic fantasies of an entire age and beyond.

All of this took place of course under the watchful and disapproving eye of the church, whose fathers, close to God in age and education, devoted themselves to the difficult task of classifying what happened in the marriage bed on the strength of what they learned from hearsay and the Bible. The evidence we have stems largely from them, so that social reports on the fine points of love, procreation, decency, propriety, forbidden sexual positions and so on in the Middle Ages are tinged with clerical displeasure. One wonders what really happened before and after everyone cleared their consciences through confession.

This cultural name-dropping at least highlights the range of possibilities which once were reality (for literature considered them worth reporting). Perhaps we are closer now to being witnesses of something beautiful, as Plato recommended, than being the uprooted plastic people we often fear. Perhaps Michel Foucault was right when in 1984, just before his death (having completed his book *The History of Sexuality*), he remarked: 'The idea of morals as something obeying a code of rules is already disappearing. And this lack of any moral code must and will be answered by the search for an aesthetic code of existence.' In place of law, moral precepts, rigidity and a hierarchy of needs Foucault proposed the ancient concept 'the art of life', 'stylizing existence' and 'developing personal qualities enabling one to make one's own life beautiful' (quoted in Schmid 1986: 680). What Olympian plans; our future neighbours will be the ancient Greeks! Or perhaps the Arabs, the Renaissance lovers, the troubadours, or some fourth, fifth or sixth group of which we as yet know nothing.

Even at the risk of distorting the wealth of evidence we have from the past, I should like to distinguish three main periods in the relationship between love and marriage (incidentally tailored to the emergence of love as a religion). The first is a long phase, covering the whole of antiquity and the Middle Ages and coming to an end in the eighteenth century. The underlying assumption was that love and passion are a sin against marriage. 'Nothing is more shameful than loving one's wife like a mistress' (Seneca, quoted by St Jerome, in Flandrin 1984: 155). At least for the nobility and ruling classes this meant that love could be refined with a mistress, unhindered by marital duties and rights.

The second period started in England in the late eighteenth century; the new middle class, prospering on the fruits of industrialism, imposed its puritanical attitudes on society, disapproving of the nobility's 'loose morals'. As a result desires went underground and variations were pushed into the category 'deviant sexual behaviour' to be treated by psychologists and physicians.

The third phase is the one discussed here. Rigid middle-class morals have awakened a surreptitious interest in forbidden and bizarre behaviour, and the most exotic fantasies have become widespread. In such a setting love seems highly tempting because as well as whetting the sexual appetite it offers a new kind of freedom. The bold ideas on which Romanticism was founded, each person seeking his or her own destiny and facing the joys and sorrows of life in defiance of middle-class norms, once the domain of the eccentric and rash, have become common property. Love as an encounter of egos, as a re-creation of reality in terms of you–me, as a trivialized Romanticism without any prohibitions attached, is becoming a mass phenomenon: a secular religion of love.

Love, monks and the pre-industrial order

'In almost all societies and almost all ages other than ours,' as Philippe Ariès and Jean-Louis Flandrin have shown in their stimulating studies, 'there was a great difference between love within marriage and love outside it' (Ariès 1984: 165; Flandrin 1984).

> Someone showing excessive love for his own wife is . . . acting shamefully. Excessive love is the unbridled passion which lovers feel outside marriage. A reasonable man should love his wife in a level-headed way, not passionately; he should restrain his desires and not allow himself to be carried away to have intercourse with her. (Seneca, quoted in Ariès 1984: 169)

Reading the reasons given for such strictly run marriages of convenience has a charm of its own. Even the wise Montaigne notes in his essays that 'matrimony is a pious and holy union' in which sexual desire is unseemly unless it is 'a serious and considered pleasure tempered by a certain strictness' or 'a so to speak careful and conscientious sensuality' (quoted in Flandrin 1984: 161). Even he was apparently under the influence of theologians who considered procreation the main purpose of marriage and in doing so supported the power structure which depended entirely on kinship and the frail male line, making heirs mandatory. The married couple, faced with such an important task, was only allegedly alone; as well as the looming figure of the father confessor they had the state to contend with, which needed male children if success in battle and statesmanship were to be assured. For fear of having to relinquish his power, court and property to his enemies, everyone had to make his contribution in this field too.

Considering that failure was tantamount to losing a war, it was merciful of the church to turn marital intercourse into a moral act with a single aim; if the social order had depended on people's feelings – love and desire – it would have abdicated its authority to uncontrollable impulses and would have mixed love with war.

In view of these attitudes the church's commitment to marriage as an institution for having and bringing up children was quite reasonable, or at least in keeping with the times. If some aspects seem mysterious to us nowadays it is worth remembering that since then the state has delegated protecting the social order to constitutionally elected bodies and a differentiated legal system, so that the ruling system is much more independent of the consequences of intercourse.

One does wonder, however, how monks and theologians carried out their delicate task:

> A man who lets himself be carried away by too much desire and to satisfy his lust attacks his wife as passionately as if she were not his wife at all and he still wanted to have intercourse with her, is committing a sin. St. Jerome seems to confirm this when he agrees with Sextus the Pythagorean, who stated that a man who is over-attracted to his wife is committing adultery . . . This is why a man should not use his wife like a harlot and the wife should not approach her husband like a mistress, because it is fitting to make use of this holy sacrament of matrimony with all propriety and respect. (Benedicti 1584, quoted in Flandrin 1984: 155)

The justifications are also intriguing. Monks of all people knew well that passions which flared up did not necessarily stay at home but could light up several delightful small purgatories elsewhere:

> Furthermore these husbands teach their wives thousands of lascivious ruses, thousands of lewd tricks, new positions, twists and turns and teach them those horrible figures by Aretino; from one fire in their bodies they light a hundred others and so they become like whores. Once they have been drilled in this way, they cannot help running away from their husbands and looking for other cavaliers. This makes their husbands desperate and induces them to kill their wives; in doing so they are very wrong. (Brantôme, quoted in Flandrin 1984: 161)

There is a mixture of moralizing and lewdness like this in many texts. The authors know what they are talking about and what they disapprove of, and do not restrain themselves. This suggests that the church parallel to its official anti-sex attitudes cultivated and preserved an underground eroticism all the more attractive for being forbidden.

Maintaining the status quo by insisting on marriage as a reproductive union had, however, another side to it: passion outside marriage, which one could find if one were wealthy or powerful enough even if the church frowned on it. A distinction was made between moral behaviour and worldly behaviour, which no doubt was sometimes awkward and could be embarrassing but did enable people to cultivate their love-lives independently of their marital duties (though selectively and often at the expense of the woman). Love was not the same thing inside and outside marriage, a fact which tended to stabilize both arrangements. Wedlock was not constantly under threat from volatile emotions, and love was protected from having to think in terms of permanence and parenthood. Over the centuries both erotic art and the art of the erotic have flourished in places where man and woman are not forced to stay together.

Even nowadays this law applies in a slightly different form: the assumption that we marry for love means we cannot resolve any contradictions between marriage and love by simply letting them exist alongside each other; our only solution is to have one after the other. Our age makes much of distinguishing functions but it lumps private life and sex life together, idealizing the belief that they are one, and turning the law of distinct functions upside down. The old monks would no doubt smile and shake their heads.

The business ethic, breaching conventions, adultery

There has been much criticism of the contrast between erotic love and the puritan ideal of marriage in early capitalist society. The pathos in the idea of freedom is not, however, just a contradiction of bourgeois society; marital fidelity is equally a contradiction to revolutionary cries of liberty and equality which the bourgeois raised against their rulers. To be successful a businessman has to break with feudal norms and restrictions and to pursue his own interests against the needs of his competitors. As soon as he gets home, however, moral order is supposed to prevail. Rational behaviour is recommended by modern philosophers as a guiding principle, ignoring both metaphysics and religion. But being rational means shrugging off restrictions, pursuing your own ends, serving no master, relying on your own intuition and experience, admittedly a freedom which depends on connections but still a categorical imperative which has to be defended against a whole range of subjective (other people's) interests.

We no longer live in a preordained world; our existence is the result of our activities and subject to them. Here Kant meets the entrepreneur, conquering the world with his financial skills. This attitude presupposes and suggests that the subject, each of us, is personally able and liable to decide on our own rights, but not where sex and love are concerned. On what grounds and with what backing?

If freedom for the businessman means ignoring the norms of an outdated feudal society, what about the right of lovers to break with prudish bourgeois conventions? These ideas are closely related, getting your way in business and getting your way in love, showing up the inherent hypocrisy in repressive middle-class morals, making them highly susceptible to furtive and outlawed kinds of love; encouraged by taboos, sex simply becomes steamier.

Love's escape from bourgeois convention is not just an escape; it also turns the conventions on themselves. The fascination love holds lies in the freedoms it seems to offer from old moral restrictions. Romanticism – understood here as unlimited subjectivity, a capacity to love and suffer – is the second possibility offered by the rise of capitalism; look at all the rapidly changing subcultures and exuberant consumerism. From this viewpoint it becomes clear that it was not a historical coincidence that the nineteenth century came up with a strict moral code for marriage, industrialization, subjectivity, the legacy of the Marquis de Sade, Romantic poetry and biographical escapades in literature and real life.

Romanticism now: love as a pop song

In line with its Romantic origins love is a conspiracy against 'society'. It knows no barriers, no classes, no laws except its own. Its subversive ideology has always had a touch of hysteria – neatly traced by Hans

Magnus Enzensberger in his 'documentary' novel (1988) on the Romantic poet Clemens Brentano:

> Auguste Bussmann to Clemens Brentano (Landshut, autumn 1808)
>
> Friday morning
>
> Oh you dreadful nasty mean hateful and beloved Clemens Clemens why do you torment me like this? Tonight you get no kiss; I'll hit you, I'll bite you, I'll scratch you, I'll crush you to death if you come and see me . . .

Three years later, having been 'crushed to death' by her love, the poet shakes off his hatred in this unique farewell poem:

> Well now, I'm finally rid of you,
> You insolent slut!
> A curse on your sinful lap
> A curse on your cheap lewd body,
> A curse on your sluttish breasts,
> Devoid of decency and truth,
> So full of shame and lies,
> A dirty pillow for each wretched lust.
> A curse on every wasted hour
> I spent with disgusting kisses
> On your lying mouth
> . . .
>
> Farewell, you liar, fare badly, there's the door,
> Where my rueful heart finally leaves, you witch,
> May every foot wither that enters your bed!
> I never knew you, I never saw you,
> It was a bad dream that must pass over . . .

> Dear unhappy Auguste [writes Enzensberger], you can hardly imagine what you and a handful of contemporaries of both sexes have done. I am not exaggerating when I say that you (a handful of people between the eighteenth and nineteenth centuries) invented 'love' – or let us say, what people up to the present day still understand as love. After all, what was there before? People got married, made a good or bad match, looked for helping hands, had children and brought them up, and accepted happiness or unhappiness, just as it came, for life. Only in your day, relatively late, did people come up with the idea that there must be something else to it, something beyond childbirth, work and possessions, as if one could take one's life into one's own hands in this respect too. What an extremely risky and momentous idea! My Self in all its glory, and its counterpart, You. Body and soul, supposed to become a small eternity. A

> stress, a set of hopes, expecting happiness which earlier generations never even dreamed of, and at the same time expecting too much of one another and opening up entirely new kinds of unhappiness. Disappointment was the reverse side of your paradise, and your new postulates gave the war between the sexes a new radical twist.
>
> I could write pages tracing the consequences, yet I fear you would not believe me. The fact that your novel set an example, in fact was the prototype for a vast literature, and that your love story still fills theatres in a thousand variations is the least of these. What you would find even more difficult to believe, Auguste, is this: your story has become ordinary, flat, trivial, it has been ruined by being repeated a million times and has been the reason for million-fold sufferings. Entire sciences are dealing with it; an army of experts, counsellors and charlatans busies itself with this endless story and the red tape attached to it, and every day it appears in court to be tried yet again. For it cannot be a coincidence that it was your day that invented divorce, in the same breath as it were as it discovered pure feelings. (Enzensberger 1988: 92, 190–1, 228–9)

Auguste Bussmann and Clemens Brentano experimented and suffered their way through this obsession with themselves and each other quite ruthlessly, pioneers of the thorny odyssey of love, but not, as Enzensberger suggests, its inventors. There is a great deal of late fragmentary Plato in the excesses and piles of rubble they left behind (the bookshops are full of popular guides to living together with a platonic tinge to them); there are also echoes from troubadour and romance literature; the wisdom of ancient India is being revived (and not surprisingly sells well); behaviour once reserved for courtly circles is being tried out in millions of flats. In other words, the allegedly individualistic goings-on stem from old traditions and norms which have been rediscovered.

Viewed in that way, love is applied reading of novels, lived-out pop songs, experimenting with the words of the ego-preachers. Personal impulses are mixed with or even dominated by fantasies invented long ago and often far away, an exoticism which is perhaps the romantic core of love.[6] The conglomeration of impressions read, heard or actually experienced means it is also love using other people's words, feelings helped by the lyrics of pop songs. Auguste Bussmann and Clemens Brentano presumably did not know whether they were writing letters or living them out. The expression of love in writing letters, looking forward to and reflecting on real encounters, picking up clues and inventing new goals has probably died out. It has been replaced, however, by *seen* and *heard* love (in fairly standardized form on television and in therapy), canned love, with a script written for thousands of home viewers.

Once love could burst family bonds and taboos. As barriers have fallen, it increasingly finds no one to shock. With no resistance, no rules to break, it no longer seems immoral or even amoral. It can only concern itself with itself.[7]

So there are endless droning exchanges on relationships, and love lies smothered beneath layers of advice and therapy, pornographic do-it-yourself hints and so much preoccupation with being in love that the person involved gets forgotten. Just like science, which no longer fights untruth with truth, but merely rubs different kinds of truth against each other, romantic love is just one kind among many, with confusion and misunderstanding as the result. Its status as a protective shield is getting lost again, for there are too many kinds around, nothing specifically ours, and often they seem interchangeable.

Because real love has become a scarce and precious commodity, it holds enormous fascination for our individualized society, and finding it has become an existential matter – for everyone, not just nineteenth-century eccentrics and heroes. Or to put it more pointedly: with the death of love, while it seems to dissolve around us into lesser loves – parental love, sex on the side, flirting, companionship and family commitment – there is a mass search under way for a holistic 'grand love'.

Shorn of class connections with their comfortable social certainties and places to meet, the isolated modern citizen has to think up his/her own kind of company. One thing idealistic Romanticism and therapeutic romanticism have in common is the notion of keeping one's distance. 'Absence makes the heart grow fonder,' and lovers tend to love the idea of loving more than confronting the banal facts about the person they have chosen to adore. Idealizing someone is easier at a distance: 'When in love I keep deluding myself about reality . . . Is illusion a prerequisite for desire?'[8]

This kind of love, as Lou Andreas-Salomé remarks, is loneliness multiplied thousand-fold, overcoming the feeling of being all alone in the world by listening to an echo. Only seeing through one's own idealizations and coming to terms with one's lover's shortcomings puts an end to it; the individuals are still alone but at least they have a kind of closeness. When normality dawns on one, keeping a distance is the only remedy to delay returning to loneliness. Or if the disappointing beloved is nearby, perhaps some self-irony and laughing about the unrealistic expectations we have of each other can soften the situation. Love like this, near and yet far, can survive; this is its romantic and realistic core, indeed its invention.

Love is loneliness for two:

> Although we foster the illusion of being completely filled with the other, we are really only filled with our own condition, which on the contrary makes us quite incapable, intoxicated as we are, of really concerning ourselves with the nature of anything. From the very beginning the passion of love is incapable of objectively seeing another person or having any real empathy with that person. It is rather our deepest penetration into ourselves, a thousandfold loneliness, but of a kind which seems to broaden out and arch over our own loneliness into an all-encompassing world, as if surrounded by a thousand sparkling mirrors. (Andreas-Salomé 1986: 59)

Love as a subjective law-giver: programmed battles and paradoxes

Now that the church has little say and the law merely reflects social change, loving seems to be a purely personal affair or at least is meant to be. The irritating aspect, and the least comprehensible one, of course, is that the rules are delegated to individuals, who find themselves caught in a certain scheme with its own logic and paradoxes invading their private lives; they are at once themselves and actors in a common play. Just like capitalism love as pure relationship has its own preordained range of behaviour and crises, affecting everybody but apparently being a matter of personal choice (see also Weitman 1994).

(1) Love is simultaneously the essential factor which provides us with a sense of personal validity and worth, and a way of avoiding being quite alone in the world. It is an alternative to loneliness, and therefore contra-individual, or more precisely a dream of being at once very close to someone else and yet quite separate and autonomous. Conversely, individualization encourages people to idealize living as partners; even realists can turn into idealists under current circumstances, for a fragmented and uncertain world drives them to invest all hope of finding safety and comfort in their private love-lives.

(2) Love's social scheme depends on an active agent, who takes on responsibility, in contrast to anonymous or mechanical models. (Its mechanics are, however, quite obvious, as we shall see.) In the realm of love, as opposed to the outside world, people seem to be free agents, personally accountable, taking decisions which are intentional and their own. It takes hold of them and they are compelled to join in; there is

no escaping. Hurled about by mighty feelings, one finds oneself playing unfamiliar and prescribed roles just at that moment when one rejoiced in the conviction 'this is how I really am, this is absolutely me.' The only way to get in touch with one's deepest and most exhilarating feelings is via such banal vehicles as sex role, labour market and economy, making one simultaneously king and slave, or legislator, judge and prison guard in one. Miracles have to be accomplished all the time to keep the most ordinary things in balance, even if one has long ago abandoned all faith in miracles or salvation.

(3) Instead of justifying love along traditional or formal lines, we do so along emotional and individual ones. It originates in what we experience, in our personal hopes and fears rather than in any superior power. The lovers, and only they, are in charge of what is true and right about their love, which means they are their own judges but equally the lawgivers who can rewrite the rules. This implies, however, that there is no such thing as injustice, even if one partner is discovered *in flagrante delicto*, and no right of appeal. Love and justice seem to belong to two mutually unintelligible languages.

(4) Love is founded in itself: its basis is always and only an emotional one. In operational terms this means that no one except the lovers can decide whether they are in love – a radical form of democracy for two, personal responsibility in its purest form. In fact it is so extreme that it includes being irresponsible, for only the lovers can decide on ending their love, i.e. one voting against the other, for the sole reason that feelings have changed.

(5) Love is our alternative to doubt: it is the place we hope to find security. In the nineteenth century love was something irrational, the opposite to bourgeois norms, uncertain and exotic, symbolized by a temptress with snake-like charms. The present situation is exactly the reverse; in view of the dissolution of so many supports, love ranks as the ultimate refuge. While love used to break up (or ignite) under the pressure of social conventions, nowadays people seek a loving relationship as a place in which to hide from an inimical world.

(6) Love is a blank form which the lovers have to fill in: how they actually organize their love-lives and what love means are decisions they must agree on, and these can vary to include different taboos, expectations and infidelities, all left to their own choice. Loving means setting oneself norms not on how one behaves but on how one reaches decisions on

how to behave, a matter of conscience. The actual content of the love package is a subjective mutual invention, and all around it are pitfalls and potential disaster. This also applies even where the couple fills up the holes in their arrangement with ready-made answers, such as moral precepts, the Kama Sutra or therapeutic know-how, to reinforce what they claim to have invented together.

(7) Love which does not have any traditional backing does not tolerate any form of deviation, or at least only individual ones. Society expects and approves only of two people consenting with one another; any disagreement or use of force is regarded as breaking the rules and officially punished.

(8) The meaning of love, of togetherness, is always at risk, another proof of its secular nature. One main threat in this system lies in who decides whether togetherness should continue, and if so in what form. The lovers have two levers to two trap-doors; the end can come very suddenly, on the decision of the other, and there is no appeal. The criteria are ultimately subjective feelings, and how each perceives the relationship in terms of his/her dreams (or competing offers which are waiting in the wings). Behind the interminable discussions on current misunderstandings looms the guillotine of unilateral decision-making, forcing the participants to scurry nervously round their mutual emotional territory like rats in a cage.

(9) Love is dogmatism for two, in delightful agreement if things are going well and in a bitter clash of faiths if they are going badly. The dogmatic side remains hidden in the harmony and exuberance of emotions but surfaces as soon as the long-term fundamental conflict breaks out between two people struggling to be 'authentic', because this alone guarantees the validity and rightness of their feelings. Being authentic turns out to include being different, and conflicting truths emerge. 'Being quite honest', 'standing up for one's feelings' suddenly implies the end of the affair, getting out, because I want it that way. The process is in itself dogmatic and not subject to individual choice, for it is inherent in the modern definition of love. Ironically lovers can decide on everything about their relationship but not the mode in which they decide, for they themselves personify this mode, their feelings decide for them. This however implies that as well as soaring to great heights of bliss they can just as easily crash on to hard and icy ground, when togetherness splits up into two rival dogmas rigidly repelling any search for compromise.

(10) Love is the opposite of instrumental rational behaviour. It is not a goal that can be aimed at, or worked for, or technically perfected. It is not even a side-effect which regularly results from another form of activity. Marriage is also no recipe or construction set for capturing or domesticating love. Love is unequally and unjustly distributed, and cannot be used to form pressure groups or parties; any political party putting love on its banner is pursuing an illusion.

(11) Love in our day is post- and a-traditional, and makes its own rules out of sexual desire now unhampered by moral or legal obligations. Love cannot be institutionalized or codified, or justified in any general sense as long as free will and mutual consent are its guiding stars. To put it another way, while a religion which is no longer preached soon loses any influence on our thinking, love as a religion without priests prospers on the force of sexual attraction. This is at least true where external standards have lost any validity and a flourishing market – from pop songs to pornography to psychotherapy – has opened the floodgates of personal yearning.

But how are heaven and hell intermeshed in this scheme? Briefly, lacking any traditional restrictions, love as pure relationship becomes a radical from of personal responsibility, a framework for hoping and acting in which issues, laws, behaviour and legal proceedings – everything in fact – are exclusively in the hands of the lovers. Its underlying patterns governing how and why decisions are made are therefore absolutely in line with modern thinking on progress and enlightenment, which converts everything which used to be preordained into a decision entrusted to individuals. This enticing notion, however, conceals a trap which one does not discover until the question of lodging appeals against decisions or judgements made against one comes up. The answer remains the same: individuals have the right to judge each other. Love is thus also a radical form of self-government, divested of checks and balances, acknowledging neither referees, norms nor legal procedures which might otherwise help to prise its dilemmas out of the sordid swamp of accusations and disagreements and take them to a neutral court. Combatants who have fallen out of love sit and declare final verdicts on one another and do their best to enforce them. So love's democracy comes full circle and turns out to be exactly the opposite: no one is there to stop the unrestrained outbursts of hatred which two people, unwillingly shackled together and subjected to the cruelty of intimacy without affection, hurl at one another, well knowing each other's weak spots. It then looks as if love has turned into a medieval religious war before the state was capable of intervention.

According to its social design, love is a fair-weather ship on a long voyage. A storm or two can be sailed through with little difficulty. Since the captain, the sails, the mast and the hull are all of a piece, however, chaos breaks out during a long storm. Leaks are plugged with ripped-out planks, if it ever gets that far, for there are suddenly two captains fighting over the charts and hitting each other with the broken rigging. As the attraction of being in love lies in the feeling of freedom, consensus and satisfaction it offers, we prefer to ignore the fact that this state of affairs is bound to result in its opposite. Something founded only on agreement and free choice cannot be modified into a conditional freedom with escape clauses when the adventurers find their treasure stolen and turn on one another in desperation and disappointment.

The trap love sets us is the downside of the security it tempts us with: we rely on subjectivity, and only that, which quickly becomes arbitrary and cruel when unrestrained by outside obligations. In creating their own laws, lovers open the door to a form of lawlessness as soon as the magic of being in love has flown away and their own interests take centre stage. Love requires that both are unreservedly open with one another, thereby handing each the evil tools of familiarity to be used against one another. As (market-trained) individuals we have recast love as its own legislator, fitting in with our own opinions and interests. That is why we experience not only the understanding and merciful God of the New Testament but also the jealous and enigmatic one of the Old Testament.

Love's inevitable battles: conditions

The mechanics of love follow a law: the law of the lawlessness of subjectivity and intimacy oriented towards personal needs, which has divested itself of all external controls and been left to its own devices.

This is of course a sketch of the 'idea' behind the changes we can observe, and hints at likely developments behind our reality, anticipating what love might well become. The factors influencing such changes are:

- men and women are becoming equals in the professional field in terms of income and status, so that economic restraints are reduced or even vanish, making love the main bond between the partners;
- *there is an increase in the number of couples from different backgrounds*, so that finding and keeping common ground to halt the centrifugal force of two very different biographies lies exclusively in the hands of the men and women involved;

- *couples rarely know or understand each other's work situations* so that there is little shared experience to bind them together;
- *the state and the church are retreating from their roles as law-givers for marriage and close relationships*, so that love has more scope to develop its inherent conflict potential as a radical, self-administered search for intimacy;
- *individualization – that is to say being dependent on one's training, mobility, commitment to the labour market and impersonal regulations* – makes love seem the best answer to loneliness, holding out the promise of a meaningful and satisfying physical and emotional experience.

There are important indicators and long-term trends (presented in various ways in this book) which suggest that such changes are under way. The divorce laws for instance internationally attest to the retreat of the state and the law, having replaced the principle of the guilty party with that of 'irretrievable marital breakdown'. This means that the guilt question is excluded and only the results have to be regulated, such as the financial side of divorce and child-rearing issues (Lucke 1990).

The same goes for the decriminalization of so-called deviant forms of love, as long as no violence is involved. This implies that the question of what is legal has been delegated to the parties involved. Certainly the church, and especially the Catholic Church, is deeply concerned about marriage and the family, as its public admonitions show, but even in strictly Catholic regions there is a striking gap between moral claims and actual behaviour. This does not just apply to birth control but equally to abortion figures, for instance in Catholic Poland, where they are among the highest in Europe.

Nowhere is the inherent logic of love so clear as in the paradoxes people wander or stumble into in their seemingly idiosyncratic way whenever this sort of behaviour is left to flourish without interference.

The paradox of freedom

If freedom is everything, restricting someone else's freedom must be the goal even if love keeps enthusing about doing quite the opposite. What is desired is someone else's voluntary renunciation of their freedom for yours. How should this be achieved? As Jean-Paul Sartre asks:

> Why should I want to appropriate the Other if it were not precisely that the Other makes me be? But this implies precisely a certain mode of appropriation; it is the Other's freedom as such that we want to get hold

> of. Not because of a desire for power. The tyrant scorns love, he is content with fear. If he seeks to win the love of his subjects, it is for political reasons; and if he finds a more economical way to enslave them, he adopts it immediately. On the other hand, the man who wants to be loved does not desire the enslavement of the beloved. He is not bent on becoming the object of passion which flows forth mechanically. He does not want to possess an automaton, and if we want to humiliate him, we need only try to persuade him that the beloved's passion is the result of a psychological determinism. The lover will then feel that both his love and his being are cheapened. If Tristan and Isolde fall madly in love because of a love potion, they are less interesting. The total enslavement of the beloved kills the love of the lover . . . Thus the lover does not desire to possess the beloved as one possesses a thing; he demands a special type of appropriation. He wants to possess a freedom as freedom.
>
> On the other hand, the lover cannot be satisfied with that superior form of freedom which is a free and voluntary engagement. Who would be content with a love given as pure loyalty to a sworn oath? Who would be satisfied with the words, 'I love you because I have freely engaged myself to love you and because I do not choose to go back on my word.' Thus the lover demands a pledge, yet is irritated by a pledge. He wants to be loved by a freedom but demands that this freedom as freedom should no longer be free. He wishes that the Other's freedom should determine itself to become love – and this not only at the beginning of the affair but at each instant – and at the same time he wants this freedom to be captured by itself, to turn back upon itself, as in madness, as in a dream, so as to will its own captivity. This captivity must be a resignation that is both free and yet chained in our hands. (Sartre 1956: 342–3)

The paradox of authenticity

Love is the first person singular for everything: my experience, my truth, my transcendence, my salvation. This presupposes authenticity, both in principle and in fact. What does honesty mean, what is it based on? How does it halt the free fall it plunges into if subjected to further questioning? Must my attitude towards a feeling be as certain as the feeling itself? How do I react when put under pressure by someone else's emotional truth, which as well as being hard for me to grasp denies my own vital interests and claims on my beloved with its own unswerving conviction. This is the paradox of authenticity. According to Niklas Luhmann what is required is

> a simple and prescribable principle which can push aside three hundred years of insight into the indissoluble connection between honesty and dishonesty in the course of human existence and love. Quite apart from

> the question whether the person one loves will allow one to say everything one wants to, should one be honest, even in moods which are constantly fluctuating? Should the other person be linked to my own temperature like a thermometer? And above all, how is one supposed to be honest towards someone who is not honest with himself? Is not every existence ultimately an unfounded projection, a plan needing supports and protective zones of dishonesty? Can one communicate one's own honesty at all without being dishonest by doing so?
>
> It is difficult to gauge the influence of therapists on morals (and of morals on therapists) but they are certainly something to fear. Instead of love they substitute the individual's shaky health, his need for support, and the only notion of love they can develop is a permanent mutual therapy based on a dishonest understanding of honesty. (Luhmann 1984: 210–11)

The paradox of action

Perhaps poverty can be eliminated, and inequalities reduced; perhaps military and technical risks too. Love, in contrast, cannot be aimed at, invoked or coerced into existence nor can any institution restrict it. It simply happens, strikes like lightning or dies out according to laws which are not open to individual or social control. The same applies to its opposite, indifference, which happens just like love or can be shattered by an attack of love. But how do we attain, preserve and survive love, if not along rational means–ends lines, the only ones available to us? What happens when everyone chases after a goal which is unattainable, at least in the way they are attempting it? What if resisting the goal turns out to be the shortest route to it? Or when reached it undergoes metamorphosis into exactly the opposite of what we hoped for?

The new era which has fallen in love with love, so to speak, at the peak of its technical and rational prowess, is abandoning itself to perhaps the last kind of happiness that resists rational powers, evades the grasp of modern thinking and draws its immense appeal for its believers and imitators from exactly this fact. Similar to anxiety, which incidentally is merely the other side of worshipping love in a society acclimatized to risk, love cannot be explained or refuted and in fact is indescribable; despite all the inflationary talk about relationships, or perhaps because of it, no one can really convey what he/she feels.

Competing viewpoints

In terms of the history of ideas, the more the theory of de-tabooed love with its own value system and behavioural logic gains ground in real life, the less convincing (at least) two currently dominant sets of ideas will seem.

First of all there is the view adopted by psychologists and psychoanalysts that the reasons for all the emotional turmoil lie almost exclusively in the personalities of the individuals and their childhood experiences.

One conclusion one can draw from the situation we have sketched is that the upsets and battles do not necessarily stem from personal neuroses or traumatic experiences. They may just as well be brought about by the inherent contradictions of love itself and its bewildering dynamics. Insisting on tracing the crashes and jolts in the system back to psychological problems and personal pasts is just as misleading as blaming mountaineering accidents on 'anal difficulties' or an inflationary economy on 'repressed libido'.

The second false conclusion is the broadly backed consensus of various social theories which assume that society needs a tradition to give it meaning, which has to be documented, transmitted, criticized and legitimated, and must be instilled into the hearts and minds of the coming generation from lecterns and pulpits to prevent it evaporating and losing its validity.

Love takes another path: having cast off traditional values and codes it has opened the gate to our sensual and emotional side. Under its influence people believe in and rely on their senses to make their lives worth living, trusting their innermost feelings and longings, doing without any of the old methods of transmitting ideas and reacting to their own conscious and subconscious drives and needs. This is an individual religion in two senses – it has its source in each individual and it promises to do away with loneliness; it is a non-tradition, or a post-tradition based on individual hopes and fears, providing its believers with a sense of purpose and a delight in discovering their own desires and strengths on love's battlefield.

A retrospective glance from the future, or the last St Valentine's Day

Let us leap into the twenty-first century and close with a report drawn from the *International Herald Tribune* which appeared while this book was being written:

> Boston – Our history books tell us now that 1990 was the year our forebears celebrated the last Valentine's Day. By then, the very idea of a national holiday for the celebration of love had become an anachronism, a holdout from the days of sex, drugs and rock'n'roll.

Certain members of Congress had never approved of V-Day and there was talk through the late '80s of withholding funds from any museum that harbored images of naked children under the pseudonym Cupid. At the very least, parents' groups believed stores should mark Valentine cards with parental warnings.

But the final blow was the commission report completed that year on love. Not surprisingly, the commission concluded that love caused what the experts labeled 'an altered state of consciousness'. That phrase had a clear and ominous meaning for the stay-straight Nineties. Love was a substance and Americans were abusers.

The symptoms were common, nationwide and alarming. People who fell in love, the commission determined, had trouble concentrating. They were often distracted, found daydreaming, or staring in space, exhibiting a condition known as 'blind love'. Many experienced loss of appetite, elevated heart rates, a certain high color to the face, an effect that was easily identifiable to the naked eye.

The health implications of what the commission dubbed love abuse were worrisome, but so were the financial ones. Lovers, it estimated, cost the gross national product millions of dollars a year in lost productivity since this unchecked emotion took precedence over, say, strategizing hostile takeovers. In contrast, the commission pointed to the Japanese, who did not officially celebrate love with a national holiday. Need the commission say more?

There had long been concerns about love in America. Half a century earlier, a generation had questioned the subliminal messages, even in the old standards such as 'Love is sweeping the country,' and 'I can't give you anything but love, baby.'

But this time the Woodstock generation, which had outgrown, worn out or given up all sorts of substances as they entered middle age, were the ones who turned their attention toward love. They searched for its telltale signs among their vulnerable children. Who could not worry about something that made people high, that produced ecstasy?

Before the Nineties, as students of history know, love had been a noun, or a verb. But by this time, love was increasingly used as an adjective, as in 'love addict' and 'love junkie'. People in love described themselves as hooked on each other. Indeed, love created dependency or, worse yet, co-dependency. This was the subject of many best-sellers during the pivotal winter of 1989–90.

By the 21st century, it would become routine for Americans to introduce themselves by their name, their gender and their 12-step support program: 'Hi, My Name is Alice and I'm in Love.' But even in 1990, millions had already formed associations based on their addictions the way their ancestors had come together by ethnic origin. No less an authority than Erica Jong, a former pusher of love potions, had turned to writing about recovery. Abstinence was going around.

All of this laid the groundwork for acceptance of the commission's recommendations in 1990. The scientific evidence of a love epidemic required action.

The Supreme Court approved random love testing for the workplace. Funding was set up for programs for people who wanted to free themselves of others. Educators were instructed to teach the young the risks of love. 'Romeo and Juliet' was banned. And in that atmosphere, Valentine's Day could no longer be tolerated.

Today Americans now date their long climb back from falling into love to that last Valentine's Day. The final and most debilitating excess, the most widespread high, was brought down to earth. Love came under control.

Occasionally, to this day, there is a report of some couple found together, faces flushed, but it is almost always after aerobics. Indeed, although recovery is never complete, it can be said that at last in the post-Valentine era we have nearly accomplished that wonderful goal of moderation in all things except misery. Thanks to our ancestors of 1990, we live in a Love Free America. (Ellen Goodman, 'The Last Valentine's Day')[9]

NOTES

Extracts with German sources have been translated from the German for this edition, unless otherwise stated.

INTRODUCTION

1 'Motive zum BGB' (motives for the Code of Civil Law), *circa* 1880, p. 562; our emphasis.
2 Individualization as concept, conjecture, explanation, remedy and damnation is on everyone's lips today. It is being discussed in connection with the so-called 'democracy of mood', the unpredictable movements of formerly regular voters, the difficulties of trade unions, who are clearly unable to maintain their membership with the old slogans and organizational forms, the stubbornness of youth ('Generation X'), and with issues of socio-structural inequalities that can only be put back together into classes with great effort in grey mass statistics. It should almost go without saying that this also applies to the very normal puzzles raised by statistics on marriage and family, on which no one is ever a completely neutral observer. For a summary of the disputes on 'individualization' see Beck 1994; Beck and Beck-Gernsheim 1994 and 1995. On the *theory* of social individualization see, among others: Elias 1991; Habermas 1988: 223ff.; Honneth 1988a and b; Luhmann 1989; Kohli 1988; Keupp 1988; Keupp and Bilden 1989; P. A. Berger 1987; Berger and Hradil 1990: Introduction; Dörre 1987: 43ff.; J. Ritsert 1987; Brose and Hildenbrand 1988; Lau 1988; Rosenmayr 1985; Hennig 1989; Esser 1989; Hornstein 1988; Flitner 1987; Weymann 1989; Klages 1988; Heitmeyer and Möller 1988; Wahl 1989; Neckel 1989; Zoll et al. 1989.
3 Foucault 1978; Burckhardt 1958; Elias 1991: vol. II. In the inward asceticism of Calvinism, Max Weber (1985) saw a release from the traditional

certainty of salvation; for him it also represented the compulsion to subdue Nature by asserting oneself, leading a careful life and accumulating wealth. For Georg Simmel (1978), the central motor of individualization lay in the finance economy; the latter opens up social circles and remixes them. Thus the theme of individualization can be traced through the epochs and social theories into the present.

4 Juridification, welfare-state protection, the break-up of traditional households, the shortening of the working week and other factors continue to play a part here (see Beck 1986: 121–30). The ambiguity of the individualization concept and its breathtaking public career stand for the insecurity of an entire society with regard to its social structure. Individualization is the code word for the fading of an old form of social inequalities and the vague emergence of a new one. On this point see *Soziale Welt*, 3/1983 as well as the special issues of *Soziale Welt* edited by Kreckel (1983) and Berger and Hradil (1990).

5 'The individualization process runs with differing speed in different milieus, and not necessarily in the same direction,' as Burkart, Fietze and Kohli show in detail (1989: 256; also pp. 11–12, 61, 195, 259); see also Bertram and Dannenbeck 1990.

CHAPTER 1 LOVE OR FREEDOM

1 The highest level was found in 1984 at 87 divorces per 10,000 existing marriages, and since then a decline has been observable: 86 in 1985, 83 in 1986; see Federal Office of Statistics (ed.) 1988: 78.

Divorces in Germany

Year	*Total*	*per 10,000 inhabitants*	*per 10,000 marriages*
1900	7,928	1.4	8.1
1913	17,825	2.7	15.2
1920	36,542	5.9	32.1
1930	40,722	6.3	29.5
1938	49,487	7.2	31.1
1950	84,740	16.9	67.5
1960	48,878	8.8	35.0
1970	76,520	12.6	50.9
1980	96,222	15.6	61.3
1984	130,744	21.3	87.1
1988	128,729	21.0	—

Sources: Federal Minister of Youth, Family and Health 1985: 57, 137; *Statistisches Jahrbuch 1983–1985*: Tables 3.32–3.34; *Wirtschaft und Statistik*, no. 8, 1989: 508.

2 Differentiated according to years of marriage, the number of divorces is by far the largest (at 360 per 10,000 marriages) among couples who have been married sixteen to twenty years and have raised children together, while divorce varies between 146 and 230 per 10,000 for couples married two, three or four years; Federal Minister of Youth, Family and Health 1985: 78. It is natural to suspect that children hold many couples together only so long as they remain at home.

3 The German Institute for Youth Research has calculated 2.5 million (1988: 156). The Allensbach Institute for Demographics, as quoted in the *Süddeutsche Zeitung* (10–11 June 1989), estimates 3 million. The frequently heard interpretation that non-marital unions are quasi-marriages or some new form of betrothal is contradicted by the composition of such unions: with or without children; before and after divorce; between material and physical victims of divorce, or so-called 'retiree concubinage' (Bertram and Borrmann-Müller 1988: 18).

4 Burkhart, Fietze and Kohli 1989: 30, 34; *Süddeutsche Zeitung* (8–9 October 1989).

5 The group of never-married singles, divorced people and married people living separately make up roughly 58% here, while widows (and widowers) together amount to 41.5%; see Federal Office of Statistics (ed.) 1989: Table 3.16 and 64ff.

6 Federal Minister of Education and Science 1988–9: 70. Among school-leavers at the top of the school, a slight decrease in the proportion of women has been observed; it was 45.7% in 1987; Federal Office of Statistics (ed.) 1988: 345f.

7 The discrepancy was even larger in universities: in the autumn term of 1987–8, 62% of the students enrolled in German universities were men and only 38% women; see Federal Office of Statistics (ed.) 1988: 359.

8 More precisely, 61% of the students in the humanities were female, 38% of those in law and economics and 31% in mathematics and natural sciences; Federal Office of Statistics (ed.) 1988: 361.

9 Federal Minister of Education and Science 1988–9: 206–8; Federal Office of Statistics 1989: 367. The proportion of women overall was 15%, with 5% of the professorial posts (not broken down by salary grade), 13% of the assistantships and 19% of the lectureships occupied by women.

10 Federal Office of Statistics (ed.) 1987: 79; this includes data on the individual productivity groups, which are sometimes quite close together. See also *Quintessenzen aus der Arbeitsmarkt- und Berufsforschung* 1984: 33f.

11 This is also reflected in the meteoric career of the individualization concept in the public sphere and scholarship. For a synopsis of the dispute and the basic arguments see Beck 1994; Beck and Beck-Gernsheim 1994 and 1995. For the area of *adolescent sociology* in this respect see Fuchs 1983; Hornstein 1985; Rosenmayr 1985; Baethge 1985; Michal 1988: 143ff.; Heitmeyer and Möller 1988. For the *working class and labour movement*: Mooser 1983; Dörre 1987. For *women's studies*: Beck-Gernsheim 1983; Bilden 1989. For *social inequality*: Berger and Hradil 1990; Neckel 1989; Mayer 1989.

For *family sociology*: Bertram and Borrmann-Müller 1988; Hoffmann-Nowotny 1988; Burkart, Fietze and Kohli 1989.

CHAPTER 2 FROM LOVE TO LIAISON

1 Rückert, reprinted in Behrens 1982: 205.
2 Proportion of girls/women:

	In grammar schools (senior level)	*Starting university*	*University students (overall)*
1960	36.5%	27.0%	23.9%
1970	41.4%	28.8%	25.6%
1980	49.4%	40.1%	36.7%
1980	49.8%	40.2%	38.0%

Source: Federal Minister of Education and Science 1989–90: 46 and 154–5.

3 In 1907 26% of the married women in Germany over fifteen years old were employed outside the home. The rate in West Germany was 33.7% in 1965, and 44.5% in 1988 (Federal Office of Statistics 1983a: 63; 1989, as reported in *Süddeutsche Zeitung* 24–5 June 1989).
4 The percentage of working women with children over eighteen years old rose from 33.2% in 1961 to 44% in 1982 (Federal Minister of Youth, Family and Health 1984: 21).
5 See the cover art for Merian 1983.
6 Wingen 1985: 348; *Statistisches Jahrbuch 1988 für die Bundesrepublik Deutschland*: 78.
7 Lutz 1985: 3; the figures refer to Austria, but the development is running very similarly in Germany.
8 The ratio of illegitimate births to all newborn children rose from 4.6% in 1967, the lowest level of the past few decades, to 10.2% in the last quarter of 1987 (Permien 1988: 20; Burkart, Fietze and Kohli 1989: 30).
9 'An illegitimate child is less and less the unwanted teenage pregnancy of earlier years, and ever more frequently the planned pregnancy of women over 25. Extramarital fertility, then, is less and less a "misfortune" of young women and rather an obviously planned or at least a consciously accepted decision of older women' (Burkart, Fietze and Kohli 1989: 34).
10 Surveys conducted in 1962 and 1983 on whether a woman should be married when she bears a child reveal that 89.4% of the girls asked in 1962 considered this to be important, but only 40% agreed in 1983 (Allerbeck and Hoag 1985: 97–8).
11 Merrit and Steiner 1984; Fabe and Wikler 1979: 122–3; 'Ledige Mütter mit Wunschkind: Geht es wirklich ohne Mann', *Für Sie*, 1985/11; 'When

Baby Makes Two: Choosing Single Motherhood', *Ms.* (November 1984); 'Having Babies without Husbands', *New Woman* (May 1995).

CHAPTER 3 FREE LOVE, FREE DIVORCE

1 Translated by Mary J. Price and Laurence M. Price as *The Feud of the Schroffensteins*, in *Poet Lore*, 1916/25/5: 518, 563.
2 This interview excerpt originates from the unpublished material in a study that was conducted within the project 'Child-rearing in the Lower Class' at the German Youth Institute, Munich. On this, see Wahl et al. 1980.

CHAPTER 4 ALL FOR LOVE OF A CHILD

1 See also *Einstellungen zu Ehe und Familie* 1985: 177.
2 For a scientific account of the stages of in-vitro fertilization see Bräutigam and Mettler 1985: 54–68.

CHAPTER 5 EVE'S LATE APPLE

1 [German] Federal Office of Statistics, as reported in the *Süddeutsche Zeitung* (24–5 June 1989).
2 Particularly Wallerstein and Blakeslee (1989) as well as Furstenberg (1987), who speaks of 'serial marriages' and 'separated parenthood' and predicts a 'matrilineal reversal' as a consequence of high divorce rates, through which the paternal commitment to the kinship system is loosened overall.
3 I owe this pointer to Ronald Hitzler; indicators for it are those who are still married but living separately or with new partners because they shy away from the cost or the emotional expense of a divorce, or because they simply want to preserve appearances. Here it becomes clear at the same time that, while the words, administrative acts and statistical depiction of marriage and divorce have remained constant, their meaning has become more formalistic and provisional. If marriage figures are once again rising, then this is also owing to the fact that marriage has shed its eternal glamour and now recommends itself as an attempt subject to cancellation, which must be tried out just like a South Seas holiday, the Octoberfest and psychoanalysis.
4 For documentable developmental lines of parents' ideas of an ideal child, see Beck-Gernsheim 1988b and 1995 and Beck 1988 (English trans. 1995; chapter 1, on the social consequences of reproductive medicine and human genetics).

CHAPTER 6 LOVE, OUR SECULAR RELIGION

1 Verses translated by Jane Wiebel, from Gottfried Benn, *Sämtliche Werke*, in an edition with Ilse Benn, ed. Gerhard Schuster, vol. 1: *Gedichte 1* (Klett-Cotta, Stuttgart, 1986), by kind permission of the publisher.

2 'It is characteristically *images* and *fantasies* of family and children which promise a meaning for life and much less the concrete experiences of a family life in the biography to date and as it appears in ordinary reality' (Wahl et al. 1980: 35).
3 This assessment, which seeks to ground love in the conflict situations of individualized lifeworlds, thus also disputes the idea that traditional milieus are *exclusively* broken up into 'small social lifeworlds' (Hitzler 1988: 136ff.). Love becomes an almost compulsory theme in detraditionalized lifeworlds; this also shows how important it is to connect inquiries into individualization tendencies with the inquiry into the newly emerging social patterns and understandings.
4 I am indebted to Christoph Lau for this quotation.
5 The classical formulation by Jürgen Habermas is 'Meaning cannot be administratively produced' (1973: 99). Summarizing a long line of argument (extending back to Adam Smith, Hegel and de Tocqueville), Helmut Dubiel writes: 'Just as industry consumes fossil resources, without being able to replace them, the stability of free-market liberal societies consumes the substances of a social morality which these societies cannot renew within their own political, economic and cultural institutions' (1987: 1039ff.) If the arguments presented here were to prove tenable, this assessment would have to be rethought in the following sense: can one conceive detraditionalized, conflict-laden love as an ever-modern source of social meaning? My answer: that is a good question. If it is true that love is one of the sources of acrimonious conflict which moves men and women in the deepest part of their being, chafing them, wounding them, and, at the same time, forcing them to rethink their course, their future, their personality, their characteristics, their will as well as their beliefs and scepticism, then it could be that this is precisely its meaning. Not some positive, pre-given, authoritarian unambiguous meaning, but rather a conflict that springs forth from the substance of life, targets it and destroys it. This would be precisely the form of the post-traditional meaning of love. The questions which well up threaten to undermine the edifice of normality from the inside, from its very foundations. This is the source of many things: retreat, bitterness and cynicism, but also, and contradictorily enough, a new horizon, a new world view, a new life style, or at least the desire for those things, even as repressed desires, in the citadel of the celebrated ego. This does not take the form of certainties or values one could simply harvest. Instead it appears as a cultural soreness, an awakened sensitivity which arouses perception and shifts priorities.

   One must, of course, agree with Thomas Luckmann (1983: esp. 188) that love as post-religion can have an effect that creates meaning only in the *private* sphere and only 'to the extent the latter is really left alone by the large institutions'; on this point see the subsection 'Love's inevitable battles: conditions' later in this chapter.
6 The concepts of Romanticism and Romantic love are doubtless vague and

ambiguous, as the debates that flared up on 'The Modernity of Romanticism' (see Bohrer 1988) have generally shown. Niklas Luhmann suspects the real core meaning, rather like we do, in that peculiar relationship between idealization and distance. Romantic love is 'ideal and paradoxical, insofar as it claims to be the unity of a duality. The point is to retain and elevate the self while giving it up, to engage in love fully and at the same time ironically. In all of that, a novel and typically Romantic paradox prevails: the experience of the intensification of seeing, experiencing and enjoying *through distance*' (Luhmann 1984: 210–11; emphasis in original); on the historical origins, see also Campbell 1987 and Honneth 1988b.

7 I owe this thought to Christoph Lau. The thesis is not identical in meaning to the 'reflexivity of life' of which Niklas Luhmann speaks (1984). The latter does not aim at a historically new state of affairs; instead it is 'when seen abstractly, a possibility for all talents and situations'.

8 Kristeva 1989: 16: 'All philosophers of thought, from Plato to Descartes, Hegel and Kant who have attempted to ensure an access to reality for the love experience, have expunged the upsetting aspects from it and reduced it to an initiatory journey attracted by the highest good or the pure spirit. Only theology . . . allows itself . . . to be lured into the trap of the holy madness of love.'

9 Ellen Goodman, 'The Last Valentine's Day', *International Herald Tribune*, 14 February 1990. Copyright © Washington Post Writers Group, by permission of Editors Press Service, Inc. on behalf of the Washington Post Writers Group.

BIBLIOGRAPHY

Adorno, T. 1978: *Minima moralia*. London (Ger. orig. 1951).

Alberoni, F. 1983: *Verliebtsein und lieben: Revolution zu zweit*. Stuttgart (*Falling in Love*, New York).

—— 1987: *Erotik: Weibliche Erotik, männliche Erotik, was ist das?* Munich.

Allerbeck, K. and Hoag, W. 1985: *Jugend ohne Zukunft?: Einstellungen, Umwelt, Perspektiven*. Munich.

Andreas-Salomé, L. 1986: *Die Erotik*. Frankfurt and Berlin.

Ariès, P. 1962: *Centuries of Childhood: A Social History of Family Life*. New York (Ger. trans. 1978).

—— 1984: Liebe in der Ehe. In P. Ariès et al., *Die Masken des Begehrens und die Metamorphosen der Sinnlichkeit*, Frankfurt (*Western Sexuality: Practice and Precept in Past and Present*, Oxford, 1985).

Ayck, T. and Stolten, I. 1978: *Kinderlos aus Verantwortung*. Reinbek.

Bach, G. R. and Deutsch, R. M. 1979: *Pairing: Intimität und Offenheit in der Partnerschaft*. Reinbek.

Bach, G. R. and Molter, H. 1979: *Psychoboom: Wege und Abwege moderner Therapie*. Reinbek.

Bach, G. R. and Wyden, P. 1969: *The Intimate Enemy: How to Fight Fair in Love and Marriage*. New York.

Baden-Württemberg Provincial Government 1983: *Bericht der Kommission 'Zukunftsperspektiven gesellschaftlicher Entwicklungen', erstellt im Auftrag der Landesregierung von Baden-Württemberg*. Stuttgart.

Badinter, E. 1988: *Ich bin Du: Die neue Beziehung zwischen Mann und Frau*. Munich.

Badura, B. (ed.) 1981: *Soziale Unterstützung und chronische Krankheit: Zum Stand sozialepidemiologischer Forschung*. Frankfurt.

Baer, J. 1976: *How to be an Assertive (not Aggressive) Woman*. New York.

Baethge, M. 1985: Individualisierung als Hoffnung und Verhängnis. *Soziale Welt*, 3: 299f.

Barthes, R. 1978: *Fragments: A Lover's Discourse*. New York.

Beck, J. 1970: *How to Raise a Brighter Child*. London.

Beck, U. 1983: Jenseits von Stand und Klasse?: Soziale Ungleichheit, gesellschaftliche Individualisierungsprozesse und die Entstehung neuer sozialer Formationen und Identitäten. In Kreckel 1983: 35–74. (Beyond Status and Class? In Meja, Misgeld and Stehr (eds), *Modern German Sociology*, New York, 1987.)

—— 1986: *Risikogesellschaft: Auf dem Weg in eine andere Modernität*. Frankfurt (*Risk Society: Towards a New Modernity*, London, 1992).

—— 1988: *Gegengifte: Die organisierte Unverantwortlichkeit*. Frankfurt (*Ecological Politics in the Age of Risk*, Cambridge, 1995).

—— 1994: The Debate on the 'Individualization Theory' in Today's Sociology in Germany. In B. Schäfers (ed.), *Sociology in Germany: Development, Institutionalization, Theoretical Disputes*, Opladen.

Beck, U. and Beck-Gernsheim, E. (eds) 1994: *Riskante Freiheiten: Individualisierung in modernen Gesellschaften*. Frankfurt.

—— 1995: Individualization in Modern Societies. In S. Lash, P. Heelas and P. Morris (eds), *Detraditionalization*, Oxford.

Beck, U., Giddens, A. and Lash, S. 1994: *Reflexive Modernization: Politics, Tradition and Aesthetics in the Modern Social Order*. Cambridge.

Beck-Gernsheim, E. 1980: *Das halbierte Leben: Männerwelt Beruf, Frauenwelt Familie*. Frankfurt.

—— 1983: Vom 'Dasein für andere' zum Anspruch auf ein Stück 'eigenes Leben': Individualisierungsprozesse im weiblichen Lebenszusammenhang. *Soziale Welt*, 3: 307–41.

—— 1988a: *Die Kinderfrage: Frauen zwischen Kinderwunsch und Unabhängigkeit*. Munich.

—— 1988b: Zukunft der Lebensformen. In J. Hesse, H.-G. Rolff and C. Zoppel (eds), *Zukunftswissen und Bildungsperspektiven*, Baden-Baden: 99–118.

—— 1989: *Mutterwerden: Der Sprung in ein anderes Leben*. Frankfurt.

—— 1995: *Technology, the Market, and Morality: On Reproductive Medicine and Genetic Engineering*. Atlantic Highlands, NJ.

Becker-Schmidt, R. and Knapp, G.-A. 1985: *Arbeiterkinder gestern – Arbeiterkinder heute*. Bonn.

Behrens, K. (ed.) 1982: *Das Inselbuch vom Lob der Frau*. Frankfurt.

Béjin, A. 1984: Ehen ohne Trauschein heute. In P. Ariès et al., *Die Masken des Begehrens und die Metamorphosen der Sinnlichkeit*, Frankfurt (*Western Sexuality*, Oxford, 1985).

Benard, C. and Schlaffer, E. 1981: *Liebesgeschichten aus dem Patriarchat*. Reinbek.

—— 1985: *Viel erlebt und nichts begriffen: Die Männer und die Frauenbewegung*, Reinbek.

Benn, G. 1962: *Leben ist Brückenschlagen: Gedichte, Prosa, Autobiographisches*. Munich and Zurich.

Berger, B. and Berger, P. L. 1983: *The War over the Family*. New York.

Berger, J. 1986: Gibt es ein modernes Gesellschaftsstadium?: Marxismus und Modernisierungstheorie im Widerstreit. In J. Berger (ed.), *Die Moderne: Kontinuität und Zäsuren. Soziale Welt*, special volume 4: 79–96.

Berger, P. A. 1986: *Entstrukturierte Klassengesellschaft?* Opladen.
—— 1987: Klassen und Klassifikationen. *Kölner Zeitschrift für Soziologie und Sozialpsychologie*, 29: 59–85.
Berger, P. A. and Hradil, S. (eds) 1990: *Lebenslagen, Lebensläufe, Lebensstile. Soziale Welt*, special volume 7.
Berger, P. L. 1973: *Zur Dialektik von Religion und Gesellschaft*. Frankfurt.
—— 1983: Das Problem der mannigfachen Wirklichkeiten: Alfred Schütz und Robert Musil. In Gradhoff and Waldenfels (eds), *Sozialität und Intersubjektivität*, Munich.
Berger, P. L. and Kellner, H. 1965: Die Ehe und die Konstruktion der Wirklichkeit. *Soziale Welt*, 3: 220–35.
Berger, P. L., Berger, B. and Kellner, H. 1973: *The Homeless Mind: Modernization and Consciousness*. New York.
Bernard, J. 1976: *The Future of Marriage*. Harmondsworth.
Bernardoni, C. and Werner, V. (eds) 1983: *Der vergeudete Reichtum: Über die Partizipation von Frauen im Öffentlichen Leben*. Bonn.
Bertram, H. and Borrmann-Müller, R. 1988: Individualisierung und Pluralisierung familialer Lebensformen. *Aus Politik und Zeitgeschichte*, supplement to the weekly *Das Parlament*, 13: 14–22.
Bertram, H. and Dannenbeck, G. 1990: Zur Theorie und Empirie regionaler Disparitäten: Pluralisierung von Lebenslagen und Individualisierung von Lebensführungen in der BRD. In Berger, P. A. and Hradil, S. 1990.
Beyer, J., Lamott, F. and Meyer, B. (eds) 1983: *Frauenhandlexikon*. Munich.
Biermann, I., Schmerl, C. and Ziebell, L. 1985: *Leben mit kurzfristigem Denken: Eine Untersuchung zur Situation arbeitsloser Akademikerinnen*. Weilheim and Basle.
Bilden, H. 1989: Geschlechterverhältnis und Individualität im gesellschaftlichen Umbruch. In Keupp, H. and Bilden, H. (eds), *Verunsicherungen*, Göttingen: 19–46.
Blixen, T. 1986: *On Modern Marriage*. New York.
Bock-Rosenthal, T., Haase, C. and Streeck, S. 1978: *Wenn Frauen Karriere machen*. Frankfurt and New York.
Bohrer, K. H. 1988: Die Modernität der Romantik. *Merkur*, 469: 179–98.
Bolte, K.-M. 1980: Bestimmungsgründe der Geburtenentwicklung und Überlegungen zu einer möglichen Beeinflußbarkeit. In *Bevölkerungsentwicklung und nachwachsende Generation*, Schriftenreihe des Bundesministers für Jugend, Familie und Gesundheit, vol. 94, Stuttgart, Berlin, Cologne and Mainz: 64–91.
—— 1983: Subjektorientierte Soziologie. In Bolte, K.-M. and Treutner, E. (eds), *Subjektorientierte Arbeits- und Berufssoziologie*, Frankfurt: 12–36.
Bopp, J. 1984: Die Mamis und die Mappis: Zur Abschaffung der Vaterrolle. *Kursbuch 1967*, June: 53–74.
Borscheid, P. 1986: Romantic Love or Material Interest: Choosing Partners in Nineteenth-Century Germany. *Journal of Family History*, 2: 157–68.
Boston Women's Health Collective (ed.) 1971: *Our Bodies, Ourselves*. New York.
Braun, D. and Wohlfahrt, D. 1984: *Ich und du und unser Kind: Tagebücher aus dem Leben zu dritt*. Reinbek.

Bräutigam, H.-H. and Mettler, L. 1985: *Die programmierte Vererbung: Möglichkeiten und Gefahren der Gentechnologie*. Hamburg.

Brinker-Gabler, G. (ed.) 1979: *Frauenarbeit und Beruf*. Frankfurt.

Brod, H. (ed.) 1987: *The Making of Masculinity*. Boston.

Brontë, C. 1966: *Jane Eyre*. Harmondsworth (first edn 1847).

Brose, H. G. and Hildenbrand, B. (eds) 1988: *Vom Ende des Individuums zur Individualität ohne Ende*. Opladen.

Brose, H. G. and Wohlrab-Sahr, M. 1986: Formen individualisierter Lebensführung von Frauen: ein neues Arrangement zwischen Familie und Beruf? In H. G. Brose (ed.), *Berufsbiographien im Wandel*, Opladen: 105–45.

Bruckner, G. and Finkielkraut, A. 1979: *Die neue Liebesunordnung*. Munich.

Bruker, M. O. and Gutjahr, I. 1986: *Biologischer Ratgeber für Mutter und Kind*. Lahnstein.

Buchholz, W. et al. 1984: *Lebenswelt und Familienwirklichkeit*. Frankfurt.

Bullinger, H. 1986: *Wenn Paare Eltern werden*. Reinbek.

Burckhardt, J. 1958: *The Civilization of the Renaissance in Italy*. New York (Ger. orig. 1858).

Burkart, G., Fietze, B. and Kohli, M. 1989: *Liebe, Ehe, Elternschaft: Eine qualitative Untersuchung über den Bedeutungswandel von Paarbeziehungen und seine demographischen Konsequenzen* (*Materialien zur Bevölkerungswissenschaft*, no. 60, ed. Bundesinstitut für Bevölkerungsforschung). Wiesbaden.

Campbell, C. 1987: *The Romantic Ethic and the Spirit of Modern Consumerism*. Oxford.

Cancian, F. M. 1985: Gender Politics: Love and Power in the Private and Public Spheres. In A. S. Rossi (ed.), *Gender and the Lifecourse*, New York: 253–65.

—— 1986: The Feminization of Love. *Signs*, 4: 692–709.

Capek, K. 1985: Romeo und Julia: Eine Erzählung. *Süddeutsche Zeitung*, 25–7 May.

Chesler, P. 1979: *With Child: A Diary of Motherhood*. New York.

Chester, R. (ed.) 1982: *Children and Marriage*. Special issue of the *International Journal of Sociology and Social Policy*, 2/3.

Christie, A. 1977: *An Autobiography*. New York.

Cohen, A. 1983: *Die Schöne des Herrn*. Stuttgart.

—— 1984: *Das Buch meiner Mutter*. Stuttgart.

Cook, E. H. and Harrell, K. F. 1984: *Parental Kidnapping: A Bibliography*. Monticello: Vance Bibliographies.

Cunningham, M. 1991: *A Home at the End of the World*. London.

Daele, W. van den 1985: *Mensch nach Mass?: Ethische Probleme der Genmanipulation und Gentherapie*. Munich.

Degler, C. N. 1980: *Women and the Family in America from the Revolution to the Present*. New York.

Demos, J. and Boocock, S. S. (eds) 1978: *Turning Points: Historical and Sociological Essays on the Family*. Chicago.

Diezinger, A., Marquardt, R. and Bilden, H. 1982: *Zukunft mit beschränkten Möglichkeiten, Projektbericht*. Munich.

Dische, I. 1983: Das schönste Erlebnis. *Kursbuch*, 72 (June): 28–32.
Dörre, K. 1987: *Risiko-Kapitalismus: Zur Kritik von Ulrich Becks Weg in eine andere Moderne*. Marburg.
Dowrick, S. and Grundberg, S. (eds) 1980: *Why Children?* New York and London.
Dubiel, H. 1987: Zur Ökologie der sozialen Arbeit. *Merkur*: 1039ff.
Duby, G. 1983: *The Knight, the Lady and the Priest: the Making of Modern Marriage in Medieval France*. New York.
Durkheim, E. 1933: *The Division of Labor in Society*. New York (Fr. orig. 1893).
Ehrenreich, B. 1983: *The Hearts of Men*. New York.
—— 1984: The Politics of Talking in Couples: Conversus Interruptus and other Disorders. In A. M. Jaggar and P. S. Rothenberg (eds), *Feminist Frameworks*, New York: 73–6.
Ehrenreich, B. and English, D. 1979: *For Her Own Good: 150 Years of the Experts' Advice for Women*. London.
Ehrenreich, B., Hess, E. and Jacobs, G. 1986: *Remaking Love; The Feminization of Sex*. New York.
Eichenbaum, L. and Orbach, S. 1983: *What Do Women Want?: Exploding the Myth of Dependency*. New York.
Elias, N. 1978: *The Civilization Process: The History of Manners*. New York.
—— 1985: Foreword. In M. Schröter, *'Wo zwei zusammen kommen in rechter Ehe . . .': Sozio- und psychogenetische Studien über Eheschliessungsvorgänge vom 12. bis 15. Jahrhundert*, Frankfurt: vii–xi.
—— 1991: *The Society of Individuals*. Oxford.
Elschenbroich, D. 1988: Eine Familie, zwei Kulturen: Deutsch-ausländische Familien. In Deutsches Jugendinstitut (ed.), *Wie geht's der Familie?: Ein Handbuch zur Situation der Familien heute*, Munich: 363–70.
Enzensberger, H. M. 1988: *Requiem für eine romantische Frau: Die Geschichte von Auguste Bussmann und Clemens Brentano*. Berlin.
Erler, G. A. 1985: Erdöl und Mutterliebe: Von der Knappheit einiger Rohstoffe. In T. Schmidt (ed.), *Das pfeifende Schwein*, Berlin.
Esser, H. 1989: Verfällt die soziologische Methode? *Soziale Welt*, 1/2: 57–75.
Fabe, M. and Wikler, N. 1979: *Up Against the Clock: Career Women Speak on the Choice to Have Children*. New York.
Fallaci, O. 1976: *Letter to a Child Never Born*. New York.
—— 1980: *A Man*. New York.
Federal Minister of Education and Science (ed.) 1982–3, 1984–5, 1988–9, 1989–90: *Grund- und Strukturdaten*. Bonn.
Federal Minister of Youth, Family and Health (ed.) 1980: *Frauen 80*. Bonn.
—— 1984: *Frauen in der Bundesrepublik*. Bonn.
—— 1985: *Nichteheliche Lebensgemeinschaften in der Bundesrepublik Deutschland* (*Schriftenreihe des Bundesministers für Jugend, Familie und Gesundheit*, vol. 170). Stuttgart, Berlin, Cologne and Mainz.
Federal Office of Statistics (ed.) 1983a: *Frauen in Familie, Beruf und Gesellschaft, Ausgabe 1983*. Wiesbaden.
—— 1983b: *Datenreport*. Bonn.
—— 1987: *Frauen in Familie, Beruf und Gesellschaft, Ausgabe 1987*. Wiesbaden.

—— 1988: *Statistisches Jahrbuch 1988 (für die Bundesrepublik Deutschland)*. Bonn.

Fend, H. 1988: Zur Sozialgeschichte des Aufwachsens. In Deutsches Jugendinstitut (ed.), *25 Jahre Deutsches Jugendinstitut e.V.: Dokumentation der Festveranstaltung und des Symposiums*, Munich: 157–73.

Fischer, E. 1983: *Jenseits der Träume: Frauen um Vierzig*. Cologne.

Fischer, I. 1989: Der andere Traum vom eigenen Baby. *Geo-Wissen, Sonderheft Sex–Geburt–Genetik* (May): 46–58.

Fishman, P. M. 1982: Interaction: The Work Women Do. In R. Kahn-Hut, A. K. Daniels and R. Colvard (eds), *Women and Work: Problems and Perspectives*, New York: 170–80.

Flandrin, J. L. 1984: Das Geschlechtsleben der Eheleute in der alten Gesellschaft. In P. Ariès et al., *Die Masken des Begehrens und die Metamorphosen der Sinnlichkeit*, Frankfurt (*Western Sexuality*, Oxford, 1985).

Fleming, A. T. 1989: When a Loving Nest Remains Empty. *New York Times*, 15 March 1989.

Flitner, A. 1988: Zerbrechliche Zukunft. In his *Für das Leben–oder für die Schule?*, Weinheim: 211–19.

Foucault, M. 1978: *The History of Sexuality*. New York (Fr. orig. 1976).

Frankl, V. E. 1984: *Das Leiden am sinnlosen Leben: Psychotherapie für heute*. Freiburg.

Fuchs, R. 1988: *Die Technisierung der Fortpflanzung*. Berlin.

Fuchs, W. 1983: Jugendliche Statuspassage oder individualisierte Jugendbiographie? *Soziale Welt*, 3: 341–71.

—— 1984: *Biographische Forschung*. Opladen.

Furstenberg, F. Jr. 1987: Fortsetzungsehen: Ein neues Lebensmuster und seine Folgen. *Soziale Welt*, 1: 29–39.

Gabbert, K. 1988: Prometheische Schamlosigkeit. *Ästhetik und Kommunikation*, 69: 85–91.

Garfinkel, P. 1986: *In a Man's World*. New York.

Gensior, S. 1983: Moderne Frauenarbeit. In *Karriere oder Kochtopf, Jahrbuch für Sozialökonomie une Gesellschaftstheorie*. Opladen.

Gerhard, U. 1978: *Verhältnisse und Verhinderungen: Frauenarbeit, Familie und Rechte der Frauen im 19. Jahrhundert*. Frankfurt.

Geulen, D. 1977: *Das vergesellschaftete Subjekt*. Frankfurt.

Gilligan, C. 1982: *In a Different Voice: Psychological Theory and Women's Development*. Cambridge, Mass.

Glick, P. C. 1984: Marriage, Divorce, and Living Arrangements: Prospective Changes. *Journal of Family Issues*: 7–26.

Goldberg, H. 1979: *Der verunsicherte Mann: Wege zu einer neuen Identität aus psychotherapeutischer Sicht*. Reinbek.

Goody, J. 1983: *The Development of the Family and Marriage in Europe*. Cambridge.

Gordon, S. 1985: Interview with Jean Baker Miller. *Ms.* (July): 42.

Grass, G. 1980: *Kopfgeburten*. Darmstadt: Eng. trans. as *Headbirths; or The Germans are Dying Out*, 1983.

Gravenhorst, L. 1983: Alleinstehende Frauen. In J. Beyer et al. (eds), *Frauenhandlexikon: Stichworte zur Selbstbestimmung*, Munich: 16f.

Groffy, C. and Groffy, U. (eds) 1986: *Das Insel-Buch der Ehe*. Frankfurt.

Gronemeyer, R. 1989: *Die Entfernung vom Wolfsrudel: Über den drohenden Krieg der Jungen gegen die Alten*. Düsseldorf.

Gross, P. 1985: Bastelmentalität. In T. Schmidt (ed.), *Das pfeiefende Schwein*, Berlin: 63–84.

Gross, P. and Honer, A. 1990: Multiple Elternschaften. *Soziale Welt*, 1.

Gstettner, P. 1981: *Die Eroberung des Kindes durch die Wissenschaft: Aus der Geschichte der Disziplinierung*. Reinbek.

Habermas, J. 1973: *Legitimationsprobleme im Spätkapitalismus*. Frankfurt (*Legitimation Crisis*, Cambridge, 1988).

—— 1988: *Nachmetaphysisches Denken: Philosophische Aufsätze*. Frankfurt.

Hage, V. 1987: Ferne Frauen, fremde Männer. *Die Zeit*, 11 December.

Hahn, A. 1988: Familie und Selbstthematisierung. In K. Lüscher et al. (eds), *Die 'postmoderne' Familie*, Konstanz: 169–79.

Handke, P. 1982: *Kindergeschichte*. Frankfurt.

Häsing, H. (ed.) 1983: *Mutter hat einen Freund: Alleinerziehende Mütter berichten*. Frankfurt.

Häsing, H. and Brandes, V. (eds) 1983: *Kinder, Kinder!: Lust und Last der linken Eltern*. Frankfurt.

Häussler, M. 1983: Von der Enthaltsamkeit zur verantwortungsbewussten Fortpflanzung: Über den unaufhaltsamen Aufstieg der Empfängnisverhütung und seine Folgen. In M. Häussler et al., *Bauchlandungen: Abtreiben–Sexualität–Kinderwunsch*, Munich: 58–73.

Heiliger, A. 1985: Alleinerziehende Mütter: Ohne Partner glücklicher. *Psychologie heute* (December): 10–11.

Heitmeyer, W. and Möller, K. 1988: Milieu-Einbindung un Milieu-Erosion als individuelles Sozialisationsproblem. *Zeitschrift für erziehungswissenschaftliche Forschung*: 115–144.

Hennig, C. 1989: *Die Entfesselung der Seele: Romantischer Individualismus in den deutschen Alternativkulturen*. Frankfurt.

Hennig, M. and Jardim, A. 1977: *The Managerial Woman*. New York.

Hentig, H. von 1978: Vorwort. In P. Ariès, *Geschichte der Kindheit*, Munich.

Hite, S. and Colleran, K. 1989: *Kein Mann um jeden Preis: Das neue Selbstverständnis der Frau in der Partnerbeziehung*. Niederhausen.

Hitzler, R. 1988: *Sinnwelten*. Opladen.

Hoff, A. and Scholz, J. 1985: *Neue Männer in Beruf und Schule: Forschungsbericht*. Berlin.

Hoffmann-Nowotny, H.-J. 1988: Ehe und Familie in der modernen Gesellschaft. *Aus Politik und Zeitgeschichte*, supplement to the weekly *Das Parlament*, B 13: 3–13.

Höhn, C. Mammey, U. and Schwarz, K. 1981: Die demographische Lage in der Bundesrepublik Deutschland. *Zeitschrift für Bevölkerungswissenschaft*, 2: 139–230.

Hollstein, W. 1988: *Nicht Herrscher, aber kräftig: Die Zukunft der Männer*. Hamburg.

Hölzle, C. 1989: Die physische und psychische Belastung durch In-vitro-Fertilisation. *pro familia magazin*, 5: 5–8.

Homan, W. E. 1980: *Kinder brauchen Liebe – Eltern brauchen Rat*. Munich.

Honig, M.-S. 1988: Kindheitsforschung: Abkehr von der Pädagogisierung. *Soziologische Revue*, 2: 169–78.

Honneth, A. 1988a: Soziologie: Eine Kolumne. *Merkur*, 470: 315–19.

—— 1988b: Soziologie: Eine Kolumne. *Merkur*, 477: 961–5.

Höpflinger, F. 1984: Kinderwunsch und Einstellung zu Kindern. In H.-J. Hoffmann-Nowotny et al., *Planspiel Familie: Familie, Kinderwunsch und Familienplanung in der Schweiz*, Diessenhofen: 77–181.

Hornstein, W. 1985: Strukturwandel im gesellschaftlichen Wandlungsprozess. In S. Hradil (ed.), *Sozialstruktur im Umbruch: Karl Martin Bolte zum 60. Geburtstag*, Opladen: 323–42.

—— 1988: Gegenwartsdiagnose und pädagogisches Handeln. *Zeitschrift für Pädagogik*, 34.

Hubbard, R. 1984: Personal Courage is Not Enough: Some Hazards of Childbearing in the 1980s. In R. Arditti et al. (eds), *Test-Tube Women: What Future for Motherhood?*, London: 331–55.

Hurrelmann, K. 1989: Warum Eltern zu Tätern werden: Ursachen von Gewalt gegen Kinder. *Forschung – Mitteilungen der DFG*, 1: 10–12.

Ibsen, H. 1986: *A Doll's House and Other Plays*, trans. Peter Watts. Harmondsworth.

Illich, I. 1985: Einführung in der Kulturgeschichte der Knappheit. In A. H. Pfürtner (ed.), *Wider den Turmbau zu Babel: Disput mit Ivan Illich*, Reinbek: 12–31.

Imhof. A. E. 1981: *Die gewonnenen Jahre*. Munich.

—— 1984: *Die verlorenen Welten*. Munich.

Institute for Demographics, Allensback/Köcher, R. 1985: *Einstellungen zu Ehe und Familie im Wandel der Zeit*. Stuttgart.

Jaeggi, E. and Hollstein, W. 1985: *Wenn Ehen älter werden: Liebe, Krise, Neubeginn*. Munich.

Jannberg, J. 1982: *Ich bin ich*. Frankfurt.

Jong, E. 1974: *Fear of Flying*. London.

—— 1985: *Parachutes and Kisses*. London.

Jourard, S. M. 1982: Ehe fürs Leben – Ehe zum Leben. *Familiendynamik*, 2: 171–82.

Kamerman, S. B. 1984: Women, Children and Poverty: Public Policies and Female-headed Families in Industrialized Countries. In *Women and Poverty*, special issue of *Signs: Journal of Women in Culture and Society*, 10/2: 249–71.

Kaufmann, F.-X. 1988: Sozialpolitik und Familie. In *Aus Politik und Zeitgeschichte*, supplement to the weekly *Das Parlament*, B 13: 34–43.

Kaufmann, F.-X., Herlth, A., Quitmann, J., Simm, R. and Strohmeier, P. 1982: Familienentwicklung: Generatives Verhalten im familialen Kontext. *Zeitschrift für Bevölkerungswissenschaft*, 4: 523–45.

Kern, B. and Kern, H. 1988: *Madame Doctorin Schlözerin: Ein Frauenleben in den Widersprüchen der Aufklärung*. Munich.

Kerner, C. 1984: *Kinderkriegen: Ein Nachdenkbuch*. Weinheim and Basel.

Keupp, H. 1988: *Riskante Chancen: Das Subjekt zwischen Psychokultur und Selbstorganisation*. Heidelberg.

Keupp, H. and Bilden, H. (eds) 1989: *Verunsicherungen: Das Subjekt im gesellschaftlichen Wandel*. Munich.

Kitzinger, S. 1980: *The Complete Book of Pregnancy and Childbirth*. New York.

Klages, H. 1988: *Wertedynamik: Über die Wandelbarkeit des Selbstverständlichen*. Zurich.

Klein, R. D. 1987: Where Choice Amounts to Coercion: The Experiences of Women on IVF Programs. Address at the Third International Interdisciplinary Women's Congress, Dublin (mimeographed ms.).

Kohli, M. 1985: Die Institutionalisierung des Lebenlaufes. *Kölner Zeitschrift für Soziologie und Sozialpsychologie*, 1: 1–29.

—— 1988: Normalbiographie und Individualität. In H. G. Brose and B. Hildenbrand (eds), *Vom Ende des Individuums zur Individualität ohne Ende*, Opladen: 33–54.

Krantzler, M. 1974: *Creative Divorce: A New Opportunity for Personal Growth*. New York.

Krechel, U. 1983: Meine Sätze haben schon einen Bart: Anmahnung an die neue Weiblichkeit. *Kursbuch* (September): 143–55.

Kreckel, R. (ed.) 1983: *Soziale Ungleichheiten*. Special issue of *Soziale Welt*.

Kristeva, J. 1989: *Geschichten von der Liebe*. Frankfurt (*Tales of Love*, New York).

Kuhn, H. 1975: '*Liebe*': *Geschichte eines Begriffes*. Munich.

Kundera, M. 1974: *Laughable Loves*. New York (Czech orig. pre-1968).

Lange, H. and Bäumer, G. (eds) 1901: *Handbuch von der Frauenbewegung, I. Teil: Die Geschichte der Frauenbewegung in den Kulturländern*. Berlin.

Langer-El Sayed, I. 1980: *Familienpolitik: Tendenzen, Chancen, Notwendigkeiten*. Frankfurt.

Lasch, C. 1977: *Haven in a Heartless World: The Family Besieged*. New York.

Lau, C. 1988: Gesellschaftliche Individualisierung und Wertwandel. In H. O. Luthe and H. Meulemann (eds), *Wertwandel–Faktum oder Fiktion?*, Frankfurt and New York.

Lazarre, J. 1977: *The Mother Knot*. New York.

Ledda, G. 1978: *Padre, Padrone*. Zurich.

Lempp, R. 1986: *Familie im Umbruch*. Munich.

Ley, K. 1984: Von der Normal- zur Wahlbiographie. In M. Kohli and G. Robert (eds), *Biographie und soziale Wirklichkeit*, Stuttgart: 239–60.

Liegle, L. 1987: *Welten der Kindheit und der Familie*. Weinheim and Munich.

Lorber, J. and Greenfield, D. 1987: Test-Tube Babies and Sick Roles: Couples' Experiences with In Vitro Fertilization. Address at the Third International Interdisciplinary Women's Congress, Dublin (mimeographed ms.).

Lucke, D. 1990: Die Ehescheidung als Kristallisationskern geschlechtsspezifischer Ungleichheit im Lebenslauf von Frauen. In P. L. Berger and S. Hradil 1990.

Luckmann, T. 1983: *Life-World and Social Realities*. London.

Lüscher, K. 1987: Familie als Solidargemeinschaft aller Familienangehörigen: Erwartungen und Möglichkeiten. In *Familienideal, Familienalltag* (Schriften des deutschen Vereins für öffentliche und private Fürsorge, vol. 226), Frankfurt: 22–37.

Luhmann, N. 1984: *Liebe als Passion: Zur Codierung von Intimität*. Frankfurt (*Love as Passion*, Cambridge, 1986).

—— 1985: Die Autopoiesis des Bewusstseins. *Soziale Welt*, 4: 402–46.

—— 1989: Individuum, Individualität, Individualismus. In his *Gesellschaftsstruktur und Semantik*, III, Frankfurt: 149–258.

Lutz, W. 1985: Heiraten, Scheidung und Kinderzahl: Demographische Tafeln zum Familien-Lebenszyklus in Österreich. In *Demographische Informationen*: 3–20.

Maase, K. 1984: Betriebe ohne Hinterland. In *Marxistische Studien, Jahrbuch des IMSF*, Frankfurt.

Mackenzie, N. and Mackenzie, J. (eds): *The Diary of Beatrice Webb, Volume Three, 1905–1924*. London.

Mayer, E. 1985: *Love and Tradition: Marriage between Jews and Christians*. New York and London.

Mayer, K. U. 1989: Empirische Sozialstrukturanalyse und Theorien gesellschaftlicher Entwicklung. *Soziale Welt*, 1/2: 297–308.

Meller, L. 1983: *Lieber allein: Zur Situation weiblicher Singles*. Frankfurt.

Merian, S. 1983: *Der Tod des Märchenprinzen*. Reinbek.

Merrit, S. and Steiner, L. 1984: *And Baby Makes Two: Motherhood without Marriage*. New York.

Metz-Göckel, S. and Müller, U. 1987: Partner oder Gegner?: Überlebensweisen der Ideologie vom männlichen Familienernährer. *Soziale Welt*, 1: 4–28.

Metz-Göckel, S., Müller, U. and Brigitte Magazine 1985: *Der Mann*. Hamburg.

Michal, W. 1988: *Die SPD–staatstreu und jugendfrei*. Reinbek.

Michelmann, H. W. and Mettler, L. 1987: Die In-vitro-Fertilisation als Substitutionstherapie. In S. Wehowsky (ed.), *Lebensbeginn und Menschenwürde: Stellungnahmen zur Instruktion der Kongregation für Glaubenslehre vom 22.2.1987* (*Gentechnologie*, 14), Frankfurt and Munich: 43–51.

Mooser, J. 1983: Auflösung der proletarischen Milieus, Klassenbindung und Individualisierung in der Arbeiterschaft vom Kaiserreich bis in die Bundesrepublik Deutschland. *Soziale Welt*, 3: 270–306.

Müller, W., Willms, A. and Handl, J. 1983: *Strukturwandel der Frauenarbeit 1880–1980*. Frankfurt.

Münz, R. 1983: Vater, Mutter, Kind. In G. Pernhaupt (ed.), *Gewalt am Kind*, Vienna: 33–44.

Muschg, G. 1976: Bericht von einer falschen Front. In H. P. Piwitt (ed.), *Literaturmagazin 5*, Reinbek.

Musil, R. 1952: *Der Mann ohne Eigenschaften*. Hamburg (first edn, 2 vols, 1930–3; Eng. trans. as *The Man without Qualities*, 3 vols, 1953–60).

Nave-Herz, R. 1987: Bedeutungswandel von Ehe und Familie. In H. J. Schulze and T. Mayer (eds), *Familie–Zerfall oder neue Selbstverständnis?*, Würzburg: 18–27.

—— 1988: *Kinderlose Ehen: Eine empirische Studie über die Lebenssituation kinderloser Ehepaare und die Gründe für ihre Kinderlosigkeit.* Weinheim and Munich.

Neckel, S. 1989: Individualisierung und Theorie der Klassen. *Prokla*, 76: 51–9.

Neidhardt, F. 1975: *Die Familie in Deutschland: Gesellschaftliche Stellung, Struktur und Funktion.* Opladen (4th expanded edition).

Nichteheliche Lebensgemeinschaften in der Bundesrepublik Deutschland 1985: Schriftenreihe des Bundesministers für Familie, Jugend und Gesundheit, 170. Stuttgart.

Norwood, R. 1985: *Women who Love too Much: When You Keep Wishing and Hoping He'll Change.* New York and Los Angeles.

Nunner-Winkler, G. 1985: Identität und Individualität. *Soziale Welt*, 4: 466–82.

—— 1989: Identität im Lebenslauf. In Psychologie heute (ed.), *Das Ich im Lebenslauf*, Weinheim.

ÖKO-TEST 1988: *Ratgeber Kleinkinder.* Reinbek.

Olerup, A., Schneider, L. and Monod, E. 1985: *Women, Work and Computerization: Opportunities and Disadvantages.* New York.

O'Reilly, J. 1980: *The Girl I Left Behind.* New York.

Ostner, I. and Krutwa-Schott, A. 1981: *Krankenpflege: Ein Frauenberuf?* Frankfurt.

Ostner, I. and Pieper, B. 1980: Problemstruktur Familie – oder: Über die Schwierigkeit, in und mit Familie zu leben. In Ostner and Pieper (eds), *Arbeitsbereich Familie: Umrisse einer Theorie der Privatheit.* Frankfurt and New York.

Palmer, C. E. and Noble, D. N. 1984: Child Snatching. *Journal of Family Issues*, 5/1: 27–45.

Papanek, H. 1979: Family Status Production: The 'Work' and 'Non-work' of Women. *Signs*, 4/4: 775–81.

Partner, P. 1984: *Das endgültige Ehebuch für Anfänger und Fortgeschrittene.* Munich.

Pearce, D. and McAdoo, H. 1981: *Women and Children: Alone and in Poverty.* Washington.

Perls, F. and Stevens, J. O. 1969: *Gestalt Therapy Verbatim.* Lafayette, California.

Permien, H. 1988: Zwischen Existenznöten und Emanzipation: Alleinerziehende Eltern. In Deutsches Jugendinstitut (ed.), *Wie geht's der Familie?: Ein Handbuch zur Situation der Familien heute*, Munich: 89–97.

Pfeffer, N. and Woollett, A. 1983: *The Experience of Infertility.* London.

Pilgrim, V. E. 1986: *Der Untergang des Mannes.* Reinbek.

Plessen, E. 1976: *Mitteilung an den Adel.* Zurich.

Praschl, P. 1988: Bloss keine Blösse geben. *Stern*, 13: 38.

Praz, M. 1933: *The Romantic Agony.* London.

Preuss, H. G. 1985: *Ehepaartherapie: Beitrag zu einer psychoanalytischen Partnertherapie in der Gruppe.* Frankfurt.

Pross, H. 1978: *Der deutsche Mann.* Reinbek.

Quintessenzen aus der Arbeitsmarkt- und Berufsforschung 1984: Frauen und Arbeitsmarkt. Nuremberg.

Rapp, R. 1984: XYLO: A True Story. In R. Arditti et al. (eds), *Test-Tube Women – What Future for Motherhood?*, London: 313–28.

Ravera, L. 1986: *Mein liebes Kind*. Munich.

Reim, D. (ed.) 1984: *Frauen berichten vom Kinderkriegen*. Munich.

Rerrich, M. S. 1983: Veränderte Elternschaft. *Soziale Welt*, 4: 420–49.

—— 1988: *Balanceakt Familie: Zwischen alten Leitbildern und neuen Lebensformen*. Freiburg.

—— 1989: Was ist neu an den 'neuen Vätern'. In H. Keupp and H. Bilden (eds), *Verunsicherungen*, Göttingen: 93–102.

Richter, H. E. 1969: *Eltern, Kind, Neurose: Die Rolle des Kindes in der Familie*. Reinbek.

Riehl, W. H. 1861: *Die Familie*. Stuttgart.

Riesman, D. 1981: Egozentrik in Amerika. *Der Monat*, 3: 111–23.

Rifkin, J. 1987: *Kritik der reinen Unvernunft*. Reinbek.

Rilke, R. M. 1980: *Briefe*. Frankfurt.

Ritsert, J. 1987: Braucht die Soziologie den Begriff der Klasse? *Leviathan*, 15: 4–38.

Rolff, H.-G. and Zimmermann, P. 1985: *Kindheit und Wandel: Eine Einführung in die Sozialisation im Kindesalter*. Weinheim and Basle.

Roos, B. and Hassauer, F. (eds) 1982: *Kinderwunsch: Reden und Gegenreden*. Weinheim and Basle.

Rosenbaum, H. (ed.) 1978: *Seminar: Familie und Gesellschaftsstruktur*. Frankfurt.

—— 1982: *Formen der Familie: Untersuchungen zum Zusammenhang von Familienverhältnissen, Sozialstruktur und sozialem Wandel in der deutschen Gesellschaft des 19. Jahrhunderts*. Frankfurt.

Rosenmayr, L. 1984: *Die späte Freiheit*. Munich.

—— 1985: Wege zum Ich vor bedrohter Zukunft. *Soziale Welt*, 3: 274ff.

Rossi, A. S. (ed.) 1974: *The Feminist Papers: From Adams to de Beauvoir*. New York.

Roth, C. 1987: Hundert Jahre Eugenik. In Roth (ed.), *Genzeit: Die Industrialisierung von Pflanze, Tier und Mensch: Ermittlungen in der Schweiz*, Zurich: 93–118.

Rothman, B. K. 1985: Die freie Entscheidung und ihre engen Grenzen. In R. Arditti et al. (eds), *Retortenmütter*, Reinbek: 19–30.

—— 1988: *The Tentative Pregnancy: Prenatal Diagnosis and the Future of Motherhood*. London.

Rubin, L. B. 1983: *Intimate Strangers: Men and Women Together*. New York.

Ryder, N. B. 1979: The Future of American Fertility. *Social Problems*, 26/3: 359–70.

Sartre, J.-P. 1956: *Being and Nothingness*, trans. Hazel E. Barnes. New York (Fr. orig., 1943).

Schellenbaum, P. 1984: *Das Nein in der Liebe: Abgrenzung und Hingabe in der erotischen Beziehung*. Stuttgart.

Schenk, H. 1979: *Abrechnung*. Reinbek.

Schlumbohm, J. (ed.) 1983: *Wie Kinder zu Bauern, Bürgern, Aristokraten wurden, 1700–1850*. Munich.

Schmid, J. 1989: Die Bevölkerungsentwicklung in der Bundesrepublik Deutschland. In *Aus Politik und Zeitgeschichte*, supplement to the weekly *Das Parlament*, B 18: 3–15.

Schmid, W. 1986: Auf der Suche nach einer neuen Lebenskunst. *Merkur*: 678ff.

Schmidbauer, W. 1985: *Die Angst vor der Nähe*. Reinbek.

Schmiele, W. 1987: *Henry Miller*. Reinbek.

Schneewind, K. A. and Vaskovics, L. A. 1991: *Optionen der Lebensgestalltung junger Ehen und Kinderwunsch, Forschungsbericht*. Munich and Bamberg.

Schneider, S. W. 1989: *Intermarriage: The Challenge of Living with Differences*. New York.

Schönfeldt, S., Countess von 1969: *Das Buch vom Baby: Schwangerschaft, Geburt und die ersten beiden Lebensjahre*. Ravensburg.

—— 1985: *Knaurs Grosses Babybuch*. Munich.

Schopenhauer, A. 1987: *Vom Nutzen der Nachdenklichkeit*. Munich.

Schröter, M. 1985: *'Wo zwei zusammenkommen in rechter Ehe . . .': Studien über Eheschliessungsvorgänge vom 12. bis 15. Jahrhundert*. Frankfurt.

Schulz, W. 1983: Von der Institution 'Familie' zu den Teilbeziehungen zwischen Mann, Frau und Kind. *Soziale Welt*, 4: 401–19.

Schumacher, J. 1981: Partnerwahl und Partnerbeziehung. *Zeitschrift für Bevölkerungswissenschaft*, 4: 499–518.

Schütze, Y. 1981: Die isolierte Kleinfamilie. *Vorgänge*, 5: 75–8.

—— 1986: *Die gute Mutter: Zur Geschichte des normativen Musters 'Mutterliebe'*. Bielefeld.

—— 1988: Zur Veränderung im Eltern-Kind-Verhältnis seit der Nachkriegszeit. In R. Nave-Herz (ed.), *Wandel und Kontinuität der Familie in der Bundesrepublik Deutschland*, Stuttgart: 95–114.

Seidenspinner, G. and Burger, A. 1982: *Mädchen '82: Eine Untersuchung im Auftrag der Zeitschrift Brigitte*. Hamburg.

Sennett, R. 1976: *The Fall of Public Man*. London.

Sichrovsky, P. 1984: Grips-Mittelchen. *Kursbuch* (May): 55–9.

Sichtermann, B. 1981: *Leben mit einem Neugeborenen: Ein Buch über das erste halbe Jahr*. Frankfurt.

—— 1982: *Vorsicht, Kind: Eine Arbeitsplatzbeschreibung für Mütter, Väter und andere*. Berlin.

—— 1987: *Wer ist wie? Über den Unterschied der Geschlechter*. Berlin.

Sieder, R. 1987: *Sozialgeschichte der Familie*. Frankfurt.

Simmel, G. 1978: *The Philosophy of Money*, trans. D. Frisby. London (Ger. orig. 1977).

—— 1985: *Schriften zur Philosophie der Geschlechter*, ed. H. J. Dahmke and K. Höhnke. Frankfurt.

Steinbeck, J. 1966: *America and Americans*. New York.

Stich, J. 1988: 'Spätere Heirat nicht ausgeschlossen . . .': Vom Leben ohne Trauschein. In Deutsches Jugendinstitut (ed.), *Wie geht's der Familie?: Ein Handbuch zur Situation der Familien heute*, Munich: 155–62.

Stone, L. 1978: Heirat und Ehe im englischen Adel des 16. und 17. Jahrhunderts. In H. Rosenbaum (ed.) *Seminar Familie und Gesellschaftsstruktur*, Frankfurt: 444–79.

—— 1979: *The Family, Sex and Marriage in England 1500–1800*. New York.
Strauss, B. 1987: Ihr Brief zur Hochzeit. *Süddeutsche Zeitung*, 24–5 Jan., weekend supplement.
Strümpel, B. et al. 1988: *Teilzeitarbeitende Männer und Hausmänner*. Berlin.
Swaan, A. De 1981: The Politics of Agoraphobia. *Theory and Society*: 359–85.
Theweleit, K. 1987: *Male Fantasies*, 2 vols. Minneapolis (Ger. orig. 1987).
Tilly, C. (ed.) 1978: *Historical Changes of Changing Fertility*. Princeton.
Tuchman, B. 1978: *A Distant Mirror: The Calamitous Fourteenth Century*. New York.
Turow, S. 1991: *The Burden of Proof*. London.
Urdze, A. and Rerrich, M. S. 1981: *Frauenalltag und Kinderwunsch: Motive von Müttern für oder gegen ein zweites Kind*. Frankfurt.
Vester, H. G. 1984: *Die Thematisierung des Selbst in der postmodernen Gesellschaft*. Bonn.
Vogt-Hagebäumer, B. 1977: *Schwangerschaft ist eine Erfahrung, die die Frau, den Mann und die Gesellschaft angeht*. Reinbek.
Vollmer, R. 1986: *Die Entmythologisierung der Berufsarbeit*. Opladen.
Wachinger, L. 1986: *Ehe: Einander lieben–einander lassen*. Munich.
Wagnerova, A. 1982: *Scheiden aus der Ehe: Anspruch und Scheitern einer Lebensform*. Reinbek.
Wahl, K. 1989: *Die Modernisierungsfalle: Gesellschaft, Selbstbewusstein und Gewalt*. Frankfurt.
Wahl, K., Tüllmann, G., Honig, M. S. and Gravenhorst, L. 1980: *Familien sind anders!* Reinbek.
Wallerstein, J. and Blakeslee, S. 1989: *Gewinner und Verlierer*. Munich (*Second Chances: Men, Women and Children a Decade after Divorce*, New York).
Wander, M. 1979: *'Guten Morgen, du Schöne!': Frauen in der DDR, Protokolle*. Darmstadt and Neuwied.
Wassermann, J. 1987: *Laudin und die Seinen*. Munich (first edn 1925; Eng. trans. as *Wedlock*, New York, 1926).
Weber, M. 1985: *The Protestant Ethic and the Spirit of Capitalism*. London (Ger. orig. 1905).
Weber-Kellermann, I. 1974: *Die deutsche Familie: Versuch einer Sozialgeschichte*. Frankfurt.
Wehrspaun, M. 1988: Alternative Lebensformen und postmoderne Identitätskonstitution. In K. Lüscher et al. (eds), *Die 'postmoderne' Familie*, Konstanz: 157–68.
Weitman, S. 1994: Elementary Forms of Socioerotic Life. MS, Tel Aviv.
Wetterer, A. 1983: Die neue Mütterlichkeit: Über Brüste, Lüste und andere Stil(l)blüten aus der Frauenbewegung. In M. Häussler et al., *Bauchlandungen: Abtreiben–Sexualität–Kinderwunsch*, Munich: 117–34.
Weymann, A. 1989: Handlungsspielräume im Lebenslauf: Ein Essay zur Einführung. In Weymann, *Handlungsspielräume: Untersuchungen zur Individualisierung und Institutionalisierung von Lebensläufen in der Moderne*, Stuttgart: 1–39.
White, N. R. 1984: On Being One of the Boys: An Explanatory Study of

Women's Professional and Domestic Role Definitions. *Women's Studies International Forum*, 7/6: 433–40.

Wiegmann, B. 1979: Frauen und Justiz. In M. Janssen-Jurreit (ed.), *Frauenprogramm: Gegen Diskriminierung*, Reinbek: 127–32.

Wiggershaus, R. 1985: 'Nun aber ich selbst': Neue Tendenzen in der Literatur von Frauen in der Bundesrepublik, in Österreich und in der Schweiz. *Die neue Gesellschaft, Frankfurter Hefte*, 7: 600–7.

Williams, L. S. 1987: 'It's Gonna Work for Me': Women's Experience of the Failure of In Vitro Fertilization and its Effect on their Decision to Try IVF Again. Address at the Third International Interdisciplinary Women's Congress, Dublin (mimeographed ms.).

Willms, A. 1983a: Segregation auf Dauer?: Zur Entwicklung des Verhältnisses von Frauenarbeit und Männerarbeit in Deutschland. In W. Müller, A. Willms and J. Handl 1983: 107–81.

—— 1983b: Grundzüge der Entwicklung der Frauenarbeit von 1880–1980. In W. Müller, A. Willms and J. Handl 1983: 25–54.

Wimschneider, A. 1987: *Herbstmilch: Lebenserinnerungen einer Bäuerin*. Munich.

Wingen, M. 1985: Leitung und Einführung zur Podiumsdiskussion 'Heiratsverhalten und Familienbindung'. In J. Schmidt and K. Schwarz (eds), *Politische und prognostische Tragweite von Forschungen zum generativen Verhalten: Herausgegeben von der Deutschen Gesellschaft für Bevölkerungswissenschaft*, Berlin: 340–51.

Wysocki, G. von 1980: *Die Fröste der Freiheit: Aufbruchphantasien*. Frankfurt.

Zinnecker, J. 1988: Zukunft des Aufwachsens. In J. Hesse, H.-G. Rolff and C. Zoppel (eds), *Zukunftswissen und Bildungsperspektiven*, Baden-Baden: 119–39.

Zoll, R. et al. 1989: *'Nicht so wie unsere Eltern!': Ein neues kulturelles Modell?* Opladen.

Zschocke, F. 1983: *Er oder ich: Männergeschichten*. Reinbek.

INDEX